World Geography

WORLD GEOGRAPHY
second edition

Edited by John W. Morris and the late Otis W. Freeman

McGraw-Hill Book Company

New York   St. Louis   San Francisco   Toronto   London

To the Memory of Otis W. Freeman,
Dedicated Geographer and Teacher

Preface

World Geography is planned to give college and university students information about nations and continents to help them in their understanding of world affairs and the applications of geography in general. The editors have chosen the study of familiar geographic areas as the primary approach to world geography because they believe that this organization will help students to learn and remember essential facts and basic principles. The book proceeds, after a general introductory chapter, from areas close at hand to those more distant. Part One, The Americas, includes (in order) the United States, Canada, Middle America, and South America. Part Two, The Old World, is divided into areas selected for convenience and location. Each chapter describes a unified area, although the factors that account for this unity are not always the same. The detail in which an area is studied depends, in part, upon its relative importance in world affairs. Some continents, such as South America and Australia, are considered as a whole; others, like Europe and Asia, are divided into groups of related countries. Because of the need for much greater knowledge of the United States, four chapters have been devoted to the study of the home country.

Throughout the text human activities have been related to the earth's relief features, climatic regions, and natural resources—soils, vegetation, supplies of water, and mineral deposits. After presenting the physical environment, the description of each area considers significant aspects of the cultural environment such as cities, industries, and other economic and cultural activities. Man succeeds most easily when he acts in harmony with nature, but modern man is not inevitably dominated by his environment, because his advancing technology has aided him in overcoming many natural handicaps. For example, man can produce power from fuels, build dams and bring water to irrigate deserts, fertilize and reclaim poor or worn-out soil, extract raw materials and transport them great distances to industrial centers where they are manufactured for local use and for distribution all over the world. World geography gives the student a conception of the broad patterns of human occupations, the distribution of population, and the important areas of commodity production. Its study contributes greatly to knowledge that will help students to understand, evaluate, and reach decisions about current world problems.

The text is intended to meet several needs. One is a survey of the countries and areas of the world to be included in the general education curriculum, especially where such a course is the only one the student will take. Another is a study of principles of geography, intended for a second course following the general survey. Institutions which offer two terms of geography, one on the Eastern Hemisphere and the other on the Western Hemisphere, will find the volume adapted to their requirements. The book will also serve as a text for courses in world-regional geography.

Geography exercises a dynamic power; daily occurrences show how current events and human relationships are affected by geographic factors. Maps, photographs, and clippings that deal with such happenings, when posted on a bulletin board or made the basis for class discussions, will help to arouse class interest in geography. The use of films and slides will enrich the course.

Geographers employ many words or terms that are not commonly used. In general, such words or phrases are defined when first used in the text. To supplement these definitions, and to aid in understanding many of the more common terms, a glossary has been added at the end of the book.

A *Study Guide* has been prepared for student use with *World Geography*. Each unit in the manual correlates with a text chapter. A map exercise, a series of true-false review statements, a list of important terms, a self-test of multiple-choice and completion exercises, a matching exercise for locations and place names, and suggested discussion questions will enable the student to check his progress.

In preparing *World Geography,* the editors have called upon a team of specialists, all experienced teachers, who combine comprehensive knowledge about the regions they describe with awareness of what information is most essential for students. All the authors have done original research on the regions about which they write, and many have made outstanding contributions in these fields.

Many public agencies, representatives from foreign lands, corporations, and individuals have supplied photographs and information used in the book, and the authors and editors extend sincere thanks for such assistance. Numerous individuals have read portions of the volume and offered suggestions which the editors deeply appreciate.

John W. Morris and
the late Otis W. Freeman
Editors

Contents

INTRODUCTION: WORLD GEOGRAPHY

THE TWENTIETH CENTURY IS A CENTURY OF activity. Since 1901 there have been two world wars and many minor wars, revolutions, and "police actions" as well as the beginnings of the exploration of outer space. Since World War I several empires have disintegrated, and many countries have changed their form of government. Most European nations have lost the major parts of their colonial empires. Since 1945 approximately fifty new nations have come into existence, and several more colonial areas are scheduled for independence in the near future. The boundaries of many older countries have been changed. The United Nations, a relatively new international body, was created at the close of World War II to help maintain world peace and improve relations among nations.

A knowledge of geography, then, is fundamental to understanding human activities in the modern world. When we scan a daily paper, read a news magazine, or view a newscast on television, we indicate our interest in national and international situations. All parts of the world are within a few hours' travel time of one another, and most are only minutes apart in communication time. The activities of any one group of people may greatly affect the work and life of numerous other groups. A definite interrelationship exists among all the groups of peoples or nations of the world. To understand why certain groups act as they do, why people prosper in some areas and are poor or stagnant in others, we need a knowledge of the various environments, both cultural and physical, which produce these differences.

For an exceedingly long time the earth has been undergoing changes. There have been upheavals of mountains, vast outpourings of molten rock, downwarps to form inland seas, and reduction, by erosion, of entire mountain chains to plains. Large areas of some land masses have been covered by glaciers; other areas have been inundated by oceans. These and other changes, such as the development and spread of plants and animals, the formation of soils, the deposition of minerals, and the changes of climate which are constantly in progress, are some of the factors affecting occupancy of the earth. In addition, man's historic and cultural inheritance influences his activities, particularly his utilization of available resources.

The surface area of the earth is 196,950,-000 square miles, of which 139,440,000 is water and 57,510,000 is land. Although the land area is but one-fourth of the total surface of the earth, to man who lives on the land the continents and islands are of far more importance than the oceans that occupy the remaining three-fourths of the surface. Actually the huge masses of land called continents, since they include the continental shelves as well as the land above water, cover about one-third of the earth's surface, and the ocean basins account for about two-thirds. Since the volume of water exceeds the capacity of the basins, ocean water has so encroached upon the margins of the continents that it has reduced the exposed land area to approximately one-quarter of the earth's surface. Encircling both the land and water masses is the vast layer of atmosphere, which not only extends out into space but penetrates both the land and water. Developments in aerial transportation, of intercontinental missiles, and of earth satellites have led to increased interest in the atmosphere and the growth of knowledge about it.

THE LITHOSPHERE

The land areas, or solid portions of the earth's surface, are called the "lithosphere." There are seven recognized continents. Asia, Africa, and Europe (sometimes called the Eastern Hemisphere or the Old World) form one continuous land mass. Australia, which lies to the southeast of this mass, is also a part of the Eastern Hemisphere. The Western Hemisphere, or New World, consists of North and South America, the two continents being connected by a narrow isthmus. Antarctica, which surrounds the South Pole, is isolated from the other continents.

Man, by positing an imaginary equator, has divided the earth into a Northern and a Southern Hemisphere. The land masses of Europe, Asia, and North America are completely within the Northern Hemisphere; Australia and Antarctica are entirely within the Southern Hemisphere. Both South America and Africa, which are crossed by the equator, are partly in both hemispheres. The greater part of the land area (about 75 per cent) is in the Northern Hemisphere.

LOCATION AND SHAPE

The shape and latitudinal location of a continent are more important and have greater influence upon human activities than does its size. North America, South America, and Africa all have triangular shapes with the base of the triangle to the north. South America, whose greatest expanse is in the equatorial belt, includes much territory with a sensible temperature and humidity not conducive to the highest types of human development under present conditions. The continent narrows considerably in the latitudes of Argentina and Uruguay. Africa is a desert land at its greatest width, since at that latitude it is crossed by the subtropical high-pressure belt, in which the air is descending and heating under compression so that moisture is absorbed rather than liberated. The central part of Africa, like the northern part of South America, is in the humid equatorial area; only where highlands offset the lowland climatic conditions, and along the northern and southern edges of the continent, has much development taken place. North America is more advantageously situated than the other two. Although it reaches its greatest width along the edges of the Arctic Ocean, much of its land is in the productive area between 30° and 55° north latitude.

The Eurasian land mass may be considered a single unit. It, too, has a roughly triangular shape, with the base along the east side. From this triangular core project

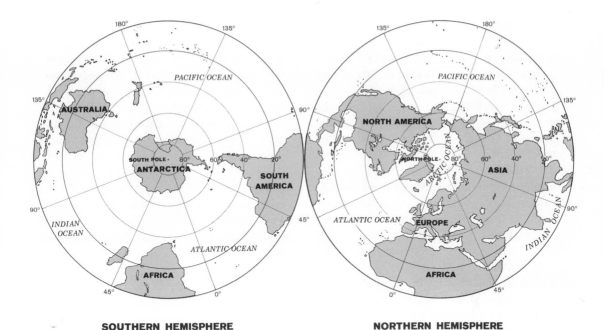

SOUTHERN HEMISPHERE   **NORTHERN HEMISPHERE**

many peninsulas, including Malaya, India, Arabia, Italy, and Iberia. In some respects the continent of Europe is but a peninsula extending westward from Asia. Although Eurasia has its greatest east-west extension from about 35° to 50° north latitude, the very size of the land mass counteracts the desirable effects of this location. High mountains and distances so great that rain-bearing winds lose most of their moisture before reaching the continental heartland result in large areas of dry land. Thus, most of the people live along the margins of the land mass.

Australia, located between 11° and 39° south latitude and 114° and 154° east longitude, has an approximately rectangular shape. Antarctica almost forms a circle. Australia, in the southern trade-wind and subtropical high-pressure belts, is largely a region of arid and semiarid lands. The mountains along its eastern coast prevent much rain from reaching the central and western interior. Antarctica, extending poleward from approximately 70° south

latitude, is a land of snow and ice, too cold for human habitation except under certain conditions which have been developed for scientific expeditions.

CONTINENTAL TOPOGRAPHY

Each continent has its areas of mountains, hills, plains, and plateaus. Frequently the continental shape is determined by the location of the younger mountains or the older, more resistant rock masses. Both North and South America have high mountain ranges along their western sides and older, worn-down mountains near their eastern borders. Wide plains fill the spaces between the mountain masses. Only narrow coastal plains are adjacent to the western mountains of the American continents, although in many places fertile coastal plains are near the eastern border of the land masses.

A long mountain axis—Pyrenees, Alps, Carpathians, Caucasus, Hindu Kush, Pamirs, Himalayas—extends across south central Eurasia. South from this axis extend such plateaus as Iberia, the Balkans, Anatolia, Arabia, Iran, and the Deccan. To the north and northwest of this mountain core lies the great lowland plain of Europe and Asia; to the east are the densely populated river valleys and coastal plains of China and Vietnam. Within the heart of this land mass are the high and dry Tibet Plateau and the Gobi. Because numerous peninsulas extend from the European part of the land mass, the coastline of Europe is longer than that of any other continent.

Africa is frequently referred to as a plateau continent since much of its interior is a great central plateau. With the exception of the Atlas Mountains in the northwest, most of the highlands are scattered along the eastern side of the continent from the Red Sea to the Cape of Good Hope. Large plains are found only in the borderlands of the Sahara. For the most part the coastal plains are narrow. The abrupt changes in elevation between the coastal plains and the central plateau that caused waterfalls and rapids near the mouths of many rivers, along with tropical climates, diseases, and unfriendly natives, discouraged the exploration of Africa for many decades.

Australia has three dominant landforms, the Eastern Highlands, the plains area in the east central part of the continent, and the western plateaus. The continent has a lower average elevation than any of the other land masses. Narrow coastal plains, south and east of the highlands, are the principal populated regions.

Little is definitely known about the detailed topography of Antarctica since most of the surface is continually covered by snow and glaciers. Some scientists now believe that the continent is a group of islands formed by mountain ranges and peaks with the entire area connected by an ice plateau, in some places over a mile in thickness.

NATIONS OF THE WORLD

Except for Australia and Antarctica, the continents are divided into independent nations and dependencies. There are approximately 200 such political units, about 130 of which are independent. Independent countries range in size from the 8.6 million square miles of the Soviet Union to the 100 acres of Vatican City. The United States, the fourth largest country, is considerably above the average in area. Europe and Africa each have more than thirty independent countries. In Europe, except for the U.S.S.R., the countries are small; France, the largest, is smaller than

TABLE 1 CONTINENTS

Continent	Area, sq. mi.	Population*	Highest peak, ft.
Africa	11,635,000	261,300,000	Mt. Kilimanjaro—19,565
Antarctica	5,250,000	0	Mt. Markham—15,100
Asia	17,035,000	1,792,000,000	Mt. Everest—29,002
Australia	2,975,000	11,000,000	Mt. Kosciusko—7,305
Europe	3,850,000	584,000,000	Mt. Elbrus—18,481
North America	7,435,000	273,000,000	Mt. McKinley—20,270
South America	6,860,000	148,000,000	Mt. Aconcagua—22,835

* Areas and populations of continents vary with authorities depending on whether or not certain islands are included in their calculations.

the state of Texas. Twelve of the African nations, however, are larger than Texas, and nine have areas in excess of 400,000 square miles.

THE HYDROSPHERE

The water parts of the earth—oceans, seas, bays, gulfs, lakes, and others—are called the "hydrosphere." The most important of these water bodies, because of their great size, are the oceans. There are three major oceans, the Pacific, Atlantic, and Indian, and one minor ocean, the Arctic. Although some maps may show an Antarctic Ocean, this so-called ocean is essentially only the continuous southern parts of the three major oceans.

LOCATION AND SHAPE

The Pacific Ocean is shaped like a huge inverted U, with the closed part at the north where the continents of Asia and North America almost meet. The eastern part of the Pacific, adjacent to the Americas, is almost free of islands, but westward from the central part of the ocean, islands both large and small are numerous. The Pacific attains its greatest width, 10,000 miles, near the equator. In area this huge body of water is greater than all the land masses of the world combined.

The Atlantic Ocean, shaped somewhat like the letter S, is east of the American continents but west of Europe and Africa. The narrowest part of the Atlantic is between Cape São Roque, Brazil, and the African coast near Dakar, Senegal, where it is only about 1,850 miles in width. Except near the continental masses the ocean is relatively free of islands. The Atlantic and Pacific join between South America and Antarctica.

The Indian Ocean, south of Asia, east of Africa, and west of Australia, is dominantly a tropical ocean. It connects with the Atlantic at the southern tip of Africa and with the Pacific through the East Indian islands and south of Australia. Like the Pacific, it has a shape rather like an inverted U. The Indian Ocean is the only ocean that does not touch North America.

The Arctic Ocean, because of its location in the north polar region, is of little importance in world trade. It is the counterpart of Antarctica and has almost the same size and shape. Most of the surface of the Arctic is covered by heavy, shifting masses of ice throughout the year. Near the shores of Eurasia and North America the Arctic sea lanes are usually open for a brief period during the short summer. The Arctic's position between Europe and North America gives it strategic importance. Air routes from North America to Eastern Europe over the Arctic Ocean are much shorter than those that follow parallels of latitude. The direct route over the Arctic shortens the flying distance between Fairbanks, Alaska, and Moscow, U.S.S.R., from about 6,000 miles across Siberia to 4,200 miles; and a flight over Greenland cuts the approximately 6,000 air miles from Chicago to Moscow to nearly 2,000 miles.

OCEANS AND MAN

The oceans, like the land, influence man and his activities in many ways. From the oceans man secures food, furs, minerals, and many other useful items. The oceans are the primary source of one of man's chief needs—water. It is from the oceans that the atmosphere secures most of the moisture which eventually falls as rain, snow, hail, or sleet, or may form a drifting fog.

Because of differences in temperature, variations in salinity, the rotation of the earth, winds, and the configuration and location of the continents on which the waters impinge, the ocean waters have definite movements called drifts and currents. Warm currents are streams of water that are warmer than the water through which they are flowing. For the most part warm currents flow generally toward the polar areas. In the Atlantic the warm Gulf Stream, flowing northward along the east coast of the United States, crosses the ocean under the influence of the westerly winds and moves northward along the northwest coast of Europe. Here the warmed waters help to produce a more moderate climate much farther north than is found on the east sides of continental masses. The Japanese Current in the north Pacific warms the western coast of North America. Cold currents are, in many ways, the opposite of warm currents. They are colder than the water through which they are flowing, usually flow equatorward, and often affect adversely the continental area past which they move. The Laborador Current, flowing south along the eastern Canadian coast, the Humboldt (Peruvian) Current, moving north along the west coast of South America, and the California Current, which flows along the California coast south from San Francisco, are typical examples. It must be remembered, however, that ocean currents have no effect on the land and man unless there is an onshore wind.

During past ages the oceans have served nations as defensive barriers, but with the air age their importance as barriers has diminished. The oceans continue, however, to furnish the cheapest means for the transportation of goods between nations; the world's greatest sea lane connects industrial Europe with industrial North America across the North Atlantic.

THE ATMOSPHERE

The layer of the atmosphere that rests on and penetrates the land and water surfaces is called the "troposphere." In this layer temperatures change, pressures vary, clouds form, moisture condenses, winds develop, and weather originates. Weather is the constant change in the atmospheric conditions; but when these conditions are observed for a period of years, fairly definite patterns of occurrence can be identified. Averaging weather data within a specified area gives climatic types, as is shown in Table 3.

TABLE 2   OCEANS

Ocean	Area, sq. mi.*	Average depth, ft.†	Greatest known depth, ft.
Arctic	5,440,000	4,200	17,850 (400 miles north of Herald Island)
Atlantic	31,000,000 plus 10,000,000 in adjoining seas	12,900	30,246 (Milwaukee Deep)
Indian	28,350,000	13,000	24,440 (Java Trench)
Pacific	64,000,000 plus 4,600,000 in adjoining seas	14,000	35,640 (Marianas Trench)

* Areas vary with authorities, depending on whether or not adjacent seas and bays are included.

† No complete ocean survey exists; therefore, this figure will change as research progresses.

TABLE 3   CLIMATIC REGIONS

Climate	Type locations	Characteristics
Rainy tropical	Amazon Basin Congo Basin Indonesia	Heavy rainfall all seasons, average temperature about 80°F. Average annual temperature range usually not more than 5 or 6°F. High humidity. All-year growing season.
Wet-and-dry tropical Savanna	Caribbean area Northern Australia East central Africa Sudan Llanos, Campos	Annual rainfall 30–60 in., uneven distribution. Hot wet season during period of greatest rainfall. Length of wet and dry seasons variable with distance from equator.
Monsoon	India Burma Southeast China	Heavy summer rainfall, dry winters. Annual temperatures usually average above 60°F.
Semiarid tropical steppe	Northern Mexico Iran Syria	Undependable, meager rainfall of 10–20 in. yearly. Low humidity. Temperatures range from below freezing in coldest months to an average of 60°F or higher during summer.
Tropical desert	Interior Saudi Arabia Sahara Australian Desert	Rainfall over much of area less than 4 in. annually. Large daily temperature ranges. Very low humidity.
Mediterranean	Mediterranean Basin Southwestern California Central Chile	Maximum rainfall during winter season with very little or no rainfall during summer. Semiarid to subhumid. Average yearly temperature about 60°F.
Marine west coast	Northwestern coast of United States British Isles—West central Europe Southern Chile	Temperate humid climate. Temperatures usually between 40–60°F. Great variation in rainfall depending on altitude. Rain all seasons, maximum winter.

TABLE 3 CLIMATIC REGIONS (continued)

Climate	Type locations	Characteristics
Humid subtropical	Southeastern United States East central China Pampa of Argentina Southern Brazil	Average hot month temperatures about 75°F. Winters usually mild. Yearly rainfall varies from 30 to 65 in. depending on distance inland.
Humid continental Long summer	Corn Belt, United States Hungary Korea	Warm to hot summers, cold winters. Rainfall varies, decreasing toward interior of continent and with increasing latitude. Usually an early summer maximum.
Short summer	Northeast United States Southeast Siberia Central Russia	Mild to cool summers. Long, cold winters. Annual rainfall about 30–40 in., fairly evenly distributed throughout the year.
Continental or mid-latitude steppe	Great Plains, United States Chaco, Argentina	Large variation in annual rainfall. Average 16–22 in. Hot summers, cool to cold winters.
Continental or mid-latitude desert	Mohave Desert, Great Basin Gobi Turkestan	Marked temperature extremes; hottest month averages 90°F. Rainfall usually less than 7 in.
Subpolar continental or taiga	Central and east central Canada Central part of Soviet Union	Long, cold winters. At least one month has average temperature above 50°F. In summer long periods of daylight during each 24 hr. Much of area receives less than 15 in. of rainfall.
Tundra or polar	Arctic coast of Asia, Europe, and North America	Very short, cool summers. Long, cold winters. Average temperature warmest month between 32–50°F. Annual rainfall usually 10–12 in.
Polar icecap	Antarctica Northern Greenland	No month with average temperature above 32°F.
High altitude	Himalayas Andes Rockies	Conditions vary with altitude in a particular latitude.

CLIMATIC ZONES

The climate of any particular place is the aggregate of its weather averaged out in terms of temperature, precipitation and humidity, pressure and winds, and location and topography. Mountains especially influence the amount of rainfall a place may receive, depending upon its location on the windward or leeward side. Storms can advance more easily over plains than in areas of rugged relief.

Climatic regions must be areas of generalizations. The boundaries of climatic regions are seldom well-defined lines as shown on maps, but are rather zones of increasing variation in rainfall, temperature, cloudiness, number of storms, and other factors. A place in western Iowa, which is in a climate boundary zone, might have a dry continental-steppe climate one year and a humid continental-interior climate the following year.

That the pattern of climates is fairly regular can be determined by a study of the map. Mediterranean climates, for example, always occur on the west coasts of continents in latitudes of approximately 30° to 40° in both the Northern and Southern Hemispheres. These regions have a pattern of winter rainfall, summer dryness, and moderate temperatures throughout the year. In like manner the humid continental climates appear within the interior or along the east coasts of the continents. In these areas the range of temperature increases and rainfall decreases toward the interior from the coast. The characteristics of each of the other climatic regions are summarized in Table 3.

CLIMATE AND MAN

The climate of an area affects, at least to some extent, what man may do to make a living. Most of the grasslands or steppes of the world are used for grazing. Humid continental interior areas are usually good farmlands; the marine west coast is, in many respects, ideal for forests. Where minerals are found, where good harbors exist, where manufacturing has been developed, climate has less influence upon the activities of man. In the not too distant future, technological advances may enable man to bring water for irrigation from the oceans, to seed clouds for rainfall when and where needed, to track and dissipate tornadoes, and in numerous other ways to adapt the climate to human needs.

Part I   The Americas

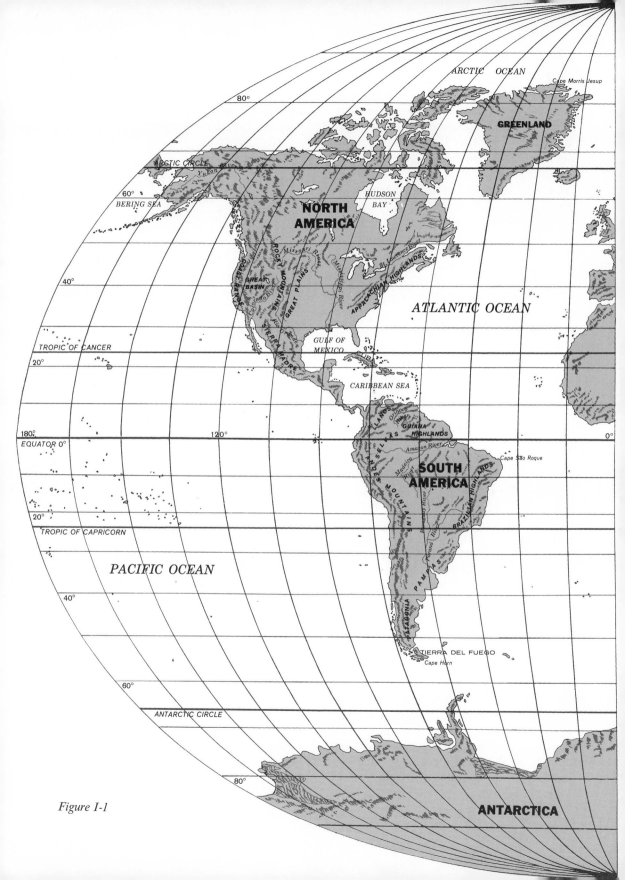

Figure I-1

NORTH AND SOUTH AMERICA ARE sizable continents, their combined area totaling more than 14 million square miles; yet when compared with Asia they are small, since that largest of all continents is over 2 million square miles greater in area than the New World. South America is southeast of its northern neighbor, with most of its west coast lying east of the meridian of New York City. Cape São Roque, the eastern-most point in Brazil, is on the mid-meridian between New York and London; Cape Prince of Wales, the most western point of the Alaskan mainland, is only 60 miles from Asia. The American continents extend between Cape Morris Jesup at the northern tip of Greenland, only 440 miles from the North Pole, and Cape Horn, at 56° south latitude, the southern tip of South America.

PHYSICAL SETTING

CLIMATE CONTRASTS

Climatically the continents have many differences. The whole area of North America is north of the equator, and only its narrowest part has a rainy, tropical climate. In contrast, since the equator crosses South America at almost its greatest width, much of that continent has a wet, tropical climate. With cold climates the reverse is true. The Arctic Circle crosses northern North America near its maximum width, and thus the far north of this continent has such a severe climate that the few inhabitants can engage in little agriculture. On the other hand, the entire continent of South America is well north of the Antarctic Circle, only stormy Tierra del Fuego and the high mountain areas having climates too cold for farming. In general, the middle latitudes have the climates most favorable for man. South America is narrow in the mid-latitude areas, but this handicap is rendered in some measure less serious because a considerable amount of tropical South America has such a high elevation.

RELIEF FEATURES

The relief features of North and South America are somewhat similar. Each continent has a mountain chain paralleling the Pacific, that in South America being much higher than its North American counterpart. East of the mountain barrier vast plains extend north-south through the continental interiors. The plains of North America are well populated in the middle latitudes, but settlement rapidly declines toward the north. In South America the widest plains are in the tropics and are poorly developed when compared with the mid-latitude plains of Argentina and Uruguay. Unfortunately, these countries are located where the continent is rapidly narrowing, so that areas of productive land and favorable climate are smaller than similar areas in the United States. Highlands, older geologically and more reduced in height by erosion than the western cordilleras, are located near much of the Atlantic coast in both continents. In general they are considerably less of a barrier than the younger, higher, and more rugged western mountains, and have less effect on climate.

PEOPLE OF THE NEW WORLD

The first people to occupy the New World were the American Indians, whose ancestors came from Asia. They eventually occupied both continents although the Indian population in neither was ever very great. Their culture depended to a great extent upon their physical environments. Where conditions were favorable, several wild plants—beans, squash, maize (corn), pumpkins, white potatoes, manioc (cassava), bananas, yams—were domesticated. Besides the dog, the llama of Peru was the only domestic animal kept by the Indians. Some groups, such as the Incas of the Andean plateaus and the Aztecs of Mexico, attained high stages of civilization by becoming both farmers and craftsmen. The Iroquoian and the Muskhogean groups, living in what is now the eastern part of the United States, developed a somewhat sedentary agricultural civilization. On the Western plains, however, the Sioux, Arapaho, Cheyenne, Comanche, Osage, and others, lived a migratory life by following the buffalo herds as they roamed the plains. Some of the Indians living in the Pacific Northwest were fishermen, whereas many of those in California were gatherers, who depended on roots and fruits.

At present North America has almost double the population of its southern neighbor. The Spanish, who settled much of the area south of the Rio Grande, came seeking riches in the form of gold and other scarce minerals. The English, who eventually dominated settlement north of the Rio Grande, came seeking places to build homes and to develop agriculture and other resources. Finally they produced manufactured goods for the markets of the world. Independence for the Colonies and the development of the United States as it expanded across the continent helped to attract thousands of migrants to the New World. Even in proportion to population, North America produces more raw materials and manufactured goods than does South America. Reasons for this greater production in North America are the large areas where soil and climate are suitable for growing wheat, cotton, corn, and other agricultural products, the far greater resources of coal, and the development of other minerals

and of water power. In addition are the less tangible but equally important contributions of inventiveness, skill in all forms of production, and political stability.

During the last century great shifts in population have occurred in the United States. From the 1860s into the 1890s most of the public land of the West passed into private ownership, and the population was predominantly rural. Thereafter industries expanded, and the cities grew until now the population is largely urban.

GEOGRAPHIC SITUATIONS

NORTH AMERICA

The western part of North America is dominated by high, rugged mountains. The Western Cordillera extends southward from the Alaskan and Brooks Ranges in Alaska and is separated in Canada into the Pacific Coast Range and the Rocky Mountains. The Coast Range, trending south and southeast, has determined much of the shape of the western edge of the continent. The Rocky Mountains in many places parallel the Coast Range, the eastern edge being about 600 miles inland. At approximately the 49th parallel, however, the Rockies form a large curve, swinging eastward into the central parts of Colorado and New Mexico, and in places are more than 1,000 miles east of the Coast Range.

In the United States, between these two mountain groups, other large mountain ranges and plateaus have developed. The Columbia Intermontane province in Washington, Oregon, and Idaho was formed mainly as a result of volcanic activity; the Colorado Plateau of Utah, Colorado, New Mexico, and Arizona has resulted from a gradual uplifting of the land. Inland from the coast, the Sierra Nevada of eastern California and the Cascades of Washington and Oregon are both higher than the Coast Range. The largest area of North America without drainage to the oceans is the part of Nevada and Utah that is trapped between the Rockies and the Sierra Nevada.

In northern Mexico the various ranges come together forming the Sierra Madre and the Central Plateau of Mexico. South of the Isthmus of Tehuantepec the mountains form a low, broken ridge to the South American border. The Western Cordillera has its greatest elevations in the north, Mt. McKinley in southern Alaska reaching 20,270 feet. The highest point in the coterminous United States is Mt. Whitney, of the Sierra Nevada in California, with an elevation of 14,996 feet.

The effect of these western mountains upon the activities of man is very distinct. Since their elevations cause the prevailing westerly winds to be cooled and thus to lose their moisture, the area between the mountains and even for some distance east of the Rockies is too dry for most types of agriculture. Grazing and irrigation farming are the dominant occupations except where mining or some specialized activity has developed. Population density over most of the area is sparse.

In the eastern part of the continent old, worn-down mountains, such as the Laurentian Highlands of Canada and the Appalachians of the United States, are bordered by low plateaus or plains. Although these mountains formed transportation barriers during the colonial period, they present only minor difficulties to modern engineering. The mountains have contributed to the growth of manufacturing since they are the source of much water power as well as of coal and iron. Much of the area, already highly industrialized and densely populated, has been aided by the completion of the St. Lawrence–Great Lakes Seaway.

The central part of North America is a vast plain. Fertile soils, moderate rainfall, and agricultural skill have made it the most productive food-supplying region in the world. American farms or ranches are highly mechanized, and with careful farm management more wheat, cotton, corn, hogs, cattle, and other farm products are grown than in any other comparable area. Highways, railways, and airways connect all parts of this highly productive area with the Eastern industrial region. Good harbors along the eastern coast give its output easy access to world markets.

Three large groups of islands—the Aleutians, the Canadian Arctic Archipelago, and the West Indies—are also part of North America. Southwest of Greenland, the world's largest island, and north of Canada lie Victoria, Baffin, Ellesmere, and many other islands, which form the Canadian Arctic Archipelago. Some have never been completely explored. Because of their high latitude and cold climate, most are uninhabited. Greenland is nearly covered by an icecap, and most of its population lives along the southern and southwestern shore. Its chief importance is as a military site. Extending westward from the Alaskan Peninsula toward Asia are the Aleutians, a group of volcanic islands of relatively little importance. Between the United States and South America are the Greater Antilles and other productive islands that make up the West Indies. Since many of these mountainous islands are greatly overpopulated, the standard of living in most instances leaves much to be desired.

SOUTH AMERICA

South America, like North America, also has a region of high, rugged, young mountains along its west coast, old, low, and worn-down mountains to the east, and large plains between the two. The Andes, a formidable barrier between eastern and western South America, rise abruptly from the Pacific and Caribbean shores of the continent. Starting with three distinct ridges in Venezuela and Colombia, they extend for 4,000 miles along the western edge of the continent to Cape Horn. In the southern part of Colombia the three ridges come together. From this point southward they separate, as in Ecuador, southern Peru, and Bolivia, leaving high intermontane basins and plateaus between the ridges. South from central Chile they form a long, high, continuous range. The Andes attain their greatest elevation on the Chilean-Argentine border in Mt. Aconcagua, 22,835 feet, which is the highest point in the Americas. Since much of South America is in the tropics, the intermontane plateaus, here about 4,000 to 7,000 feet in elevation, are among the more desirable places for human habitation. It was in these plateau basins that the Indians reached their highest stage of civilization.

In the eastern part of the continent, the older highlands and plateaus of Brazil and the Guiana Highlands of Venezuela are somewhat comparable to the highlands in eastern North America. On the plateaus and highlands of eastern Brazil that country has its greatest agricultural, mineral, and manufacturing development and its greatest population density.

Except for part of the Pampa, the large plains areas of South America are poorly developed. The Llanos of Venezuela and Colombia, the Amazon Basin of Brazil, and the Gran Chaco of Paraguay and Argentina are all sparsely settled. Climatic conditions, which vary seasonally from droughts to periods of excessive rainfall, and an all-year high temperature tend to retard settlement. The Pampa of Argentina and Uruguay, in an area of temperate climate, is one of the world's leading producers of cattle, sheep, and wheat. Again with the exception of the Pampa, which has a well-developed railway network, the South American plains lack transportation systems other than their rivers. The Amazon River, which carries more water than any other in the world, drains the large Amazon Basin. The Orinoco serves the Llanos, and the Gran Chaco depends upon the Paraná and its tributaries for a part of its transportation.

Since the coastline of South America, except for the southern third of Chile, is very regular, the continent has few good harbors. None of southern Chile's many islands are important. The large island of Tierra del Fuego is at the southern end of the continent, from which it is separated by the Strait of Magellan; the Falkland Islands, controlled by Britain but claimed by Argentina, are about 300 miles east of the Strait of Magellan; the Galapagos Islands, owned by Ecuador, are approximately 600 miles west of that country. None of the groups contribute much to world economy.

chapter 1

THE UNITED STATES:
THE NORTHEAST

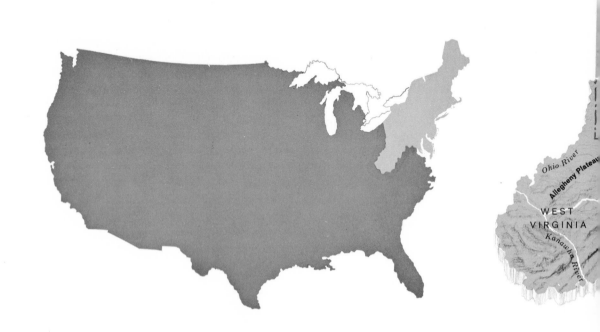

Figure 1-1 The physical landscape of the Northeast is characterized by numerous mountain ranges and ridges interlocked with a series of elongated valleys and bordered, in part, by plateaus.

*T*HOSE OF US WHO LIVE AND WORK IN the United States of America are convinced that this nation enjoys advantages beyond those of any other political unit or region on the face of the earth. Every American should be thoroughly familiar with the geographic conditions that prevail in his country and should understand the sources of its strength—a strength that has placed it among the leading industrial, agricultural, and military nations of the world.

Over three centuries ago European immigrants began to settle in North America, clear the forests, till the fertile soil, and develop the abundant resources of the New World. They came to a sparsely inhabited continent whose natural resources were almost undeveloped. Today the United States with an area of over 3,628,-000 square miles and a population of more than 180,000,000 persons ranks fourth among the nations in both size and total population. Within this vast area can be found examples of practically all the variout types of physical and cultural environments that exist in the world. In many parts of the United States changes in the natural environment and adjustments to it have been unique. Sometimes large amounts of a natural resource have been wasted or destroyed or human resources have been carelessly used; but in general the interrelationships between man and his surroundings have served to develop for most citizens of the United States the highest standard of living possessed in any nation on the earth.

Because of the wide variety of physical areas involved, the variations in economic development, and different conditions of cultural adjustments, the study of the United States has been divided, in this book, into four chapters, dealing respectively with the Northeast, the South, the Midwest, and the West. The bases for the divisions are largely locational, and state boundaries are ordinarily used. But aside from its geographical position, each division also has characteristics of physical and cultural environment that help to distinguish it from all the other areas. Of course no area in the United States or in the world stands alone, for each is an interdependent part of the whole. Regardless of where the boundaries of an area or region are drawn, they are not definite lines as shown on maps, but are rather zones in which the activities of man and nature gradually change from one situation to another.

The Northeast, as designated in this study, extends southward from northern Maine to the Potomac River and westward from the Atlantic Coast to western New York, Pennsylvania, and West Virginia. This Northeastern division differs from the other parts of the United States by reason of its vast urban development. Of a total population of over 50 million persons, almost 80 per cent of them live in approximately 1,400 incorporated places. The only state in the area where more than half of the population do not live in urbanized areas is Vermont; no more than 38.5 per cent of its people are so classified. Of the ten largest cities in the United States having populations of 750,000 or more, four—New York, Philadelphia, Baltimore, Washington—are in the Northeastern part of the nation. In this part of the United States the incorporated places dominate the landscape and have formed the great American megalopolis, the largest continuous urban area in the world. Here, in the Northeast, live over 25 per cent of the nation's population on less than 6 per cent of its area.

Although the Northeastern section is only a small part of the United States, it has long been a leader in the culture, commerce, and skilled manufactures of the

PHYSICAL REGIONS OF THE UNITED STATES

0 | | | | | 500 MILES

Figure 1-2   On the basis of landform and geologic structure the United States is divided into eight physical regions. Where adjacent to Canada or Mexico the regions extend into those countries.

APPALACHIAN HIGHLANDS: *New England, Piedmont Plateau, Blue Ridge, Ridge and Valley, Appalachian Plateaus*

COASTAL PLAIN

INTERIOR HIGHLANDS: *Ozark Plateau, Ouachita Mountains*

INTERIOR PLAINS: *Central Lowlands, Great Plains*

CANADIAN SHIELD: *Adirondack Mountains, Superior Highlands*

ROCKY MOUNTAINS: *Northern Rockies, Wyoming Basin, Southern Rockies*

INTERMONTANE REGION: *Columbia Intermontane Province, Basin and Range Province, Colorado Plateau*

PACIFIC REGION: *Sierra Nevada–Cascade Mountains, Pacific Ranges and Valleys*

nation. The first settlers came from Great Britain, the Netherlands, and Sweden. Since forests covered most of the region, land had to be cleared of trees before settlers could begin farming. Moreover, glaciers that once covered the northern two-thirds of the area had deposited stones that had to be picked off the fields before tillage could begin. Frequently the climate was severe; much of the land was hilly, and the soil was generally poor. Constant hard work was necessary if men were to make even a scant living on the small farms.

PHYSICAL SETTING

RELIEF FEATURES

The dominant physical region in the Northeastern area is the Appalachian System that extends southward from northern

Figure 1-3   The Northeast is a region of relatively small states that have many large cities. In most parts of the area towns, hamlets, and villages are never far apart.

Maine to northern Alabama (Figure 1-2). In New England the highland areas are continuous with those of eastern Canada. After being formed, the Appalachian System was eroded to a peneplain (almost a plain). Since then the system has been uplifted, extensively dissected by erosion, and the northern part glaciated. The upland areas of rough, irregular topography are inland, at no point extending to the sea. The Coastal Plain, beginning with Cape Cod and Long Island, extends only a few miles inland in the Northeastern area, but increases in width to the southward. The Adirondacks, lying between Lakes Champlain and Ontario and north of the Mohawk Valley, are separated from the Canadian section of the Canadian Shield by the St. Lawrence Lowland. A northeastward extension of the Central Lowlands occupies a small area south of Lake Ontario (Figure 1-2).

NEW ENGLAND   New England has diverse relief, with hills predominating; there are large areas of highlands and smaller areas of lowlands. The major uplands are the Green Mountains of Vermont, the White Mountains of New Hampshire, the Berkshire Hills in Massachusetts, and the Maine Uplands. In general, these upland surfaces exceed 2,000 feet in elevation with a few peaks attaining heights in excess of 5,000 feet. Many of the lowlands are located where the rocks offering the least resistance to glaciation occur. Lowlands include the Housatonic, Connecticut, and Merrimac Valleys, the Lake Champlain trench, the Narragansett, Portland, and Boston Basins, and the Aroostock area in northeast Maine. Most of the agriculture in New England is carried on in these valleys and basins; and in them are located also a great majority of the important New England cities.

The entire surface of New England has been glaciated. The tops of many hills and mountains were scraped off; weak rocks were gouged away. In some places rivers were dammed, and elsewhere glacial till, or moraines, were spread over large areas. Glacial lakes are numerous; but only a few are large enough to serve as sources of municipal and industrial water supply. On the other hand, the lakes do regulate stream flow, serve as recreation sites, and add beauty to the landscape. Glaciers and glacial deposits often changed the course of rivers, causing waterfalls or rapids to form at outcrops of resistant rocks. Many factory towns were founded at such power sites. Along the ocean shore, the glaciers dug deep troughs below sea level in the river valleys that permit the sea to penetrate far inland.

NEW YORK LOWLANDS AND THE ADIRONDACKS
New York State is crossed by two lowland areas. Along its eastern side the state is separated from New England by the Hudson River–Lake Champlain Lowland. Extending east-west across the state and separating the Adirondacks from the Appalachian Plateaus, is the Mohawk Lowland. The two lowlands, which are at

Figure 1-4   Glaciers once covered most of the region. The tops of many hills and mountains were scraped off. (Courtesy of Vermont Department of Highways.)

right angles to each other, form the much used land and water transportation route from New York to Buffalo and the interior of the United States. The Hudson River is so deep that oceangoing ships can go upstream as far as Albany. Smaller ships can navigate to Troy or through a canal to Lake Champlain and then through the Richelieu River to the St. Lawrence.

The chief tributary to the Hudson River is the Mohawk, which flows east to join the major stream at Cohoes. Through the Mohawk Valley and the lowlands to its west, was built the Erie Canal. Between 1905 and 1918 the Erie Canal and the canalized Mohawk River were deepened and widened to form the New York State Barge Canal, which extends from Troy on the Hudson River to Tonawanda on the Niagara River, from which point it connects with Lake Erie. Branch canals provide access to Lake Ontario ports. Along this same route has also developed an extensive system of railways and highways.

The Adirondacks, lying between Lakes Champlain and Ontario and north of the Mohawk Valley, are a part of the Canadian Shield but are separated from it by the St. Lawrence Lowland. During the glacial period the ice sheets removed the surface materials, smoothed and rounded the bedrock, and deepened the valleys. As the ice retreated the area was left covered with till (glacial debris), which deranged many of the streams, forming waterfalls, rapids, and lakes. Although some of the lakes have disappeared as a result of filling or draining, the Adirondacks are still a region of lakes.

ATLANTIC COASTAL PLAIN The Atlantic Coastal Plain has a nearly level surface and rises toward the interior in a series of low terraces. The great irregularity of the coastline is due to the drowning of river mouths by the invasion of ocean water.

The resulting estuaries, or tidewater bays, include Delaware and Chesapeake Bays and the Potomac River. Inland a scarp (low cliff) marks the contact of the Coastal Plain with the Piedmont. Where streams cross this scarp, there are rapids or falls, according to the differences in the hardness of the rocks. The resulting feature, known as the Fall Line, determines the head of navigation on most major rivers of the area as well as the site of numerous water power developments. Many cities, including Trenton, Baltimore, and Washington, are located along the Fall Line, and their elevations vary from near sea level to over 300 feet.

NORTHERN APPALACHIAN HIGHLANDS The Northern Appalachian Highlands, like their counterpart in New England and eastern Pennsylvania, greatly influenced the early activities in the region. The Ridge and Valley area, with its curving depressions, plus the width of the rugged Allegheny Plateau, presented many problems to the development of transportation systems and lines of communications.

The northern Allegheny Plateau includes the Catskill and Pocono Mountains as well as the Finger Lakes district of New York. Along with portions of northwest Pennsylvania and northeast Ohio, this area has been glaciated and is more extensively eroded than the land farther south. Many lakes are scattered among the forest-covered hills. In the Poconos, Catskills, and Finger Lakes areas a thriving tourist industry has developed. Cool summers, scenic hills, and placid lakes with large cities nearby are all inducements to the vacationer.

CLIMATE

The climate of the Northeastern area is of a continental type (Figure 1-5). Near the coast it is somewhat modified by the winds

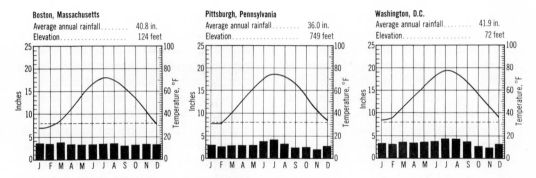

Boston, Massachusetts
Average annual rainfall........ 40.8 in.
Elevation.................... 124 feet

Pittsburgh, Pennsylvania
Average annual rainfall........ 36.0 in.
Elevation.................... 749 feet

Washington, D.C.
Average annual rainfall........ 41.9 in.
Elevation.................... 72 feet

Figure 1-5   Climate graphs of selected stations.

that blow from the sea a part of the time. Away from the coast, toward the interior, the length of the growing season decreases markedly and rapidly, being only 159 days in Burlington, Vermont, as compared with 199 days in Boston. The length of the growing season also increases southward; it is as much as 200 days in some parts of Lancaster County, Pennsylvania. Rainfall occurs during each month of the year, the heaviest rainfall usually coming during the summer. Temperatures range from below freezing in the winter months to well above 80°F during the summer.

ECONOMIC DEVELOPMENT

The people of the Northeastern area make their living in numerous ways. Agriculture, forestry, fishing, and the various recreational activities are all important producers of income. Manufacturing and the industries associated directly with it, however, bring more wealth into the area and employ more people than do all other kinds of economic development combined. Because of the relationship of manufacturing to urban areas and urban development, that economic activity will be discussed in connection with the various cities.

AGRICULTURE

Early settlers in the Northeastern area came seeking a living from the land. Farming in New England although handicapped by cold winters, short, cool summers, thin, stony soils, poor transportation, and a limited market survived as a major activity until the opening of the Erie Canal, the building of railroads, and the development of manufacturing. Importation of cheap wheat and other farm products from the interior brought about the abandonment of many farms, especially those at high elevation; fields reverted to scrub and forest, and houses settled into ruin. A part of this erstwhile farmland is now in state and national forests. Some abandoned farms, however, have been reoccupied by European immigrants and by city folk desiring to own land or a country home.

In many sections of New England specialized farming prevails. Dairy farming is highly developed, and dairy products normally account for about one-third of the cash income from agriculture. During the cool, wet summers, hay and pasture grasses grow well even on steep slopes with poor, leached soils. From 80 to 90 per cent of the cropland harvested in the Vermont and New Hampshire uplands is devoted to hay. Corn is grown for grain and silage, and near the large industrial cities, the dairy industry uses large quantities of imported feed concentrates. Improved handling of fresh milk and the large urban demand for milk products have enabled dairy farmers remote from markets to operate successfully. The Lake Champlain Lowland of western Vermont ships milk and cream to Boston, southern New England cities, and New York.

Specialty crops are locally important. Sumatra leaf tobacco, which is used for cigar wrappers, is grown on the terraces of the lower Connecticut River. The crop is shielded from the sun by cloth netting supported by poles and wire, whereas tobacco for cigar fillers is grown in the open. In the Aroostook Valley of Maine the sandy, porous soils and the cool, rainy summers delimit an area where potatoes are grown; because of their superior quality and the care used in production and grading, many of these potatoes are sold for seed. Another Maine specialty is sweet corn for canning, the climate keeping the corn at just the right degree of succulence for a considerable period. Onions and a variety of market vegetables come from suitable land near the cities. Many hardy fruits, especially apples, are grown. On Cape Cod cranberries improved from the wild variety are planted in swampy mucklands. Maine harvests and cans large quantities of wild blueberries. Maple syrup is also a specialty product, especially in Vermont, where the long, cool springs with freezing nights and thawing days result in a flow of sap sufficiently prolonged to justify the labor and expense of tapping the sugarbush.

Agriculture has also long been an important activity on the Coastal Plain. The earliest settlements in tidewater Maryland, Pennsylvania, and New Jersey were generally rural. Towns were few

because most plantations and many farms had frontage on tidewater. Planters often shipped directly to England and received imports from the mother country at their own landings. The wide-spreading bays, an advantage for commerce in colonial days, became a liability in later times when land routes largely replaced waterways. As a result, parts of peninsular Maryland east of Chesapeake Bay became isolated, and a quiet rural life survives there in contrast with the more common suburban developments around the many great cities near the inner margin of the Coastal Plain.

Much of the Coastal Plain is covered with light sandy soils. The ground is easily tilled, and many truck farmers produce early- and late-season vegetables and fruits for the urban markets. On drained swampland and loam soils in northern New Jersey, the truck farms are meticulously tended and yield abundantly. Other sections of northern New Jersey and peninsular Maryland are also intensively farmed, much fertilizer being used to increase production. In the Delmarva Peninsula poultry raising is of prime importance, for the area is one of the nation's leaders in the broiler industry. Besides the fruit, vegetables, and poultry that are sped by rail or truck to the cities, great quantities are canned or frozen. More than 400 canneries and other food-processing plants operate in and around Baltimore. Other hundreds operate in the Camden and Philadelphia district.

In the Piedmont area of Pennsylvania, especially near York and Lancaster, careful rotation of crops—corn, wheat, hay, oats—and the practice of mixed farming with livestock production have prevented erosion and even increased the original fertility of the soil. Grass and hay crops thrive. Here the farmers are prosperous, and the rural population is increasing. The big barns, houses, and other farm build-

Figure 1-6   Much of the land of southern New Jersey is in truck farms. Here, near Riverton, a field is being planted with carrots. (Courtesy of Riverton News and Views.)

ings are evidence of good farming practices.

In the Allegheny Plateau area are numerous dairy farms, from which fresh milk is shipped to city markets or processing plants. Although much land is in pasture, hay, corn, and small grains are the usual crops. Farming on the steep slopes has frequently resulted in badly eroded fields, land abandonment, and a decrease in the local farm population. In Pennsylvania, especially in Indiana County, tree farming has been instituted. Millions of conifers have been planted on the gullied hills, from which they are harvested and sold as Christmas trees.

FORESTS

A view of the New England landscape from an airplane or mountain peak gives the impression of extensive forests broken by small cultivated areas and settlements. Often small communities are half hidden by the tall shade trees that give an added charm to the fine old dwellings. Over 75 per cent of New England is under some sort of forest cover. These forests are the recreation playgrounds and sports areas for the large urban communities of the Northeastern United States. Besides the

woodlot found on nearly every farm, commercial forests cover large areas.

For over two hundred years the region supplied lumber for building, wood manufacturing, ships, and fuel. During many decades, Bangor, on the Penobscot River, was the preeminent sawmill center of the nation. After the virgin forests had been cut, the new growth was useful chiefly for pulpwood and cordwood. Today the pulp and paper industry is the largest consumer, although the forests still produce other materials in reduced amounts. Improved forest management is a definite regional need, although some of the paper companies manage their large forest holdings so efficiently that their pulpwood requirements can be supplied permanently. National, state, and community forests, along with some privately owned land, are being developed for growing timber. Usually pulp and paper mills are located along rivers, which can be used for power, log storage, and manufacturing needs, just as the sawmills were built on comparable sites before the timber was largely exhausted. New England today has less standing saw timber than any other forested region in the nation.

Along the irregular coastline of New England are many harbors useful to both local fishermen and ocean commerce. The abundance of excellent timber—white pine for masts, spruce for spars, and oak for framework and planking—helped to make shipbuilding profitable in the days of wooden sailing vessels, and pine trees also provided tar, pitch, and turpentine—the so-called naval stores. There are still many boatyards and shipbuilding establishments.

FISHERIES

In the shallow waters adjacent to New England is one of the major fishing grounds of the world. Here the banks, usually less than 100 fathoms in depth, are important feeding grounds for cod, halibut, haddock, mackerel, and herring. Fisheries have been an important source of income since colonial days. Although the catch varies, it is approximately a billion pounds annually, and two-thirds of it enters through Massachusetts ports, especially Gloucester and Boston. Fish are sold fresh in local markets, and are also quick-frozen, canned, salted, dried, or smoked. Shore fisheries supply clams, oysters, crabs, and lobsters. Some by-products of the industry are fish meal, fertilizer, and vitamin oil. During the century preceding the 1870s New England dominated the whaling industry, and the whalers, together with the commercial trading fleet, carried the American flag to all shores of the world. Profits from the whaling industry furnished some of the capital for the construction of textile mills such as those in New Bedford and Fall River.

Fish have always been an important source of food along the Coastal Plain. Chesapeake and Delaware Bays lead the United States in the production of shellfish. Oysters grow in the warm, shallow water that is relatively free from silt and mud. Overexploitation of the beds has led to the development of oyster farms, where the oysters are propagated scientifically. Locally, herring, shad, flounder, mackerel, and bluefish are taken by offshore fishermen, and quantities of menhaden are netted, which, though inedible, are used in the fertilizer industry. Owners of small craft often take parties of vacationers "deep-sea fishing" in the shallow waters of the Continental Shelf.

MINERALS

Mining is not a major activity of New England as the area contains no coal or petroleum, and deposits of metals are of small importance. Building stone, however, is quarried extensively. Barre, Vermont, is famed for granite, and marble is produced in several localities. Stone is now used mostly for decorative purposes and monuments. It has been largely replaced by concrete, steel, and glass in large structures because these materials cost less, use less labor, and so make building more economical. Iron ore is mined in small quantities in the Adirondacks and eastern Pennsylvania. The most active mining period in recent years was during and immediately after World War II. Near Syracuse salt deposits are exploited by the chemical industries.

Pennsylvania and West Virginia are the important producers of mineral fuels; the principal anthracite coal mines of the United States are near Scranton and Wilkes-Barre. Anthracite is mined from those parts of the Appalachian ridges which were subject to intense pressure. Because of the competition of petroleum and natural gas, production of anthracite has declined since 1945.

In the western part of the Appalachians the rocks have not been as intensively folded as in the eastern area. In western Pennsylvania and West Virginia lies the most productive part of the Appalachian coalfield, an area of high-grade bitumi-

Figure 1-7   West Virginia is one of the leading producers of high-grade bituminous coal. Here a tug pushes several barges of coal down the Monongahela River. (Courtesy of Dravo Corporation.)

nous coal. The availability of this source of power is the most important factor in the location of the manufacturing belt in the United States, the area known especially for the manufacture of iron and steel and other heavy goods. Here the towns are generally of two types, farm-market centers with fine old houses and shady streets, and mining towns, in many of which the operators have built the houses all alike. These latter towns are frequently ugly, devoid of trees, and situated in a landscape dominated by huge piles of waste rock. Bituminous coal production is highly mechanized both in the surface, or strip, mines and underground. Cutting, loading, sorting, cleaning, chemical treatment, and blending of the coal is done by machines.

Petroleum and natural gas are two other sources of available power. The first oil well in the United States was drilled in 1859 in northwestern Pennsylvania. The names of Oil City and Titusville were famous in the early days of the oil industry. Much high-grade petroleum is still pumped from the oil fields of Pennsylvania and West Virginia.

RECREATION

Recreation in the Northeastern part of the United States is favored by the beauty and variety of the landscapes and inland resorts, and by the nearness of the play-

grounds to New York, Washington, Boston, and other large cities. The area offers mountains, hills, forests, lakes and rivers, irregular coasts varying from sandy beaches to rock-girt harbors, hunting, fishing and boating facilities, deep, long-lying snows for winter sports, interesting historical sites and architectural gems, national, state, and community parks, and a closely woven net of highways and railroads. There are varied accommodations for people of different means. An increasing appreciation of the importance of industry has stimulated willingness to cater to various wants and tastes. Thousands of people are supported by the recreation industry, which brings to New England alone an estimated income of more than half a billion dollars annually. The development of recreation and summer residence in localities once hard to reach was made possible by the automobile and by paved highways along the ocean shores, to inland waters, and to mountain views.

Upper New York State, north of the Mohawk Valley, is a rugged, mountainous country. A region of peaks, forests, lakes, and scenic beauty, the Adirondacks serve as an important recreation area, and many hunters and fishermen are attracted to the region. The Adirondack Forest Preserve covers much of the section. Resort hotels have been built along the shores of Lake

Placid, Lake George, and other bodies of water; and during the winter season the resorts remain open for such activities as skiing, sledding, and ice skating. Transportation routes by both rail and highway cross or penetrate the region.

Along the Coastal Plain the tourist and recreation industry is also big business, amounting to several hundred million dollars annually. Summer resorts have developed along the seashore, where sandy beaches are within easy reach of the larger cities. Among these resorts Atlantic City, with its famed 7-mile-long boardwalk, Asbury Park, Jones Beach, and Coney Island are perhaps the best known.

CITIES AND INDUSTRIES

From Portland, Maine, to northern Virginia stretches an almost continuous series of cities. Functioning as seaports and railroad terminals, or as manufacturing, financial, and political centers, they form the American megalopolis. The focal point of the cities in this strip is New York. Between the major cities of this urbanized zone are situated mills, factories, and refineries at spacious sites convenient to transportation, great numbers of suburban communities, and thousands of country homes. Transportation by private

Figure 1-8   A large majority of the people of the Northeastern United States live in urban areas. Only in one state, Vermont, is more than one-half of the population classed as rural.

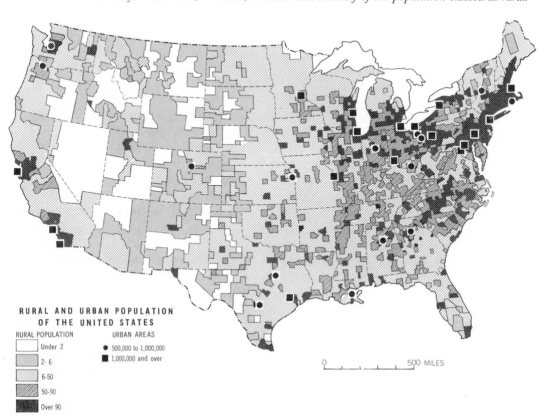

RURAL AND URBAN POPULATION
OF THE UNITED STATES

RURAL POPULATION   URBAN AREAS

☐ Under 2

▨ 2- 6   ● 500,000 to 1,000,000

▨ 6-50   ■ 1,000,000 and over

▨ 50-90

▨ Over 90

0   500 MILES

automobile, trucks, buses, and commuter trains makes living in the country or suburbs as convenient as living in the big cities. So many people prefer homes outside of the city limits that, since 1920, the suburbs have grown much faster than the cities themselves. Within the Northeastern area, in 1960, there were 52 metropolitan areas with a total population of almost 35 million persons. In fact, many cities recorded decreases in population between 1950 and 1960.

Because the Appalachian Highlands separate this urbanized zone from the populous and productive Ohio Valley and the southern Great Lakes region, the corridors that connect the coastal and interior cities are of major importance. Railroads and highways cross the mountain barrier from Washington, Baltimore, and Philadelphia, but the lowest route, and one that is without steep grades, is in the Hudson-Mohawk lowlands between New York and Buffalo. The route extends north from New York to Albany and then west to Lake Erie. Indians and fur traders first used the route, and wagons followed. In 1825 the Erie Canal, now the New York State Barge Canal, was opened, and New York became the seaboard terminus of the only low-level water route from the rich and rapidly developing interior lowlands. In 1851, a through railroad was completed between Buffalo and New York. The combination of canal and rail services so stimulated commerce and settlement that New York quickly outgrew its former rivals, Boston, Philadelphia, and Baltimore, in trade and population. Along the Hudson-Mohawk route, an urbanized belt, containing scores of cities, has developed. The excellent transportation has led to the establishment of many manufacturing plants which provide employment.

A large majority of the people of New England live in cities, where they work in

Figure 1-9   Waterways have played a large part in the development of the Northeastern states. Large quantities of fuel, grain, and bulk goods are transported over the New York State Barge Canal system. (Courtesy of New York State Department of Commerce.)

factories, engage in commerce, trade, and service occupations, or follow some craft or profession. Also important are financial businesses such as investments and banking, insurance, importing and exporting, and the management of large corporations. The region is a hive of industry, producing nearly 10 per cent of all manufactures of the United States, an achievement the more noteworthy since few raw materials are secured locally.

New England produces little wool and no cotton; yet it leads the country in the fabrication of woolens and manufactures much cotton cloth. Concord, Manchester, Nashua, Lowell, Lawrence, Fall River, New Bedford, Providence, and numerous other cities are important for textiles. Although not notable for the production of hides and leather, the region leads in making women's shoes and ranks high in the production of men's shoes; Brockton, Haverhill, and Lynn are noted for footware. The region also manufactures a large quantity of electronic and electrical materials, machinery, household equipment, tools, hardware, wire, and other steel products; among the cities known for these items are Springfield, Worcester, New Haven, Hartford, and Bridgeport. Ships are built at Quincy and other port cities. Hundreds of factories make specialty products such as watches at Waltham and Waterbury, optical goods at Southbridge, jewelry and emblems at Attleboro, hats at Danbury, canoes at Oldtown, fine paper at Holyoke, and all kinds of grinding equipment at Worcester. Providence, New Haven, Bridgeport, and Hartford all have a large variety of manufactures. Few parts of the world make so much, so well, with so few local resources. Among the factors accounting for New England's industrial importance are an early start and a reputation for producing excellent goods, skilled labor, efficient management, proximity to local markets, and capital for investment.

Although coal, oil, and natural gas are imported, New England has much water power. Before the development of electric power transmission, mills and factories were located at falls and dams where machinery could be run directly by waterwheels, and as a result many towns were crowded into narrow valleys where water power was available. Manufactures are heavily concentrated, for as an industry succeeds, competitors follow, their enterprise favored by the skilled labor that has been trained for certain methods of production. Concentration, however, also has disadvantages. If a factory which is the main support of a community ceases operations, moves to some other site, or works on a part-time basis, the entire community suffers. Competition from Southern textile mills, which have expanded until they now surpass New England mills in output of cottons, has closed many New England mills. Some affected cities have been able to secure new industries, but others have suffered from unemployment and loss of population.

Many industrial cities have developed in the Mohawk Valley. Started because of some particular advantage of site, the cities have continued to grow because of improved transportation and their concentration upon producing industrial specialties. Albany is near the intersection of the Barge Canal and the Hudson River with the Lake Champlain Lowland route to Montreal. Rochester, at the falls of the Genesee River, early developed waterpower resources. Syracuse exploited local salt deposits to build a significant chemical industry. Some cities profited by utilizing the skills of early settlers: Gloversville was settled by immigrants trained in glove making, Utica by those skilled in the knitting industry. The important industries of other cities capitalized inventiveness or commercial acumen: Troy is noted for its manufacturing of shirts, Schenectady for electrical goods, and Rochester for the production of photographic equipment and scientific instruments.

Buffalo, the second largest city in New York, is located at the eastern terminus of water-borne traffic on the four western Great Lakes and at the western end of the Mohawk Lowland. This situation is excellent for receiving iron ore, limestone, and grains from upper lake ports. Coal comes from the Allegheny Plateau. The harbor, which has connections with the Atlantic Ocean via the St. Lawrence Seaway, has been extended and improved to accommodate large lake vessels, and docks and wharves are mechanized to speed loading and unloading. The western terminus of the New York State Barge Canal is an integral part of the waterfront. Originally primarily a transshipment point, Buffalo is today a great manufacturing city utilizing power from coal and from Niagara

Figure 1-10 Buffalo is an important terminus of waterborne traffic. It has large facilities for receiving iron ore, limestone, and grains. (Courtesy of Buffalo Chamber of Commerce.)

Falls for flour and cereal manufacture, steel fabrication, and chemical, electrical, and other industries.

The Pittsburgh district leads the world in the manufacture of iron and steel. The abundance of high-grade coking coal, the ease with which iron ores are imported from the Lake Superior region and Canada via the St. Lawrence Seaway, the early start of the industry, and the huge demand from nearby industries help to account for the regional importance of iron and steel manufacturing. Pittsburgh is located at the junction of three navigable rivers—the Ohio, the Monongahela, and the Allegheny—on a usable water route to the interior and the Gulf of Mexico, and it also has excellent railroad and highway connections. Although Pittsburgh, is located in the Northeastern area, its activities are closely related to those of other steel centers in the American Midwest. Youngstown, Wheeling, and Johns-

town are but a few of the many other steel centers. Besides steel, the district manufactures a great variety of products.

In spite of the importance of truck farming, fishing, and the tourist industry, most of the people living on the Coastal Plain in New Jersey, Pennsylvania, Delaware, and Maryland reside in cities and are employed in manufacturing, commerce, retail trade, and various service occupations. Situated on the eastern edge of the manufacturing belt, the area makes at least some of almost every product manufactured in the United States—iron and steel, oil products, chemicals, transportation equipment, electronics, radios and TV sets, clothing, textiles, electrical goods, and thousands of other articles. Most large cities of the Coastal Plain developed along the Fall Line, where water power, protection from storms and open sea, and the necessity for bulk breaking and transshipment led to early settle-

Figure 1-11 Steel-producing plants are located on both sides of the Monongahela River in and near Pittsburgh. This view shows large blast furnaces. (Courtesy of Jones and Laughlin Steel Corporation.)

ment and continued growth. Several of these cities have become major seaports, and nearly all are manufacturing centers. The large population of the region provides a huge market for all kinds of goods.

The low relief of the plain further aided manufacturing by permitting easy construction of railroads and highways, but the broad tidewater bays in many places prevented construction of routes along the coast. This problem has led to the building of great highway bridges over several of the bays—bridges rising so high above the water that ocean ships pass freely underneath the spans. Some examples are the Delaware, Chesapeake Bay, Potomac, and York bridges, in addition to those across the Hudson River. Combined with the turnpikes (toll roads) the bridges have greatly reduced travel time from New York to other Northeastern cities as well as those to the south and west. In addition, numerous railroads and many highways connect the industrial and seaport cities with the uplands and interior plains.

This large development of metropolitan regions and urban areas has been called the "main street and crossroads of the nation." In this megalopolis are five very large cities—Boston, New York, Philadelphia, Baltimore, Washington—about which the numerous agglomerations function. The almost continuous urban buildup accounts for the greatest concentration of population in the United States and the high density of population in the states of Rhode Island (812 per square mile) and New Jersey (806 per square mile), the two most densely populated states in the nation.

BOSTON

Southern New England is a land of cities; thirty-three urban areas have populations of 50,000 or more. Boston, the largest of these, is frequently called the "hub of New England." The city has an excellent harbor with deep entrance channels and an extensive frontage for berthing ships. Its sea-borne imports are largely coal and petroleum products, together with a variety of raw materials and commodities that are either consumed in New England or manufactured there. Imports far exceed exports both in tonnage and value. Like many of its old colonial neighbors, Boston is a city of narrow, crooked streets, historical landmarks, noted educational institutions, fine old residential districts, and cultural tradition.

Massachusetts Institute of Technology and Harvard University, both located in nearby Cambridge, as well as Boston University and several other Northeastern colleges and universities—Yale, Princeton, Syracuse, Clark, Pennsylvania State, Johns Hopkins—are noted institutions of higher learning. On the faculties of these colleges and universities are some of the outstanding research workers and teachers of the nation. Research is carried on in medicine, space exploration, weather, food, and var-

Figure 1-12 Sketch map of the New York harbor area showing major rivers, bays, and ship canals. (Adapted from a map of the Corps of Engineers, United States Army.)

ious other technological fields. Numerous foundations such as Ford, Carnegie, the National Science Foundation, and the Office of Naval Research contribute generously to the support of these activities in which people are paid to think. The discoveries resulting from such work have aided not only the people of the United States, but the people of the entire world.

NEW YORK

New York, the largest city in the Western Hemisphere, has developed from the settlement made as New Amsterdam in 1626 at the southern end of Manhattan Island. Now covering approximately 300 square miles and having a population of about 7,800,000, the city is the core of the Greater New York metropolitan area. Within this area of over 2,600 square miles live some 14,000,000 persons who reside in approximately 400 different municipalities. The metropolitan area includes such cities as Newark, Hoboken, Paterson in New Jersey, Stamford in Connecticut, and Yonkers and New Rochelle in New York. New York City alone now covers Manhattan and Staten Islands, part of Long Island, and some territory on the mainland. Politically, the city is divided into the five boroughs of the Bronx, Brooklyn, Manhattan, Queens, and Richmond.

Manhattan Island is the heart of the New York business district. Upon this island has been built the greatest group of skyscrapers in the world, many buildings exceeding fifty stories in height. Within these great buildings are housed the headquarters of the leading commercial, industrial, and financial enterprises of the United States. The density of population in the entire area of New York City exceeds 25,000 per square mile. During the daytime working period, in many of the Manhattan business districts the density is greater than 100,000 persons per square mile.

The intermingling of land and water hampers the movement of goods and people. Vehicular and railroad tunnels plunge under the water; enormous and costly bridges stretch high above, while tugs, barges, lighters, and ferryboats plying on the surface facilitate the movement of both people and goods. Twelve major railroads serve the port, although only three of them have terminals on Manhattan Island. Since most of the streets are narrow and sometimes winding, traffic congestion makes delivery by trucks slow and costly. Most New York residents do not try to drive cars to work, but even so, vehicular tunnels, subways, and throughways for automobiles have relieved the traffic only in part. Hundreds of thousands of office workers, professional persons, and laborers commute daily to Manhattan Island from Long Island, New Jersey, Connecticut, and Hudson River points, and at the rush hours the subways, suburban trains, ferries, and buses are filled to capacity in transporting suburbanites into or out of the metropolis.

One of the principal problems faced by New York, as well as by most other major cities of the nation, is that of water supply. Each day 1,200 million gallons of water are used by its industries and people. The cost of constructing aqueducts and tunnels to bring the city water from sources east of the Hudson and from the Catskills, west of the river, exceeds the cost of the Panama Canal or the Grand Coulee project.

Housing such a large population is also a problem of great concern. The population is polyglot, for people move into the metropolis from every country on earth; for example, special homogeneous groups live in Negro areas, Spanish Harlem, and Chinatown. Unfortunately, many New Yorkers live in crowded and often unhealthful apartments, and parks for playgrounds are inadequate, although progress is being made in providing recreation areas. The movement of many residents into the suburbs, in order to secure more favorable living conditions, lessens the number of taxpayers and increases the financial problems of the city.

Most of the world's great business firms maintain offices in New York, and large corporations are usually managed from the city. As the nation's financial center, New York dominates banking, investment, and insurance. Industries such as garment and jewelry manufacturing, which produce high-value, high-style items in relatively small space, remain in midtown Manhattan, where buyers congregate. The city leads in the styling and production of clothes. It makes or controls the manufacture of most toys, novelties, pharmaceuticals, books, and periodicals. New York managers present the country's major concerts, plays, and musical attractions and staff most of those sent on tour.

As a result of congestion and high land values, industries requiring large space for their operations have sought sites in neighboring areas. Many of these outlying cities have other complementary and supplementary functions in the metropolitan area—providing residential sections for people who work in New York, terminals and freight yards for railroads that do not go into Manhattan, dockage for coastal vessels and tramp ships, and storage facilities. Several cities that share the environmental advantages of New York have become centers of commerce and industry in their own right; among them are Bayonne, an oil-refining center; Perth Amboy, noted for the refining of metals and the importation of coal; Jersey City and Hoboken, the location of many huge factories, shipyards, and docks; Elizabeth, famous for petroleum refining and manufacturing sewing machines; Newark, with a wide diversity of manufactures; and Paterson, a textile center.

One of the principal reasons for the great development in the New York vicinity is the excellent harbor. A marvelous system of protected and interconnected waterways, well sheltered from, but easily accessible to, the sea, is the focus of routes to and from the ocean and the continental interior. Eight bays and six rivers afford more than 700 miles of water frontage, along which extend 200 piers equipped to service oceangoing vessels; in addition, there are hundreds of smaller docks and piers. The Hudson River has a channel deep enough to accommodate the largest ships, and tides and currents are strong enough to help keep it scoured out. There are no natural obstacles to shipping since the tidal range is small and the waters are ice-free during the whole year. Ten thousand or more vessels utilize the port facilities annually. The New York area normally handles 40 to 50 per cent of the nation's imports and 30 to 40 per cent of its exports. Its total of well over 150 million short tons yearly is more than twice that of any other United States port.

PHILADELPHIA

Philadelphia, the fourth largest city in the nation in population, is located at the junction of the Delaware and Schuylkill Rivers. This city, founded by William Penn in 1682, has continued to develop according to the plan he approved. City Hall Square forms the heart of the business district, and a gridiron pattern of streets extends from there to all parts of the city. Philadelphia contains many historical shrines: Independence Hall, where the Declaration of Independence was signed, still stands; nearby are such buildings as Betsy Ross House, Carpenter's Hall, where the first Congress met, and Christ Church, where many of the nation's founders worshiped. Modern Philadelphia is among the top-ranking seaports of the nation. The Delaware River, navigable for oceangoing ships as far as Trenton, ranks second to New York City in commercial tonnage. Proximity to coal and other resources has furthered the growth of Philadelphia. The city has a great diversity of industrial enterprises—chemicals, printing, tobacco, hats, rugs, foodstuffs, and radios—which have benefited from excellent transportation, access to markets both at home and abroad, and the early start of the city. Just across the Delaware River, in New Jersey, is Camden, which is an important producer of food and electronic products. Nearby, in Delaware, is Wilmington, the center for chemical industries.

BALTIMORE

Baltimore, on the west coast of Chesapeake Bay, is one of the area's larger cities and one of the chief seaports of the nation. Like Philadelphia, Baltimore is an old,

Figure 1-13   Skyline view of Baltimore, showing inner harbor and downtown area. (Courtesy of Baltimore Association of Commerce.)

historic city as well as a modern commercial and manufacturing center. Along its waterfront are numerous shipbuilding and dry docks, grain elevators, oil-storage facilities, and ore piers. Sparrows Point, a suburb, has one of the largest steel mills in the world and an enormous shipyard. Transportation in the Baltimore area is excellent. Chesapeake Bay is connected to Delaware Bay by a canal.

WASHINGTON

Washington, D.C., the nation's capital, is unique among the cities of the nation. Although its urban population exceeds 1,000,000 persons, manufacturing is of minor importance. The city has just one important industry—government. Many varied service enterprises care for the thousands of government workers and the numerous tourists and visitors. For the most part, the city is a place of beauty. The site was selected by Washington and the city plan designed by L'Enfant. Wide avenues radiate from the Capitol somewhat like the spokes of a wheel, and in addition the city is overlaid by a gridiron pattern. Trees shade many of the main avenues as well as streets in the residential areas. Government buildings, many built of light-colored stone, are located along Constitution, Pennsylvania, and other avenues. Large parks, the Mall, various monuments and shrines, museums, and archives are all places of interest. The present city has outgrown the District of Columbia, and expanded into Maryland and across the Potomac into Virginia. Washington, like most large cities in the United States, decreased in population between 1950 and 1960, but the population of the suburbs is rapidly increasing. Most wage earners and "white-collar" workers are employed by the government or are in service occupations.

In the Northeastern states, as in the other parts of the nation, the problems of urbanization are critical. Good housing, slum clearance, an adequate road and highway net for rapid ingress and egress, sufficient and properly spaced parks and recreational areas, necessary supplies of pure and fresh water, and good educational and health programs are basic requirements for modern city development. So important is a satisfactory solution to these community problems that the Federal government now has nearly fifty major programs affecting urban development and redevelopment. Practically all cities have planning boards, and many work in conjunction with county or metropolitan boards. Since more people in the United States now live in urban than in agricultural areas, many government leaders believe that a Secretary of Urban Affairs should be added to the national Cabinet.

SELECTED REFERENCES

Atwood, Wallace W.: *Physiographic Provinces of North America,* Ginn and Company, Boston, 1940.

A description of the physiography of North America in one volume that is well written and has many illustrations. Good reference for chapters 1–5.

Fenneman, Nevin M.: *Physiography of Eastern United States,* McGraw-Hill Book Company, Inc., New York, 1938.

A detailed study of landform development in the eastern part of the United States. A well-illustrated volume. Good reference for chapters 1–3.

Gottmann, Jean: *Megalopolis: The Urbanized Northeastern Seaboard of the United States,* The Twentieth Century Fund, New York, 1961.

A comprehensive study of urban development in the Northeastern states. Many maps and tables explain vividly the problem from Boston to Washington.

Klimm, Lester E.: "The Empty Areas of the Northeastern States," *Geographical Review,* vol. 44, no. 3, pp. 325–345, July, 1954.

A study of the vacant, or nonoccupied, areas in the Northeast. The relationship between population and landforms is illustrated.

Wallace, William H.: "Merrimac Valley Manufacturing: Past and Present," *Economic Geography,* vol. 37, no. 4, pp. 283–308, October, 1961.

A study of changing manufacturing conditions and situations in the heart of industrial New England.

White, C. Langdon, Edwin J. Foscue, and Tom McKnight: *Geography of Anglo-America,* 3d ed., Prentice-Hall, Inc., Englewood Cliffs, N. J., 1964.

A standard college text of Anglo-America with chapters usually developed about physical regions.

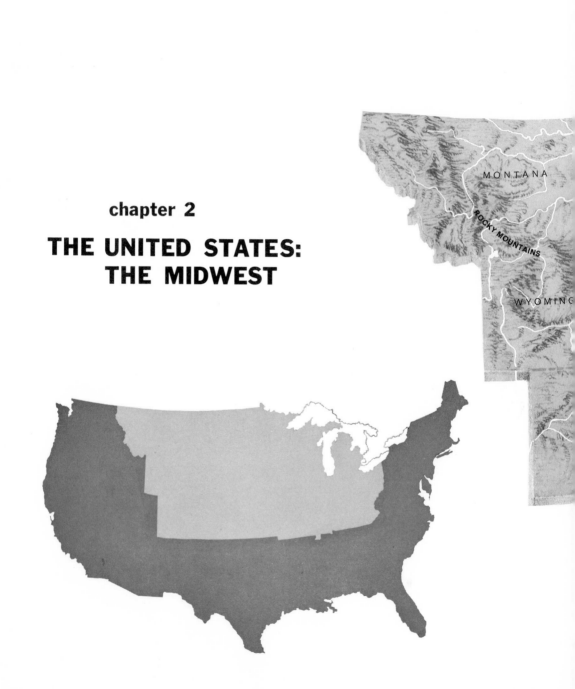

chapter 2

THE UNITED STATES:
THE MIDWEST

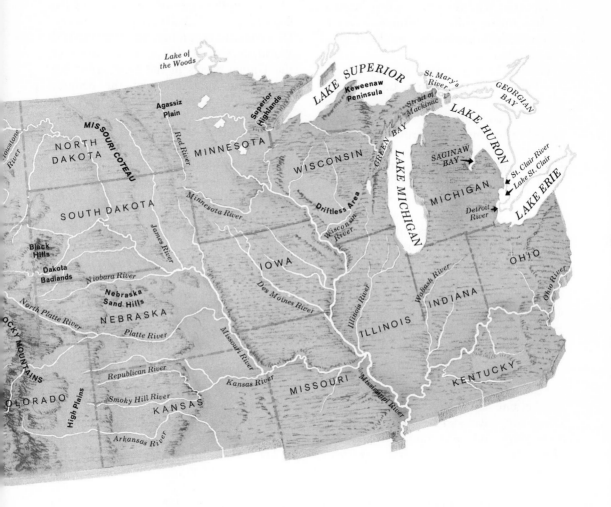

Figure 2-1 *The American Midwest is largely an area of vast plains and grasslands. In general, the part of the region north of the Ohio and Missouri Rivers has been glaciated.*

*A*MERICAN SOCIETY EVOLVED DURING the expansion of settlement from the Atlantic fringe westward across the continent to the Pacific. An important factor in the development of this changing society was the frontier. The immigrants first faced a million square miles of primeval forest, swarming with game and populated by a few hundred natives.

Before the new nation could be fully developed the land had to be transformed. In America the frontier was a zone between a comparatively stable and well-settled region and one hardly touched by civilization. It was thinly occupied by Indians and offered abundant opportunities for development although at the cost of risk and hardship. As the zone of settlement was extended, forests were cleared, the sod broken, crops and orchards planted, homes and villages built, railroads and highways constructed, and a savage wilderness and a seemingly endless grassland were transformed into farms and cities.

The century following the independence of the United States saw territorial gains that extended the nation across the continent to the Pacific. Frontier settlements spread across empty areas until the country became a united whole. Abundant cheap land gave poor men an opportunity to become landowners quickly. Although the chance to acquire good free homestead land virtually ended in the early twentieth century, the human characteristics developed on the frontier still affect the American people and their way of life. The experience of overcoming natural difficulties and the thrill of taking part in the settlement and expansion of the country colored and shaped the thinking and culture of Americans. Great and untouched natural resources and the economic needs of both the new land and the Old World furthered the development of lumbering,

mining, and manufacturing. Men who tilled their own land, however, often did not want to work for wages in industry, and their independence led to a shortage of labor, high wages, the immigration of up to a million persons a year, and the invention of labor-saving machinery. Descendants of immigrants from the Old World developed the peculiar culture of the United States in the New, while the power and production of the country expanded beyond the most optimistic forecasts.

For many years the American frontier existed in the old Northwest Territory. An important route of migration from the seaboard colonies followed the Hudson-Mohawk Lowlands to Buffalo and along the southern shore of Lake Erie. Other routes, such as the Braddock and Forbes roads, crossed the Appalachians by following rivers and low divides to terminate in Pittsburgh at the confluence of the Allegheny and Monongahela Rivers, and from there down the Ohio River southwestward. The National, or Cumberland, Road also crossed the plateau and headed west over the plains toward St. Louis. During later decades the Mormon Trail, Oregon Trail, and Santa Fe Trail originated in the Midwest, and along them the frontier continued to move westward across the plains to the mountains.

The advancing frontier brought to the Midwest immigrants from many lands, people who were used to hardships, work, and want. As each adapted his methods to the varying natural environment, progress was made, and the area grew into one of the most productive and wealthy parts of the world. Such superlatives as "Center of American Industry" and "Breadbasket of the Americas" have been applied. The Midwest, an area extending westward from Pennsylvania and New York to the Rocky Mountains and southward from the

Figure 2-2   The population and therefore the size of settlements decrease from east to west across the Interior Plains.

Canadian border to the South, is truly the "Heart of the Nation."

The "Heart of the United States" is located on the extensive Interior Plains region, the largest physical region in North America. The Plains extend westward from the Appalachians to the Rockies and southward from the Arctic Ocean to the Rio Grande. In the United States the area between the Appalachians and the Mississippi River slopes gently westward; that between the Rockies and the Mississippi River slopes eastward. The two chief tributaries of the Mississippi, the Ohio and Missouri Rivers, mark the approximate southern boundary of the area once covered by continental glaciation. The region is usually divided into two large subregions, the Central Lowlands and the Great

Figure 2-3   Near Cairo, Illinois, is the confluence of the Mississippi and Ohio Rivers. Note the broad meanders of the Mississippi and the agricultural use of the land.

Plains, both of which have a moderately rolling surface. The Bluegrass area of central Kentucky, the Nashville Basin of middle Tennessee, and the Osage Plains of Oklahoma and Texas are southward extensions of the Central Lowlands that, because of historical background and cultural development, are considered a part of the American South. The southern extension of the Great Plains is also historically connected with the South.

CENTRAL LOWLANDS

The Central Lowlands are superlatively endowed by nature. Included in the northwestern portion of the Eastern states, the region extends from the Eastern Highlands to the Great Plains, and from the Canadian border to the Ozarks and the South. The surface is level to moderately rolling; the soil is generally fertile; and the Great Lakes offer advantageous inland transportation. The region has a stimulating continental climate with adequate rainfall ranging from 25 to over 45 inches annually, and a growing season sufficiently long (about 200 days along the southern border to 140 along the northern) for midlatitude crops such as corn, oats, and soybeans. Minerals found in the region include large deposits of bituminous coal, petroleum and natural gas, iron ore, cop-

per, lead, zinc, and building materials. There is some available water power, many rivers for transportation, and water for industries. The original vegetation cover was varied. Large forests of conifers predominated around the upper Great Lakes; a mixed forest of broad-leaved deciduous species was found in the middle United States; and tall-grass prairies extended from Illinois westward to the Great Plains.

In utilizing these resources man has developed numerous and varied activities. Within the Central Lowlands is the world's largest corn-producing area, the Corn Belt. Few parts of the world equal the region in the production of pork, beef, and dairy and poultry products. Large crops of hay, soybeans, wheat, oats, and other grains are harvested; and manufactures are notable, especially the output of steel and machines. Rail transportation is highly developed, and the largest freshwater freighters in the world ply the Great Lakes. Within this region is the nation's center of population as well as the center of its agricultural activity.

AGRICULTURE

Although the Central Lowlands rank high in manufacturing and mining, agriculture is the foundation of the region's development. Since the area is so large, diversities

Figure 2-4 Climate graphs of selected stations.

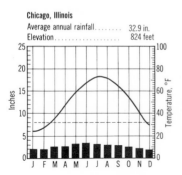

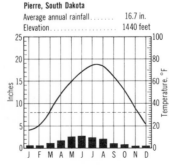

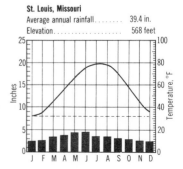

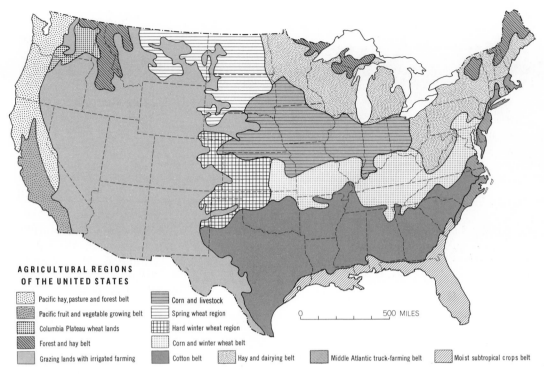

AGRICULTURAL REGIONS
OF THE UNITED STATES

Pacific hay, pasture and forest belt

Pacific fruit and vegetable growing belt

Columbia Plateau wheat lands

Forest and hay belt

Grazing lands with irrigated farming

Corn and livestock

Spring wheat region

Hard winter wheat region

Corn and winter wheat belt

Cotton belt

Hay and dairying belt

Middle Atlantic truck-farming belt

Moist subtropical crops belt

0   500 MILES

Figure 2-5   The agricultural regions of the United States are the result of both the physical and cultural activities of the areas. Although one or two principal crops may be important, each region grows many crops, and each has a large variety of land uses.

in the length of the growing season, soils, topography, and distance from markets have brought about differences in agricultural practices, crops, and livestock. The northern half of the region was repeatedly covered by continental glaciers which strongly modified the surface features; glacial erosion and the damming of drainage by debris dropped by the melting ice resulted in the formation of tens of thousands of lakes, ponds, and swamps. When drained, the beds of shallow lakes and swamps usually make superior farmland, especially good for the production of corn, sugar beets, celery, and other varied crops. Glacial soils may be stony, but they are fertile, for the soils have been formed of mixtures of rock waste and humus derived from many sources, and the limestone and

other soluble materials have not been leached as much as in unglaciated soil. The best soils south of the limits of glaciation are those of alluvial origin, usually found on the valley floors, and the prairie soils, where the topsoil is deep and an abundance of humus has been derived from plant stems and roots. Soils which developed under a cover of deciduous trees contains more humus and are more fertile than those formed in areas of pine forests, where the soils are apt to be leached and low in usable plant foods.

The Corn Belt, actually an area of diversified agriculture, extends from western Ohio to eastern Nebraska and from central Minnesota to central Missouri. The region dominates the country's agricultural production. In this area, glaciers

Figure 2-6   An aerial view of contour strip-cropping near Garnavillo, Iowa. In most parts of the Corn Belt the best farming practices are used; as a result, the region is the best agricultural area in the nation. (Courtesy of Soil Conservation Service.)

generally leveled the topography and improved the soils. Summers are rainy and hot—just what corn needs for best growth—and the region has assured markets since it is close to the center of the nation's population. Corn is grown extensively outside this central area, but nowhere else does it so dominate the cultural landscape. Nevertheless, although more land is planted in corn than in any other crop, little corn is marketed as grain; much of it is fed to hogs and beef animals and marketed in the form of meat. Also, many food products are made from corn. In addition to corn, many other crops such as oats, wheat, barley, soybeans, and hay are planted, making the area important for its diversified farming. Frequently, such legume crops as clover and alfalfa, because of the nitrogen-carrying nodules that develop on their roots, are plowed under to enrich the soil. This favorable combination of climate, soil, and topography along with man's good use of these

natural resources has resulted in (1) intensive land use for agriculture, (2) a large percentage of the rural area in crops, (3) a conversion of much of the crop output into livestock production, and (4) high land values. Good farm practices, such as crop rotation and soil conservation, and an income from a variety of crops and livestock are basic to Corn Belt farming.

Excellent and extensive groups of farm buildings are characteristic of most farms. Large, two-story homes fully equipped with electricity and running water are common. Butane gas is frequently used for fuel. Big barns, tall silos, equipment sheds, chicken houses, hog pens, and feed lots occupy the barnyard. Near this complex will be the garden plots and possibly a small orchard. Most farmers use gasoline for power and tractors instead of horses as well as other agricultural machinery. Railroads and highways form a close net over the Corn Belt, no farm being over a few miles from a town or shipping point. Since the eastern part of the Corn Belt was originally covered with a forest of mixed hardwoods, an adjunct of most farms is the woodlot. Woodlots add beauty and variety to the scenery, supply fuel and posts, provide a refuge for birds and small game, and furnish some saw logs for sale. Where the prairies once were, the country is still open, but crops have replaced the native grasses. Trees were frequently planted to shelter the houses, and groves around the farmsteads stand out on the level land. On the Great Plains, however, even the farmsteads may be treeless.

Winter wheat, planted in the fall, is the chief crop southwest of the Corn Belt; to the northwest spring wheat, sown in the spring, is most widely grown. These two crops predominate in the zone of transition between the Central Lowlands and the Great Plains, where the rainfall is not sufficient to produce good corn or where the growing season is too short for its maturing.

Northward from the Corn Belt the winters increase in length and severity. The summers are rainy and long enough for excellent hay and forage crops, and although the growing season is too short for corn to mature, much corn is produced for use as silage. Pastures are generally good, and most areas of swampy, hilly, and cutover land can be used for grazing. In this region of rather short summers, farmers get better results by using land for forage crops and hay rather than for grains. Small amounts of rye and barley are usually grown as cash crops since they are hardier than wheat or corn.

Dairying is the primary type of farming. Jerseys, Holsteins, Brown Swiss, and other breeds of dairy cattle are numerous. Not only are climatic conditions favorable for forage, but the region is close to the markets of Minneapolis, Chicago, Detroit, and other large cities. Cooperative creameries and cheese factories, the latter a specialty of Wisconsin, provide an additional market for cream, milk, and milk products that can be stored and distributed throughout the year. Milk-condensing factories are also numerous. Throughout the dairy region are big, well-built barns that protect the animals during the long, cold winters and also provide storage space for hay and other feeds. This is the area where a young couple, beginning as dairy farmers, are told, "Build your barn first, and your barn will build your house." Near cities most milk and cream are marketed fresh. Increasing remoteness from market is reflected in more specialization in butter and cheese or condensed and powdered milk. Farmers who separate their milk and sell only the cream use the skimmed milk as feed for poultry and pigs. The regular marketing of calves and some beef animals gives the dairy farmer an additional income from meat products.

Some parts of the region produce such specialty crops as the sugar beets raised in the lowlands of the Saginaw Valley in Michigan. Potatoes grow fairly well on the relatively poor soils and in the short summers of northern Michigan and Wisconsin. Many large truck farms are located near the urban areas.

Of special importance is fruit. Numerous orchards have been planted along the shores of the larger lakes. The eastern shore of Lake Michigan is one of the principal fruit-growing areas of the nation. Large quantities of apples, peaches, pears, grapes, cherries, and other noncitrus fruits are shipped from this area each year. Practically all kinds of mid-latitude berries—gooseberries, loganberries, dewberries, raspberries—are grown. The lakes have a strong effect upon the climate and influence the kind of crop produced. In the spring cool, westerly winds blowing off the lakes retard plant growth and thus prevent damage by late frost. During the fall the lakes warm the winds and delay the killing frosts, so that the farmer has time to gather his ripened crop and prepare his orchard for winter. The effects of these winds extend from 20 to 25 miles inland. The Door Peninsula of Wisconsin and the southern shore of Lake Erie are also famous for fruits. The fruit business is helped by the nearby large urban markets. Although some fruit is sold fresh, much of the crop is processed by freezing, canning, or preserving for marketing throughout the year.

MINERALS

The Central Lowlands are well endowed with fuels, iron, and other minerals. The Eastern Interior coalfields of Illinois, southwestern Indiana, and western Kentucky rank next in production after the Appalachian fields, and some coal is also mined in Kansas, Missouri, and Iowa. Although most of the bituminous coal is not as suitable for coking as that from the Appalachian fields, it is an excellent power resource. The iron and steel manufacturing centers are so located that imports from mines in Pennsylvania, West Virginia, and eastern Kentucky are easily accessible.

Petroleum and natural gas, produced locally, have contributed much to the industrial progress of the Central Lowlands. The principal producing fields entirely within the area are the southern Illinois and Kentucky field and various pools of Indiana, Ohio, and Michigan. The Mid-Continent field, largest in the nation, extends northward from Oklahoma into Kansas. Some natural gas is produced in connection with the petroleum, especially in the Mid-Continent field. Large oil refineries that receive petroleum from

Figure 2-7 An open-pit iron mine at Eveleth, Minnesota. The ore is mined by power shovels, then transported by trucks of 30-ton capacity to loading stations, from which the ore is further raised to the surface by means of a conveyor belt. (Courtesy of United States Steel Corporation.)

these and other fields are located in many places; some of the most important are in Whiting and East Chicago, Indiana, and Wood River, Illinois.

The iron ore deposits in Minnesota, Wisconsin, and Michigan are actually in the Superior Highland section of the Canadian Shield rather than in the Central Lowlands. (Since this region is small in area it will be discussed with the mineral section of the Central Lowlands.) The Superior Highlands, the most important source of iron ore deposits in the United States, supply about 80 per cent of the nation's output of approximately 90 million tons per year. The Mesabi Range in Minnesota is the most productive single source in the United States, furnishing over 50 per cent of the total output. Most of the mining is from deep open pits. The Cuyuna and Vermilion Ranges, also in Minnesota, the deep mines of the Marquette, Iron Mountain, and Menominee Ranges of Michigan, and the Gogebic Range in both Michigan and Wisconsin are other sources. Enormous deposits of taconite, a low-grade ore, are now being developed in Minnesota. By concentrating this material it will be possible to maintain production long after the high-grade hematite ore has been exhausted. The iron-mining district has cold, snowy winters and short summers. Once the area was well forested, but uncontrolled cutting of the trees and forest fires have depleted this resource. The conditions of soil and climate are unfavorable for crops other than hay. Without the mining-company taxes that support good schools and public services in well-built cities like Virginia and Hibbing, Minnesota, this area would have few inhabitants, except dairymen and resort operators.

Copper from the Keweenaw Peninsula in northern Michigan was known to the Indians and was developed by white men over a century ago. For many years the peninsula was the leading copper-producing area of the world, but as mines became deeper and ores less rich, the increasing costs forced some mines to close.

Rock, clay, sand, and gravel deposits are widely distributed. Limestone for building is quarried in central Indiana, for flux in steelmaking in northern Michigan, and for cement in practically all Middle Western states. Clay is used in making brick, tile, and other ceramic products. Brick and tile plants are common because of the amounts of good clay available and the large markets. Glacial deposits of sand and gravel are used in road making, building construction, and railroad maintenance. The tonnage used is enormous; transportation of these raw materials, the finished clay products, and cement is facilitated by level topography and numerous water routes.

FORESTS

Originally forests covered much of the eastern part of the Central Lowlands; in the western part of the region vegetation graded from forests to prairies to short grasses, with trees being found only along streams in the latter areas. The central hardwood forest extended westward from Pennsylvania to Illinois. This forest was of mixed hardwoods, including oak, ash, elm, beech, maple, walnut, and hickory, with minor stands of pine and hemlock. Much of this forest has now been cleared and the land used for agriculture.

The northern forests of Michigan, Wisconsin, and Minnesota consisted of white pine, spruce, fir, and other conifers, with some hardwoods, especially maple, oak, birch, and aspen. Most of the white pine has been cut, and great inroads have been made on other species. Many cutover areas have been replanted, and numerous

tree farms are being developed. Some states have zoning regulations that prevent certain types of areas from being used for purposes other than forests. Although the quality of the second-growth timber is usually poorer than the original, it is suitable for use as pulpwood. Many large paper mills, for example, those in International Falls and Grand Rapids, Minnesota, produce papers of varying grades. Where suitable lumber can be cut near at hand, furniture factories continue to be of local importance. Grand Rapids, Michigan, is nationally known for its manufacture of quality furniture.

TRANSPORTATION

The five Great Lakes and their connecting waterways form the busiest inland water route in the world. The long lake freighters equal many ocean carriers in size and carrying capacity. The large lake-port cities, long shorelines, and rich hinterlands make the Central Lowlands a populous and busy commercial and industrial region.

Traffic on the Great Lakes totals about 200 million tons of freight annually. Four commodities—iron ore, coal, limestone, and grains—make up 90 per cent of the tonnage. Lying between producing and consuming regions, the waterway provides the world's cheapest freight rates per ton-mile for transporting materials in bulk. The major movement is down the lakes, from western Lake Superior to the southern shores of Lake Michigan and Lake Erie, carrying iron ore and grains. Limestone is moved from quarries near the water's edge in the vicinity of Alpena, Michigan, to dockside steel mills. Coal from Lake Erie ports is transported up the lakes.

Since ice usually closes the lakes to navigation for three to five months of the

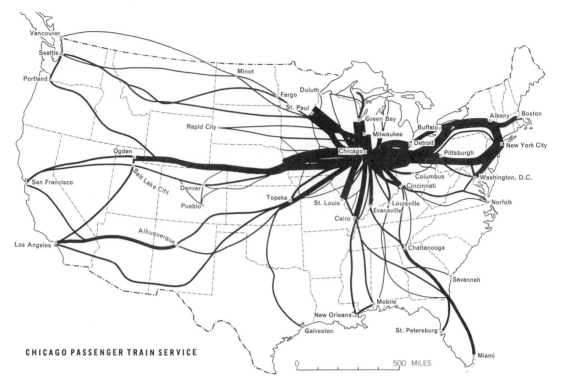

CHICAGO PASSENGER TRAIN SERVICE

Figure 2-8   The high nodality of Chicago is vividly shown in this diagram. Note especially the heavy passenger traffic between Chicago and the East. (Adapted from a map, courtesy of Chicago Association of Commerce and Industry.)

year, ships make as many trips as possible during the open season. To facilitate quick turnaround, the docks, loading and unloading devices, and the ships themselves have been especially designed. Channels have been dredged and four big locks built to form the Soo Canal so that ships may be lifted and lowered between Lakes Superior and Huron. To help the automobile and truck traffic between Canada and the United States, a large bridge has been built over, and a tunnel dug under, the Detroit River. A gigantic bridge has been erected over the Straits of Mackinac. A few car ferries, built to break through the ice floes, operate across Lake Michigan all winter.

More than 60 million tons of iron ore

are moved over the Great Lakes each year. At the upper lake ports of Duluth, Superior, Two Harbors, Marquette, and Escanaba ore trains run along docks, on high trestles, 2,000 and more feet long. The ore is dumped into pockets, from which chutes carry it into the open holds of vessels. Ships of 12,000 to 16,000 tonnage can be loaded, if necessary, in an hour or two. At lower lake ports such as Conneaut, Cleveland, Erie, and Buffalo, huge clamshell unloaders bite the ore out of the holds with almost equal speed. Cargoes of coal, limestone, and grain are likewise loaded and unloaded in remarkably short times.

The completion of the St. Lawrence–Great Lakes Seaway offers an improved opportunity for oceangoing vessels to dock at inland ports. The present Canadian Welland Canal connecting Lakes Erie and Ontario, now rather narrow and not designed for use by the largest lake freighters, is being deepened, widened, and straightened for greater usefulness. Large and modern docks have been built in Chicago, Cleveland, and other cities. These cities, although far inland, are becoming important ocean ports. Small craft can reach the Mississippi River from Chicago, via a canal and the Illinois River through Illinois from Lake Michigan.

Inland transportation facilities in the Central Lowlands are better than those in any other region of the United States. The country is crisscrossed by a railway network that extends to practically every town and city as well as to numerous villages and hamlets. Chicago is recog-

nized as the leading railway center of the nation. Its location near the southern tip of Lake Michigan and the level topography of the area make the city the focus of rail lines from west, south, and east. In addition to the Great Lakes waterway, which serves most of the larger cities of the region, the Ohio and Mississippi Rivers and some of their tributaries are important arteries of transportation. Coal, sand and gravel, and other bulk goods, in addition to bargeloads of automobiles and oil, are frequently moved by water. Wide, paved highways connect most of the cities, and the towns are connected by all-weather roads. Toll roads, freeways, and bypasses now enable the traveler to drive long distances without passing through congested areas. All the larger cities and many of the smaller ones are served by national and international airlines.

Figure 2-9   The St. Lawrence Seaway was developed by both Canada and the United States. A series of six locks and three dams was constructed between Montreal and Lake Ontario. Ships are lifted from 22 feet above sea level at Montreal to 246 feet in Lake Ontario. The Welland Canal and the Soo Canals make it possible for ships to move as far inland as Duluth.

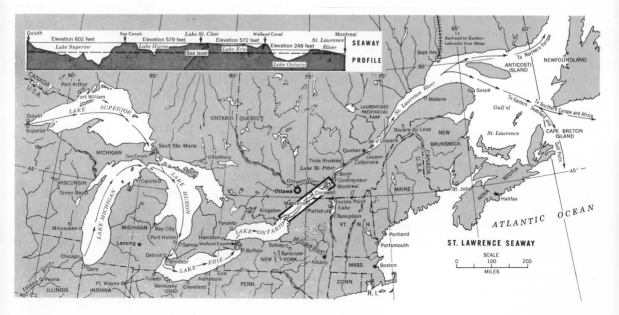

Figure 2-10 Airview of Santa Fe Railway's electronic retarder yard, Corwith, Illinois. (Courtesy of Santa Fe Railway.)

INDUSTRIES AND CITIES

A large part of the manufacturing belt of the United States is located in the northeastern part of the Central Lowlands. The industries range in size from the one-man or one-family activity, such as broom making, to the largest assembly plant in the world, River Rouge near Detroit. So varied are the manufactures that they are frequently grouped under three headings: (1) heavy industries dependent upon adequate mineral supplies and cheap transportation—steel mills in Gary, Detroit, Cleveland, Duluth, (2) manufacturing that is directly related to agricultural activities, such as flour milling in Minneapolis and Milwaukee, making of farm equipment in Moline and Indianapolis, and meat packing in Chicago, Omaha, and Cincinnati, and (3) medium and light industries such as the manufacture of

glass, scales, rubber goods, furniture, paper products, and plastics. In some parts of the manufacturing belt industries of certain types tend to group together, for example, heavy industry in the Youngstown area; but in other sections, as in central Illinois, a variety of industries may be found. Agreeable climatic conditions, navigable waterways, favorable topography, a large supply of mineral fuel, and a variety of raw agricultural products have caused and aided the development and expansion of manufacturing.

In the Midwest, as in the Northeast, there are numerous metropolitan areas. The Midwest, however, does not have a megalopolis to compare with that extending from Boston to Washington. In the not too distant future, though, it is conceivable that urbanization will expand across the rich agricultural lands between such large cities as Buffalo, Cleveland, Toledo, and Detroit so that farms, hamlets, villages, and towns will form an almost continuous built-up area along the shore of Lake Erie and the Detroit River. Another Midwest megalopolis now developing about the southern part of Lake Michigan includes the territory from Milwaukee through Chicago to Gary.

Along the southern shore of Lake Erie, from Buffalo to Toledo, lies one of the chief manufacturing regions of the nation. Although each city makes a variety of products, many are also noted for some specialty. Toledo is famed for glass, Lima for diesel engines, Akron for rubber goods, Lorain for iron and steel pipe, Sandusky for paper products, and Cleveland for steel. The Detroit area, to the west of the Detroit River and Lake St. Clair, is the heart of the world's automobile industries. Huge plants in this vicinity and in Flint, Pontiac, South Bend, and Toledo have turned out more than 6 million cars within a year. A host of Middle Western cities manufacture parts for automobiles, trucks, and aircraft.

Around southern Lake Michigan, from the Door Peninsula on the west to Grand Rapids on the east, is a manufacturing area that processes vast quantities of the agricultural products grown in the Central Lowlands. Large meat-packing plants are located in the Chicago area; quantities of grains are used in the Milwaukee brewing industries; most towns and cities have creameries and canneries; hides are processed and made into shoes in Milwaukee, Chicago, and other places. Nationally important manufacturing centers include Gary (steel); Grand Rapids (furniture); Battle Creek (breakfast foods); Green Bay (papermaking); Indianapolis (pharma-ceuticals); and Moline (farm implements).

Smaller manufacturing areas have developed around the larger river cities. Minneapolis and St. Paul, the Twin Cities, together form the greatest market, manufacturing, and distribution center in the upper Mississippi Valley. St. Paul, located at the head of river navigation, later became a railroad headquarters, and is famed for wholesaling, meat-packing, and general industry. Minneapolis, at the Falls of St. Anthony, began as a sawmill town, then turned to flour milling. It is now the greatest wheat-storage center in the nation. Minneapolis is also noteworthy for general manufacturing, trade, and financial activities.

Figure 2-11 The principal manufacturing region of the United States is located in the northeastern quarter of the nation. An ample supply of fuel, large reserves of iron ore nearby, natural deepwater transportation, and industrious people combine to make this the world's most productive area. Smaller regions are to be found in the South and West that have certain specific advantages.

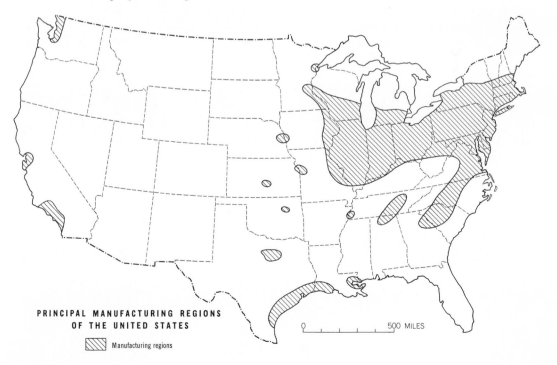

PRINCIPAL MANUFACTURING REGIONS
OF THE UNITED STATES

0 _____ 500 MILES

⬛ Manufacturing regions

St. Louis, the tenth largest city in the nation, began as a fur-trading post in 1764 near the junction of the Missouri and Mississippi Rivers. Founded by the French, it later attracted so many German people that the pronunciation of its name was changed. St. Louis is a river port as well as an important rail and air center. Its population exceeds 750,000, and the metropolitan district has a population of over 2 million people. Manufactures include beer, cereals, garments, shoes, chemicals, electrical goods, and articles made of iron. Smelting and meat-packing are carried on across the river in Illinois at East St. Louis.

Louisville and Cincinnati are both important Ohio River ports. Cincinnati has large factories that produce soap and machine tools. Louisville is an important distillery center and tobacco market. Kansas City and Omaha are the largest industrial centers on the Missouri River; each has large stockyards, meat-packing plants, and flour mills, as well as factories that produce agricultural equipment. Other highly industrialized cities include Fort Wayne, South Bend, Evansville, Racine, and Peoria.

Many cities and towns that are not on waterways have also developed industrially as well as commercially. One such area extends from central Ohio across Indiana to central Illinois. Dayton, noted for the making of cash registers and refrigerators, is an important rail and distributing center. Columbus, Indianapolis, and Springfield, each the capital of its state, are wholesale and retailing centers for their immediate areas and manufacture some of the agricultural machines used in the Corn Belt. Near the western edge of the Central Lowlands are several smaller cities of special local importance. Des Moines is the capital of Iowa, a center for manufacturing farm machinery and processing local raw materials. Wichita processes wheat, meat, and oil, all produced in the state of Kansas; the city is also a leading center for the making of airplanes. Lincoln, Sioux City, Sioux Falls, and Fargo serve as distribution and processing centers of their respective areas.

Chicago, with a population of 6.2 million people in its metropolitan area, is the largest city in the Central Lowlands and the second largest in the United States. The city is frequently referred to as the transportation center of the world; it is the focus of many major highway routes, a railway center where twenty-three trunkline railroads and many terminal lines meet, an international airway port, and also an important waterway terminal since it is located on the shore of Lake Michigan and has canal and river connections with the Mississippi River and the Gulf of Mexico. The St. Lawrence Seaway gives it direct connection with the Atlantic Ocean. With such adequate transportation, the city has developed as the natural processing place for the Corn Belt and the hay and dairy region. Chicago is a leading meat-packing center, a manufacturer of flour and other food items, an important producer of agricultural machinery, and the retailing and wholesale center for the Middle West. The city is also noted for its Natural History Museum, Shedd Aquarium, and the Chicago Art Institute, as well as for several outstanding universities.

Detroit, the fifth largest city in the nation, has more than 3.7 million people in its metropolitan area, or approximately one-half of the population of Michigan. Located on the west bank of the Detroit River, the city developed because of its strategic position between Lake Huron and Lake Erie. Among the first manufactures were carriages. Partly because of the early start in this type of industry and

Figure 2-12 Aerial view of the Rouge River plant, centering around the boat slip and showing the blast furnaces and coke ovens on the left. (Courtesy of Ford Motor Company.)

inventions by its citizens, Detroit became the leader in the automobile industry. Other numerous and varied industries such as saltworks and the production of chemicals, aircraft, drugs, and furniture have also developed.

Cleveland, the largest city on the shore of Lake Erie, has a metropolitan population of 1.7 million. The city is near the center of the Lake Erie industrial region, which extends, almost without breaks, between Ashtabula and Toledo. Cleveland serves as a transshipment point for Mesabi iron ore going to the Pittsburgh and Youngstown areas as well as for coal being shipped westward from the Appalachian field. Large steel mills, oil refineries, machine shops, and food-processing plants are among its many industries. Like Chicago and Detroit, the principal retail district is near the lake shore.

RECREATION

The vacation and tourist industry brings hundreds of millions of dollars in income to residents of the Great Lakes states and lesser amounts to the people in other parts of the Central Lowlands. Excellent beaches, forested surroundings, and fishing are among the attractions. Then, too, highways, railroads, and airways make it possible to reach the resort areas in a few hours, or at the outside in a day's travel,

from the big Middle Western cities. Along the shoreline of the Great Lakes region are hundreds of resorts. Inland Michigan, Minnesota, and most of Wisconsin have been strongly glaciated, with the resulting formation of thousands of lakes—17,000 in Minnesota alone. Thousands of private vacation cabins and many resorts have been built along the lake shores and river banks. In the fall the forests of northern Michigan, Wisconsin, and eastern Minnesota are visited by hunters after deer and other game. The amounts spent on recreation, hunting, and fishing support many communities which, after the decline of the lumber industry, would have been depopulated without this outside income. Many state parks, such as Itasca State Park at the source of the Mississippi River in Minnesota, have been established. Isle Royale National Park, the only national park in the region, is on an island in Lake Superior. During the winter many fishermen move small cabins onto the ice-covered lakes. After the cabins are in place they cut a hole in the ice floor so that they may fish. In some cabins a small oil heater will be used for warmth. Winter recreation areas with ski jumps and ski trails have been developed in several places where the topography was suitable.

The part of Minnesota between Lake Superior and the International Boundary is called the "Arrowhead Country" because of its shape. In the northern part of this region is a large area of virgin forest growing in the midst of numerous lakes and small streams. This forest, known as the Quetico Forest, extends into Canada. No railroads or highways have been developed, and plans indicate that none will be. The many lakes, footpaths, and canoe trails make it an outdoor paradise. In this wild area only the real nature lover spends his vacation.

GREAT PLAINS

The Indians who lived on the broad and grassy Great Plains depended in large part upon wild animals—principally the bison, or buffalo—for their food, shelter, and clothing. The meat from these creatures was a staple food that could be dried for future use. Hides formed the Indian tepee, and hairy robes made warm beds and clothing. Dry droppings, called "buffalo chips," were the common fuel used by pioneers for cooking in this nearly treeless country. Other game and fur-bearing animals supplemented the buffalo. The Plains tribes were nomadic, and after the introduction of the horse about 1550 the tribesmen were able to hunt bison from horseback. Horses were also used to pull burdens placed on a set of poles called a "travois"; a pair of shafts was stretched from the back of the horse and was dragged over the ground.

PHYSICAL SETTING

RELIEF FEATURES   The Great Plains slope eastward from the Rocky Mountains from an elevation of 4,000 to 6,000 feet to about 500 to 1,600 feet where they merge with the Central Lowlands. In this subregion of fertile soil, frequently deficient in mois-

ture, the plant life of the Great Plains is dominated by shortgrass, bunchgrass, tumbleweeds, and other subhumid vegetation. Numerous sectional names are applied to parts of this area: The northern section, in Montana, North Dakota, and South Dakota, is frequently referred to as the Missouri Plateau; the Nebraska Sandhills cover a large area in the north central part of that state; and the part of the southern section of the Great Plains west of the 101st meridian is known as the High Plains, where alluvial materials washed from the Rockies were deposited on top of an older surface, causing a greater elevation. In general the surface of all the High Plains appears almost flat, being broken only by the streams that cross it. The Great Plains extend southward into Texas and as such are a part of the South.

The High Plains are broad, relatively level, treeless uplands that extend for miles. Over this level surface, winds having an average velocity between ten and fifteen miles per hour blow much of the time, during the night as well as the day. At varying intervals the High Plains are cut by narrow, steep-sided valleys that trend in general from west to east. In these valleys are to be found the narrow rows of trees—cottonwood, locust, cedar, and others—that are typical of the plains. The level uplands between the valleys are largely agricultural areas devoted to wheat growing and grazing. Some of the rivers such as the Platte, Republican, and Arkansas have developed wide valleys containing rich alluvial soil.

Two areas in the Great Plains, the Bad Lands and the Black Hills of western South Dakota, contrast vividly with their surroundings. The Bad Lands have been formed in an area of easily eroded shale bedrock. The downpours of occasional thunder showers have caused considerable erosion, creating deep valleys and steep-walled gullies. In some places sharp pointed hills stand several hundred feet above the valley floors. The core of the Black Hills is an uplift of igneous rock, largely granite, around which the sedimentary rocks have been eroded. The Black Hills are high enough above the surrounding plain to receive sufficient rain to support forests of spruce and pine. The sandstones that outcrop around the central core serve as the source of water and as aquifers for much of the artesian water used in eastern South Dakota.

Streams on the northern Great Plains are mainly tributary to the upper Missouri River; those of the southern Great Plains flow into the Mississippi or Red Rivers. Channels of the streams are often shallow, with broad, low banks, and some stream gradients are so low that many rivers have braided (multiple) channels. Where the channels are deeply cut, badlands of steep and eroded slopes develop between the nearly level interstream divides and the river floodplains.

CLIMATE The weather of the Great Plains is of the semiarid steppe or continental type, with severely low temperatures in winter during cold waves, though there is a high frequency of sunlit days. Well-defined warming winds called chinooks often sweep southeastward down these plains in winter and spring. The chinooks are welcomed by the ranchers for they rapidly melt snow and ice by evaporation making it possible for the animals to graze. When the strong winter windstorms called blizzards occur with their drifting snow, transportation is impeded and grazing becomes difficult for the cattle. Summer days may be hot, but nights are cool. The annual temperature range—the difference between the mean temperatures of the coldest and warmest months—may be as great as 60°F or more.

Figure 2-13 Windbreaks, made by rows of trees, have been developed in many parts of the Great Plains. Windbreaks help to prevent soil blowing and also shield the wheat or other crop until it has a good start. (Courtesy of Soil Conservation Service.)

Rainfall of about 10 to 20 inches a year necessitates irrigation or special dry-farming methods of raising crops. If the precipitation on the plains were dependable, farming would be more profitable. Where ranchers must obtain water from mountain streams or reservoirs if irrigation is to succeed, they must make a great expenditure of time and money. Nevertheless, many reservoirs have been built in the shallow natural basins and the low-banked river channels, and the water is used to irrigate sugar beets, alfalfa, and other crops. The more elevated surfaces, locally called "benches" in Montana, are devoted to dry farming. In the better areas the farms are smaller and the population correspondingly larger than in the dry-farming regions.

The native grasses, before destruction by overgrazing or cultivation, provided a moderate income, since they were suitable for large-scale pasturage, but so much grassland has been destroyed that each year sees less of it available for commercial purposes. Once destroyed, the grass is difficult and expensive to replace. For this reason, conservation of vegetation and soil

Figure 2-14 In the Wheat Belt land use is extensive, farmsteads are often far apart, and settlements are small. (Courtesy of John W. Morris.)

in the semiarid Great Plains is of prime importance to a grazing economy—a matter all too often ignored or misunderstood by those who live in the humid realm of the United States.

AGRICULTURE

In the mid-nineteenth century the white men began to displace the Indians and to replace the herds of buffalo with herds of cattle. Sheepherding became a secondary activity where native fodder was too sparse for grazing cattle. This extensive grazing economy prevailed until the last quarter of the nineteenth century when, after a series of humid seasons and high prices for wheat, much of the native grass was plowed under and the land planted to grain. For a time the change to extensive wheat farming paid, but it took only a few years of subnormal precipitation to make this type of agriculture unprofitable. Eventually the plowed land was abandoned, and then, after a period of humid years, the cycle was repeated.

Kansas and Oklahoma are the principal winter-wheat states, and the Dakotas lead in spring-wheat production. The Wheat Belts continue eastward into the Central Lowlands. Wheat farms are large, becoming greater in size toward the west as the amount of yearly rainfall decreases. Wheat is raised as an annual crop or in rotation with grain sorghums or other suitable crops.

The Wheat Belts are a contrast to the Corn Belt. Here agriculture is extensive and less varied. Farm houses are far apart, and the villages are smaller and have fewer functions. Grazing is an important source of income in the Winter-wheat Belt. The wheat, after being planted in the fall, comes up and may be pastured by feeder stock during the winter. In the spring these animals are sold through various markets to the farmers of the Corn Belt or to others who buy feeder stock. The wheat then develops and is harvested. Practically all work is done by machines. Groups of combines, with their crews, start working the wheat harvest as the crop begins to ripen first along the southern margin. The crews then move north with the season, many starting the harvest in Oklahoma or Texas and ending it in the Prairie Provinces of

Canada. Numerous elevators are located along railroad sidings far from hamlets or villages, and during the harvest season, activity around these elevators is great. Long strings of boxcars are often stationed near them just before harvesting starts, so that wheat may be moved to the larger centers as rapidly as possible. Enid, a small city in northern Oklahoma, has the second largest wheat-storage capacity in the nation—approximately 70 million bushels. Minneapolis, to which much of the wheat from the Dakotas is shipped, ranks first, with a storage capacity of approximately 100 million bushels.

Since grain farming brings uncertain profits, and since neither wheat fields nor beef cattle can support many people, throughout most of the rural Great Plains the population density is less than twelve per square mile, and vast areas cannot support more than two per square mile. In some areas the wheat farmers no longer live on their farms. Many have moved into nearby villages or towns, where they engage in other business activities; others employ some individual to look after routine farm activities and return to the farm only two or three times a year. Such farmers are frequently referred to as "carpet-bagger" or "suitcase" farmers. Once the crop is planted there is little to do until the following harvest season. The area in which the feeder stock is to be grazed can be easily controlled by movable electric fences.

In the Great Plains grazing competes with wheat growing as the chief user of the land. Beef cattle have always been the dominant domestic animal of the area. Even prior to and during the days of settlement the large cattle companies of Texas, Montana, and other places used the land for grazing. Many famous early cattle trails crossed the Great Plains to such well-known railhead cattle towns as Abilene and Dodge City. Since about 1925 the number of cattle in the area has varied with (1) climatic conditions, (2) the market demands for beef, and (3) the market demands for wheat. A sufficient supply of water is always a problem. Most ranches have strategically placed windmills or pumps in addition to the water in rivers, creeks, or ponds. Animals are seldom more than one mile from water. Even though sheep were brought into the Great Plains at an early date, they never became an important part of the economy, partly because of the attitude of the cattlemen, but largely because cattle brought greater financial returns.

Figure 2-15 Cattle and ranches are common sights on the Great Plains. Roundup time is always important in ranch life. (Courtesy of Montana State Planning Board.)

Ranch life is not an unpleasant existence. Good automobiles and improved roads, many paved, put almost all ranches within an easy drive of a town. Most ranch homes are modern in all respects; they have running water, electricity from the local REA, and butane for heating. The condition of the inside of the home is never to be judged by the looks of the outside. Strong winds blowing for only a short period but carrying sand and gravel can soon take the paint off the outside of a house, barn, or other building.

Although grazing has always been a leading industry in the northern Great Plains, the settlers soon recognized that the large variability in the amount of the annual rainfall would present serious water problems. By 1900 dams and reservoirs were in operation or planned, whereby flood waters might be impounded and then distributed to the fertile areas east of the Rocky Mountains. An early project of this type centered in the vicinity of Greeley, Colorado, and there have been many since. Later, under the auspices of the Bureau of Reclamation and other Federal agencies, the building of many irrigation projects has allowed a more intensive use of the land. One of the largest constructions is the Fort Peck Dam on the Missouri River in Montana; built to control floods, it also impounds water for irrigation. Other projects are located in the Yellowstone River near Billings, the Milk River plain in Montana, near Williston, North Dakota, and north of the Black Hills on the Belle Fourche River. Alfalfa, sugar beets, and grains are important irrigated crops, and the rural population has increased in density on the reclaimed lands.

Water supplies are precarious in the Great Plains south of the Nebraska Sand Hills, where evaporation frequently exceeds precipitation. Irrigation projects in Nebraska, Kansas, and Colorado have reclaimed some land. Water is taken from the Platte, Arkansas, and other rivers, as well as from lakes and deep wells, to irrigate such crops as grain sorghums, sugar beets, alfalfa, melons, and vegetables, especially onions and beans. Although these crops do not occupy large acreages, they are of special importance to the area in which they are produced.

MINERALS

The most important mineral resources of the Great Plains are (1) the petroleum and natural gas deposits in both the northern and southern parts of the region, (2) the rock salt deposits of Kansas, and (3) the lignite deposits of the Dakotas and Kansas. Although the mineral industries employ many hundreds of persons and add materially to the economy of the area in which they are mined, their economic contribution to the Great Plains is much less than that of the agricultural and ranching activities.

Petroleum is common in both the northern and southern parts of the Great Plains. The Williston Basin in North Dakota and Montana is one of the more recently developed fields of the nation. In Wyoming petroleum is of local importance. The great Mid-Continent petroleum field of the South extends northward from Texas and Oklahoma into Kansas. In petroleum production Kansas ranks sixth and North Dakota eleventh among the oil-producing states.

The largest natural gas field in the United States, the Hugoton, extends southward from near Garden City, Kansas, into the Texas Panhandle. Much gas is piped to urban areas in other parts of the nation for use as fuel. Carbon black is made from the gas in some plants located in the field.

Figure 2-16   A not uncommon sight on the Great Plains is the combination of oil and wheat. Here a combine harvests a field of wheat while oil is being pumped. (Courtesy of Northern Pacific Railway.)

Large salt mines have been developed near Hutchinson, Kansas. The salt deposits came from a great inland sea that covered much of central Kansas about 275 million years ago. Salt deposition began when an isolated arm of the sea began to dry up through evaporation. The salt deposits formed into a thickening mass about 45 miles wide and 100 miles long. During later geologic periods sediments buried the salt and compressed it into dense rock salt about 300 feet thick. The deposit was discovered in 1889 when oilmen drilled into the salt. Mining was begun in the early 1920s when the first shaft was dug. It has been estimated that this deposit holds enough salt to meet the needs of the United States for 250,000 years.

Lignite is found in the northern part of the Great Plains, but the lack of a market discourages mining. Gold ores and a few other metals occur at Lead and Deadwood in the Black Hills. The Homestead Mine at Lead has produced over 200 million dollars' worth of gold ore. There is, however, little activity in the area today.

SETTLEMENTS

Villages, towns, and cities in the Great Plains are usually small, widely spaced, and bear strong resemblance to each other. Communities sprang up, at first, in connection with railroad lines crossing the plains, because of the need for farm and ranch service centers. The region is not noted for its large cities or manufactures. Towns are frequently located near stream channels where water is obtainable, or along railway lines where the inhabitants can maintain contacts with distant places. Each town or village will have a small commercial center with a few stores that can supply the necessities of life. In many places one or two large general stores will sell everything, from food and clothing to drugs and machine parts. In many, the two dominant places of activity will be the stockyards and the elevators, especially during the marketing season. A large consolidated school, a few churches, and several modest homes will be adjacent to the business district.

By far the largest and most important city of the Great Plains is Denver, which not only commands the plains, but lies so near the Southern Rockies that it serves both these extensive regions. It is particularly important for wholesale and retail trade. Several main highways and transcontinental railways focus on Denver. It is also district headquarters for numerous agencies of the Federal government. Tourism is a major industry of this mile-high city.

Smaller cities are of local importance. Some, like Great Falls, Montana, and Trinidad, Colorado, became highly important points for the connection of land travel routes and for the shipment of mining products from the Rockies. In later years their character changed somewhat; Colorado Springs has become a popular high-altitude resort and an aviation center for the United States Air Force. Pueblo is now a trading and iron-smelting center. Scottsbluff is the trade center for the irrigated agricultural area known as Goshen Hole. Rapid City, second largest city in South Dakota, is an Air Force base and a mining and agricultural center. Dodge City, famous for its history as a frontier town, is the trade center for an extensive stock-raising and agricultural area. Casper, Wyoming, and Williston, North Dakota, are important oil centers, La Junta, Colorado, and Garden City, Kansas, are shipping centers for irrigated agricultural products, and Harve, Montana, is a center for the shipping of livestock. Bismarck, Pierre, and Cheyenne are not only the capital of their respective states, but each is also a local retail and wholesale outlet for its area.

RECREATION

Living in the Great Plains has been picturesque if not easy. The landscape is wide open, without the polluted air of Eastern cities. Though ranches are very large, they can be operated with relatively few laborers and cowhands. In the early history of the plains, labor-saving devices such as barbed wire, the high windmill, and mechanical pumps aided the rancher in changing the landscape from cattle kingdom to wheatfield. More recently, the radio, automobile, and electric pump have been important to the farmers. Distinctive features of the Great Plains' cultural environment have spread throughout the United States. Perhaps the greatest contribution to recreation from the area has been cowboy music, certain words and phrases of our speech, Western motion pictures, Western fiction, and Western clothing, all derived from the pattern of the Great Plains cattle ranch of the late nineteenth century.

Set in the midst of the northern Great Plains, the dome of the Black Hills offers sharp contrast to the surrounding lands; here are forests used for their timber supply. The rugged mountains—including Mount Rushmore, famous for its giant carved heads of four presidents—the relatively pleasant summer weather, and the forests combine to make this part of South Dakota attractive to tourists. Rapid City, east of the Black Hills, serves as a point of entry and as a service center.

Several other areas are becoming nationally recognized as places of interest for tourists. A short distance west of the

Black Hills is a national monument known as Devils Tower. This oddity, visible for many miles, rises for almost a thousand feet above the surrounding plain. It is the central core of an ancient volcano. An excellent highway has been built through the Dakota Bad Lands making it possible for tourists to view the erosional features from several points. The area is also frequented by fossil hunters, many well-preserved fossils of prehistoric animals having been discovered. Various Indian reservations, located near the Bad Lands, also attract thousands of tourists each year.

Recreational areas are also being developed along or near many of the large man-made lakes. Places of historical interest along the Oregon and Santa Fe Trails— Mitchell Pass, Fort Laramie, Council Grove, Pawnee Rock—also attract numerous visitors. A few former cow towns like Dodge City have reconstructed their "Boot Hills" and "Front Streets" to encourage tourist trade.

SELECTED REFERENCES

Alexandersson, Gunnar: "Changes in the Location Pattern of the Anglo-American Steel Industry: 1948–1959," *Economic Geography*, vol. 37, no. 2, pp. 95–114, April, 1961.
A study of the shifting location pattern of the steel industry as influenced by location of iron ore fields, markets, and shipping ports for ore.

Garland, John H. (ed.): *The North American Midwest*, John Wiley & Sons, Inc., New York, 1955.

A geography of the Midwestern states, discussing such topics as physiography, economic production and development, and rural and urban areas.

Harris, Chauncy D.: "Agricultural Production in the United States: The Past Fifty Years and the Next," *Geographical Review*, vol. 47, no. 2, pp. 175–193, April, 1957.
A study of the changing agricultural situation and some of the problems to be considered.

Hidore, John J.: "The Relationship between Cash-Grain Farming and Landforms," *Economic Geography*, vol. 39, no. 1, pp. 84–89, January, 1963.
A study of the influences of landforms upon the types of crops planted.

Krenzell, Carl F.: *The Great Plains in Transition*, University of Oklahoma Press, Norman, Okla., 1955.
A discussion of the climate, soils, economic development, and problems of the Great Plains in the light of their history and regionalism.

Lounsbury, John F.: "Industrial Development of the Ohio Valley," *Journal of Geography*, vol. 60, no. 6, pp. 253–262, September, 1961.
A study of the changing industrial developments in the Ohio River Valley.

Weaver, John C.: "Crop Combination Regions in the Middle West," *Geographical Review*, vol. 44, no. 2, pp. 175–200, April, 1954.
A study of crop-combination regions (not agricultural regions) pertaining to land-use association of crops. Many good maps.

Webb, Walter Prescott: *The Great Plains*, Ginn and Company, Boston, 1931.
The classic volume dealing with the Great Plains from an historical-geographic approach.

chapter 3

THE UNITED STATES:
THE SOUTH

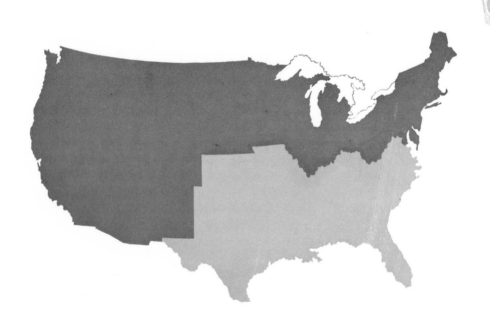

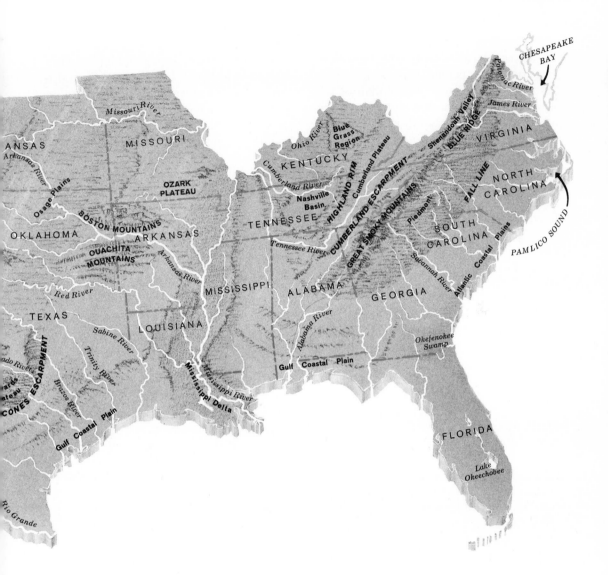

Figure 3-1 Plains are the dominant physical feature of the South. The Fall Line and numerous rivers were of special importance during the early development of the region.

THE PART OF THE UNITED STATES COMmonly referred to as the South is probably the least-understood section of the nation. Far too many people think only of the South's historical past rather than of the modern, progressive developments in the area. At present the South is in a state of transition, changing from cotton to a great variety of agricultural activities, from rural to urban life, from man power to mechanical power, from a static to a mobile population, from conservatism to liberalism. True, other parts of the nation have gone through similar changes, but not in so short a period of time. More changes have occurred in the South during the past thirty years than took place in the Northeast in over a century.

The South is a sprawling area extending from the Atlantic Ocean westward into the Great Plains and northward from the Gulf of Mexico to the Ohio River and the Ozark Plateau. Prior to the discovery of America the area was inhabited by Indians in various stages of civilization, ranging from the Plains tribes who followed the buffalo for sustenance to those living in the southeast who had developed a primitive type of agriculture by planting such crops as corn, beans, and squash. The first Europeans to settle in America were the Spanish. Before 1550, De Soto, De Vaca, Coronado, and other explorers had crossed and recrossed parts of the area. The first permanent settlement in what is now the United States was St. Augustine, established in 1565.

For many decades the South has been a region of economic maladjustment. The history of its people and their activities has been a record of turbulence. Before the Civil War the economy was based on cotton plantations and slavery, after the war on cotton and tenant farmers or sharecroppers. Various political conditions, along with declining soil fertility and poor farming methods, made recovery slow, but

by 1900 a semblance of agricultural adjustment had occurred. Because of the high cotton prices during and immediately after World War I, however, much eroded and infertile soil was planted in cotton. In the Depression years of the 1930s the South, with the rest of the nation, found its economy again shattered and many of its people in want. In several respects the South, with its dominant one-crop system and tenant farmers, became the economic problem of the nation.

Since 1935 a new South has been in the process of formation. Recognizing the need for diversification of crops, better soil and forest conservation, and the development of industries, the people of the South, with the aid of the Federal government, again began an economic adjustment. No longer is the region just a "land of cotton" and small farms. Although cotton is still widely grown and there are numerous small farms, the tendency now is toward consolidation of holdings; increased attention to livestock, with greater acreages planted to soybeans, peanuts, and hay crops; terracing, contouring, and fertilizing of the soil; and the development of industries to use the natural resources of the region.

The South, as delimited in this study, occupies much of the Coastal Plain, the southern half of the Eastern Highlands, and southward extensions of the Central Lowlands and Great Plains. All of the Interior Highlands are considered a part of the South.

PLAINS OF THE SOUTHLAND

PHYSICAL SETTING

COASTAL PLAIN   Most of the Atlantic and all of the Gulf Coastal Plains are in the South. Varying in width from less than 50 miles to approximately 500 miles where it follows the Mississippi River northward

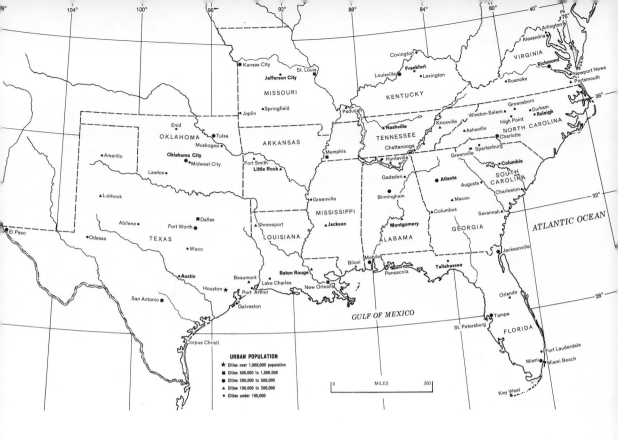

*Figure 3-2   The South is a large area, extending from the Atlantic Ocean westward into the
Great Plains. Locations of the largest cities are largely the result of cultural factors.*

to southern Illinois, the plain is a region
of relatively recent sedimentary deposits.
Much of the Coastal Plain is a nearly flat
lowland that slopes gently toward the
ocean. The Virginia and North Carolina
coastline is very irregular because of the
drowning of river mouths by the sinking
of the coast and thus the invasion of ocean
water. The resulting estuaries, or tidewater
bays, include Delaware and Chesapeake
Bays, the lower Potomac, James, and York
Rivers, and Albemarle Sound. In places
low hills, which mark the outcrop of more
resistant rocks, rise above the lower lands
formed of silt, clay, and limey marl.
Florida is a peninsula built mostly of limestone, in which many lakes have been
formed in natural depressions or by solution. From the southern end of the peninsula a festoon of keys extends into the Gulf

of Mexico. Along and near the shore of the
Coastal Plain are several great swamps
like the Dismal Swamp in Virginia and
North Carolina, Okefenokee in Georgia,
the Everglades in Florida, and much of the
lower Mississippi Delta in Louisiana. Just
offshore, in many locations, long, narrow
sand islands have been formed.

The Mississippi Embayment, which
separates the East Gulf Coastal Plain from
the West Gulf Coastal Plain, has been
filled by river sediments. In these lowlands
the Mississippi meanders over a wide
alluvial floodplain. Along each side of the
river are low bluffs. The vast amount of
sediment which the river carries constantly extends the large delta, making it
hard to tell where land ends and the sea
begins. The Mississippi, with its tributaries, broad flood plain, and delta, is the

major river and the dominant feature that divides the Gulf Coastal Plain into two nearly equal parts.

Florida and the Gulf Coast enjoy a humid, subtropical climate with little or no frost. Inland, during two or three months, freezing temperatures occur, and many plants become dormant. Rainfall is usually distributed and generally totals 40 to 50 inches annually. At some Gulf stations the annual rainfall may exceed 80 inches, but inland, to the west and northwest, the total decreases to 25 or 30 inches. The principal weather handicaps are hurricanes that occasionally affect the coasts, winter cold waves that bring freezing temperatures injurious to fruits and vegetables, and occasional droughts. In general, the northern boundary of the Coastal Plains coincides with the 200-day growing season.

INTERIOR PLAINS　Parts of the Interior Plains extend from the Midwest into the South. The section of the Central Lowlands in middle Tennessee and central Kentucky contains the famous Bluegrass section and the Nashville Basin, the latter surrounded by the Highland Rim. In general the area is undulating and the soils rich. West of the Interior Highlands, the Osage Plains section of the Central Lowlands extends across Oklahoma into central Texas. For the most part the area is a rolling plain with the native vegetation changing from forests and prairies to short grass toward the west. In southern Oklahoma the remains of two eroded mountain groups, the Arbuckles and the Wichitas, contrast in roughness of topography and elevation with the surrounding plain.

The Great Plains extend southward across the Panhandle of Oklahoma and western Texas to the Rio Grande. The southern extension of the High Plains part of the Great Plains is comparable to the area in Kansas and Nebraska. South of the Canadian River, the High Plains are called the Llano Estacado or Staked Plains; the southern part is known as the Edwards Plateau. The eastern edge of the High Plains is marked by an escarpment, or a narrow zone of rough topography, known as the Break of the Plains.

The climate of the Bluegrass region–Nashville Basin as well as the eastern part of the Osage Plains is of the humid, continental, long-summer type. Summers range from warm to hot with short periods of cold weather in winter. In the eastern areas rainfall is adequate, but in the Osage Plains rainfall decreases to about 25 inches yearly toward the west. Usually the maximum rainfall is in early summer.

Most of the Southern High Plains are handicapped by the lack of rainfall, the yearly average being between 15 and 20 inches. Evaporation is so rapid that in some years the meager rainfall is inadequate to support good pastures or dry croplands. Usually winters are moderate to mild, although freezing blizzards are not unknown. Summers are warm to hot. The mean January temperature at Amarillo is 35°F, that for July, 77°F.

AGRICULTURE

Agriculture is the basic occupation in much of the Coastal Plain. The long growing season and abundant rainfall favor corn, cotton, and many other crops—peanuts, soybeans, tobacco, melons, sunflowers. Only the lower Rio Grande Valley requires regular irrigation. The soils are highly variable. Those in the river bottomlands and deltas and the zones of marls and silts inland from the coasts are very fertile; in contrast are the poor soils of the pineflats and sandy hills. When drained, muck soils of the Everglades of

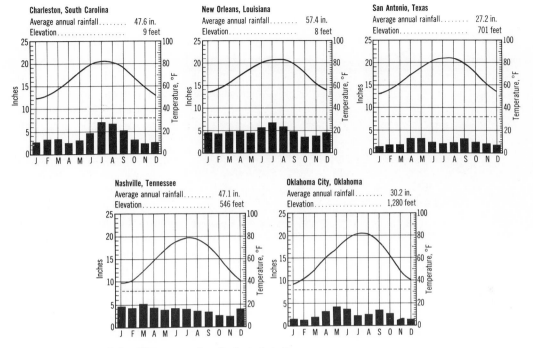

Figure 3-3 Climate graphs of selected stations.

Florida and along parts of the Gulf Coast are well suited for vegetables and sugar cane. All through the South marked changes are taking place in agriculture, particularly in the use of machinery, marketing methods, and variety of products grown.

For over 150 years, cotton has so constantly been the money crop that the region is often called the Cotton Belt. The crop has an annual value of over 2.5 billion dollars. The best soils planted to cotton are those of alluvial origin along the Mississippi, Yazoo, Arkansas, and other rivers. The very fertile, black, waxy prairie soils of Texas are also excellent producers of cotton. The southern Piedmont and a zone of sandy loams on the inner coastal plain from Georgia into North Carolina are traditionally of great importance. Since 1900, however, production in these eastern sections has declined

because of soil erosion or depletion, infestation by the boll weevil, replacement by other farm products, especially corn, fodder, and pasture crops, and competition for labor from industry. Cotton lands are increasingly dependent on the use of fertilizers.

Since 1920 a westward shift in cotton production has been due largely to the growing of cotton in newly developed irrigated areas in Texas, New Mexico, Arizona, and California. Even though many farmers living outside the principal producing areas of the old Cotton Belt continue to plant one to five acres in cotton, the product does not occupy as great an acreage as corn. So discontinuous is cotton acreage in the old Cotton Belt that today many publications are referring to the area as the "Shattered Cotton Belt." During the past quarter century the cotton farmer, like the wheat, corn, and peanut

Figure 3-4   The principal areas of cotton production have shifted from the Coastal Plain to the irrigated part of the High Plain. Mechanical cotton pickers are widely used on the large western farms. (Courtesy of Harlingen Chamber of Commerce.)

farmer, has been limited in the number of acres he could plant in cotton by government regulations which he voted to follow. Frequently the cotton farmer has been paid large sums to let a part of his land lie fallow (be nonproductive) instead of putting it into production. In spite of the fact that cotton is now planted on a smaller acreage, the total production has increased. The use of better seed, more efficient farming methods, and a regulated water supply through irrigation, plus spraying for insects, have helped to account for the larger crop.

The High Plains in western Texas and southwestern Oklahoma have largely replaced the southeastern areas in cotton production. Near Lubbock, Texas, is the nation's leading cotton-producing region. Water is pumped from deep wells for irrigation. Mechanization in caring for and picking the crop, together with the development of varieties suited to a drier climate, has made possible the expansion of the industry into these western lands. Since cotton must be picked in dry weather, only small amounts are grown along the southern coast where autumn rains may delay or prevent the harvest.

In the nonmechanized areas, much labor is needed to produce a good cotton crop. After planting, the farmer must cultivate and chop (hoe) the growing crop for thinning and weeding. Until the 1930s the picking of cotton by hand required much cheap labor, but since then cotton-picking machines have been increasingly used, especially in the newer producing areas to the west where farms are larger than in the older districts. After the cotton has been picked, it is taken to cotton gins, where the seeds are removed and the fibers are pressed and bound into bales. Cottonseed is a valuable by-product, used for edible oils, soap, and other items. In addition to the large quantities consumed by mills in the United States, cotton is exported to many textile-manufacturing countries, for the South (Piedmont, Coastal Plain, and High Plains of west Texas) grows approximately 25 per cent of the world's cotton. The location of principal seaports, like Houston and New Orleans, which are close to the cotton fields, is advantageous for export.

Although citrus fruits are grown along the outer margins of the Coastal Plain, central Florida and the lower Rio Grande

Valley in Texas are so seldom reached by frosts that they produce most of the South's commercial crop. Oranges, grapefruit, tangerines, and limes are most important in Florida. Grapefruit is a specialty in Texas. Normally, citrus fruits come on the market in quantity only at certain seasons; to prolong the marketing season and preserve the products, therefore, nearly one-half of the crop is processed into canned fruit and juice, frozen concentrates, and marmalade. Over 50 million gallons of orange juice are frozen and processed yearly in Florida. Non-citrus fruits are grown in almost all inland sections of the region; important commercial crops of peaches are marketed in South Carolina and Georgia. Oklahoma and Texas are among the nation's leaders in pecan production. Large orchards of tung trees, whose seeds supply an oil for varnish, have been developed in northern Florida and southern Alabama.

Sugar, rice, corn, peanuts, tobacco, and winter vegetables are among other South-ern crops. Sugar cane is grown on the lower Mississippi Delta, especially in southern Louisiana, and to some degree in southern Florida. Although there is danger of crop injury from cold, the development of cold-resistant hybrid varieties has lessened this danger and also doubled acreage yields. Southern Louisiana is a land of big plantations. Planting and caring for the crop, harvesting and transporting the cane, and extracting the sugar at the mills and refineries require large capital investment. Southern rice, like wheat, is planted and harvested by machine methods. Level land underlain by impervious clay is surrounded by dikes to retain the water in which rice stands during much of its growing season. Louisiana, Texas, and Arkansas produce over 60 per cent of the domestic rice. More acres are planted in corn than in any other crop, for corn is the common grain crop of the South. As corn bread, hominy, and grits, corn is widely used for food as well as feed for livestock. Peanuts grow well on

Figure 3-5   Flooding in progress in the final preparation of seeding rice field near Stuttgart, Arkansas. (Courtesy of Arkansas Publicity and Parks Commission.)

depleted soils. They are used for food, for processing into other food products, and as raw material by chemical industries.

Truck crops are grown by intensively specialized methods in a number of limited areas. Most of the products, such as vegetables and strawberries, move first from the more southerly areas to Northern markets during the early winter. Within a few weeks a more northerly locality will then come into production. Some growers plant two crops annually, one for the early and one for the late market. The drained muck lands of southern Florida and the silts of the lower Rio Grande Valley are among the principal producing sections. Thousands of carloads of Southern fruits and vegetables are delivered in season to Northern markets by refrigerator cars and trucks.

Livestock is of increasing importance, notably on the depleted soils of the older settled sections of the South. Fodder crops like lespedeza, kudzu, and cowpeas are good stock feeds and grow well on worn-out land, which they enrich while they help hold eroding soils in place. The recent growth in production of cattle, pigs, and poultry east of the Mississippi is quite noteworthy. The cattle industry benefits from the mild temperatures; the even rainfall that facilitates rapid growth of hay and forage crops makes pasturage available most of the year. Because pork products are popular in the South, corn and hog raising has prospered. The poultry business has expanded, especially in northeastern Georgia; quantities of fowls are now being processed for shipment to Northern markets. Mild temperatures and available feed are favorable; but the "know-how" of hatching, feeding, processing, and marketing poultry is even more important. Although natural conditions favor dairying, its development has lagged, partly because many farmers lack experience. An effort is being made to

develop breeds of dairy cows that will be unaffected by the long, hot summers. Beef cattle production also is increasing, and crossbreeding of Hereford and Angus stock with the Brahmas of India is providing good beef cattle that can withstand the heat of the long summers. Many former cotton plantations are now prosperous livestock farms.

The High Plains of Texas have long been noted for the production of beef animals, especially feeder stock that is marketed in the Corn Belt. Ranches are numerous, and ranch life does not differ greatly from that of the northern Great Plains. The milder winters minimize the danger of animal loss from freezing. Ranches often include more than 25 sections of land. The King Ranch, the largest in the United States, located in southeast Texas, covers a discontinuous area as large as the state of Rhode Island. On the brush-covered Edwards Plateau the grazing of sheep and Angora goats is of prime importance. The goats produce mohair.

An agricultural transition zone is found between the Corn and Cotton Belts from the Cumberland Plateau to the Mississippi River bottoms. This hilly region includes the Ohio Valley and central and western Kentucky and Tennessee. Some fertile valleys and wide basins occur. Much of the hill land is wooded, and the landscape is varied. Frequently steep slopes have been cleared and planted to corn and tobacco, but heavy rains on the bare, cultivated slopes have caused much erosion and contributed to the poverty of the hill farmers. In the fertile river valleys and the Bluegrass and Nashville Basin areas, farming is generally very successful. There is a striking difference between the big mansions, blooded livestock, and well-tilled, productive fields of the fertile areas, and the unpainted shacks, skinny mules, and eroded, weed-infested plots characteristic of some of the hill country.

Although corn is widely grown—with poor success on eroded hills and with good results on river bottoms and fertile plains—it is not a dominant crop. Tobacco is the major cash crop. Though total production is large, heavy labor demands and the exacting soil requirements restrict the amount of land planted in tobacco to from 4 to 10 acres on most small farms. The large and well-managed estates may plant much more. Burley tobacco, used in making cigarettes, is preferred in the Kentucky Bluegrass, but in western Kentucky and north central Tennessee dark-fired tobacco, used for snuff and chewing tobacco, is grown. The Kentucky Bluegrass and the Nashville Basin, being areas of fertile limestone soils, are regions of superior pastures, where purebred cattle and blooded horses are raised.

FORESTS

The South is a natural woodland area. Because of its long growing season and ample rainfall, trees make double the growth of those in northern climates. Pines

Figure 3-6   The Bluegrass area is noted for its blooded horses and its picturesque countryside. (Courtesy of Kentucky Tourist Division.)

predominate on the flat plains; hardwoods are found in the river bottoms; and in areas of hilly land the two are frequently mixed. Except on natural prairies in Texas and Oklahoma, farmland, when abandoned, is quickly seeded from the nearby woods and is in a short time covered with a

Figure 3-7   Southern pines are especially good for the making of wood pulp. Here, in Louisiana, a company has established a wood-concentration yard, where farmers can sell their wood. It is then moved by barge to a mill. (Courtesy of International Paper Company.)

second-growth forest. In thirty to forty years the pines become large enough for saw logs. A chief obstacle to reforestation in the coastal sections is the large number of forest fires. Few national forests have been established, but large acreages under private ownership are scientifically handled and form the basis for permanent lumber and pulp or paper enterprises. Logging is possible throughout the year, and the logs are delivered to the mills by truck and rail. Many mills are located at seaports or so near them that lumber can be easily exported. Mississippi and Louisiana are the leaders, but lumber is marketed from every Southern state. In total output, the South is second only to the Pacific Northwest. Lumber used for construction, naval stores, and wood pulp are the principal products of the Southern forests. The sawing of hardwood lumber is especially important in Tennessee and Arkansas.

The southern pines are the principal source of naval stores. Resin, the basic element, is a thick, amber-colored liquid that flows from the tree when a gash is cut in the trunk. Since the resin flows into cups which have been attached to the tree, this activity is called "cupping." After many years of cupping the trees are cut for lumber. The chief naval store products are pitch, which is used in caulking wooden ships, tar for waterproofing, and turpentine. Resin is also used as a raw material for the chemical industries. Savannah and Jacksonville lead in the exportation of naval stores.

The pulpwood and kraft (wrapping) paper industry has had a phenomenal development. Many paper mills have been built, especially in Georgia and the Gulf states. Since trees become large enough for pulpwood in ten to fifteen years the paper and pulpwood industry can be established on a permanent basis. Tree farming is now an important activity in many parts of the South.

FISHERIES

Shrimp, sponges, oysters, and crabs provide the principal source of income from the Southern coastal fisheries. Inshore

Figure 3-8   Commercial fishing and shrimp boats docked in Galveston. (Courtesy of Galveston Chamber of Commerce.)

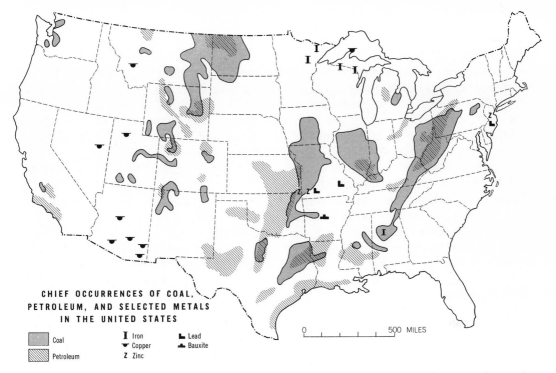

CHIEF OCCURRENCES OF COAL,
PETROLEUM, AND SELECTED METALS
IN THE UNITED STATES

	Coal	**I** Iron	**L** Lead
	Petroleum	**▼** Copper	**⊥** Bauxite
		Z Zinc	

Figure 3-9   The South is well supplied with mineral fuels. Many other minerals are also mined in the area.

waters, especially along the lagoons of the Mississippi Delta, supply small shrimp and crabs. Large shrimp are secured by trawlers, fishing at night, in the deeper Gulf waters. Corpus Christi and Galveston are important shrimp ports. From these and several other ports, shrimp are shipped fresh or as frozen or canned products. Oysters are taken mainly from the lagoons on the coasts of Louisiana and Florida. The center of the sponge industry is Tarpon Springs, Florida. Sponges are taken largely by divers.

In a few places snapper and other fish are caught for local markets. In the Mississippi, Arkansas, Red, Tombigbee, and other rivers in the region, both large and small, fishing for catfish, bass, perch, and other fresh-water fish greatly supplements the local food supply and furnishes very desirable recreation.

MINERALS

In total value the South produces over 25 per cent of the nation's minerals. Petroleum, coal, iron ore, sulfur, phosphate, and salt are produced in large quantities; the South exceeds all the rest of the nation in the production of petroleum. Building stones and numerous minerals of lesser importance such as asphalt, glass sand, and kaolin are of considerable local importance. One of the most important factors in the industrial development of the South has been this large and varied mineral reserve.

The Mid-Continent oil field, the most important producer of petroleum in the world, is largely in the South. Included in this field are producing areas in Arkansas, northern Louisiana, Oklahoma, and much of northern and western Texas. The Gulf Coast field, the second most important petroleum field in the United States, is located along the Gulf of Texas and Louisiana. Because of the large production of this field, along with that of the Mid-Continent, Texas ranks first among all states in petroleum production, Louisiana third, and Oklahoma fourth. Arkansas and Mississippi are also important producers of petroleum. During the period 1955 to 1960, the average yearly production of petroleum in the United States was 2,553 million barrels of which 1,600 million barrels were produced in the South.

The exploitation of petroleum makes startling changes in the landscape. Small agricultural hamlets, sleepy cow towns, or somnolent fishing villages may become booming cities almost overnight. Derricks, pumps, storage tanks, oil-field camps, and all the other accompaniments of this industry completely change the activities of the communities in which oil is found. New residential and commercial additions, in many instances whole new towns, have been built for and by the influx of workers required to carry on the various phases of the industry. Good transportation is essential. Along the coast, harbors have been improved and sometimes created by dredging, and breakwaters and docks built to service the tankers that transport petroleum and its products to Atlantic Coast ports and abroad. Pipelines, railroad tank cars, and highway tankers distribute oil products inland.

Seemingly insuperable difficulties have been overcome in developing oil fields along the Gulf of Mexico. Much oil lies beneath coastal swamps and even under the ocean floor. Drilling operations proceed on platforms in quagmires or in open waters. Transporting men and materials over swamps and waters requires wholly new types of vehicles and amphibious boats. Some producing wells are 10 miles offshore in the shallow Gulf waters, and the seaward limit of the oil fields has not yet been determined.

Coastal centers famous for oil production include Beaumont and Port Arthur, Texas, and Lake Charles, Louisiana. Texas City, Houston, and New Orleans all have great oil refineries. More than 40 oil refineries are located along the Gulf Coast of Texas and Louisiana, among them four of the five largest in the United States. Two refineries in Port Arthur and one in Beaumont have a daily crude capacity of over 200,000 barrels each. The largest American refinery, in Baton Rouge, has a daily capacity greater than 350,000 barrels. Smaller cities, such as Tyler and Kilgore, have developed in the East Texas oil fields. Tulsa is one of the leading oil financial centers of the world.

Natural gas, usually associated with petroleum, is found in enormous quantities. Formerly much of this excellent fuel was wasted because there were no markets nearby. The invention of spiral steel pipe and machines to lay and weld the sections quickly has made possible delivery of gas from the South to Northeastern industrial and seaport cities. Natural gas is considered the ideal fuel for heating and cooking in homes. Some gas is burned to make carbon black, a product used in many chemical industries. Two large helium plants have been built in the Hugoton Gas Field that extends southward from Kansas across the Oklahoma Panhandle to near Amarillo. Natural gas is used also as a raw material in certain chemical industries and is considered the best fuel for the making of glass.

Five Southern states—Alabama, Arkansas, Georgia, Oklahoma, and Texas—have reserves of bituminous coal. Arkansas and Texas also have deposits of lignite. Excellent bituminous coal, which can be

Figure 3-10   A general view of the Esso refinery located in Baton Rouge, Louisiana. This refinery, the largest in the United States, processes 340,000 barrels of crude oil daily. (Courtesy of Esso Standard Oil Company.)

used to make coke, is mined in Alabama near the end of the Appalachian Plateau and is used in the iron and steel industries of that state. Coking coal is mined in eastern Oklahoma and shipped to the steel center in Daingerfield, Texas.

The largest production of sulfur in the world is on the Gulf Coast of Louisiana and Texas. Water heated under pressure to temperatures higher than 300°F is forced into the sulfur deposits. At such temperatures the sulfur becomes soluble. The liquid is then forced to the surface by compressed air, run into large storage bins, and allowed to cool and solidify. Gulf Coast sulfur is shipped to chemical plants throughout the world. The chief product made from sulfur is sulfuric acid, but the mineral is also used in making drugs, paper, fertilizer, and a variety of other products.

Phosphate, iron ore, and salt are also mined in the South. Phosphate rock, used for fertilizer, is mined in the Tampa area. This part of Florida supplies 80 per cent of the phosphate used in the United States and exports a large amount besides. The chief iron ore mining region is near Birmingham and is close to good coking coal and limestone. These resources are the basis for the largest iron and steel production in the South. Some iron ore is mined

in northeast Texas and forms the base for a small but expanding industry near Daingerfield. Large quantities of salt are mined along the Texas-Louisiana coast.

MANUFACTURING AND TRANSPORTATION

Within the past decade the number of manufacturing establishments in the South has greatly increased. Factors that favor the industrial development of this region are (1) vast reserves of petroleum, natural gas, and coal that can be used both for power and for chemical raw materials, (2) resources of timber, minerals, and agricultural products available for processing, (3) a large supply of labor, and (4) good transportation by sea and land. Among the handicaps are (1) a shortage of local capital and lack of industrial experience, (2) the competition of Northern mills which have established reputations, (3) the lack of skilled labor, and (4) the greater distance to the large markets.

Although the South is less densely populated than the Northeast, it has an adequate supply of potential industrial workers. Some of them come from the farms where mechanization, soil depletion, and changes in crop systems have reduced the number of laborers needed.

In general, living costs less in the South, and wages have usually been below those of the North. Many branch plants of Northern-owned corporations have been located in the South to supply the demands of the region for nationally distributed articles. Examples include assembly plants for automobiles, farm machinery, and heavy goods, on which important savings in freight charges from the home plants to the South can be made.

The pattern of manufacturing in the Coastal Plain is characterized by wide distribution and great diversity. The Texas Gulf Coast area, particularly in and around Houston, is especially important for chemicals, machinery, oil refining, and shipbuilding. Elsewhere, Birmingham leads the South in steelmaking. Memphis processes agricultural products and lumber. The Dallas–Fort Worth section has a variety of industries including meat packing, the making of wearing apparel, automobile assembly, and airplane manufacture. In the vicinity of New Orleans, Mobile, Tampa, and other Southern cities, smaller industrial districts make practically all types of manufactured goods.

Transportation in the region is easily managed. Except for the necessity of bridging the rivers, the broad lowlands offer few hindrances to the building of railroads and highways. There are many navigable rivers, of which the Mississippi is the major artery for bulky freight. The Black Warrior River in Alabama is used to carry coal. A few canals are noteworthy. Houston, an inland city, has become a great seaport by dredging and improving a shallow river and developing the Houston Ship Canal. A canal connects Galveston with the Mississippi River. A dredged waterway connecting the Mississippi and Lake Pontchartrain has greatly increased waterfront land available to industrial development in the vicinity of New Orleans. The Intracoastal Waterway is located through much of its route from New Jersey to Miami in waters protected by offshore islands. Thousands of pleasure craft travel on this waterway yearly.

CITIES AND TOWNS

The uniform flat surface of the rural Coastal Plain favors a fairly even distribution of population. Only the swamps and areas with the poorest of sandy soils have few inhabitants. Zones of superior soil like the black, waxy prairie in east central Texas and the Yazoo bottomlands of northwestern Mississippi support many prosperous farms. Rural hamlets and villages are numerous throughout the region. In most of them a consolidated school and a post office serve the immediate vicinity. A small general store or two, filling stations, and possibly a drug store, garage, and cotton gin comprise the local business establishments. Two or three small churches are found in almost every village. Many of the people drive to the larger towns or cities to buy most of their needs.

Forty cities in the South have populations of 100,000 or more and twenty-five of these are on the Coastal Plain. The four cities with the largest populations are, in order, Houston, Dallas, New Orleans, and San Antonio, each having over 500,000 inhabitants.

Houston, with a metropolitan population of over a million, has developed rapidly during the past decade. The city is one of the principal cargo ports of the nation. It is connected with the Gulf of Mexico by the 50-mile-long Houston Ship Canal. The chief exports are petroleum, sulfur, cotton, grain, and chemical products. Numerous imports from the Latin American countries are received. The city is noted for its petrochemical industries and other manufactures based upon the natural resources of the region. In tonnage of trade, Houston ranks among the first ten ports of the nation.

New Orleans, located 90 miles upstream from the mouth of the Mississippi River, is one of the principal southern seaports and ranks in tonnage among the first ten ports of the United States. Water transportation is important; along the banks of the Mississippi are many docks, wharves, grain elevators, cotton warehouses, and numerous other commercial and industrial activities. Much Latin American trade moves through New Orleans. Often called America's most interesting city, New Orleans is not only a famous resort center, but also a popular shopping center for travelers from both Middle and South America.

Texas has more large cities than any other Southern state. Eleven places, including Houston, have populations in excess of 100,000. Near the Balcones Escarpment, the boundary between the Coastal Plain and the Interior Plains, such major cities as San Antonio, Austin, and Dallas have developed in addition to smaller cities like Waco and Temple. Dallas is a major cotton market and a

leader in women's fashions. The city is the principal banking and insurance center in the southwestern part of the nation. Because of its central position, adequate railroads, good highways, and airlines the city is one of the leading wholesale and retail centers of the United States. San Antonio, established in 1718, is a tourist and ranch center. Its pleasant climate, its wealth of historical associations—Alamo, the Spanish Governor's Palace, the San Antonio River that winds through the city—and its large Spanish American population have all played a part in the city's development. Corpus Christi, Texas City, Galveston, Port Arthur, and Beaumont are important Gulf ports. Many cities of the Interior Plains have won national recognition. Fort Worth is noted as a meat-packing and distribution center. Amarillo and Wichita Falls are wholesale centers for large petroleum and agricultural areas. Lubbock is famous as a center for irrigation agriculture.

In many instances some local factor has spurred the development of cities. Memphis, located on the Chickasaw Bluffs overlooking the Mississippi River, is the world's largest cotton market. It is also the

Figure 3-11   Dallas is a major cotton market and a leader in women's fashions. (Courtesy of Dallas Chamber of Commerce.)

national center for cottonseed products, such as shortening, vegetable oils, and stock feed. Memphis is also noted as the nation's largest inland hardwood market. Birmingham is the steel-producing center of the South. Newport News is famed for shipbuilding and the export of coal. Miami and Miami Beach are noted recreational centers. Ports on the Atlantic, like Wilmington, Charleston, Savannah, and Jacksonville, which have smaller hinterlands than the Gulf ports, have less ocean-borne trade, although some, in particular Charleston, have magnificent harbors. Oklahoma City, Jackson, Little Rock, Montgomery, Richmond, and Nashville are not only state capitals, but serve as retail-trade outlets for various large areas.

RECREATION

Tourists and vacationists spend hundreds of millions of dollars in travel through the South and in sojourning at coast resorts from the Carolinas to Texas. Both the Atlantic and Gulf Coasts of Florida are major resort areas. More visitors come in the winter season, but many are encouraged to vacation in the summer by the cheaper rates of the off season. Streamlined trains, airplanes, buses, private cars, and pleasure boats bring thousands of visitors to Florida daily at the height of the season. Miami Beach stretches for 9 miles on an island offshore from Miami. It boasts of approximately four hundred hotels with a capacity to care for visitors far in excess of most larger cities. Palm Beach, Fort Lauderdale, and Daytona Beach are a few of the Florida east-coast resort towns in the section between Jacksonville and Key West, which is at the end of a noted overseas highway that follows a row of coral islets. Resorts in west Florida center around Tampa Bay, and include the cities of Tampa and St. Petersburg. The

central Florida lake district is of increasing popularity with vacationers and retired Northerners. Westward along the Gulf of Mexico are numerous resort areas, including Gulfport, Biloxi, and Galveston. The warm sunshine, freedom from frost and snow, sandy beaches for sun and water bathing, and sport fishing are the leading attractions. Many retired elderly people move to Florida.

The Coastal Plain has an attractive and restful landscape with many places of historical interest as well as some unique natural attractions. The Everglades National Park, at the southern tip of Florida, has virgin swamps and forests famous for birds, alligators, wild animals, and curious plants. The flowers in season are an attraction in themselves. The gardens and old mansions of Charleston, South Carolina, are world-renowned, as are the old buildings in St. Augustine and New Orleans.

SOUTHERN APPALACHIAN HIGHLANDS

The southern part of the Appalachian Highlands is almost a direct contrast to the adjacent Coastal Plain. Because of extreme variations in soils, relief, and mineral resources, the distribution of population is very irregular. Compared with the adjacent lowlands, the highlands have few large cities, since factors favoring urban growth are seldom present. Forests and woodlands occupy one-half of the area, and many of the higher ridges or more rugged slopes are uninhabited. In some areas deer, bear, and other wild game are common.

The Appalachians have had marked effects on transportation, since railroads and highways had to be built in the valleys and over the passes that afford the lowest or easiest routes. Until roads were constructed, travel was so slow and difficult that settlement was restricted to the coastal lowlands and the Piedmont. The eighteenth century was more than half gone before frontiersmen searched out the gaps in the mountain barrier and began settling in Tennessee, the fertile Bluegrass region of Kentucky, and the Ohio Valley. These early settlers were generally farmers. Today, although there are some highly productive farming regions, many of the farms are small, and income from them is often considerably below the national average. Exploitation of the forests and mineral resources had little significance until after the mid-1800s, when railroads, the development of industry, and the growth of lowland cities provided markets.

PIEDMONT

Extending eastward from the Blue Ridge or other front ranges of the Appalachian Mountains to the Fall Line is a hilly belt or low plateau, known as the Piedmont, whose rolling surface is underlain by hard, crystalline bedrock. The region is approximately 50 miles wide in northern Virginia, increasing to 120 miles in South Carolina. On the east, at the Fall Line, elevation of the Piedmont is generally 200 to 400 feet, rising to 1,400 feet near the Blue Ridge. Many streams cross the region, and the valleys which have been eroded into the bedrock offer numerous sites for generating electricity.

The Piedmont is very productive. Its wooded hills and broad cultivated slopes are attractive to both residents and visitors. Agriculture was originally favored by the generally fertile, reddish loam soils, an abundant rainfall of 40 to 50 inches annually, and a long growing season ranging from 180 to 240 days. After the forests had been cleared and row crops of corn, cotton, and tobacco raised, erosion of the hilly land became a problem. This is especially true in the Carolinas. In some areas, because of the long frost-free and rainy season, three-fourths of the topsoil has been removed and great gullies have been formed, thus hindering farming operations on the sloping land. Many upland farms have been abandoned. Damage by floods has increased, and reservoirs built for the storage of water for hydroelectric plants are being filled with silt. Some owners are now rehabilitating gullied land by seeding permanent pastures. This has resulted in a shift from tilled crops to the raising of beef and dairy cattle. The Piedmont in Virginia has long been important for the raising of livestock, especially cattle.

Tobacco is a leading cash crop in North Carolina and Virginia. Tobacco culture requires careful preparation of the soil, transplanting of seedlings from seedbeds, cultivation, spraying, removal of worms, topping, and curing. Need for hand labor in this work limits the amount of land planted to the crop as much as does the soil or climate. On an average farm tobacco is usually planted on only 8 to 14 acres. If tobacco is raised steadily on a piece of land, the fertility of the soil is exhausted in a few years. Some farmers, especially those in the southern Piedmont, then abandon the field and clear new land for tobacco; others add commercial fertilizers to maintain production.

Much of the Piedmont is included in the manufacturing belt of the United States. Coal can be secured from the Appalachian Plateaus, and much water power has been developed, especially in North Carolina. Here are numerous manufacturing centers. High Point is famous as a producer of furniture. Greensboro, Raleigh, and Charlotte are cotton and synthetic-fiber mill towns. Winston-Salem and Durham also produce textiles, but are better known for their manufactures of tobacco, especially cigarettes. Besides Greenville, Columbia, and Spartanburg, South Carolina has many small textile towns. In Georgia, the cities of Augusta, Macon, and Columbus are noteworthy for manufacturing textiles, chemicals, and other products. Atlanta, near the southern end of a high mountain barrier, serves both the Coastal Plain and the Piedmont. It is the inland railroad and distributing center of the South, and has also a large variety of manufactures. Cheap water power, an abundant labor supply, and raw materials available nearby are among the factors favoring the expansion of manufacturing. The southern Piedmont is the leading cotton-textile manufacturing region in the world, both in the number of active spindles and in fabric production. Much rayon is also manufactured.

APPALACHIAN RIDGES AND VALLEYS

The Appalachian Mountains are composed of closely folded sedimentary rocks that were once deposited on the floor of an ancient sea. The rocks—mainly sandstone, limestone, and shale—differ greatly in hardness. After millions of years of prolonged erosion, the more resistant rocks now form a series of ridges; the exposures of weaker rocks have been removed to such an extent that they form valleys. As a result, the region is characterized by alternate rows of ridges and valleys that extend northeast to southwest from New York State to Georgia and Alabama. The ridges are discontinuous and may end with the dying out of the fold that caused them. In some instances a river may cut through a ridge and form a water gap. Such gaps, or passes, were important in determining the routes followed by the travelers on early trails and the pioneer settlers, and later by

the canals, highways, and railroads. In the generally fertile valleys farming is frequently very successful. The ridges are used for forest land and have few permanent inhabitants. Forestry, mining, and tourism are the leading activities.

The Blue Ridge, the name applied to the eastern-facing front of the Appalachians, is the longest uplift. At about the Virginia–North Carolina boundary a series of ridges and ranges forms a rough mountain area. Just west of the Blue Ridge are such groups as the Unakas and the Great Smokies. In North Carolina and Tennessee, the Great Smokies and the Blue Ridge attain a width of 70 miles. In this section many peaks exceed 6,000 feet in elevation, Mt. Mitchell, 6,694 feet, being the highest in the eastern part of the United States. These mountain masses form important barriers to the east-west movement of goods and people. Areas of hardwoods as well as forests of pine and fir extend the length of these mountains and support a lumber industry. More important, however, is the resort and tourist industry, which is favored by the scenic beauty of the region and its coolness in summer. The Great Smoky Mountains National Park, the most used of all national parks, Blue Ridge Parkway, Cumberland Gap, and other national monuments have been established in this area. Only a little subsistence agriculture has been developed in protected valleys.

The Great Valley lies west of the Blue Ridge and is the most important depression in the Appalachian Ridge and Valley area. It includes parts of 8 states, is 1,000 miles long, and averages about 20 miles in width. Many rivers—Potomac, Shenandoah, James, Roanoke, New, Holston, Tennessee, and Coosa—occupy portions of the Great Valley. Locally the valley is known by various names, among them the Shenandoah, Valley of East Tennessee, and Cumberland. The state of Virginia calls it the Valley of Virginia. Although the Great Valley reaches 2,000 feet in elevation in southern Virginia, the floor is generally flat; the divides between rivers are so gentle that there are no obstructions of importance. The bedrock is a limestone in which many caves and the Natural Bridge of Virginia have been formed. This valley has served as an important artery for travel and commerce for the last two centuries. Soils in the region are fertile, and diversified farming with dairying and livestock production is dominant. Since the valley slopes are relatively free from harmful frosts, apples and other orchard fruits are produced on a large scale, especially in the Shenandoah Valley. During the Civil War this route was used by both the Northern and the Southern armies. Among the cities in the Great Valley are Winchester and Roanoke in Virginia, and Knoxville—famed for atomic energy and the TVA—and Chattanooga in Tennessee.

Between the Great Valley and the Appalachian Plateaus are the many ridges and interwoven valleys that form the remainder of the region. In certain sections, forest-covered ridges dominate over valleys and may be without permanent population. In other places the valleys, although short and narrow, are floored with fertile soil and support productive farms similar to those in the Great Valley. Some lumbering is done.

The scenery, cool summers, and occasional hot springs have stimulated the development of many resort centers among the Appalachian ridges. Asheville, in a fertile basin near the Great Smoky Mountains National Park, is a famous resort city. Other resort centers include Gatlinburg, Tennessee, and Cherokee, North Carolina.

The Tennessee Valley Authority essentially covers the watershed of the Tennessee River. Government agencies, with the approval of Congress, organized and developed the project. The TVA was to serve as a pilot plan for regional development and to act as a guide for future planning in other regions such as the Arkansas,

Figure 3-12 The Shenandoah Valley of Virginia is noted for its large apple orchards. (Courtesy of Virginia Chamber of Commerce.)

Missouri, and Columbia River valleys. Specifically, it was intended to (1) create a 9-foot channel from Knoxville to the mouth of the Tennessee River at Paducah, (2) provide for flood control and the development of hydroelectric power, (3) develop soil conservation and erosion control, (4) provide fertilizers for the rehabilitation of agricultural lands, and (5) encourage the development of agriculture and manufacturing. The Tennessee River is formed by the confluence of the Holston and French Broad Rivers in the valley of east Tennessee. With the construction of several dams across the main channel, the river has become almost a series of connected lakes. Nine dams—including Wilson, Kentucky, Watts Bar, Chickamauga—have been built across the river proper. Numerous other dams, such as the Norris, Douglas, and Cherokee, have been built on tributaries of the Tennessee. Chemical, aluminum, and other manufacturing plants have located in or near Knoxville and Chattanooga because of the available hydroelectric power. The first atomic energy plant was developed at Oak Ridge. Since 1950 many TVA power installations have been expanded and supplemented by coal-generating plants.

CUMBERLAND PLATEAU

West of the Appalachian Ridges and Valleys is a plateau area extending southward from central New York to northern Alabama, usually referred to as the Appalachian Plateaus. The southern part of this area, southward from the Kanawha River in West Virginia, is known as the Cumberland Plateau, and its steep eastern edge is called the Cumberland Escarpment. In spite of the hilly aspect of the area, if one looks over the country from a high viewpoint it is apparent that all the summits are of nearly the same height and that they were once joined to form a flat surface. The bedrock is similar to that in the Ridge and Valley area; however, it was only gently warped during its uplift instead of being closely folded. The hills, then, are the result of erosion of the uplifted plateau by thousands of streams. In general, the plateau is so deeply and widely dissected that only remnants of the former surface remain. Southwestward the plateau slopes down and gradually merges with the Interior Plains and the Coastal Plains. Small areas of flatland occur along the river bottoms and, with the gentler slopes of the usually steep-sided valleys, are the principal sites of farmland. More than half the plateau is wooded, and although the best timber has been cut, some logs and mine props are still produced.

Starting in West Virginia, the Cumberland Plateau extends through eastern Kentucky and Tennessee into northern Alabama. Much of the plateau is extremely dissected, producing some of the most rugged hill country in the entire Appalachian Highlands. In Tennessee and Alabama the plateau is less dissected than the Allegheny, the valleys being narrower and the divides wider. Coal is the principal mineral resource of the Cumberland Plateau. The mines of eastern Kentucky, western Virginia, and southern West Virginia rank second only to those in Pennsylvania and northern West Virginia. Most of the coal mined in this region is shipped either to the Great Lakes ports or the Hampton Roads area. Petroleum and forests are also important resources. Although tillable areas are small, subsistence farming is the chief support of many people. There are no large cities, and except for the mining communities, the towns are few and small. The population is predominantly rural.

The Cumberland Plateau was originally settled by people of English, Scotch, and Irish stock, moving on upstream eddies of the tide of westward migration. They came so far, and went no farther. This seemed good country to most pioneers, for the land was well forested. Game and fish abounded and the little coves of flatter land were adequate for early subsistence agriculture. As the population increased, isolation and inaccessibility continued, putting more and more pressure on the meager resources. Lacking better land, descendants of the pioneers planted corn, their chief crop, on increasingly steeper slopes. Here, within a few years, erosion ruined the fields, and the crops grown on the hill lands became so pitifully small that they provided only the barest living. In the more remote areas houses, with their furnishings, were built by the people; in a few places much of the clothing is of home manufacture. In some areas people still hunt game to supplement the larder and gather wild herbs to sell for a little cash. The development of coal mining and lumbering provides work for some. With the improvement of roads more visitors will enter the district, but since there are few facilities for their entertainment, the tourist business brings little cash.

INTERIOR HIGHLANDS

The Interior Highlands, composed of the Ouachita (pronounced Washita) Mountains, part of the Arkansas River valley, and the Ozark Plateau, are located largely in Arkansas and Missouri, with a smaller area in Oklahoma. This region of folded mountains and dome-shaped plateau is completely surrounded by the plains of the Central Lowlands and the Coastal Plain.

In many respects the region is much like the Ridge and Valley area and the Cumberland Plateau.

White people began settling in the Ouachitas and Ozarks soon after the United States acquired the land through the Louisiana Purchase, usually migrating from the older Southern states. These early settlers established subsistence farms and grazed livestock, which was driven to market, and in some remote areas this pattern of life still persists. The Oklahoma part of the Ozarks, however, was set aside as Indian land for the Cherokees, and the Ouachita area in Oklahoma was given to the Choctaws. In many instances, the Indians made more progress in their development than did the whites. The boundary line between Arkansas and Oklahoma has been referred to as a "cultural fault line" since it so definitely marks the division between people of two races, two cultures.

OUACHITA MOUNTAINS AND ARKANSAS RIVER VALLEY

The Ouachita Mountains are formed by a series of steeply folded sandstone ridges that have elevations up to 3,000 feet and extend in a general east-west direction. Because of these ridges, the rainfall of the region is considerably above that of the surrounding plains, many stations recording over 60 inches annually. Forestry and grazing are the principal activities. Coniferous trees, especially pines, grow well on the poorer, sandy soils. A variety of deciduous trees, dominantly oak and hickory, is found in the valleys. The Ouachita National Forest covers about one-fifth of the total area, and there are several state-supervised forests in the rest of the region. Both hardwoods and softwoods are cut, sawed, dried, and marketed for flooring, siding, and general construction. Fence

Figure 3-13 Many farmers of the Springfield Plain specialize in the raising of turkeys and chickens. Most of the turkeys are marketed for the Thanksgiving and Christmas season. (Courtesy of Massie—Missouri Resources Division.)

posts are also a common product. In many parts of the mountains, cattle graze over the open range, and the fields are fenced to keep the cattle out. The only important source of bauxite, the ore of aluminum, within the United States is in the Ouachitas, the region mining about 98 per cent of the domestic supply. The large open pits near Benton, Arkansas, have been greatly expanded during the past decade.

Hot Springs, at the eastern edge of the Ouachitas, is the largest city in the area. Noted for its hot baths and the Hot Springs National Park, it has become an attractive resort.

The Arkansas River, flowing in a general easterly direction, separates the Ouachita Mountains from the Ozark Plateau. The valley floor is flat and the soil rich; much of the land is in pasture or is used for specialty crops. There are coal mines within the area. The most important function of the valley is as a transportation route through the adjacent higher, rougher areas.

OZARK PLATEAU

The Ozark Plateau is a dome-shaped uplift with streams radiating from the broadly rolling central portion, deepening and widening their valleys as they approach the perimeter. The southern edge of the Ozarks, known as the Boston Mountains, is higher and has a rougher topography than the rest of the area.

Although much of the more rugged area is forest-covered, and lumbering is an important industry, agriculture and grazing are of prime importance. In northwestern Arkansas the broiler industry has been highly developed; many acres are planted in vegetables, and vineyards are common. Wineries and canneries in the nearby communities buy and process the crops. The rocky hills in both Arkansas and Oklahoma produce large quantities of strawberries. The Springfield Plain in southwestern Missouri is among the important dairy regions of the nation.

Lead, zinc, and limestone are mined or quarried in the Ozarks. The Joplin or Tri-state district of Oklahoma, Kansas, and Missouri mines much lead and was for many years one of the principal zinc-producing areas of the world. Southeastern Missouri leads in lead production.

Recreation is rapidly becoming the most important industry in many parts of this area. With the construction of large dams for flood control, power, and recreation, artificial lakes such as Lake-O'-The Cherokees, Fort Gibson, and Tenkiller Ferry in Oklahoma, Norfolk and Bull Shoals in Arkansas, and Lake of the Ozarks and Table Rock Lake in Missouri have been formed. Each lake is larger than many of the large natural lakes in the eastern part of the United States. Several picturesque limestone caves and big springs also add to the tourist attractions.

SELECTED REFERENCES

Clark, Thomas D.: *The Emerging South,* Oxford University Press, Fair Lawn, N.J., 1961.

A good discussion of the changing economic conditions (agricultural, industrial) as well as of the political and cultural situations, 1920–1940.

Doerr, Arthur H., and John W. Morris: "The Oklahoma Panhandle—A Cross Section of the Southern High Plains," *Economic Geography,* vol. 36, no. 1, pp. 70–88, January, 1960.

A study of the Oklahoma Panhandle as a representative area of the Southern High Plains.

Ford, Thomas R. (ed.): *The Southern Appalachians: A Survey,* University of Kentucky Press, Lexington, Ky., 1962.

An analysis of the social, economic, and cultural aspects of the area with special attention devoted to the attitudes of the people.

Goldschmidt, Arthur: "The Development of the U.S. South," *Scientific American,* vol. 209, no. 3, pp. 224–232, September, 1963.

A discussion of the changing of the South to a modern industrial area.

McKnight, Tom L.: "The Distribution of Manufacturing in Texas," *Annals of the Association of American Geographers,* vol. 47, no. 4, pp. 370–378, December, 1957.

A discussion of the geographical distribution and the reasons for the distribution of manufacturing in present-day Texas.

Parkins, A. E.: *The South: Its Economic-Geographic Development,* John Wiley & Sons, Inc., New York, 1938.

The Classic historical geography of the South. Although old, it points up reasons for many of the current economic and cultural problems of the area.

Prunty, Merle, Jr.: "The Renaissance of the Southern Plantation," *Geographical Review,* vol. 45, no. 4, pp. 459–491, October, 1955.

A study of plantations from antebellum days to 1955. Reviews the changing occupance patterns and economic activities.

chapter 4

THE UNITED STATES: THE WEST

Figure 4-1 Physical factors dominate in the determination of regional boundaries. Mountains form many of the definite boundaries.

*E*VEN OMITTING ALASKA AND HAWAII from consideration, we find that sharp geographic contrasts are characteristic of the Western states. Land relief ranges from the summit of Mt. Whitney, 14,495 feet, to the depths of Death Valley, 282 feet below sea level. In northwestern Washington rainfall exceeds 100 inches yearly, but southwestern Arizona receives only 2 or 3 inches. Localities in Montana have experienced temperatures nearly 70° below zero; Death Valley suffers under the highest recorded temperature on the continent, 134°F. Point Reyes, 40 miles north of San Francisco, holds the record for high winds, with an average velocity of 34.5 miles per hour for May. Near the coast grow the tallest trees, but vegetation is almost absent from the Death Valley landscape. Salt Lake City, Seattle, and Los Angeles represent advanced phases of urban and industrial geography, in which geographic relationships are complex; in contrast, a cattle ranch located in one of the Nevada basins has a simple type of economic activity. In the West, dense population and intensively farmed irrigated land may adjoin unpeopled and untilled deserts and wilderness, but most land in the Western states is used for grazing of range livestock. Alaska, Arizona, Nevada, New Mexico, Utah, and Wyoming, with 31 per cent of the land area of the nation, have only about 2 per cent of the total cropland area, and the farm population in the Western states totals only 9 per cent of their total population.

The Western United States occupies approximately a little less than half of the total continental area of the nation. Beginning with the 49th parallel at the north, the boundary extends to the Pacific at the Strait of Juan de Fuca, then southward along the ocean to Mexico, where the irregular border is partly defined by the Rio Grande. The eastern boundary of the "West" is not well defined except as it appears in the eastern face of the Rocky Mountains.

Though geographically detached from the rest of the nation, the states of Hawaii and Alaska rightfully belong to the Western United States. The boundaries of both states are sea-girt, with the exception of the eastern boundary of Alaska, where that state borders Canada.

ROCKY MOUNTAINS

North America's backbone—the Rocky Mountains—is a natural feature so impressive to the traveler that it becomes a milestone on any journey across the United States by train, automobile, or air. Here in imposing grandeur from Canada to Mexico stretches a wilderness of peaks and valleys, separating the streams that flow west to the Pacific from those that flow east to the Atlantic. On these mountains are the beginnings of the Western forests whose tree species differ from those of the woodlands east of the grass-covered Great Plains. Rugged mountains, deep snows, and wide vistas make crossing these mountains a memorable experience.

Indians used the Rockies for hunting, fishing, and berry picking. They usually wintered in protected valleys or basins when the heavy snows made the mountains inhospitable. During the first half of the nineteenth century traders, gold seekers, and farmers struggled over the Santa Fe, Overland, and Oregon Trails to New Mexico, Utah, California, and Oregon. When gold was discovered in the Rockies, swarms of miners searched every mountain gulch for placers and quartz mines. Of hundreds of settlements founded by miners, many remain, though many more have become ghost towns. Railroads and highways were built to serve the mines, and transcontinental routes to Pacific Coast cities were located through valleys

Figure 4-2   In general, the cities and towns in the western part of the nation are smaller than those in the eastern part. Note that only one city exceeds 1 million in population and that large areas have only a few small towns.

and passes over the continental divide. Stockmen and farmers made permanent settlements, and even dry valleys became prosperous when irrigated. The present population is scanty, however, and except for some mining towns, settlements are in the valleys.

NORTHERN ROCKY MOUNTAINS

The Rocky Mountains are divided roughly into the Northern and Southern Rockies, with the central Wyoming Basin as the point of partition. These mountains reach their greatest width in Montana, Idaho, and Colorado. In the north the trend of the ranges is generally northwest to southeast; in the south their alignment is about north to south. Some ranges such as the Big Horn and Wind River Mountains in Wyoming are distant from the main system. In the Northern Rockies individual ranges

are often separated by long, narrow, depressed valleys called trenches. The longest of these is the Rocky Mountain Trench, extending northwest for over 1,200 miles, from Bitterroot Valley in Montana into Canada. In much of Idaho the mountains resemble deeply eroded plateau uplands rather than elongated ridges. South of Yellowstone Park is the rugged Grand Teton Range.

The width and ruggedness of the Northern Rockies have made this part of the United States not easily accessible, and parts remain underdeveloped in spite of timber and mineral resources. Millions of acres lie within national parks or forests and are protected against commercial exploitation. Although most mountains are covered with conifers, much accessible commercial timber has been cut.

The original appearance of the higher parts of the mountains has been altered by

Figure 4-3   Climate graphs of selected stations.

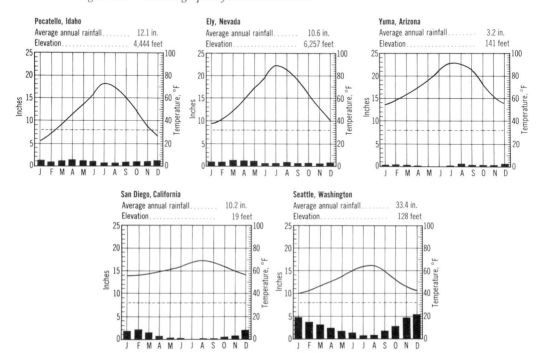

extensive glacial action, and altitudes are so great that even today snow remains on the higher summits throughout the summer, providing a constant source of water for the streams which flow deeply trenched through mountain canyons—the Columbia, Snake, Missouri, and Yellowstone Rivers in the north. Canyons provide reservoir sites, and hence large amounts of power are being developed, as well as storage for irrigation and flood control. The mountain states have more acreage under flood-control projects than any other section of the nation. Hungry Horse Dam in northwestern Montana, completed in the early 1950s, helps to control the Columbia River flow and amplify present power sources. Other dams and power plants are on the Clark Fork, Snake, and other tributaries to the Columbia.

In the early years of settlement, the height and ruggedness of the Rocky Mountains tended to repel travelers. Passes at low altitudes are generally lacking, and since the higher passes are snowbound during much of the year, westward-moving traffic by land was impeded. Fur trapping occupied those Europeans who first penetrated the mountains, and their early-day trading stations and supply bases (sometimes fortified against Indian incursions) represent the beginnings of permanent settlement along the Snake, the Green, and many other streams. But the Rockies in general attracted few immigrants until the discovery of gold and the completion of the Union Pacific Railroad in 1869.

Mining has been a great source of wealth in the Rockies, and it is still one of the leading occupations of this part of the West. In the north, the mountains of western Montana and parts of Idaho and Utah have been noted for their production of copper, gold, lead, silver, and other metal-

lic ores. Wyoming has some deposits of bituminous coal and petroleum fields in the Basin. Colorado has been an excellent source of gold, silver, lead, and other minerals.

Throughout the northern Rocky Mountains the present-day settlements often represent concentrations of population whose principal incomes have been from mining—Butte in Montana, Wallace, Kellogg, and Mullan in Idaho, and Salida, Cripple Creek, Ouray, and Leadville in Colorado. In places where conditions have been unfavorable for mining as a steady source of income, through exhaustion of ores or for other reasons, the community associated with the mine continues to exist even without its principal source of income. Then it becomes a "ghost town," or sometimes, like Central City, Colorado, it attracts tourists who are interested in living conditions of the past.

Grazing of both sheep and beef cattle is widespread throughout the Rockies, but it is a particularly important occupation in the southern sections of Colorado, Wyoming, and New Mexico, where the climate is generally too arid to provide extensive forest cover. Although summer pastures are used on the upper slopes, the animals must be brought to lower elevations where winter winds and heavy snows do not interfere with grazing. Much pasturage of this type takes place on government reservations, and in places the forage is so poor that excessive grazing induces serious soil erosion. The carrying capacity of these mountain tops tends to be low.

Lumbering is a more profitable enterprise in the Northern Rockies, since the altitudes are somewhat lower and the water supply available for forest growth is greater. Here the timber resources are richer and more accessible. Most of the timber is of the needle-leaved evergreen type, frequently located in national forests, in which the care and use of the wood is under government control for the sake of conservation of the resource. Much of the timber is of excellent quality, as is true in the Idaho white-pine forests, but the processing and marketing of the lumber is sometimes handicapped by the great distance to consuming markets and by the expense and difficulty of building highways or railways through the steeply sloping canyons to reach the timber-cutting operations.

By usual American standards, settlements in the Rocky Mountains may be considered small. Some have developed as ranch-supply centers; others have grown at foci of land-transport routes; some provide servicing for rail or highway employees; a few originated as resort communities and some as lumber towns. But the limited natural resources, difficult access, severe winters, or other repressive environmental factors have prevented the growth of cities of large size. Cities of moderate size, such as Missoula, Kalispell, Bozeman, or Livingston, usually serve rather large surrounding areas.

Mountain scenery justifies three national parks, and the mountain states have a larger total area of land used for public parks than any other part of the United States. Yellowstone National Park in northwestern Wyoming is noted for Yellowstone Lake, Yellowstone Falls, and the many evidences of active vulcanism, such as hot springs, mud pots, and geysers. Yellowstone National Park is reached by both highways and railroads, and is sufficiently accessible to attract well over a million visitors each summer. Adjoining on the south is the impressive ridge of the Grand Tetons, included in a national park near the Jackson Hole country of Wyoming. Tourism and grazing are the chief industries of this part of western Wyoming. Glacier National Park in northern

Montana has jagged peaks, mountain lakes, mountain glaciers, and sparkling waterfalls.

In many sections of the Rockies, rugged landscapes appeal to the tourist who prefers to spend his vacation hunting, fishing, or camping. Some mountain valleys favored by campers are occupied by natural lakes; among the better-known are Priest, Pend Oreille, and Coeur d'Alene in Idaho, Flathead in Montana, and Yellowstone and Jackson Lakes in Wyoming. These mountains and valleys have no good east-west passes; indeed there is no crossing without steep grades, swift streams, canyons, and peaks. High altitudes with heavy snows and low winter temperatures make road construction and maintenance difficult. Railways traversing these mountains do so only at great expense for both construction and operation.

WYOMING BASIN

The Wyoming Basin in central and southwestern Wyoming separates the Northern and Southern Rockies. Its geographical conditions resemble those of the Great Plains, from which it is nearly isolated by the Big Horn and Laramie Mountains. Rainfall is deficient, and the Basin remains largely a land of open, grass-covered slopes that provide for grazing of cattle and sheep on large ranches, although some irrigation is developing along the edges. Small supply towns are strung along transcontinental railways and highways. Coal is mined in the southwest at Rock Springs, and Casper and Rawlins represent the larger settlements. Petroleum is of importance at Salt Creek. This open basin, because it nearly severs the Northern and Southern Rockies, has been an important transport route for rail and highway for more than a century. Travelers on the Oregon Trail made full use of its springs, and at a later date the railroads found it the easiest transmontane route. Today the Wyoming Basin provides a gateway through the Rockies for transcontinental railways and highways.

SOUTHERN ROCKY MOUNTAINS

South of the Wyoming Basin, the long, narrow trenches of the Northern Rockies are replaced by the high-level, basin-like North, Middle, South, and San Luis Parks of Colorado, and the Estancia, Roswell, and Tularosa Basins of New Mexico. In Colorado, the Front Range rises abruptly to more than 14,000 feet at Longs Peak, Pikes Peak, and other summits. Farther west is the Sawatch Range, and then a confused maze of mountains in southwestern Colorado, of which the most prominent are the San Juan Mountains. The Wasatch Range, with its eastern extension in the Uinta Mountains, dominates Utah. Travel in an east-west direction through the mountains and basins is difficult.

Where water supplies can be obtained from nearby mountains, as in the vicinity of Grand Junction, Colorado, intensive agriculture may be practiced, and the population density is correspondingly greater. In the grazing areas population density is low, with widely dispersed ranch settlements.

The Southern Rockies are so rugged and in places so arid that agriculture is practically impossible; but streams from their summit snows and rains, particularly the water courses on their eastern slopes, provide excellent water supplies for the higher parts of the Great Plains. Water from the western slopes normally drains into tributaries of the Colorado or the Rio Grande, but in places it is possible to tap these western waters and divert them for the benefit of improved irrigation of land east of the mountains. One such diversion project, along the Fryingpan and Arkansas Rivers, will pipe water from the west slope and convey it to irrigate fertile fields along the Arkansas River on the east slope, as well as to provide urban supplies and hydropower for Pueblo, Colorado Springs, and other cities of the western Great Plains. When completed, the project will benefit people in an area two-thirds of the size of the state of Colorado.

Minerals, including molybdenum and uranium ores, have been exploited, and some towns, like Leadville in western Colorado, depend upon mining. Cripple Creek is a gold-mining town near Colorado Springs and Pikes Peak. Except for mineral wealth, the paucity of resources within the mountains prevents great economic expansion; the urban centers related to this area are located in adjoining regions and include Cheyenne, Boulder, Denver, Colorado Springs, Pueblo, and Trinidad, a coal-mining town, as well as Las Vegas and Santa Fe. Several of these cities are outstanding tourist centers.

To some extent, the presence of mountain passes has furthered the development of nearby cities. Travelers may avoid difficult routes by taking the broad gap through Wyoming up the North Platte Valley between the Big Horn and Laramie Ranges, and west across the Great Divide Basin and South Pass into the Great Basin and Snake River country. Passes across the Colorado Front Range lie at high altitudes. Raton Pass, 7,834 feet, crosses the Southern Rockies between Trinidad, Colorado, and Raton, New Mexico, and is traversed by main-line railway and highway. Some passes are higher than 10,000 feet. Lack of a convenient pass west of Denver was partly overcome by building the Moffat tunnel through the mountains 50 miles west of that city. The Arkansas River crosses the southern end of the Front Range through the Royal Gorge, a deep, narrow canyon very impressive to tourists. West of Denver, Rocky Mountain National Park contains Longs Peak and has major resort areas nearby. In New Mexico, the Southern Rockies are reduced to low ranges, and the wide basins or valleys become of correspondingly greater importance for grazing; generally they are too dry for much other activity.

New Mexico represented the northern limit of Spanish settlement in the seventeenth century, but Spanish settlers did not entirely supplant the Indian population, with the result that present cultural and racial patterns are mixtures of Indian, Spanish, and American. New Mexico shares with California, Arizona, and Texas a strong Spanish-American influence that is discernible in language and architecture. Santa Fe, the state capital, founded by the Spaniards, is famed as the terminus of the Santa Fe Trail in covered-wagon days and is visited by many tourists. Taos and other Indian pueblo towns in this region also are popular with tourists.

Despite the completion of many reclamation projects, including the Elephant Butte Reservoir, farming in southern New Mexico basins is mostly limited by the amount of water obtainable from the Rio Grande or its tributaries. The prospect of expanding the cultivated land is not bright, though in recent years the population has grown, especially in Albuquerque, New Mexico's largest city. Nearby is the Los Alamos reservation for testing atomic weapons.

In the western elbow of Texas, the Rocky Mountains are even more broken than in New Mexico. In the Davis Mountains they rise higher than 8,000 feet in a section so dry that agriculture is precarious and extensive cattle ranching is the chief economic activity. For this part of the country, El Paso is the urban and transportation center as well as the gate-way to Mexico. The city is important for general trade and for smelting local ores. Below El Paso, the Rio Grande enters a mountainous country so impressive that the Big Bend has been set aside as a national park, although most of the region is used for grazing.

INTERMONTANE PLATEAUS, BASINS, AND RANGES

Between the Rocky Mountains and the combined Sierra Nevada–Cascades is a large region generally deficient in rainfall. Though it includes all or parts of nine states, it is sparsely populated. The altitude varies from below sea level to over 12,000 feet—the elevation of several peaks. Relief features are diversified and include many broad plateaus, scores of mountain ranges, and extensive basins and valleys. Most of Nevada, half of Utah, and large expanses in other states have no drainage that reaches the ocean. The climate varies from near-tropical deserts to continental extremes of temperature. Vegetation is usually of the desert and steppe type, although the higher plateaus and mountains support forests of conifers because of the greater rainfall at these altitudes. Much of the region is used for grazing cattle, but some sections toward the north have enough rainfall for wheat cultivation; in others, crops are irrigated. This intermountain region with its wide variations in geography is divided into four parts, the Colorado Plateau, the Southwestern Basin and Range province, the Great Basin, and the Columbia Intermontane province. Much of the region is a barrier to be crossed by rail lines and highways leading to the cities and populated valleys of the Pacific Coast; locally there are important centers of settlement in the interior.

COLORADO PLATEAU

The Colorado Plateau is centered around the junction of the four states of Arizona, New Mexico, Colorado, and Utah. It consists of uplifted rock strata reaching 5,000 to 10,000 feet in elevation. The surface has been eroded by streams under arid conditions, with the result that deep canyons, arroyos (gullies), gorges, badlands, and other evidences of extreme erosion have become features of the plateau surface.

The most striking effect of stream trenching occurs in the northern part of Arizona, where the Colorado River has eroded a canyon about a mile in depth, cutting its way through many strata of sedimentary rocks, forming a gorge 12 miles or more in width. This spectacular feature attracts many tourists each year, and the canyon walls have been set apart as Grand Canyon National Park; other nearby canyons are only slightly less impressive in coloring and magnitude of scenery. Beautiful as the river and its tributaries may be, the streams contribute little real wealth to the plateau area since the trenching is too deep to permit water from the canyon bottoms to be used for irrigation or power.

Downstream from the Grand Canyon the river itself is important since it provides water and power for urban centers of southern California, and irrigation water for the Imperial Valley and Arizona, an accomplishment made possible by several dams. Hoover Dam impounds Lake Mead, and though both dam and lake are tourist attractions, they contribute little to the wealth of the Plateau. Besides the Grand Canyon, national parks have been established in southern Utah at Zion and Bryce Canyons, both spectacular examples of erosion in multicolored sedimentary rocks. In addition there are several national monuments such as Cedar Breaks in Utah, and sites of historical and archeo-

Figure 4-4   Glen Canyon unit of the Colorado River Storage Project, under construction in 1962; view looking upstream. Note the horizontal rock strata of the Colorado Plateau, with a gorge incised by stream action. (Courtesy of Bureau of Reclamation.)

logical interest in Arizona. In southwestern Colorado the Mesa Verde National Park contains outstanding examples of ancient Indian cliff dwellings.

Though most of the rock is sedimentary, there are some volcanic materials in Arizona where the San Francisco Peaks, a group of extinct volcanoes, rise to a maximum altitude of 12,794 feet. The usual appearance of the plateau surface in this section of northern Arizona is that of a sunburned landscape of buttes and mesas with sharply defined vertical walls, broad sweeping slopes, and sandy-bottomed stream channels that remain dry throughout much of the year. Plant life is scant, with some open pine forests or thickets of scrub such as the piñon and juniper at moderate altitudes, and sagebrush and short grass at low elevations.

Since the altitude and latitude of the area combine to prevent large amounts of precipitation except on the very highest plateaus, a steppe climatic condition prevails throughout much of this section of the United States; that is, summers are warm to hot, winters are cold and snowy. Moisture is insufficient to permit agriculture except where occasional springs provide a small flow of water, or along canyon bottoms in alluvial material where occasional "flood farming" is practiced by those who make their homes in this unprepossessing environment.

Though the surroundings seem repressive to human development, the Colorado Plateau was the setting for the Indian villages called pueblos. Their high cultural level was apparent from the excellence of their stonework, basketry, pottery, and weaving. In a land deficient in rainfall, the Indians carried on irrigation by flooding, depending upon maize as their staple crop. After the introduction of sheep, cattle, and horses by Spaniards, their food supplies improved. Today the picturesque life of the pueblo villages attracts tourists, and

Indian tribal products and customs are on display at the annual celebration in Gallup, New Mexico. The Indian hogans (huts) are an interesting feature. On the lands in northeastern Arizona which have been set aside for the exclusive use of the Indians there is only a meager water supply. Although the Indians receive some income from flocks or herds, economic conditions are generally unsatisfactory, and poverty is widespread.

Except for one transcontinental railway line across northern Arizona and some good highways, few routes traverse the Colorado Plateau. Some towns are located with reference to rail facilities, and from the former mining center of Kingman on the west through Williams, Flagstaff (a popular winter-sports resort), Winslow, Holbrook, and Gallup eastward to Albuquerque the settlements are expressions of railroads and highways. Distances between settlements are great, and outlying centers take on the aspect of Indian trading posts, with a general store, service station, and a few necessary services, such as the agencies of the Bureau of Indian Affairs, which administers relations of the American government and members of the Indian nations. Perhaps the least-settled part of the United States is the rough terrain surrounding the "four corners" where the states of Arizona, Utah, Colorado, and New Mexico meet.

For permanent residents, the resources of the Colorado Plateau are limited. Petroleum and natural gas are produced, and in uranium mining New Mexico leads all states. Commercial timber is available only on the higher lands because of serious moisture deficiency at lower elevations. Grazing is the most important industry throughout the area and is widespread among both white settlers and Indians. Water, or its absence, controls the distribution of settlements. Small farms are found in deep canyons where temperature is warm throughout the year, or on the plateau surface where some farm crops can be grown if there are steady springs, or if underground water supplies can be obtained. Such enterprises, however, are relatively few in number; more common are ranches with herds of cattle or flocks of sheep.

SOUTHWESTERN BASINS AND RANGES

The southern rim of the Colorado Plateau descends to lower altitudes in a series of cliffs. Southwest of these steep escarpments lies an arid and semiarid land marked by tilted-block ranges resulting from faults. These fault-block mountains alternate with basins or "valleys" covered with debris washed from the mountains. This Southwestern Basin and Range province occupies parts of these states and includes the Imperial and Coachella Valleys of California, the Salt River valley of Arizona, and the upper Rio Grande Valley in New Mexico.

For decades southern Arizona was regarded as unfit for habitation by white men and was left to its primitive inhabitants. When water is available, its fertile soils are productive, and therefore, important irrigation projects have been completed in the valley of the Salt River, tributary to the Gila River. Here, where ancient prehistoric people irrigated their crops, modern irrigation works have been built to make the valley a prosperous producer of winter-grown vegetables and citrus fruits near Tempe, Mesa, and Phoenix. The area is dominated by the city of Phoenix, the state capital, which has also gained greatly from the winter tourist trade, and the establishment of many industries, especially in the field of electronics.

In southeastern Arizona, Tucson, a university town and aircraft-manufacturing center, attracts tourists with its clear, sunny, and almost frostless winter weather, although the summers are excessively hot. Farther south Bisbee, Ajo, Globe, and Morenci are copper-mining towns; the last is the largest producer in the state. The newest development, San Manuel, northeast of Tucson, has an output of about 100,000 tons of copper per year, making it the fourth largest producer in the United States. Nogales is a border town dependent upon income from transportation. In the southwest, Yuma is reached by one transcontinental railway line and highways that serve the transportation needs of southern Arizona and New Mexico. Most residents are bilingual because numbers of Spanish-Americans have taken up permanent residence north of Mexico. They have left an indelible stamp on the culture of this part of the Southwest.

In spite of desert landscapes, relics of former civilizations, and pleasant winters, this is a region of limited economic potential, resembling the Mexican Plateau across the international boundary. Although summer temperatures mount well above 100°F, low relative humidity keeps the weather endurable. Rainfall is only 3 to 5 inches a year, but erratic cloudbursts sometimes occur. No dense population has developed except in irrigated valleys, and small settlements are more characteristic than urban areas. Without irrigation, these drought-ridden lands have a climate too unfavorable for the support of many people, although residents obtain water from the few perennial streams or underground sources. When sufficient water is available, high summer temperatures provide excellent growing conditions for specialized crops.

The most extreme subtropical desert in the United States is located in the Imperial Valley, a region of interior drainage in southeastern California.

Figure 4-5   Harvesting carrots on irrigated land near Indio, California, in the Coachella Valley. Temperatures in the valley are so mild that winter-grown commercial vegetable crops are grown with profit. (Courtesy of Bureau of Reclamation.)

These lowlands represent the old sea floor which has been cut off from the northern end of the Gulf of California by the Colorado Delta. The valley is so hot and dry in summer that before 1900 it was regarded as worthless land; earlier, it was a difficult obstacle to immigrants arriving in California by the southern route. Although desert conditions are still apparent, water is now obtained from the Colorado River, transforming an otherwise barren landscape into a hothouse for whose products the rest of the nation pays high out-of-season prices.

The early-day agriculture of the cotton fields in the Imperial Valley and the Gila Valley has been replaced by high-value intensive farming of carrots, melons, citrus fruit, dates (in the Coachella Valley), and alfalfa. Land values have increased correspondingly, and this formerly barren desert now includes some of the highest-priced farmland in the entire United States. The prevailing agricultural economy is based upon air and rail transporta-tion and upon refrigeration facilities which preserve perishable commodities as they are carried to markets outside California. This has been accomplished at considerable expense by installations such as the All-American Canal, the principal distributing system for water from the Colorado River. The northern part of the basin (Coachella Valley) specializes in grapefruit and dates. The city of Palm Springs has become a popular winter resort because of its sunshine and mild weather at that season. Between the Coachella and Imperial Valleys lies a salt lake, the Salton Sea, about thirty miles long, formed by an accidental diversion of the Colorado River in 1905.

GREAT BASIN

The Great Basin is a region of interior drainage between the Wasatch Mountains on the east and the Sierra Nevada on the west. The term "basin" is somewhat misleading because the region is broken by fault-block ranges aligned north-south, and separated by intervening basins filled with debris washed in from higher altitudes. In structure both the Sierra and the Wasatch Mountains are larger counterparts of the fault-block ranges. The Mojave Desert of California is a southern extension of the Great Basin, whose northern section, sometimes called the Basin and Range province, merges with the Columbia Intermontane province.

Since most of the Great Basin is in a rain-shadow position, the mountains and basins have insufficient precipitation for agricultural activities other than grazing. The lower parts of the basins are so completely sheltered from sources of rain and snow that their character is usually that of a mid-latitude desert. Their deep deposits of alluvial material, accumulated through many centuries, frequently become storage basins for quantities of water, which can be obtained by sinking artesian wells or by pumping from the underground supply. Thus the floors of many basins may be used for year-round pasturage of beef cattle, or may even have sufficient water to support small amounts of irrigated hay crops; but agriculture in general is not a profitable enterprise throughout most of the Great Basin. Ranches devoted to grazing operations account for much of the dispersed settlement and for settlement nuclei. There is a tendency for settlements to become highly specialized in function: ranch centers, mining towns, tourist accommodations, and centers for recreation.

Population is relatively small in the state of Nevada, although it doubled between 1940 and 1960 and now exceeds 285,000. The land will support few people. With care, its residents can carry on grazing with profit, but others may live in decadent mining centers once famous for gold and silver ores; these include Virginia City, Goldfield, Bullfrog, and Tonopah, which are so picturesque that they attract many tourists.

On the western side of the Basin the largest community is Reno, a university

Figure 4-6   Salt Lake City, Utah, from the northwest, with the fault-scarp of the west-facing Wasatch Range in the distance. Utah state capitol, left center, with central business district at right center, and the city extending eastward up the slope of the wide alluvial apron at the base of the mountains. (Courtesy of Salt Lake City Chamber of Commerce.)

and trading and transportation center. Reno has also many gambling places, since gambling is legal in Nevada. In southern Nevada, Las Vegas, famed for its gambling and resorts, is also important for chemical manufactures. Salt Lake City is located on the broad piedmont between Great Salt Lake and the western face of the Wasatch Mountains and serves as a trade, commercial, educational, religious, tourist, and rail center as well as the state capital. Its prosperity is based partly on irrigated grain farms and fruit lands extending northward and southward along the piedmont. Its plentiful and excellent water supply comes, not from the Great Basin, but from melting snows which accumulate in depth during the winter on the Wasatch Mountains to the eastward.

To the north lies Ogden, a railroad and supply city. A short distance west are the salt flats of the Salt Lake Desert and the saline deposits of Lake Bonneville, ancestor of the present Great Salt Lake. This whole region is deficient in agriculture, but some grazing is carried on, and the mineral wealth is of importance, especially the copper ores at Bingham, Utah, and Ely and Yerington, Nevada. Provo, Utah, is near sources of coal and iron and has an iron and steel plant. Other mines produce coal, silver, lead, and zinc.

A few places in the Great Basin have water supplies, particularly those along the Humboldt River in northern and western Nevada until the stream disappears in the Humboldt Sink. Among them are communities such as Winnemucca, Elko, and Fallon plus a few settlements along transcontinental highway routes. Carson City has the smallest population of any of the nation's state capitals. In general, the economic future of this part of the United States seems limited.

To the southwest, along the eastern face of the Sierra Nevada, at an altitude of more than 3,500 feet, lies the long trough-like depression known as Owens Valley. Here in a mid-latitude steppe developed a profitable grazing economy and some fruit growing, but in 1909 the demand for water by residents of the city of Los Angeles prompted purchase of water rights from the valley for urban use, forcing the abandonment of Owens Valley agriculture. Prospects for any further development are poor as long as water is carried by aqueduct southward to Los Angeles. Nearby, a large basin of interior drainage contains Searles Lake, actually a marsh, which is an important source of commercial borax, potash, and other salts. In the Mojave Desert in the south, conditions are more favorable for agriculture, particularly in its western angle, the Antelope Valley, which obtains water by pumping from wells. In the heart of the Mojave, the town of Barstow serves as an important rail junction.

Southeast of Owens Valley lies a similar but much deeper trough, Death Valley, 282 feet below sea level. Of all places in the United States it seems least suited for human occupation, but pleasant winter weather attracts some tourists, and the desert scenery is so impressive that the valley has been set aside as a national monument. The exceedingly high summer temperatures discourage visitors. Some years ago deposits of borax in this valley were developed, but cheaper sources are now available, and the Death Valley borax works have been abandoned. Though other minerals occur, lack of water is a handicap to development.

COLUMBIA INTERMONTANE PROVINCE

The Columbia Intermontane province lies between the Rocky Mountains on the east and north and the Cascade Range on the west, and grades into the Great Basin

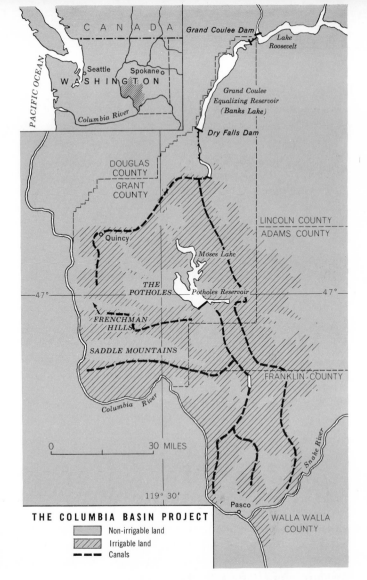

THE COLUMBIA BASIN PROJECT

Non-irrigable land
Irrigable land
Canals

Figure 4-7 Water is supplied to the irrigable land from the Grand Coulee Equalizing Reservoir, not from the Columbia River or Lake Roosevelt. Gravity flow carries the water to the irrigated fields.

to the south. The province, formerly called the Columbia Plateau, varies in elevation from a few hundred to over 10,000 feet above sea level, and is a region of diverse relief features—plains, plateaus, ridges, mountains, and hills. It can be divided into the Snake River plains and the Columbia Basin, which are separated by the Blue Mountains and associated uplifts. The Snake River plains occupy a broad crescent-shaped basin from Yellowstone Park on the east across southern Idaho into Oregon. Idaho and eastern Oregon drain into the Snake River, which has cut a deep canyon into the lava flows.

The Columbia Basin occupies parts of eastern Washington and Oregon and western Idaho. Irregularly saucer-shaped, it is enclosed by the Cascades on the west, the Okanagan Highlands on the north, the Rockies on the east, and the Blue Mountains on the south. The bedrock is a lava called basalt, covered in places by recent sediments. The Columbia River crosses the region and receives water from the Snake and other streams. Near the northern edge of the basin are the "channeled scablands," formed during the glacial period by floods of melt water that eroded channels. These were later abandoned,

Figure 4-8   Contour farming, crop rotation, green-manuring, strip-cropping, and stubble mulching are practiced simultaneously on this field near Lewiston, Idaho.

leaving deep, rock-walled, dry gorges in the "scabrock," as the bare lava is called locally. The largest of these, Grand Coulee, which extends from the Columbia River to the desert, has been reclaimed by the Columbia Basin Project. In eastern Washington near Idaho are the Palouse Hills, covered with fine, fertile loess; they receive sufficient precipitation for raising wheat and peas without irrigation.

The Snake River plains in southern Idaho are the most highly developed part of that state. The climate is continental, with low winter and high summer temperatures. Rainfall is often less than 10 inches a year, and irrigation is necessary for most crops. Originally the plains were covered with grass and sagebrush and were used for grazing cattle and sheep. This industry still continues, and many lambs are fattened for market on the irrigated crops of the plains. The Snake River has cut a canyon below the general level, in which dams and reservoirs are under construction, especially at Hell's Canyon. The soil on the plains is fertile and is productive where irrigated. Crops include alfalfa, wheat, beans, sugar beets, hardy fruits, and the famous Idaho potatoes which comprise about one-sixth of the United States' yearly potato production.

For years this part of Idaho was thinly settled because of aridity, but since 1900 many reservoirs have changed the situation. Good soils and water have attracted settlers, and today prosperous modern cities line the Snake Valley from Idaho Falls through Pocatello and American Falls as far west as Twin Falls. Elsewhere irrigation prospects are less promising, and the surface is generally unsatisfactory for farming, except in lowlands near the Oregon-Idaho boundary, where prosperous little cities like Caldwell are found. The capital at Boise, near the foot of the mountains, dominates a local fruit and grain district and was once a supply center for gold and silver mines in the mountains.

The Blue Mountains, the Wallowas, and other mountains lie in the path of winds blowing up the Columbia Gorge and receive the rainfall required by the forests that cover them. Logging, mining, and grazing are important industries. The supply cities, Pendleton, La Grande, and Baker, are located in valleys or at the foot of the ranges.

In the nearby Columbia Basin precipitation is greatest in the subhumid higher rim, decreasing to an arid condition on the plains in the lee of the Cascades. Maximum precipitation occurs in winter. The moderate annual temperature range is intermediate between that of the marine west coast and the continental interior.

From the late 1860s into the 1880s, the Columbia Basin in eastern Washington and parts of Oregon and Idaho was devoted to grazing cattle and sheep on the open range. In the 1880s, wheat replaced livestock on the good Palouse Hills soil and in other areas where rainfall was sufficient. With the coming of the railroads, wheat growing greatly expanded. Today this Inland Empire produces over 100 million bushels of winter and spring wheat annually from 4 million acres, as well as dry peas and other crops. Between 1949 and 1959, however, wheat acreage in the Western states fell from 58 million to 38 million. In the midst of the Columbia Basin dry farming was uncertain, and irrigation was begun before 1900; thereafter it was known that, with water, the soils and climate in valleys east of the Cascades were well adapted to fruits. The development of the Yakima, Wenatchee, Okanagan, Walla Walla, and other valleys in Washington and the Hood River valley in Oregon followed, using sources of water from the Cascades; the Blue Mountains supply Walla Walla. These valleys furnish one-fourth of the nation's commercial apple crop as well as quantities of pears, apricots, cherries, and peaches. The Yakima Valley is noted for such irrigated crops as alfalfa, sugar beets, and potatoes.

Since the plains in the central part of the Columbia Basin lie too high above the entrenched Columbia River to secure its abundant flow, this region long remained a thinly populated, poor grazing country. In the 1930s the Federal government began construction of the multiple-purpose Grand Coulee Dam. During the 1940s the dam supplied hydroelectric power for atomic energy, aluminum, and other metallurgical plants, and by the 1950s irrigation was begun. A million acres of land in the Columbia Basin will ultimately be reclaimed and devoted to intensive farming. Here some 40,000 farms of 10 to 40 acres, where farmers grow fruit, alfalfa, sugar beets, beans, melons, potatoes, and other irrigated crops, will offer a strong contrast to the large mechanized wheat farms of 1,000 acres or more in the Palouse Hills, where there is only enough rainfall for dry farming.

Communities such as Yakima, Walla Walla, and Wenatchee serve local farm needs; Moscow, Idaho, and Pullman, Washington, are educational centers. Pasco is a railroad center, and with Kennewick and Richland, forms the Tri-Cities area, near which are the Hanford plutonium works.

At the north, Spokane dominates this part of the Columbia Basin as well as tributary valleys in the mountains of Washington, Idaho, western Montana, and British Columbia. The city is a creation of the railroad age; passes immediately eastward permit rail lines to cross the Northern Rockies. Westward the city has excellent rail connections with Seattle; it is a rail and air center of major importance. Spokane's industrial complex includes flour milling, meat packing, sawmills, pulp and paper manufacture, and the extraction and fabrication of aluminum.

The Columbia Basin and adjacent areas have enormous potential water power. The dams at Grand Coulee, Chief Joseph, McNary, Bonneville, and The Dalles are projects of the Federal government. Dams at Priest Rapids and other sites on the Columbia and Snake Rivers were financed from other sources. There are privately owned hydroelectric plants on the Snake, Spokane, and Clark Fork Rivers. The total rated capacity of hydroelectric power plants in the region is nearly 6 million horsepower, and new plants under construction will effect an increase.

This part of the nation faces a difficult problem. The relatively great distance from centers of population and the larger urban districts necessarily imposes a degree of isolation upon the Columbia Basin—a problem which cannot be entirely overcome. The first great route into this area by way of the Oregon Trail in the 1840s failed to bring many permanent settlers to the Basin, for they were headed for the more humid and desirable lands west of the mountains. The opening of the Columbia Basin to settlement by people of European stock was delayed until the construction of the great railroads to the Pacific Northwest. Population growth began to be most noticeable during the 1880s, but in those years the length and difficulty of the rail trip inhibited settlement. Other settlers arrived with the coming of the automobile and good roads in the 1920s, but today much of the traffic in and out of this part of the country depends upon air transport. To this extent the element of isolation due to geographic location has been overcome.

CASCADE MOUNTAINS AND SIERRA NEVADA

The Cascade Range throughout its north-south extent is of a height sufficient to serve as a barrier to eastward-flowing surface winds which might otherwise be able to penetrate deeply into the heart of the continent. Instead, they are forced to reach such heights in crossing the mountains that they necessarily lose the greater part of the moisture they contain on the western slopes. Thus, while heavy rains support a dense forest, mainly of softwoods, on the western side, the eastern slopes are nearly barren except where

water is available along streams such as the Yakima, Wenatchee, and Hood Rivers, tributary to the Columbia.

The Cascade Mountains and Sierra Nevada extend from the Canadian border across Washington and Oregon as far as southern California. They function as a geographic divide, despite differences in landscapes, structure, and resources, since they separate two very different regions. West of the ranges lie fertile, well-watered, well-populated lowlands and valleys. East of the dividing crest is the semiarid and desert intermountain region with its sparsely populated basins, plateaus, and ranges. The railways and highways across the Rocky Mountains, the intermountain region, and the Cascade–Sierra Nevada region were built to reach Pacific Coast cities and favored lowlands like the Willamette Valley. Since comparatively few people stopped along the route to settle in the mountains or deserts, only small amounts of freight and few passengers originate there today. The Cascades and Sierras are impressively scenic, with resources of timber, minerals, and water power, but they will never support a large population. Their resources are exploited mainly by those who live near the Coast; and this natural wealth helped the growth of Coast cities and industries.

CASCADE MOUNTAINS

The Cascades are built mainly from volcanic materials that form a broad platform, above which tower snow-capped volcanic peaks; only the southernmost, Lassen, has erupted in this century. The range is from 50 to 100 miles wide and extends from Lassen Peak into British Columbia. Summits exceed 10,000 feet, and in Washington they include Mt. Rainier, 14,408 feet, Mt. Adams, Mt. Baker, Mt. St. Helens, and Glacier Peak;

in Oregon are Mt. Hood, Mt. Jefferson, the Three Sisters, and Mt. Thielson; and in California, Mt. Shasta and Lassen Peak. Crater Lake in southern Oregon occupies the site of a former volcano as high as Shasta. River and glacial erosion has been very active, and the mountains are characterized by steep canyons, rugged ridges, and glacial lakes. There are many existing glaciers, 28 on Rainier alone. Much of the Cascade Range is included in national forests, ensuring conservation of the forest reserves and the maintenance of the tree cover needed to control the flow of streams used for power, irrigation, and the water supply of cities.

The Cascade Mountains are impressive in their elevation and in the grandeur of the tall green forests that clothe their western slopes. Above the general summit level of about 6,000 feet rise snow- and ice-covered peaks that seem like white sentinels looking down upon the lowlands. The Cascades are a major barrier, both climatic and economic. They function negatively in the geographic pattern since they pose transportation problems that are overcome only at great cost. The north-south trend of the range places it at right angles to the principal traffic movements; it therefore becomes imperative to seek passages for highways and railroads. Land transport is difficult across these crests, particularly in winter when summits are snowbound. In the Cascade Range the most famous pass is the Columbia River Gorge, through which the river crosses the mountains at such low levels that the stream has been canalized. Northward from the gorge are passes of moderate altitude, useful through most of the year. Best-known and lowest is Snoqualmie Pass, 3,127 feet, connecting the Puget Sound Lowlands on the west and the Columbia Basin on the east by highway and rail. Other passes in western Washington

include Naches, Stampede, Stevens, and White. There is some east-west traffic across the Cascade Range in Oregon, with one railroad and several highways crossing the mountains.

Lumbering dominates most human activity on the western slopes, where a wealth of mid-latitude softwoods of high commercial value has been exploited for a century or more. Settlements of the western slopes, therefore, are an expression of lumbering, though of late years, with improved highways and trucks, there is less need for the small town and its sawmill to be located near the timber supply. Today much of the lumber moves by truck down the slopes to large mills and settlements in locations that are more convenient for processing the raw material, either as lumber or as paper pulp, of which the Pacific Northwest is a large producer.

Irrigated agriculture in the bottoms and dry-farmed grains and grazing characterize the dry ground distant from sources of water. This, like so many other sections of the American West, is a region of extractive industry, supplemented by agriculture and grazing. Towns and cities are small by American standards, and serve mainly as supply centers, either lumber towns or farm- and ranch-service centers.

In these volcanic mountains are few valuable minerals except in northern Washington, where mines produce gold, copper, and zinc. Some coal is mined near Roslyn. In northwestern Washington are beds of limestone utilized for portland cement. The principal economy depends on the vast timber resources and hydroelectric power supplied by mountain streams and dams on the Skagit, Lewis, Snoqualmie, and other rivers. Mountain resources support many people on nearby lowlands; for example, east of the crest, Bend and Klamath Falls in Oregon are devoted to handling lumber, and river valleys tributary to the Columbia are developed for the irrigation of choice apples and soft fruits. Mountain uplands along the east-facing Cascades provide summer sheep pasture; in winter the animals are kept on irrigated lowlands of the Yakima and Kittitas Valleys.

Mt. Hood, Mt. Baker, and other peaks and passes in the Cascade Range attract many visitors by fine scenery and good opportunities for winter sports. There are three national parks; that of Mt. Rainier includes the most extensive ice fields in the United States. The southernmost park is Lassen, set aside because of its distinctive volcanic features. In southern Oregon a volcanic crater in Crater Lake National Park apparently was enlarged by a catastrophic eruption and is now occupied by Crater Lake, noted for its depth, nearly 2,000 feet, and its deep blue color. Between Oregon and Washington, where the Columbia River crosses the Cascades in its gorge, the landscape is covered with forests and is distinguished by cascading streams plunging over cliffs to join the Columbia. Set in this gorge is Bonneville Dam, built by the Federal government for hydroelectric power. It is tied by transmission line to the Grand Coulee and other power dams in the Columbia Basin and on the western side of the mountains. This abundant power has encouraged the expansion of industrial output in the Pacific Northwest, especially in the fields of electrochemistry and aluminum refining.

In the vicinity of the 42d parallel, the Oregon-California boundary, the Cascades and Sierra Nevada merge with an old mountain system or plateau known as the Klamath Mountains. Here a confusion of ranges rises over 7,000 feet and interposes a barrier between the Willamette and Sacramento Valleys of Oregon and California.

SIERRA NEVADA

This impressive mountain range, with Mt. Whitney as its highest peak exceeding 14,000 feet, extends from the southern end of the Cascade Range near Lassen Peak southward for a distance of approximately 400 miles, to join the transverse ranges of southern California. The Sierra Nevada of California is almost a single granitic mountain mass, asymmetrical in cross section, with its steeper and shorter slope facing eastward and overlooking the Great Basin. Its western face is a long and relatively gentle slope descending to the foothills and the piedmonts of the Great Valley of California. The higher altitudes, as well as the western slope, have been profoundly affected by the scouring of numerous glaciers, for ice and snow accumulated in depths sufficient to supply glaciers of the past and many mountain streams of the present. Most ice action has been concentrated on the western face, where deep gorges have been etched by tributaries of the Sacramento and San Joaquin Rivers; further entrenchment has usually been due to glacial scour.

The high mountain barrier of the Sierra Nevada greatly interferes with east-west transportation in northern California since heavy winter snows often make trans-Sierra travel difficult. Although the northern Sierra is not so high as the southern, its ruggedness prevents easy crossing. The Feather River Canyon is used by railroad and highway at considerable expense. Near Lake Tahoe are several passes; Donner, 7,189 feet, which is also traversed by rail and road, is the most useful of them, but winter snows are so deep that the pass is kept open only with great effort. South of Lake Tahoe most of the passes are higher than 9,000 feet and are useless except in midsummer. For more than 100 miles, the east-facing escarpment is so steep that no wheeled vehicle can traverse this barrier. In the south, Walker Pass, 5,248 feet, is used for highway travel, but only at the southern end of the Sierra, at Tehachapi Pass, 3,790 feet, can railways find a route through the mountains.

Since the western mountain slope receives the full force of Pacific storms, precipitation is sufficient for extensive forests. For years softwoods have been produced commercially, but cutting of the accessible timber will limit further expansion of this industry. Several groves of big trees, or sequoias, have been set aside in national parks, and much timbered land has been placed on a reserve basis as national forests. Yosemite National Park, famed for its waterfalls and canyon, attracts more than a million visitors annually. Kings River Canyon and Sequoia are other national parks.

Zoning of temperature and precipitation has caused zoning of vegetation on the western slope of the mountains. In the foothills below 2,000 feet, chaparral mixed with digger pines covers the eroded slopes. From 2,000 to 5,000 feet, because of greater precipitation, there is a zone of western yellow pine, sugar pine, and the big trees. In the zone from 5,000 to 7,000 feet are several varieties of pine. Up to 9,000 feet juniper and mountain hemlock grow, with unforested mountain meadows above that elevation. Commercial timber is obtained chiefly from altitudes below 5,000 feet and is taken by highway or rail to towns for processing and shipment.

Grazing of animals pastured on upper slopes during summer and on lower slopes during winter is a further resource. Such migration occurs particularly in the pasturing of flocks of sheep, but sheepherders are few in number.

Midway up the western slope, geologic conditions have favored the formation of a zone about 150 miles long, called the Mother Lode, in which gold quartz was deposited as part of the geologic complex. From this source westward-flowing streams carried eroded bits of gold down toward the valley, and from these alluvial deposits at lower levels and quartz mines at higher levels the Californians removed quantities of the valuable metal and ore between 1849 and 1855. During this period of the Gold Rush, rapid settlement of the western slope of the Sierra occurred, and many small mining towns were established. Today, with increased costs of mining and the exhaustion of the placers and ore bodies, the remnants of the settlements attract tourists to this part of the Sierra. Except for gold, however, mining has not been an important economic activity of these mountain regions.

The combination of mountain meadow, impressive stands of trees, cool and clear summers, and streams stocked with fish attracts many tourists to these mountains each year. The season generally is limited to summer, though in Yosemite and some other places winter sports draw visitors. Peaks of the Sierra Nevada take the form of sharp-edged pinnacles posing a challenge to experienced mountain climbers, with altitudes so great and approaches so rugged that they are climbed only by the hardy.

Many of the canyons cut by stream and glacier on the west slope are spectacular; best known and most frequently visited is that of the Merced River at Yosemite Valley. Less well known to tourists is Kings Canyon National Park, farther south. These canyons, where they need not be preserved for park lands, provide excellent sites for the installation of dams and reservoirs, from which a steady supply of water is obtained for both irrigation and for electrical power. Since California generally lacks resources of energy, except petroleum, the presence of these large amounts of hydropower, developed at relatively moderate cost, provides the state with a highly valuable and important resource.

In northern California, Shasta Dam impounds waters of the upper Sacramento and provides electricity for northern California cities and farms. Shasta Dam has other functions; it controls the flow of water in the Sacramento so that the valley

is less subject to floods, and it regulates river flow in summer to aid navigation and provide water for irrigation when rain is slight. Additional dams on tributary streams are needed for further flood control, irrigation, and power. Work has begun on Oroville Dam on the Feather River, from which by 1972 southern California will obtain fresh supplies of water. The western slope of the Sierra Nevada also provides water for Millerton Lake at Friant Dam and for the power and water installations on the Tuolumne and Mokelumne Rivers, which serve San Francisco

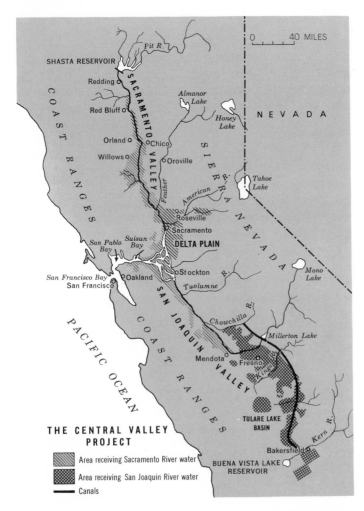

Figure 4-9 Note that Sacramento River water is being used in the San Joaquin River valley. Some of the water stored back of the Shasta Dam in northern California is used to irrigate fields in the south central part of the Great Valley of California.

and Oakland respectively. Other reservoirs conserve water on the San Joaquin and provide power for smaller cities and for local irrigation of suitable land.

The leading human activities of this mountain range, then, include a little mining, some lumbering, attractions for tourist trade, the production of electrical power, and some grazing. Perhaps more important than any single one of these, however, is the fact that the water coming from the mountains may be led to lower ground to the west, east, and south, where it may be used for agriculture in the valleys or for the growing urban populations of the Western Coast.

CALIFORNIA VALLEYS AND COAST RANGES

The valleys and coastal lowlands of California support more inhabitants than all the rest of the Western United States. One of the chief reasons for this is the Mediterranean climate, so attractive to visitors and so favorable for growing fruits, vegetables, and all kinds of farm crops. California has one-third of all the acreage planted to fruits and nuts in the United States, and leads in acreage devoted to commercial vegetable farming. Large areas of fertile soil, water for irrigation, and resources of petroleum and accessible timber further economic growth. In addition, there are terminals for the outlets of a vast hinterland and seaports where transcontinental routes meet ocean shipping. Largest production and the most populous areas are in the Central Valley and the Los Angeles lowlands. From these, many smaller valleys penetrate the mountains or lie within the Coast Ranges which parallel the Pacific Ocean and form the western boundary of the Central Valley.

CENTRAL VALLEY

The Central Valley of California, often called the Great Valley, consists of lowlands about 400 miles in length, drained by the Sacramento River from the north and the San Joaquin from the south, except for a small basin of interior drainage at the southern end. The eastern slopes abut against the lower slopes of the Sierra in the form of very large alluvial fans or piedmonts, deposited there by streams flowing from mountains to valley. The valley is bordered on the east by the Sierra Nevada and on the west by the California Coast Ranges. At the confluence of the Sacramento and San Joaquin Rivers is an extensive delta, formed where the combined streams flow through Carquinez Strait into San Francisco Bay. Shut off from the moderating effects of the Pacific Ocean, the Central Valley in summer is generally warmer than are the coastal areas. The Sacramento-Stockton region, however, is somewhat tempered by afternoon breezes from San Francisco Bay.

The broad floodplains and alluvial piedmonts of the Central Valley, with their warm summers, mild winters, and meager winter rains, supported only a small population of primitive Indians before 1849. The coming of the Americans brought a brief period of dry farming of small grains, followed by irrigation. Today this valley is prime farmland. Peaches, pears, asparagus, celery, potatoes, beans, and sugar beets are grown on the delta lands. Melons, cotton, citrus fruits, and alfalfa, as well as wine and table grapes, are grown in the San Joaquin section. Even the dry southern end of the Great Valley produces cotton, alfalfa, and potatoes. California is a major dairying area, and it is the leading state in production of poultry (turkeys) and sugar beets (23 per cent of the United

States total production). In this type of production Colorado is second to California.

The disintegration of the large cattle and grain ranches, characteristic of the early years of the valley, was accelerated after 1875 upon completion of the Southern Pacific Railroad. Small farm-service centers were established, and many communities specialized in high-value subtropical crops. In the Sacramento Valley, for example, Yuba City and Marysville now specialize in canning peaches, and Willows is the production center for one-fifth of the United States' rice crop. Sacramento owes its agricultural origins to the miner's needs; but its later growth came from its importance as a state capital, and as an urban center it dominates its part of the Great Valley.

Small communities in the delta process fruit and vegetable crops, and the port of Stockton, connected with the sea by a channel dredged deep enough for ships, is locally important. Nearby Lodi is noted for wine and table grapes. In the San Joaquin Valley, almost every small community has its own agricultural specialty. Fresno is a center of dried-fruit production, particularly raisins; other towns ship melons, table grapes, and figs. A common thread—dairying—runs through the economic fabric, and the valley has many milk condenseries.

The southern part of the Central Valley is dominated by Bakersfield, important for railroad activities. In the last quarter century the fertility of this area, combined with water from the mountains, has given impetus to the city's growth. In addition, this section of the valley has been important for petroleum, and Bakersfield is a center for the sale of oil-well supplies. Most oil production has been north and northwest of Bakersfield in the desert on the western side of the valley. Here are the McKittrick and Coalinga oil fields. Agricultural land near Bakersfield is farmed in wheat and irrigated cotton; these developments have nearly drained several large shallow lakes lying west and north of the city.

A major problem in converting the valley to profitable farmland has been solved with much success by means of a vast system of water redistribution. For many decades the northern section (Sacramento Valley) was plagued by floodwaters when mountain snows poured their streams down to the valley floor, creating flood hazards along the Sacramento River and its tributaries. At the same time, water could not be obtained in quantities needed in the southern part of the valley (San Joaquin and the interior basins to the south). In the 1930s under the auspices of the Federal government, a gigantic reclamation project was undertaken, whereby dams were built to impound flood waters of the north, and aqueducts were built to convey surplus water supplies to the south, crossing the delta of the two rivers by a flume or canal. This water was used by ranchers and fruitgrowers along the San Joaquin River, even though it must be pumped *upgrade* to reach them. Power for pumping operations was readily available from plants installed at the dams and reservoirs in the mountains. Thus the damaging floods along the Sacramento River were eliminated, or their threat was greatly reduced.

After the San Joaquin River bottom-land residents were supplied with water as described above, they no longer needed supplies from the Sierra Nevada streams; a second aqueduct, parallel to the mountain base, was therefore built to divert water from these streams (San Joaquin, Merced, Tuolumne, Kings River) and carry it southeastward into the interior basins, where it now irrigates large acreages of cotton, potatoes, and alfalfa in the former lake beds north of Bakersfield. Further development of this part of the Central Valley Project is under way, consisting of a dam, reservoir, canals, and pumping system in the dry southeastern section of the valley. This is the San Luis unit, jointly financed by the Federal and state governments.

SOUTHERN CALIFORNIA

Many visitors, especially winter tourists, think only of southern California when the state name is mentioned. The area is roughly triangular, extending from Santa Barbara on the west to San Bernardino and Riverside on the east, and south to San Diego and Mexico. Inland the region is rimmed by the San Gabriel and San Bernardino Ranges on the north and the

San Jacinto and other ranges on the east. The Los Angeles lowlands, heavily floored by sediments washed from the mountains, are divided by low ranges or hills into a number of valleys including the San Fernando, Ventura, Santa Maria, and San Bernardino. Southward the mountains crowd nearer the coast, leaving lowlands but a few miles wide between Los Angeles and San Diego. Offshore the tops of submerged Coast Range peaks project above the Pacific as small rugged islands, of which only Santa Catalina Island, a popular resort, is important.

Parallel mountain ridges are obstacles to transportation in the southern Coast Ranges, but a few passes connect desert and coast. Of these, Cajon Pass, 3,623 feet, and San Gorgonio Pass, 2,559 feet, are occupied by railroad and highway. Los Angeles has poor approaches from the

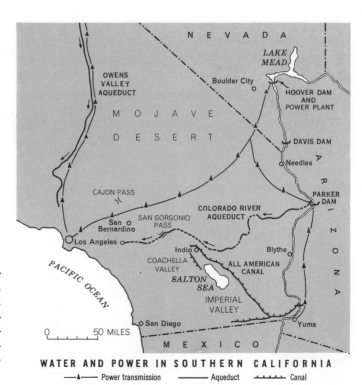

Figure 4-10   The Colorado River is of special importance to southern California. Note that it furnishes water for irrigation in the Imperial Valley and also for municipal use in the Los Angeles area. Electricity is generated at Hoover Dam.

WATER AND POWER IN SOUTHERN CALIFORNIA

north, although Tejon Pass, traversed by highway, connects the southern San Joaquin Valley and Los Angeles. West from the city for 100 miles, the steep faces of the Santa Monica Mountains descend abruptly to the shore. Though a highway has been notched from the sea cliffs, it is not a first-class route and is expensive to maintain. Southward, two main routes lead to San Diego along the coast and through interior valleys.

Favored by sunny weather, mild winters with little threat of frost, fertile alluvial soil, and moderate supplies of water for irrigation, the lowlands and valleys of southern California have experienced an extraordinary agricultural development. Small though the area is compared with other farm regions of the United States, its

Figure 4-11 Picking oranges in southern California. The pickers use small clippers to cut the orange from its stem. Note the deep and well-cultivated soil in this grove and the use of white labor for this operation. (Courtesy of Los Angeles County Chamber of Commerce.)

production of citrus and other fruits, nuts, melons, vegetables, sugar beets, and hay, along with dairy and poultry products, puts Los Angeles County among the nation's leading counties in value of agricultural output.

In southern California climate is a fundamental resource. During the last quarter of the nineteenth century, out-of-state visitors began to be attracted by the warm, sunny winters, and the great influx of settlers and migrants began. Nearly 9 million people live in the Los Angeles lowlands and adjacent valleys and coastal areas, and California has become a leading state in total population, with over 17,000,000 residents.

The coastal lowlands, originally covered by short grass and scrub trees, were the first part of Upper California encountered by the Spaniards in their northward march from Lower California. The mission fathers brought seeds and cuttings with them—many grains, citrus fruits, grapes, figs, and olives. They introduced horses, cows, and sheep. In these imports lay the foundation of California's rise as an agricultural state. As soon as the Americans tapped water sources for irrigation, the grazing economy of the Spanish-Mexicans gave way to land subdivision in the late nineteenth century. Smaller tracts were then supplied with water, and the land was brought under cultivation, specializing in subtropical fruits. Accommodations for winter tourists were expanded rapidly, and many visitors became permanent residents. This phase of life in the southern valleys continued until the 1900s, when discovery of new petroleum fields—the first oil well was drilled in 1880—provided fuel for industry and helped to spur a growth of population which eventually became more urban and established a large consumer market. The Los Angeles lowlands are one of the country's leading sources of petroleum. Without coal and remote from large hydroelectric plants, industry in southern California depends primarily on petroleum and natural gas for its development.

The city and county of Los Angeles, with over 8 million inhabitants, soon took the lead from surrounding communities, and urban growth has eclipsed agricultural activity in southern California. Although water supply, transportation, and location were poor at Los Angeles, the city progressed in spite of its geographical environment. Los Angeles went far outside southern California for water, obtaining supplies from Owens Valley and later from the Colorado River by way of the Metropolitan Aqueduct. There was no good natural harbor; the present harbor, 18 miles south of the city, is artificial. No good land connection with the rest of California or the nation was established until the Southern Pacific Railroad reached Los Angeles in 1875 and the Santa Fe in 1887.

Aggressive advertising has advanced the growth of Los Angeles. To southern California have come population and wealth out of proportion to available resources. California's pressing needs for cheap farm labor brought a diversity of people into the area, Japanese, Mexicans, Negroes, and Europeans. Now these people provide labor for many southern California industries such as petroleum refining, tire manufacture, fish processing, fruit packing, motion picture production, and the aviation industry. In recent years production has expanded to include plastics, light-metal wares, synthetic fabrics and fibers, pottery, automobiles, steel, and a long list of goods for which no geographical explanation is apparent. Though coastal southern California clings to its Spanish-Mexican past, evidently only a trace of this background remains.

Many cities around Los Angeles are agricultural centers, though they are affected by industrialization. Older and distant communities like Ventura, Oxnard, Santa Maria, San Bernardino, and Riverside are pleasant towns, where farmers and ranchers still grow subtropical crops. Towns and cities nearer Los Angeles may carry on some industry as well as serve nearby farms. They include San Fernando, Santa Ana, and Anaheim. Originally some outlying centers were winter resorts, but this aspect of existence has disappeared in the larger communities, particularly in Santa Monica, Redondo Beach, and Long Beach. Beverly Hills, Pasadena, Van Nuys, Westwood, and Inglewood are dormitory towns and may, like Beverly Hills, be surrounded by the city of Los Angeles and yet retain separate municipal identity and function.

Westward from Los Angeles, facing the sea and backed by the Santa Ynez Mountains, the city of Santa Barbara is secluded, for it cannot be reached easily from the land side and has no satisfactory harbor. Reflecting its character as one of the earlier mission communities, it has never been important for industry or agriculture. Like Pasadena, its principal development has been residential; it has the characteristics of a superior year-round coastal resort.

In the extreme southwest, on an excellent harbor, the city of San Diego occupies a remote location, somewhat handicapped by inadequate water supply and by a hinterland limited in extent by the mountains and desert to the east and the Mexican boundary to the south. As a port, however, it serves importantly as a base of naval operations. To a limited extent it has developed light industry (food processing, aircraft), for local demand has been strong, labor supply plentiful, and year-round working conditions suitable for specialized industries.

CALIFORNIA COAST RANGES AND VALLEYS

The Coast Ranges forming the western rim of the Central Valley of California are made up of ridges and basins whose direction is roughly parallel to the coast itself, a condition associated with faulting. The Coast Ranges present a bold face to the Pacific, but the submerged northern ends of some of the troughlike valleys provide access to the interior and the Central Valley. Thus the submerged block forming San Francisco Bay is a breach in the Coast Ranges leading to the San Joaquin Valley. The most significant parts of the Coast Ranges are not the mountains themselves but the intervening valleys, in which are all of the cities and most of the people. The mountains are sparsely populated.

The Indians who formerly lived in the Coast Ranges were low in the scale of civilization and had inadequate food. Like Indians of the Northwest Coast they relied largely on fish; other food included acorn meal and small animals that could be trapped. Though they lived in villages they had little social organization. With the coming of the Spaniards, Mexicans, and Americans, the human economy of this region shifted to higher levels.

In spite of proximity to the coast, people who live in the Coast Range valleys are not directly concerned with the sea, though fishing is important in a few places. Most valleys are occupied by farmers or, as they are known in the West, ranchers. Their farming is dependent on the marine climate, particularly in the production of specialty crops such as artichokes, flower or mustard seed, lettuce, sugar beets, apples, grapes, and apricots. On some of the mountains there is good grazing land, and here beef cattle are raised on big ranches. Between 35° and 38° north latitude, the central Coast Ranges enjoy more precipitation than do the southern mountains, and their summits receive amounts sufficient to support forest growth. In sheltered valleys the Coast redwoods extend from Oregon to 100 miles south of San Francisco. Where water is obtainable, most valleys are used for raising specialty crops; where drought prevails, there are traces of the old-time, large-scale ranch economy. The central Coast Ranges and their valleys all but prevent penetration from the sea, and indeed no first-class harbor can be found between Los Angeles and San Francisco.

Largest and longest of the valleys is the Salinas, through which the Salinas River flows for more than 100 miles to reach Monterey Bay. The upper valley has scattered farms, but the lower section is intensively farmed in irrigated sugar beets, lettuce, alfalfa, melons, and near Watsonville, apples. The urban center, Salinas, is derived from earlier ranching activities.

Inland from Salinas is the Santa Clara Valley, growing specialty crops and fruit in its lower northern portion. The crops, however, differ from those in the Salinas region; the lower Santa Clara is dominated by large groves of prunes, apricots, and peaches. Of some importance are alfalfa and dairying. The urban center is San Jose, like Los Angeles one of the early Spanish pueblos but lately a processing center for fruits. This valley is faced with a problem of subsurface seepage of salt water coming from San Francisco Bay.

South of the 38th parallel, San Francisco Bay is the most conspicuous geographic feature of the coast. Much of the bay is shallow, but inside the Golden Gate and a little to the south, depths are sufficient for large vessels. The eastern side of the bay has been dredged to allow ocean vessels to reach the port of Oakland. Two peninsulas impinge upon the Golden Gate like a pair of tongs; the southern prong is occupied by San Francisco, confined to its peninsula, which is only 7 miles wide; the northern (Marin) peninsula is very rugged. Highway connection between the two is maintained over the Golden Gate Bridge.

San Francisco failed to develop under Mexican rule. With the discovery of gold in California and the subsequent rush of immigrants, the city became a disembarkation point for settlers entering the state by sea. Thus the character of the city as a center of trade and commerce was established, and though San Francisco now has industries such as coffee roasting, metal processing, and sugar refining, its dominant function is that of a trading and financial center. A century ago, common labor in California was in such demand that many immigrants were non-English, including Latin-Americans, French, Germans, and Chinese. Each of these stocks left its imprint upon the life of the city, and their variety has given San Francisco a cosmopolitan tinge not duplicated in any other Coast city.

On the eastern side of the bay, the separate municipality of Oakland is part of the San Francisco metropolitan area. Here are industries that were unable to find sufficient cheap land in San Francisco, and Oakland is noted for its food processing, milling, and other industries. North of Oakland, specialized satellite cities line the shore to a point beyond Carquinez Strait. Among these cities are Berkeley, a residential and university center, Richmond and Martinez with oil refineries, Crockett with a cane-sugar refinery, and Pittsburg, Hercules, and Giant, with chemical plants.

The total population of the Bay area towns and cities (that is, the metropolitan area around the bay) is 2,783,000. Their economy is widely diversified, the emphasis being on light and medium industries even though raw materials for manufacturing are not generally abundant in this part of the country. Fuel in the form of imported petroleum products and hydropower is obtained with relatively little difficulty, but mineral resources of use to major industry are not at hand. Food processing is important in the economy, both for grain and for fruits produced in the San Francisco Bay hinterland and for imported foodstuffs such as coffee and sugar cane, brought to the bay ports in quantity by ocean freighters.

The northern California Coast Ranges are unlike the central and southern ranges. Since they are more rugged and have less access to the sea, inferior harbors, and few passes, they are more isolated. The mountains lack intervening valleys, and transport is restricted to routes parallel to the coast. Only in the southern section facing San Francisco Bay are there valley floors suitable for agriculture, those of the Santa Rosa, Sonoma, and Napa Rivers. Although there is water in these lowlands for irrigating alfalfa and vineyards, the land available for agricultural expansion is limited. Dairying is associated with excellent pasture afforded by the long, narrow, coastal terraces kept moist by cool, damp air. Except in the Salinas, Santa Clara, and a few other smaller valleys, this region is incapable of supporting many people, and most towns are small. Some dry or remote valleys are used more for grazing than for crops. In the north, in the lowlands at the mouth of the Eel River dominated by the towns of Eureka and Arcata, the economy is based on lumbering, especially of the Coast redwoods.

PACIFIC NORTHWEST COASTAL PROVINCE

Between the Cascade Range and the Pacific Ocean and from Canada into the Klamath Mountains of northern California lies a humid region with mild winters and cool summers. Here, in a belt about 100 miles wide from west to east, the Douglas fir, western hemlock, cedar, and spruce attain their maximum growth, and the region might well be called "Evergreen Land." The marine west-coast climate not only favors tree growth, but makes possible dairying and growing small fruits in the wider valleys.

Most of the people live in the Puget-Willamette Lowlands between the Cascade Range and the Coast Ranges adjoining the Pacific Ocean. The lowlands are a troughlike basin, whose northern part is submerged to form Puget Sound. The rivers in the north drain into Puget Sound or Grays Harbor on the Pacific, and those in the south flow into the Columbia or the Willamette, its major tributary.

COAST RANGES OF THE PACIFIC NORTHWEST

The mountains of the Pacific Northwest Coast lie almost parallel to the Pacific shore and are somewhat lower in altitude than the Coast Ranges of California.

Figure 4-12 Douglas fir and western hemlock forest in the Olympic Range, northwestern Washington. "Block cutting" leaves a part of the forest remaining so that natural reseeding may be speeded. (Courtesy of U.S. Forest Service.)

Coastal uplift has produced a series of marine terraces like giant steps facing the sea; this is a rugged and scenic coast, with few corridors connecting with the interior and without the long, narrow valleys of the California ranges. The principal opening through the Oregon and Washington coast mountains is the wide estuary of the Columbia River, which breaches the mountains at right angles at 46° north latitude. This and the opening at San Francisco Bay are the only routes by which ocean vessels may navigate West Coast streams to reach Portland or Stockton. The mightiest break through the coastal mountains is the Strait of Juan de Fuca connecting with Puget Sound and leading to protected ocean ports far inland. Elsewhere in Washington a wide gap of the Chehalis River connects Grays Harbor with the Puget Lowlands, and a narrower route connects the lowlands with Willapa Bay. In Oregon, Coos and Tillamook Bays are connected with the Willamette Valley by fairly satisfactory routes through the Coast Range. A mountain knot, the Olympics, occupies northwest Washington, separated from the Cascades by Puget Sound and from Vancouver Island by Juan de Fuca Strait. The Olympics reach elevations that support glaciers and snow fields, and part of the area is set aside as a national park. The highest peak is Mt. Olympus, 7,954 feet.

In Oregon and Washington the Coast Ranges generally are lower in altitude and more easily traveled than those of California. Nevertheless, construction of railways and highways in this terrain is so expensive that some sections are isolated. The northern mountains are forest-covered, chiefly with coniferous softwoods. This timber is of great economic importance. In the wider valleys specialized farming is carried on. To some extent the deep forests have been exploited for timber, but much untouched forest serves as a scenic resource. Since only the edges of the mountains are reached by highways, tourists attracted by scenery or fishing are fewer than visitors to the Cascade parks. Because of the forests and the expense of clearing, agricultural land is at a premium except in sheltered places on the eastern side of the Olympic Peninsula. South of the Olympic Mountains the landscape is moderately dissected, and there the coast is submerged at Grays Harbor, Willapa Bay, and the Columbia River embayment. Fishing, lumbering, and paper manufacture are found here, but like the mountains to the north, the region is remote, and its population density is low.

The Columbia River estuary is so broad and deep that it used to be a major interruption to any north-south travel between northwestern Oregon and southwestern Washington; but a bridge across the river now connects Astoria and the northern shore. Astoria, on the south shore, is so far distant from other activities in Oregon that its growth has been slow, in spite of its fur-trade fame and its location on deep water. South of Astoria the Oregon coast is rugged but not high, with shallow harbors at Coos Bay and Tillamook. Since some short streams cross the mountains to reach the sea, residents of the Willamette Valley go to the coast if they wish a seaside vacation, and in spite of heavy fog there are many summer resorts. Lumbering is the leading industry, and dairying has been profitable; but although some minerals have been located in southwestern Oregon, mining is small in scale.

Flats along the upper Rogue River valley and the Umpqua have good soil and conditions suitable for deciduous fruits. The Rogue Valley is famous for its pears. Small centers such as Medford and Roseburg supply the needs of fruitgrowers, farmers, and lumbermen.

The moderate climate of the Pacific Northwest imposes few hardships on those who live there. Winter is the rainy season, and the days are short, with much cloudy weather and high relative humidity. The temperature range is small throughout the year. Summers are pleasant, and high temperatures are rare. The landscape remains green all winter, and except in the higher mountains, the snowy ground characteristic of winter in the Northeastern United States is lacking near the Northwestern Coast.

PUGET-WILLAMETTE LOWLANDS

West of the Cascade Range and parallel to it lies a depressed block of the earth's crust. Its southern portion is drained by the Willamette River, a tributary of the Columbia. In the north several small streams provide drainage, but the landscape is confused because of the intensive effects of glacial deposition in some places and extensive submergence of the northern part of the lowlands forming Puget Sound. In this longitudinal position and west of the Cascade heights, this depressed area is subjected to the full force of prevailing westerly winds which cross it at right angles, though some protection against marine influence is provided by the lower mountains of the Oregon and Washington Coast Ranges, the Olympic Range, and Vancouver Island.

The marine windward climate of these lowlands provides sufficient rain (occurring mainly in the winter season) and enough high temperatures during summer to support excellent growth of trees and grassland, though most of the forests have been removed for the sake of commercial timber. In the Willamette Valley the forest cover was interrupted by occasional open stretches of prairie land. Most of the trees were softwoods—Douglas fir and hem-

Figure 4-13   Loading Ponderosa pine logs on a wide truck with a "shovel" loader in the Malheur National Forest, Oregon. Modern machinery has reduced the numbers of men needed for this type of operation. (Courtesy of U.S. Forest Service.)

lock. With rainfall of moderate amount, leaching of soils was not a serious deterrent to farming of the lowlands, though occasional flood problems arose when mountain snows melted too rapidly in spring and summer.

Of the two sections of the lowlands, the Willamette Valley is the more productive agriculturally. It has not been subjected to heavy glacial deposits, and its alluvial soils may be farmed with relative ease. Drainage, at least for agricultural purposes, is excellent most of the year. Winter temperatures, though they approach the freezing point for short periods, are seldom so severe that farm animals must be securely protected against cold, and pasturage to maintain the animals is available throughout the winter season. Grain crops (especially wheat), forage, small fruits such as berries, the stone fruits of the mid-latitudes, and bulb crops all thrive in this environment. Dairy products, wool, nut crops, apples—these and many other agricultural resources contribute to the economic wealth of the valley.

As the Willamette Valley and the Puget Lowlands were explored, Americans interested in agricultural potentialities came to the Pacific Northwest between 1842 and 1848 and began farming the land. It was

in this period that numerous settlements began. Although land and water transport was inadequate and markets were distant, development continued. The Gold Rush to California in 1850 created an excellent market for lumber in that state. Supplies of fruit, grain, and fish were ample, and fortunately the Indians offered little effective opposition to the new settlements.

Wealth was available from forests, but commercial exploitation of timber resources came only with improved transportation after 1900. Since then lumbering has proceeded at such a pace that the possible exhaustion of this resource is now a matter of concern. Conservation measures look toward cropping Northwestern forests on a sustained-yield plan that will make it possible for the Pacific Northwest to continue as a major lumber producer. The forests of the Northwest provide us with paper, shingles, plywood, building material, telephone poles, and other necessities of modern life.

The lowlands of western Oregon and Washington have been famous for a century for certain crops; indeed, the fertility and cheapness of land in the Willamette Valley attracted settlers over the Oregon Trail to the Northwest. Since they could raise many crops with which they had been familiar in the East, the settlers tended to establish Eastern farm practices in the Northwest; hence, parts of this valley resemble Ohio or Illinois, with their barns, farm animals, and houses repeating the mid-nineteenth century rural complex of the American Middle West. In addition to staples such as oats and potatoes, Northwest agriculture developed some specialty crops—berries, mint, spring-flower bulbs, and commercial seeds.

With mild winters, plentiful rain, and a long growing season, agriculture normally is profitable, although occasional summer drought makes it desirable to irrigate some land in July and August. Though native grasses and introduced forage plants do well and beef cattle and sheep are raised, the concentration is on dairy products. In some localities the emphasis on dairying is so great that exports of processed milk, cheese, and butter are large. Other industries include poultry and small fruits. The expansion of commercial farming is limited by the extent of valley lands and by the cost of removing stumps from farmland and pasture.

Fishing, especially for salmon and halibut, is a third economy in the Northwest. Demand for salmon has been so great that sea and streams have been overfished, and production is less than formerly. Commercial fishing is maintained largely through conservation measures such as restocking streams, restrictions on the gear used, and specifying the time of year when fish may be caught. Minor economies include manufacturing, tourism, and mining. Recent exploitation has demonstrated that the Northwest has mineral wealth or is accessible to mining centers. As a result, and with the aid of hydroelectric power, industrial growth has been speeded.

The Willamette Valley, only 125 miles long and about 35 miles wide, is highly productive. It contains three-fourths of Oregon's people in 5 per cent of the state's area. Its grain, wool, lumber, fruit, fish, and other commodities have provided cities with material for manufacturing a variety of goods and so attracting increasing numbers of permanent residents.

The one major resource that is deficient in the Willamette region is mineral fuels. Oil and coal are lacking in any quantity, but the abundant water supply of streams flowing down the western slope of the Cascade Range provides conditions suitable for the generation of hydropower, which is used liberally throughout the Northwest on farms and in factories. Urban communities have grown, especially the city of Portland near the confluence of the Willamette and Columbia. To secure outlets for the productiveness of the region, the lower Columbia has been dredged, making Portland a seaport 100 miles distant from the Pacific. Portland, however, is not wholly dependent upon the products of western Oregon; the city taps eastern Washington and Oregon by a transportation corridor through the Cascades at the Columbia River Gorge. Portland's location, combined with actual and potential water power, has led to industrialization, population increase, and expansion of markets.

Smaller cities of the Willamette Valley serve both general and specific functions. Salem is a center of the state's political activity, Corvallis, the site of Oregon State College. Eugene, with the University of Oregon and woodworking plants, Oregon City, with pulp and woolen mills, and other communities prosper from broad agricultural and economic bases. Few centers in the Western United States have raw materials, power, and other advantages to the same degree as towns and cities of the Willamette Valley.

Northward from the river at Portland the lowlands extend to Puget Sound. Unlike the Willamette, dense forests once prevailed here, occupying terrain whose features were determined by heavy glacial outwash and deposition. Disturbed drainage patterns and deposits of stony till hinder farming, even after clearing of timber. Forest clearing has left much land covered with stumps and intractable for intensive farming except in fertile alluvial valleys. Milk, poultry, vegetables, bulb and seed crops, and small fruits are among the farm products, but most of the lowlands are unsuited to growing grain other than oats. The average farm size in one county is only 5 acres.

The northern Puget Lowlands are submerged by the waters of Puget Sound. Long, narrow, deep channels make up the Sound, whose confused landscape includes irregular peninsulas and many small islands. Originally virgin forests reached the shore, but today the lumber mills have left only second- and third-growth coniferous and deciduous trees.

Seattle is the dominant city, though it must compete with neighboring Tacoma. Of the two, Seattle enjoys the superior geographic position nearer the open sea, enhanced by the Snoqualmie and other passes east of the city. As recently as 1935 Seattle and Tacoma were regional capitals for the Puget Lowlands, both meeting the needs of local markets, and Seattle maintaining trade with Alaska and the Orient. That trade continues, but since 1940 both cities have emphasized diversified manufacturing; the processing of fish, foods, and timber, flour milling, meat packing, boatbuilding, furniture making, copper smelting, aircraft manufacture, and other industries are important. The manufactures are mostly of the lighter type, dependent on supplies of cheap hydroelectric power. These cities, after receiving their growth impetus from the establishment of sawmills, then became inactive until mining attracted large numbers of people to Alaska and the Yukon. Although the ports remain transportation centers, now Seattle and Tacoma have joined other manufacturing cities of the nation.

HAWAII

Several geographical features distinguish the state of Hawaii; the fact that the state occupies a position distant from the mainland, with more than 2,000 miles of water intervening, places Hawaii in a location of maritime significance; indeed, insular Hawaii is the only state in the Union whose political boundaries are entirely defined by shorelines. Its climate, too, is unique among the states. Though Florida's location approaches the tropics, only the extreme southern part of that peninsula can be regarded as genuinely tropical; the rest of the state is subtropical. In contrast, Hawaii, south of the Tropic of Cancer, is in the most tropical environment anywhere in the United States, though surrounding seas somewhat modify tropical conditions. Hawaii also claims the distinction of having a high degree of uniformity in her soil condition, as the direct result of the presence of active and inactive volcanoes, and of corals in the encircling waters. These two materials make up the main part of the underlying rock of the islands, and in turn affect the productive capacity of Hawaiian soil.

The people of Hawaii are distinguished by the exceptional racial mixtures, which developed mainly during the last century. Possibly no other section of the nation has harbored such a diversity of peoples and experienced such blending of racial color, language, and culture. Economically these people depend upon the political geography of their state for the largest part of

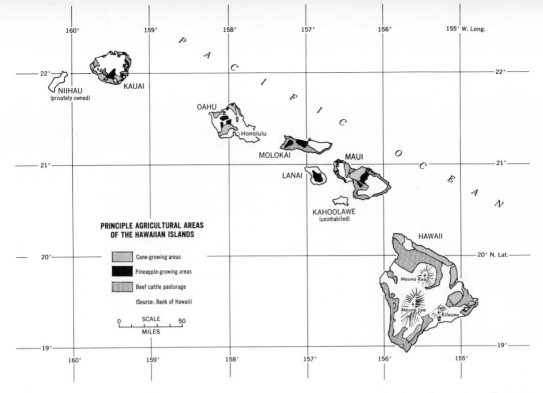

Figure 4-14   The state of Hawaii is composed of five major islands and several smaller ones. Note that Honolulu, the largest city, is on the island of Oahu.

their financial support, since the location of the islands in mid-Pacific makes them a highly strategic base for naval and air operations in that part of the world; the bases in turn call for expenditures of Federal funds for defense installations on a scale not generally present to the same degree in other states.

Hawaii's geography, then, is vastly different from that of other Western states; yet its human activities are irrevocably tied to the mainland, for the islands of the archipelago are not self-supporting in manufactured goods or in food supply. Thus the capital at Honolulu must maintain close working relationships with mainland ports such as Seattle, San Francisco, and Los Angeles in order to carry on the trade and provide the transport facilities essential to the well-being of residents of the islands.

Hawaii, viewed as a part of Polynesia by anthropologists, is made up of a large number of Pacific islands, of which the largest and most important are Hawaii, Maui, Oahu, Molokai, Lanai, and Kauai; Niihau and Kahoolawe and other islets remain relatively uninhabited and unproductive. The larger and higher islands are principally composed of volcanic material; the lower islands are often of coral. At present most of the volcanic activity is centered on the island of Hawaii at the craters of Kilauea, Mauna Kea, and Mauna Loa. Lavas, ash, and other extruded substances are the principal source of soils on these islands, and despite the rapidity of tropical leaching, their native fertility supplies soils of high quality which sustain a profitable tropical agriculture of the plantation type. Most of the volcanic soils are dark in color—brown or black—with some tendency toward the reddish shades of the tropical laterites.

Hawaii, at approximately 20° north latitude, lies in the zone of the northeast trade winds most of the year, enjoying a tropical climate free from snow or frost (except on the highest mountains) and steady sea breezes on its northeastern shores throughout the year. Low islands under the trades normally experience deficient rainfall, but the larger Hawaiian islands are so mountainous (with altitudes exceeding 13,000 feet) that onshore winds from the northeast sweep against mountain slopes, chilling as they rise. Thus the northeastern mountain faces are deluged with heavy rain through most of the year—as much as 400 to 600 inches in places, though the average amount is much smaller. The heavy rains on these slopes tend inevitably to induce excessive erosion even when land surfaces are protected by tropical vegetation; the island landscapes in places are scored deeply by canyons and gorges, through which many streams find their way to the sea over impressive waterfalls.

On the leeward side—the southwestern—offshore winds produce only small amounts of precipitation, for here the air has descended the slopes of the mountains and is both warming and drying in its effects. The larger islands, therefore, present two quite different geographical faces: tropical downpours, eroded gorges, rugged precipices, and Amazonian foliage on the windward shores; near-desert grasslands and shrubs with occasional cactus varieties on the leeward slopes.

As long as the Pacific remained relatively uncharted and traversed only by sailing vessels, the Hawaiian Islands made few advances in population or in economic life. After the opening of the Orient to commercial vessels in the mid-nineteenth century, however, the islands served increasingly as a base of naval supplies and as an outfitting point for commercial shipping. With the development of commerce between the eastern and western Pacific nations, the islands gained greatly in population and in importance, and cargoes of tropical foods were shipped to mainland ports in return for the manufactured wares that Hawaii lacked. As soon as trans-Pacific air travel mounted to major proportions, the islands became a way-station for long-distance flights to such an extent that Hawaii is sometimes called the "crossroads of the Pacific."

In recent years military operations in the Pacific have led to concentration of defense expenditures in Hawaii; this income, together with that derived from a healthy tourist trade, contributes the major share of the support of permanent residents of the islands. Agriculture, the

Figure 4-15   Climate graphs of selected stations.

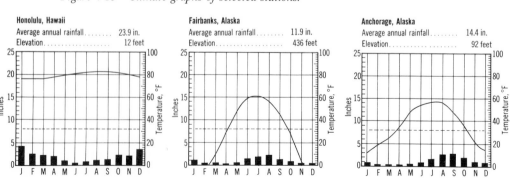

Honolulu, Hawaii	Fairbanks, Alaska	Anchorage, Alaska
Average annual rainfall....... 23.9 in.	Average annual rainfall....... 11.9 in.	Average annual rainfall........ 14.4 in.
Elevation.................. 12 feet	Elevation.................. 436 feet	Elevation.................. 92 feet

dominant activity of a half century ago, has become relatively less important, and since commercial products of the soil consist mainly of cane sugar and pineapples, the income from that source seems unpromising for future development on any large scale. Cane sugar from Hawaii must compete against cane sugar from other tropical locations, as well as the beet sugar of the mid-latitudes, but Hawaii, with less than half of the sugar acreage of Louisiana, produces twice as much cane each year. Pineapples represent a pleasant variety of tropical fruit, but on the market they compete against fruits such as bananas. Pineapple cultivation is concentrated mainly on the islands of Oahu, Maui, and Kauai, in that order. The "sugar" islands are Hawaii, Maui, and Kauai, in about equal value of production, and Oahu. Relatively minor Hawaiian crops include coffee and tropical flowers for shipment by air. All told, Hawaiian agriculture uses about 500,000 acres of cropland.

On some of the less-inhabited islands, where cultivation of the soil fails to bring good returns, grazing of beef cattle on an extensive scale has been the principal occupation, but on almost 80 per cent of the total area of Hawaii neither grazing nor cultivation of the soil is profitable. Since the total area of all the islands is little more than 4 million acres, its limited usability does not promise well for future expansion of agricultural activity.

In common with other tropical islands, Hawaiian agriculture tends to be the product of the plantation system, with all its advantages and disadvantages. In earlier years native Hawaiians of Polynesian stock failed to supply the amount or type of agricultural labor needed by the plantations; whereupon owners of cane and pineapple properties introduced a working population from many other parts of

Figure 4-16 Aerial view, showing the geometrical pattern of planted pineapple fields in the Hawaiian Islands. Hawaii's output of canned pineapple exceeds that of all other regions of the world combined. (Courtesy of Northwest Orient Lines.)

the world—China, Japan, the Philippines, Portugal (Madeira and the Azores), Puerto Rico, Korea, and Spain. Intermarriage was extensive and common among the migrants, with the result that the present population of Hawaii is very largely of mixed ancestry. It is estimated that only about 12,000 pure-blooded Polynesians remain on the islands today. Among the immigrants, the Japanese are present in greatest numbers. Perhaps no other state in the Union has experienced such a high degree of racial intermixture, as a direct result of the insistent demand for farm labor. For many years the supply of labor in Hawaii remained well below the saturation point, but recently the mechanization of sugar and pineapple plantations has made Hawaii's farm-labor problem less acute. So far the installation

Figure 4-17 Waikiki Beach at Honolulu, tourist attraction of the island of Oahu, in the state of Hawaii. Diamond Head, an extinct volcanic cone, appears in the distance. (Courtesy of Hawaii Visitors Bureau.)

of defense works has taken up the slack, but a major problem of unemployment is in prospect for Hawaii unless work can be found in occupations other than agriculture and military operations.

Tourists bound for the Hawaiian Islands are attracted by tropical conditions uncommon in other states—a mild year-round low-latitude weather condition (temperatures are nearly seasonless throughout the year) modified by the surrounding seas; exotic vegetation; and the prospect of year-long outdoor fishing, bathing, and golfing. These basic factors are widely advertised, along with luxury hotels and a type of island life that is entirely foreign to most mainland Americans. In addition, nature has provided

many features of active vulcanism—violent eruptions and lava flows—all readily available to the sightseer by means of air or sea transport. Hawaii's Volcanic National Park includes the active volcanoes Kilauea and Mauna Loa. Much of the tourist income in Hawaii has come from improved incomes and standards of living of mainland residents who feel able to afford a brief stay (averaging thirteen to eighteen days) in these tropical surroundings.

Though Hawaii is the largest island, Oahu is by far the most densely populated, since it includes the capital city of Honolulu and the defense installations at Pearl Harbor. Large and deep embayments created by lava flows and coastal erosion provide excellent protected anchorage for commercial and naval vessels alike. Of the total population of the islands (633,000) about 500,000 live in Honolulu; the rest live in small villages and outlying centers, and one island, Kahoolawe, is uninhabited.

Thus Hawaii is a strongly urban state, dependent mainly on its activities as a center of trade and transport rather than upon any wealth of natural resources which might contribute to industrialization. The islands provide no local sources of mineral fuel; coal and petroleum must be imported, and until other fuel resources are available in quantity, it seems unlikely that Hawaii will advance industrially, though strenuous efforts to develop local industry are in progress.

ALASKA

The territory of Alaska was purchased by the United States from Russia in 1867. Essentially an isolated peninsula, situated at the northwest corner of North America, Alaska sprawls over 586,400 square miles, nearly one-fifth of the area of the forty-eight coterminous American states. The Aleutian Islands extend toward the Kamchatka Peninsula of Siberia, nearly 1,000 miles west of eastern-most Asia, and the coastal panhandle reaches to within 400 miles of the state of Washington. The territory is crossed by the Arctic Circle, and interior Alaska has a severe continental climate, unlike the milder marine climate of the south coast.

PHYSICAL SETTING

RELIEF FEATURES   The landforms of Alaska range all the way from flat, marshy plains to the highest mountain peak in North America. At the northwestern end of the Cordilleran region, the landform patterns are generally a continuation of the ranges, valleys, and plateaus of the Cordillera of British Columbia and Yukon Territory.

The St. Elias Mountains rise to altitudes of 10,000 to 15,000 feet in southeastern Alaska, where Yukon Territory, British Columbia, and Alaska all come together. The St. Elias Range breaks into a complex of mountains to the northwest, such as the Chugach and Wrangell Mountains, and then separates into two definite chains. The southerly spur is the Kenai Mountains which form the backbone of the peninsula of the same name and reappear as the rugged parts of Kodiak Island.

The main mountain chain arcs northward as the Alaska Range, which averages 8,000 to 10,000 feet in elevation, but is crowned by North America's highest peak, Mt. McKinley, 20,300 feet. The Alaska Range has several mountain chains within it and in places is about 150 miles wide. The mountain system swings southwestward through the Alaska peninsula and merges with the sharp, volcanic peaks of the Aleutian Range. Many peaks of this latter range are above 10,000 feet in altitude, but elevations decrease westward across the Aleutian Islands, where peaks are generally between 4,000 and 5,000 feet high. Some of the mountains of this long island arc are still active volcanoes.

The central part of Alaska is a region of broad plateaus and plains, quite different in appearance from the mountainous southern section. The land slopes to the west from altitudes of about 2,000 feet at the Yukon border to broad swampy lowlands at the delta of the Yukon River on the Bering Sea coast. Across the rolling region the Yukon River and its main southern tributary, the Tanana, have cut broad valleys, and the streams flow generally over flat-bottomed valley floors.

The northern wall of interior Alaska is formed by the high barren mountains of the Brooks Range. It broadens to about 200 miles in width across north central Alaska. The mountains are quite rugged, with some peaks above 10,000 feet, but the ranges are broken by a few valley passes. The western end of the mountain system consists of lower ranges (2,000 feet), the rounded Delong and Baird Mountains near the Arctic Ocean coast.

North of the Brooks Range a broad foothill belt slopes down to a tundra-covered, lake-dotted coastal plain. Several rivers wind across the plain and have entrenched slightly into the glacial deposits. Permafrost, which underlies the Arctic lowlands, is one of the reasons for the many lakes and swamps across the surface (Figure 5-15).

CLIMATE   Alaska is a land of diverse climates. The many misconceptions of Alaskan climate are frequently due to a vagueness as to which part of Alaska is being discussed.

South central Alaska and the Panhandle have a marine climate quite different from the interior. Temperatures are moderated by the relatively warm water lying offshore in the Gulf of Alaska. Summers are generally cool, with July average mean temperatures of about 55°F. Winters are surprisingly mild for the northern latitude. The January average mean monthly temperatures are about 30°F, which is only about 10 degrees cooler than Seattle. Precipitation is very heavy in this south coastal area. Storms from the Aleutians come upon the mountainous coast throughout the year, but drop the greatest quantities of rain and snow from September to December. Most settlements, unless they are sheltered behind island mountains, average about 100 inches annually. Some stations have recorded as much as 150 inches of precipitation. Rainfall generally decreases to the westward along the southern coast, about 60 inches being a common average.

Central Alaska has a continental climate characterized by cold winters and relatively warm summers. Average January temperatures are slightly above zero near the Bering Sea coast, but are −10 to −15°F in the east central interior. Extreme temperatures of −60 to −70°F may be experienced at some time during most winters. Summers are cool near the Bering Sea (50 to 55°F for the July averages), but may become warm inland. Extremes rising into the 80s are common. Because of interior position, annual precipitation is only 10 to 20 inches, with a maximum of rainfall coming in the summer months.

The northern Arctic coast and most of the Brooks Range have a true Arctic climate in which summer monthly averages remain below 50°F. Although the winters are longer than those of interior Alaska, extreme temperatures are not so low, because of the modifying influence of the waters of the Arctic Ocean which, though cold, are warmer than the land.

RESOURCES AND ECONOMIC DEVELOPMENT

Most of the people of Alaska live in the south central and southeastern sections of the state. Fishing is one of the major occupations. Trading for fur seals and sea otter skins brought Russian ships to the Alaskan coast more than 150 years ago and the expeditions resulted in several Russian settlements and many Russian place names. The Pribilof Islands remain one of the world's major sources of fur seals, thanks to the present wise management and controlled harvesting of the herds.

Salmon packing began to expand at the turn of the century, particularly with improvements in the canning industry, and is a chief reason for many of the Panhandle settlements. Declining catches since 1950 indicate that the fishery may be overexploited. Salmon are netted and trapped as they approach the coastal rivers in summer; a large number of seasonal workers usually migrate into southeastern Alaska, especially to work in canneries located at Ketchikan, Wrangell, and Petersburg. Although the salmon catch makes up a large part of the value of the fishing industry, there are also catches of halibut, herring, cod, smelt, and king crab.

Placer gold was the attraction that made Alaska famous at the turn of this century; the gold rushes to Nome and Fairbanks occurred at about the same time as those to the famous Klondike region in Yukon Territory. Gold continues to be an important base for the mining industry, the greatest activity of production being near Juneau and Fairbanks. Mining declined in Alaska during World War II and has not yet regained its former status. Alaska has produced several strategic metals such as tin, tungsten, platinum, antimony, and mercury, but deposits have not been large enough or of sufficiently high grade to withstand high production costs. Most mines have operated near the coast, where accessibility has been an advantage in lowering costs. In the interior, the coal of the Nenana region along the railway is used, as is coal from the Matanuska Valley. A petroleum reserve has been established near Point Barrow for the use of the United States Navy, but finds have not been especially promising.

Alaska's forest industry has not yet developed to a large scale though there are several lumber mills on the coast and some processing of pulp at Ketchikan. The largest and heaviest timber stands are in the south central and southeastern coastal areas. Central Alaska is part of the Boreal Forest region, which covers Yukon Territory and much of north central Canada. Trees are smaller than those along the coast, and forest cover is interspersed with many swamps, muskegs, and small lakes.

Agriculture may be the future method of attracting a larger permanent population to Alaska, but progress is slow. To be sure the coastal regions, which have growing seasons of 140 or more days and ample precipitation, experience cool summers and have very little level ground. Crops can, and do, grow well in Alaska, but the agricultural sections have always suffered from economic problems such as high production cost and shortage of local markets. Subsistence farming for local needs is usually practicable in some sections, but commercial agriculture as it is known to most Americans faces many difficulties.

With less than 25,000 acres of cropland in the entire state of Alaska, agriculture is still a minor activity. This acreage is, however, but a small part of the potential arable land. The principal farming regions are in the Matanuska Valley and on the Kenai Peninsula. The former, settled in the mid-1930s, is now Alaska's chief agricultural region, marketing its produce inland along the Alaska Railway and in nearby coastal cities such as Anchorage. Farming is also practiced, on a smaller scale, in the Fairbanks area of the interior.

POPULATION

Alaska's population almost doubled in the decade 1940 to 1950, and now totals about 226,000, an increase that has been due almost wholly to the movement of population from the northern states. The military population is not included in this estimate. Native population has remained fairly stable; in 1960 there were 33,000 Eskimos, Indians, and Aleuts.

About two-thirds of Alaska's white population are found in the small cities around the Gulf of Alaska coast. Most of these people are urban dwellers, concerned with fishing, transportation, defense, local manufacturing, and business. Anchorage, the largest city, is growing rapidly. About one-third of the population live in the Cook Inlet region. In the Panhandle the two largest centers are Juneau, the capital, and Ketchikan, each with about 7,000 inhabitants.

About 42,000 Americans were living in the central part of Alaska in 1960, about two-thirds of them near Fairbanks, which is the important transportation hub for the Alaska Highway, the Alaska Railway, and air travel.

Three groups of native peoples occupy parts of Alaska. The Eskimos are found mainly on the west coast near the mouths of the Kuskokwim and Yukon Rivers and along the northwest coast to Point Barrow. Most Eskimos live in small villages near the coast, though they tend to migrate toward towns such as Nome, Kotzebue,

Figure 4-18 Fairbanks is the largest interior city of Alaska. This aerial view shows the principal business section, a bridge spanning the Chena River, and a highly developed residential area. (Courtesy Alaska Division of Tourism.)

and Barrow. Their way of life is changing rapidly but is still based on wildlife resources—fur-bearing animals, caribou, fish, seals, and in some places, reindeer.

The Aleuts are hardy inhabitants of the barren and foggy Aleutian Islands. They rely mainly on fishing. Alaskan Indians occupy parts of southeastern Alaska and the interior. Those along the coast are primarily fishermen, who live in small villages among the panhandle islands or along the irregular shores.

Thus Alaska, the largest of the American states in area, provides the greatest extent of undeveloped and unoccupied land in the entire nation. In many ways its human geography suggests the frontiers of North America over a century ago—a widely scattered population of low density, a wealth of natural resources yet to be tapped, an environment seemingly hostile. Mountain barriers, only recently breached by air travel, impede normal methods of land transport, and forest barriers are nearly as formidable. Rugged terrain, flooding streams, precipitous coasts, and frozen soil, combined with the severe winters of the northern latitudes, must be overcome before this state can be enabled to produce a decent living for many people. Alaska still has much to offer to the American pioneer.

IN PERSPECTIVE

THE UNITED STATES, PROBLEMS OF A WORLD LEADER

During the century that followed the winning of independence, the people of the United States busied themselves with expanding the Republic to the Pacific, consolidating political control over its 3 million square miles, and developing its widespread resources. The energy of the people went into clearing and plowing land for farms, founding new cities, logging the great forests, discovering and exploiting minerals, building railroads, starting and expanding manufacturing industries, and conducting the many other enterprises required by the complexities of modern life.

The country showed small concern for international relations, although the Monroe Doctrine did oppose further foreign colonization in the Americas. Two world wars compelled the United States to discontinue a policy of isolation and to concern itself with foreign problems as well as with those of domestic importance. Without deliberate intention, the country has grown to the status of a world power. It has become a defender of democratic institutions everywhere, a supplier of goods, money, and trained advisers to many peoples who need help. It has tried to maintain peace in a world torn by political turmoil. In a word, the United States has grown from a youthful, agricultural country preoccupied with developing its own resources, into a mature, industrial nation that is a pivotal factor in world affairs.

In its growth to economic maturity the United States made mistakes. It often permitted needless waste in destruction of wildlife, in soil erosion, deforestation, and wasteful mineral exploitation; but once the injurious practices were recognized, remedies were devised. A strong effort is being made to use land more efficiently than in the past. The major uses of land in various sections of the country are shown in Figure 4-19.

The highest proportion of cropland is in the Central Lowlands and Great Plains states, where over one-half of the land is tilled. Here are plains with good to excellent soils, adequate rainfall, and a moderately long growing season. No other part of the country has nearly so much cropland. The South has 23 per cent, the Northeast 19 per cent, the Mountain states less than 10 per cent, and the Pacific states 13 per cent. Improved farm practices, the substitution of tractors for hay-eating

Figure 4-19   The difference in land utilization in the various regions depends upon the adjustments made between man and nature. In the Corn Belt and Northern Plains about 50 per cent of the total area is classified as cropland. In the Mountain states and the drier areas to the west, over 60 per cent is used for grazing. Note the area in the Eastern states used for industry.

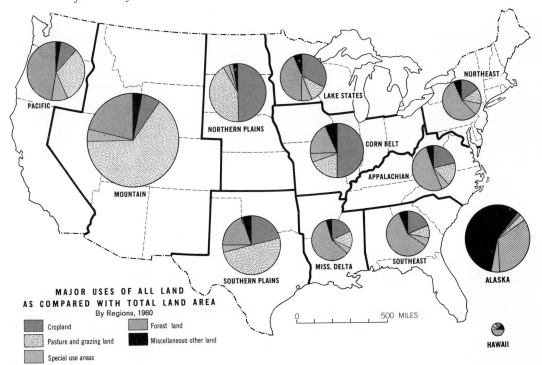

MAJOR USES OF ALL LAND
AS COMPARED WITH TOTAL LAND AREA
By Regions, 1960

Cropland

Pasture and grazing land

Special use areas

Forest land

Miscellaneous other land

horses, the use of fertilizer, control of pests and diseases, and the development of hybrids or other improved plant species help to account for increased production on the farmland of the United States.

Grazing and pasture land is concentrated in the Mountain and Pacific states, where 57 and 26 per cent of the land respectively is in this category. Here inadequate rainfall restricts crops mostly to those produced by irrigation or dry farming. East of the Great Plains, pastures amount to less than one-fifth of the total area. Forests occupy 59 per cent of the total land in the Northeast. The South, excluding the southern plains, has from 50 to 60 per cent of its land in forests, and the Lake states nearly 45 per cent. The three Pacific Coast states have 47.4 per cent of their area in forests or woodland, and the Mountain states 26 per cent. The smallest area of forest land is in the northern Great Plains, where only 3 per cent of that region is so classified. These statistics indicate that there is enough forest land in the United States to grow most of its timber requirements if the forests are well managed. Great improvement in forest management has been made since the turn of the century, and waste has been reduced.

The United States is fortunate in the variety and amount of minerals mined. Although the nation is the largest producer and consumer of bituminous coal and petroleum, at the present rate of usage the reserves of each will continue to meet the needs of the nation for a long period of time. Iron ore is not as easily procured as in the past, but large quantities of some grades are still available. Lead, zinc, copper, and bauxite are mined in various parts of the country. Nonmetallic minerals such as fertilizers, building stones, and sulfur are more than sufficient to meet the national needs.

Since 1900 the United States has become the leading industrial nation of the world. The accessibility of raw materials for manufacturing, the ease with which various types of transportation could be developed, the large supply of fuel and water power available, intelligent labor, and a surplus of capital have been responsible for the rapid growth. The giant industrial centers of Chicago, Pittsburgh, Cleveland, Detroit, Philadelphia, Baltimore, and St. Louis as well as numerous smaller cities and towns have made the northeastern quarter of the country the leading industrial area. New York, Norfolk, Boston, and other ports have aided this growth by giving easy access to the markets of the world. Smaller industrial areas have developed around some of the larger cities in other parts of the nation, along the Gulf Coast of Texas and Louisiana, and about the larger cities near the Pacific. Almost 17 million persons are now employed by manufacturing industries, which have an annual payroll approximating $90 million. The value added to the goods manufactured exceeds $160 billion yearly.

Since 1950 the population has increased at a rate of nearly 3 million persons each year. To support such a rapidly growing population, land and other resources must be used in an efficient manner. More careful use of natural resources gives further evidence of the nation's maturity.

SELECTED REFERENCES

Atwood, Wallace W.: *The Rocky Mountains,* Vanguard Press, Inc., New York, 1945.

A description of the physiography of the region. Well written, with many illustrations.

Fenneman, Nevin M.: *Physiography of the Western United States,* McGraw-Hill Book Company, Inc., New York, 1931.

The classic summary of the landform development of the United States. Though not of recent date, no other volume quite takes its place.

Freeman, Otis W., and Howard H. Martin: *The Pacific Northwest: An Overall Appreciation,* John Wiley & Sons, Inc., New York, 1954.
The standard reference work for the Pacific Northwest. Though the date is not too recent, most of the information in this volume is correct, barring a few statistics.

Griffin, Paul F., and Robert N. Young: *California: The New Empire State,* Fearon Publishers, San Francisco, 1957.

The treatment of the subject in this volume is mainly economic.

Highsmith, Richard M., Jr.: *Atlas of the Pacific Northwest,* Oregon State University Press, Corvallis, Ore., 1962.
An atlas dealing with the physical and economic aspects of the area.

Lantis, David W., Rodney Steiner and Arthur E. Karinen: *California: A Land of Contrast,* Wadsworth Publishing Company, Inc., Belmont, 1963.
A regional geography of California with detailed studies of the numerous subregions. Much interesting descriptive material.

Zierer, Clifford M.: *California and the Southwest,* John Wiley & Sons, Inc., New York, 1956.
For a general summary of the geography of California, this is still the standard accepted work. More recent material is available but not in quite such convenient form.

chapter 5

CANADA AND GREENLAND

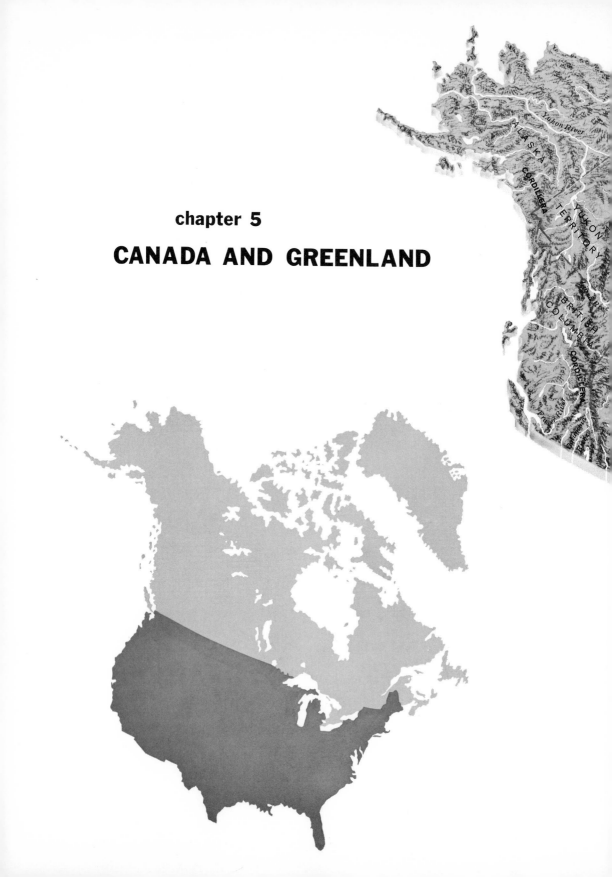

Figure 5-1   Many of the physiographic regions of Canada are continuous with those of the United States. Note that the Canadian Shield extends southward from Canada into the area around the Great Lakes.

*A*LTHOUGH CANADA IS LARGER THAN the United States it has only one-tenth as many people. Canadians inhabit only the southern part of their country in significant densities. Probably about 70 per cent of the Canadians live within 100 miles of their border with the United States. Much of Canada is not a favorable physical environment for agricultural settlement, but the resource potential of this vast land, in terms of minerals, forests, and power, is becoming more apparent. As Canada becomes an industrial and manufacturing nation, though its population will probably continue to concentrate in the cities of the southern parts, the remainder of the country will be significant in the production of raw materials. Settlement spread across Canada from east to west in the first half of this century, and now hardy people are expanding the exploitation of resources to the northward. Although many settlements in eastern North America started about the same time in the seventeenth century, the Canadian physical environment did not attract as many immigrants as did the regions to the south. Despite environmental differences, the peoples of these two countries have many things in common in their history and culture; but in Canada as in the United States there are great differences from place to place.

Canada is a self-governing, independent nation, having a total area of 3,851,809 square miles, extending some 2,800 miles from the tip of southern Ontario, jutting into Lake Erie at 42° north latitude to the icebound northern coast of Ellesmere Island at 83° north latitude. Canada's width is 3,000 to 3,500 miles, but its eastern and western tips are about 88° of longitude apart, or about one-quarter of the distance around the world.

Politically, Canada has a federal government, consisting of the union of ten provinces and two territories (Figure 5-2). Even though the Queen of England is recognized as the nominal ruler of Canada, the monarchy has no authority, and is represented at ceremonial occasions by a Governor General, who is a Canadian nominated by the Canadian government. Although a member of the British Commonwealth of Nations, Canada is completely independent in her domestic and foreign relations.

The Canadian provinces fall into regional groupings. The Atlantic provinces consist of Nova Scotia, New Brunswick, Prince Edward Island, and Newfoundland. The latter was added in 1949, having been a self-governing dominion in its own right. Central, frequently "eastern," Canada comprises the densely populated provinces of Quebec and Ontario; Quebec, Canada's largest province, is twice the size of Texas. The Prairie Provinces of Manitoba, Saskatchewan, and Alberta actually have more forest area than prairie grassland, but settlement is mainly across the southern grasslands. In the far west the mountain province of British Columbia covers as much area as California, Oregon, and Washington together. Northern Canada is sparsely settled, and this large area of 1⅓ million square miles remains in territorial status, being governed from the federal capital in Ottawa.

PHYSICAL SETTING

MAJOR LANDFORMS

Canada's large area has a variety of landforms (Figure 5-1). In a general way, the northern half of North America can be likened to a saucer, the center of the depression being shallow Hudson Bay and its adjoining lowlands. The outer parts of the continent tend to be high or rugged; the interior areas are low or rolling.

Figure 5-2 Politically, Canada is divided into ten provinces and two territories. Each province, like the states of the United States, has its own capital. Ottawa is the national capital.

APPALACHIAN-ACADIAN REGION Atlantic Canada is part of the Appalachian Mountain System which extends southwest-northeast across eastern North America. The Canadian part of the Appalachian System has linear hills and low mountains extending northeastward from the Green and White Mountains of New England. The low Boundary Ranges of southeastern Quebec and the flat-topped Shickshock Mountains of the Gaspé peninsula have their counterparts in the Long Ranges of western Newfoundland Island.

East of the linear mountains is a lower

region of hills, uplands, and plains known as the Acadian section. Central New Brunswick is hilly, but the eastern part consists of lowlands which could be considered as a small-scale equivalent of the Atlantic Coastal Plain east of the Appalachians in the Eastern United States. These lowlands include all of Prince Edward Island province and the north coast of Nova Scotia. Although much of Nova Scotia and northeastern Newfoundland Island is less than 500 feet in altitude, the coastal areas are rugged and indented with numerous bays and inlets. Level land is quite limited.

GREAT LAKES AND ST. LAWRENCE LOWLAND. The lowland jutting southwestward toward the United States is the most important region in Canada. Although it occupies about one-fiftieth of the country's area, it has more than one-half of the population, and produces almost three-fourths of the total value of Canadian manufactures. The lowland is a northeastern extension of the Central Lowlands region of North America. In Canada it is broken into two sections by a rocky southern arm of the Canadian Shield, which crosses the St. Lawrence River and appears as the Adirondack Mountains of New York State. The eastern part of the St. Lawrence Lowland in southern Quebec is extremely flat. The western part—the peninsula between Lakes Huron, Erie, and Ontario—has a rolling surface resulting in part from glacial deposition.

THE CANADIAN SHIELD The largest physiographic region in Canada forms a huge horseshoe of almost 2 million square miles of exposed ancient Precambrian rock around Hudson Bay. These worn-down hills and uplands have a rough, rocky, knobby character over most of their surface. Relief is seldom over 500 to 1,000 feet. There are many lakes of glacial origin and a few level areas marking the bottoms of large former glacial lakes. Although the Canadian Shield is valuable for its mineral, forest, and power resources, the physical characteristics of rough topography, thin soils, and poor drainage have discouraged agricultural settlement and transport.

THE HUDSON AND JAMES BAY LOWLANDS West and south of Hudson Bay, between Moose River, Ontario, and Churchill River, Manitoba, are flat-lying, young sedimentary rocks which have a landform character different from that of the old hard rocks of the Canadian Shield. The lowlands are poorly drained; streams wander slowly across the boggy surface, after having dropped over several rapids across the Shield.

THE INTERIOR PLAINS Gently dipping sedimentary rocks lie west of the Canadian Shield. The Interior Plains rise in altitude across the southern part of the Prairie provinces. The Manitoba lowlands are generally under 1,000 feet in elevation; the plains of southeastern Saskatchewan are about 2,000 feet above sea level; the plateau of southwestern Saskatchewan and southern Alberta slopes upward from 2,500 feet to almost 5,000 feet in the foothills at the base of the Rocky Mountains. The Plains narrow to the northward and become lower in the broad Mackenzie River valley.

CORDILLERAN REGION In Canada the Cordilleran region is much narrower and more compressed than in the United States. The linear ranges and valleys are not so wide, and the plateaus are smaller than they are to the south. The eastern rampart is the scenic Rocky Mountains, which end in the plain along the Liard River of northern British Columbia. The eastern wall continues to the northeast in the Mackenzie Mountains, which curve toward the Brooks Range of Alaska. Along the Pacific, the Coast Mountains have some of the most spectacular scenery in Canada, since they rise 7,000 to 9,000 feet directly from sea level above the many twisting fiords that indent the coast. Throughout the interior of the Cordillera several broad plateaus or basins are incised by deep river valleys.

ARCTIC ISLANDS   These islands have very little landform similarity throughout, but are grouped together because of their island character. Landform features range all the way from the high, alpine, ice-capped peaks of Baffin, Ellesmere, and Axel Heiberg Islands, to flat, lake-covered lowlands such as eastern Victoria, southern Prince of Wales, and King William Islands. Many of these northern islands are large: Baffin Island is almost as large

as the province of Manitoba or four times the size of New York State; Victoria Island is twice the size of the state of Ohio. The channels between the islands are filled with solid or moving ice most of the year.

GREENLAND   As a county of Denmark, the large island of Greenland is politically separate from North America, but its landform character and icecap are similar to those of the nearby Canadian Arctic Islands. The east and west coasts have high mountains. Filling the space between the mountains and rising above them in a flattened dome is the huge mass of ice which constitutes most of the surface of Greenland. Most Greenlanders live on the ice-free strip of fiorded coast in the southwest.

CLIMATE

Canada's large area has a variety of climates as well as several types of landforms (Figure 5-4). There are regions of

Figure 5-3   Glaciers are beautiful rivers of ice as they flow down from the Coast Mountains inland from Knight Inlet, British Columbia. Westerly winds that rise over the Coast Mountains drop their snowfall on the western slopes. The packed snow turns to ice and begins to move. (Courtesy of R.C.A.F.)

continuous cold and some that are mild most of the year. As in the adjoining United States, some areas are very wet and some are dry; there are regions of high heat in summer, and icecaps where summer never comes.

The climate of western and northern Canada is influenced by the warm water of the Pacific Ocean and the cold water of the Arctic Ocean and Hudson Bay. The air masses that pass over the Pacific Ocean bring mild temperatures to the west coast throughout the winter, and the nearby water keeps the coastal summers cool. During winter, these air masses drop heavy precipitation on the western slopes of the Cordilleran mountains as the air is forced upward to cross them. The Arctic Ocean is the source of cold air masses, which, in winter, move southward, spreading over the Prairie provinces and pushing into the United States. In summer,

northeastern Canada has a cool climate, owing to the cold waters around the coast. This Arctic climate, which covers about one million square miles of Canada's area, extends far south of the Arctic Circle on both sides of Hudson Bay.

Most of Canada has a continental climate, cold in winter and warm to hot in summer. The large indentation of Hudson Bay in the northeast prevents the climate from being more continental; the bay has cold water in summer, which cools the land masses near it, particularly to the eastward. Although the bay is covered with ice by January, the land masses nearby do not become so severely cold as, for example, the great land mass of Siberia. Since most Canadians live in the southern part of their country, they experience climates quite similar to those of the adjoining United States. The west coast is the wettest part of Canada and

Figure 5-4   Climate graphs of selected stations.

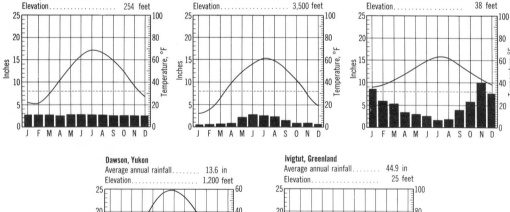

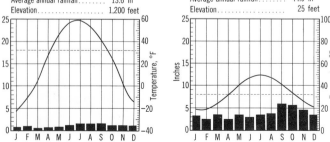

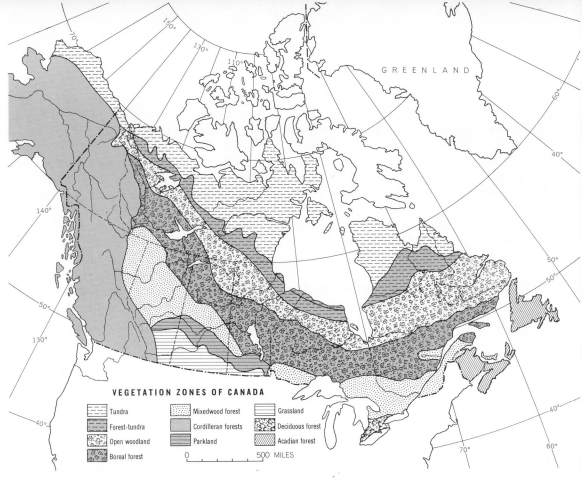

VEGETATION ZONES OF CANADA

Tundra	Mixedwood forest	Grassland
Forest-tundra	Cordilleran forests	Deciduous forest
Open woodland	Parkland	Acadian forest
Boreal forest	0 500 MILES	

Figure 5-5   East of the Cordilleran forests the vegetation zones of Canada trend in an east-west direction, as do the climate belts. Note that the zones are wider along the Atlantic shore than in the western part of the nation.

the mildest in winter; the east coast is about half as wet and has colder winters than the west coast. Central Canada is warm in summer, but the longest growing season of the interior is in the most southerly areas of Ontario, surrounded by the Great Lakes. Most of Canada is cold in winter; the coldest areas of the mainland are northwest of Hudson Bay.

VEGETATION

Since natural vegetation is a good indicator of climate, the map of vegetation zones is suggestive of the climatic regions of Canada (Figure 5-5). Canada's forested area, although the third largest in the world, covers only 45 per cent of her total area—about 1,700,000 square miles of forest. Because of unfavorable physical environmental conditions, the trees in almost half of this area are small and grow too slowly to be classed as productive forest. This leaves a remainder of about 1 million square miles of Canada—less than 30 per cent of the country's area—which is productive forest. This productive forest belt stretches across central Quebec and Ontario, north of the main agricultural areas.

A small area of deciduous forest, similar to the northern hardwoods of the

United States, was located in southwestern Ontario, north of Lake Erie. Because these trees indicated favorable environmental conditions of soil and climate, much of the forest was cut down and is now agricultural land. Maples and elms are the common trees remaining.

North of the Great Lakes and the St. Lawrence River is a transitional forest zone, containing both deciduous and coniferous trees. The deciduous trees become fewer to the north and are replaced by the hardier conifers such as spruce, pine, balsam, and tamarack. This forest region, which is close to the industrial centers of central Canada, supplies much of the forest wealth of eastern Canada.

To the north the Boreal (Northern) Forest region stretches from the Coast of Labrador to northern British Columbia and Yukon Territory. More than 80 per cent of Canada's forested area is classified in the Boreal Forest region. It is mainly a coniferous forest, although there are stands of deciduous birch and aspen in the southern sections, notably across the central Prairie Provinces. Within the forest zone are innumerable lakes, swamps, muskegs, and bare rocky hills—all treeless areas, the results of continental glaciation. These open areas are most prominent in the northern sections of the Boreal Forest.

North of the Boreal Forest about 27 per cent of Canada is in the treeless Arctic. The 50° July isotherm, which defines the southern limit of the Arctic as a climatic region, coincides closely with the northern limit of tree growth. North of the tree line, tundra vegetation (mosses, lichens, grasses, and low bushes) is confined to the lowlands, and most of the rocky hills and glacial deposits are barren of vegetation. Another treeless area is the narrow strip of grassland which lies south of the Boreal Forest in the Prairie Provinces—the result of low annual precipitation. This latter grassland zone is the northern end of a larger grassland region in the United States.

Because of the variety of climates and landforms found in British Columbia, the vegetation regions are small and complex. They frequently have a pattern of vertical zones, with grasslands in the valleys, tall straight conifers on the lower slopes, and smaller conifers on the steeper upper slopes. Many of the mountain ranges, particularly northward in Yukon Territory, rise above the tree line, adding to the amount of treeless area in Canada.

SOILS

Because agriculture has been confined to the southerly areas of Canada, many of the northern soils have not yet been mapped in detail. The best agricultural lands are the gray-brown forest soils in the Great Lakes and St. Lawrence lowlands of Ontario and Quebec. Most of these soils have been developed from glacial materials, and their exact character varies greatly within small areas. Much of eastern Canada has poor, acid, and leached soils called podsols. Soil cover is by no means complete in the Canadian Shield, where there are bare rocky ridges and many lakes, swamps, and muskegs. The northern parts of the Shield and the Mackenzie Valley are underlain by permanently frozen subsoil (permafrost), which increases drainage problems and makes the soils cold for root crops. In eastern Canada a few million acres of arable land are still unoccupied and available for settlement as required, but much of the surface is not favorable for commercial-crop production.

The utilized soils of western Canada are found chiefly in the grassland and parkland vegetation regions. They have developed over young sedimentary rocks but have been modified by glacial deposition. Some of the soil zones are like those found in longitudinal arrangement across the Great Plains of the United States, but in Canada the pattern is concentric. The brown soils are in the center, in the driest parts of southern Alberta and Saskatchewan; the dark brown soils are around them; and farther outward are the black soils, which receive more effective precipitation. North of Edmonton and Prince Albert the gray forest soils are poorer, and clearing for agriculture has been difficult. These soils extend northward into the Mackenzie River valley. Although the gray forest soils can grow crops in some places, agriculture is moving into these areas very slowly; at present it appears more economical to develop lands closer to the markets of southern Canada.

The soils of the Cordillera are complex, as might be expected in a mountainous region. The useful soils are quite limited in area and are confined to narrow river valleys or lie across the Interior Plateau. Some of the coastal soils, if they are not alluvial flood-plain deposits, are strongly leached because of heavy rainfall.

POPULATION DISTRIBUTION

Canada's population of more than 19 million (1964) is spread thinly along the southern part of the country. More than half of these people are concentrated in the small area in southern Ontario and Quebec where the original settlements were located and prospered.

In 1961 there were almost 2 million persons in the Atlantic provinces. Because of limited economic opportunities on the eastern edge of Canada, population increases have been siphoned off to industrial Ontario, to the agricultural west, or

to the Northeastern United States. Newfoundland had 460,000 persons in 1961. Because the island first drew settlers for fishing and the interior has not been attractive, 90 per cent of the people live on or near the coast. There is only one large city, the port of St. John's. The rest of the population is scattered along the coast in hundreds of small towns and villages ("outports"). The Coast of Labrador, which is part of Newfoundland politically, is sparsely occupied, with about 14,000 people in an area of 112,000 square miles.

Nova Scotia, with a rocky interior and good fishing banks offshore, also has a coastal pattern of settlement. New Brunswick has a peripheral settlement distribution, but the greatest concentration of the province's 600,000 people is along the valley of the St. John River in the western interior. Much of rough, forested central New Brunswick is unoccupied. Tiny Prince Edward Island, Canada's smallest province, is almost fully occupied, as is indicated by the virtually static population of 100,000 persons in this century.

The province of Quebec had 5,260,000 people in 1961, the majority being descendants of about 60,000 original French settlers. Most of the people live in the St. Lawrence Lowland, with smaller populated pockets northeast in the Saguenay Valley and northward in the Clay Belt. In the center of the southern Quebec population core is Montreal, a hub of transportation and Canada's largest city, which contains about one-tenth of Canada's population. As in the rest of Canada, rural population has declined steadily in Quebec, and about 70 per cent of the people live in urban areas.

Ontario, with 6,240,000 people, has the largest population of any Canadian province. As in Quebec, about 85 per cent of the population live in the southern one-tenth of the province. The average density in rural areas is about 100 persons per square mile, but most people live in cities or small towns. After most of the good soils were occupied in the last century people began concentrating in the cities to process the agricultural resources of southern Ontario and the forest and mineral resources to the north. Northern Ontario has several cities based on mining, forestry, or transportation, but the general pattern of settlement is spotty. Most of northwestern Ontario, like most of central and northern Quebec, is still virtually untouched by white settlement. These regions of gravel soils, rocky hills, and muskeg valleys will never support agricultural settlers but may see the rise of mining communities.

Manitoba's population of 930,000 is found mainly in the narrow belt between Lake Winnipeg and the United States border. More than one-third of the provincial population live in the urban area of Greater Winnipeg, Canada's fourth city. The remainder are farmers on large grain or livestock farms to the west across the fertile black soils. Although called a Prairie Province, the northern two-thirds of Manitoba is in the forested, lake-covered Canadian Shield, and is occupied chiefly by Indians. Although the Churchill Railway gave Manitoba a northern outlet after 1930, the development of its northern resources did not become significant until after 1950.

Saskatchewan's population, mainly wheat farmers, remained fairly stable from 1931 to 1951, but increased again to 925,000 by 1961 following a greater diversification in the province's resource base. The rural population, occupying large, mechanized farms, is spread across the black and dark brown soils; average densities are about 5 to 8 persons per square mile. The discovery of petroleum and natural gas and the increased use of irrigation have brought significant changes in the Saskatchewan economy. The northern half, however, in the stunted forests and lake-covered Shield, still remains almost unoccupied.

Because the width of the settled area across the Interior Plains increases from east to west, almost half of Alberta is occupied. As a result of new oil and natural gas fields, Alberta became the province with the highest percentage of population increase in the decade 1951 to 1961, and supported 1,330,000 people in the latter year. The main belt of population concentration is a south-north zone from Lethbridge through Calgary to Edmonton. An outlying pocket of settlement is growing to the northwest in the Peace River area. Agricultural settlement has been confined primarily to the black- and dark brown–soil regions and in the parkland vegetation zone. The two large cities of Edmonton and Calgary have growing industrial and commercial functions and promote a friendly rivalry as to which shall be the larger.

Although British Columbia is Canada's third-ranking province in population, most of its area is not occupied. Of the total population of 1,650,000 about three-quarters are concentrated in the southwest—in the large urban area of Greater Vancouver, the nearby lowlands of the Lower Fraser River, and on southeastern Vancouver Island. The rest of the population is scattered along the linear valleys between high mountain ranges of the southern and southeast interior. Although population has increased throughout the interior, except in the almost empty northwest, the greatest increases continue to come to the mild and scenic southwestern corner.

The two northern territories have only a few thousand people. Yukon Territory, a vast region of 207,000 square miles, has 14,000 people, more than one-third of

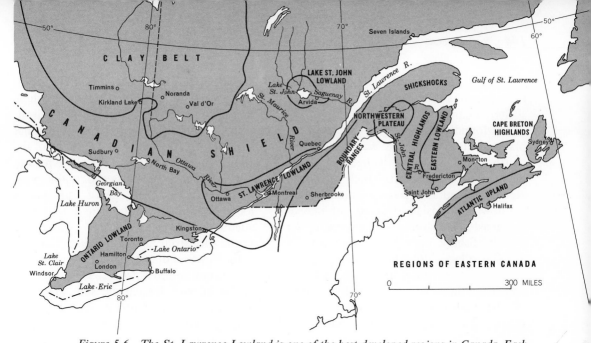

Figure 5-6   *The St. Lawrence Lowland is one of the best developed regions in Canada. Each region has its own cultural and physical characteristics.*

whom live in or near the capital, White-horse. In the Northwest Territories most of the 10,000 white inhabitants live in small villages along the Mackenzie River or on the shores of Great Slave Lake. Although Canada is often cited for its northward movement of population, the numbers involved are still small, and most of the economic expansion is in the southern sections or across "middle" Canada. In northeastern, or Arctic, Canada there are about 11,000 Eskimos, most of whom live in the Territories, although some inhabit the coast of northern Quebec. These migratory people are spread thinly along the coasts of the southern Arctic Islands and the adjoining mainland, with an average density of one Eskimo for about 100 square miles.

THE REGIONS

ATLANTIC PROVINCES

LANDFORMS Although the east-coast area of Canada is hilly, several landform regions give variety to the landscape (Fig-

ure 5-6). Northwestern New Brunswick is an upland, partly surrounded by low mountains. It slopes down to the northwest, through a gap in the Appalachian chain across the Gaspé peninsula. This pass is an important transport route between New Brunswick and the densely settled lowlands of southern Quebec. Central New Brunswick is hilly, with some rounded peaks over 2,000 feet in altitude. From this rugged, forested core rivers flow out to the flat lowlands along the east coast, or race westward to drop down into the St. John River valley. Only a few land-transport lines penetrate these central highlands. The eastern lowlands include Prince Edward Island and northwestern Nova Scotia, where altitudes are all under 500 feet. On Prince Edward Island most of the lowlands have been cleared of forest for agricultural development, but across eastern New Brunswick most of the plain remains in forest cover.

Nova Scotia has an interior rocky, rough upland. Relief is not very great, but nearly everywhere there are rounded hills, stony soils, and disrupted drainage. Much of the upland rises directly from the sea in an indented coastline noted for its many sheltered harbors.

Newfoundland Island is an elevated plateau, highest on the west where the North and South Long Ranges have altitudes of over 2,000 feet. Much of central Newfoundland is a barren upland, sloping down to an island-fringed, submerged northeast coast. About 40 per cent of the island's fishing population are scattered in small villages along this indented northeast coast. Northern Newfoundland, known as the Coast of Labrador, is part of the Canadian Shield physiographic region. This rugged upland has lower regions along the Hamilton River and its highest sections in the alpine peaks of the Torngat Mountains at the northern tip of Labrador.

CLIMATE The Atlantic provinces have a marine climate on the coasts, with mild winters, cool summers, and ample rainfall, but the interior valleys and northwestern New Brunswick have a continental-type climate, with cold winters, warm summers, and a higher percentage of snowfall. Average monthly temperatures in winter are mildest in southern Nova Scotia because of the influence of the warm Gulf Stream offshore; harbors do not freeze over, and thus Halifax and Saint John are important winter ports for eastern Canada. Similarly, southeastern Newfoundland is the least cold part of the island, but the northern peninsula has cold winter temperatures similar to those of the Coast of Labrador. The frost-free season averages about 120 days in some valleys; many of the uplands, however, have a marginal climate for agriculture with less than 80 days without frosts. Daily temperatures in midsummer are frequently higher than 80°F, particularly in western New Brunswick; but summer days are cool along the coast.

RESOURCES AND ECONOMIC DEVELOPMENT Although the four Atlantic provinces show broad similarities in physical environment, local differences produce distinct variations in the major occupations of the people in each section. The whole region, however, suffers from its geographic position on the eastern edge of Canada. Its local population is too small to be an adequate market, and it can export little to the industrial areas of central Canada.

In Newfoundland fishing is the major occupation of most people. Many sections of the interior are barren, soils are poor, and the summers are too cool for good crop growth. Throughout the history of the island, settlers have had to make a living from the sea with its plentiful fish. Fishing villages dot the bays of the northeast coast and Avalon Peninsula, and nets are set close to shore off the many headlands or islands. The catch of cod, which is cured by traditional family methods in the small villages and is dried or salted, has produced a low-quality product and low incomes for the fishing people. Fish filleting and freezing plants are being established at the main settlements to improve the quality of the export product. Some fishermen, with new trawlers and draggers, fish off the south coast of Labrador in summer or go out with the fleets of other nations on the Grand Banks, southeast of the island. In general, however, lack of capital and vessels has prevented Newfoundland fishermen from taking a large share of the fish catch of the Grand Banks.

Parts of the west and northeast of Newfoundland have coniferous forests which supply pulp and paper to the two large mills at Corner Brook and Grand Falls. The only railway in Newfoundland helps to bring pulpwood to these mills and transports the newsprint and pulp to ports when they are ice-free. Many fishermen become loggers in the winter, and the addition of their labor increases the significance of forestry in the provincial economy.

The mineral wealth of Newfoundland has been only partly explored. One of the oldest mines produces iron ore on Bell Island in Conception Bay. Much of the production moves to the coal deposits of Cape Breton Island, to become the basis of the steel industry at Sydney, Nova Scotia. Lead and zinc are mined in central Newfoundland, and copper comes from Tilt Cove on the northeast coast. Newfoundland shares with Quebec the rich iron-ore deposits of the Ungava-Labrador region of the Canadian Shield.

Newfoundland has a coastal population-distribution pattern, due partly to the settlement of the northeast and east coasts by fishing people, and also to the coastal position of many of its resources. Fishing is an obvious attraction, but most of the mines are also coastal, as is one of the two pulp and paper mills. Despite the fact that most of the people live near the ocean, only Avalon Peninsula has a connected coastal road system. Most people of the northeast and south coasts must rely on summer water transport for supplies.

In Nova Scotia the good valley land was occupied in the preceding century, and many of the clearings in the poor soils of the uplands were abandoned in this century. Present agricultural land use is chiefly for hay and pasture as a basis of a livestock and dairy industry. A major agricultural region is the apple and mixed-farming area of the Annapolis-Cornwallis Valley. Although once important as the chief source of export apples in Canada, the Annapolis Valley lost its markets in Britain after 1940. The apple producers reduced the number of fruit trees, turned more to processed apple products for the Canadian markets, and increased other agricultural products, such as poultry.

The forested uplands of Nova Scotia, which look much like parts of New England, supplied timber for shipbuilding in the last century and still are a source of lumber for export and for some pulpwood.

The sheltered harbors of an indented coastline, together with one of the world's good fishing grounds offshore, were long ago natural attractions to Nova Scotia fishermen. As in Newfoundland, most of the fish catch comes from inshore waters along the coast, but many schooners and draggers go out into international water above the Sable Island Banks. An increasing amount of fish is filleted and frozen into blocks for export to the New England fish-stick processing plants.

As in the other Atlantic provinces, mining is not a significant part of the Nova Scotia economy, except for the coalfields of Cape Breton Island. Bituminous coal is obtained in the Sydney-Glace Bay area from seams that dip down under the sea. Although the coal is used locally for the steel industry, production has declined as a result of competition from imported petroleum. Despite tidewater location, high production costs have limited the export value of Cape Breton coal. Nova Scotia is Canada's chief producer of gypsum, for export to the Eastern United States; it also mines salt for the fishing industry.

Nova Scotia has a more balanced economy than does Newfoundland. Both provinces have a coastal population distribution related to local inshore fisheries, export mineral production, and export forestry production. Nova Scotia, however, has a broader agricultural base and a significant development of manufacturing in the large cities like Halifax. Some of this manufacturing is the result of coastal location and is based on imported raw materials, for example, petroleum, sugar, and cacao.

The economic development of New

Figure 5-7   The indented coast of Nova Scotia has only scattered areas of agriculture. The remaining sections of the province are densely forested. The town of Chester (above), on Mahone Bay, is a summer resort. (Courtesy of R.C.A.F.)

Brunswick comes chiefly from its land resources. The long, fertile valley of the St. John River is a major agricultural region of the Atlantic provinces. The green of hay and pasture is the usual summer landscape, and dairying or the sale of livestock products is the main source of agricultural income across southern New Brunswick. The upper St. John Valley specializes in potato production, partly for export, and adjoins the noted Aroostook potato region of Maine. Potato production in New Brunswick is hindered by a lack of processing plants which could ship to the urban markets of central Canada.

About 80 per cent of New Brunswick is under forest cover. Forest production, mainly for pulp and paper, is the leading export from the province. Mills are located at the mouths of rivers emptying along the northeast coast, and in the upper and lower St. John River valley. For many of the subsistence farmers of the northeast coast and part-time fishermen, an additional source of income is obtained by cutting pulpwood in the forest in winter.

The herring fishery of the Bay of Fundy supports several canneries in southern New Brunswick. Many of the fishing villages along the east coast bring in the catch of lobsters from Northumberland Strait. Most of the fishermen are French-speaking Canadians, descendants of the original Acadian French who settled in the Moncton region.

Prince Edward Island is sometimes

called the "garden province." Not only is it small in size, but much of it is cleared and fully used in farmland. The picturesque countryside is green in summer from the rolling fields of hay, pasture, and oats, which contrast with the distinctive red soils. The sale of livestock products, including butter, cheese, and hams, is the chief source of agricultural income. The island is noted for its disease-free seed potatoes, which are exported to the Southern United States and the Caribbean region. Farming is the major occupation of the people, but there are a few fishing villages along the coasts. Charlottetown, the capital, is the only city on the island.

POPULATION   There are only a few cities in the Atlantic provinces; they are manufacturing centers or ports. St. John's, the capital of Newfoundland, has most of the small amount of manufacturing of the island. Corner Brook, on the west coast, has one of the world's largest pulp and paper mills. Halifax, the capital of Nova Scotia, has a number of manufacturing plants using imported raw materials. The city's port functions are important, but it is also the administrative and cultural center of the province. The port of Saint John is the largest city of New Brunswick. Its manufactures are based partially on local agricultural and forestry resources, but also upon imports. Fredericton, the capital, is an administrative and educational city, and also the distribution center of the central St. John River region.

The Atlantic provinces have many characteristics in common with the adjoining New England states. In both regions forests dominate the landscape, agriculture is mainly in narrow strips along the roads, fishing villages dot the indented coast, and mining is of lesser significance in the economy. The main difference is the lack of manufacturing in the Atlantic provinces in comparison with its development

in southern New England. Perhaps the major reason for this difference in economy is that New England is close to the major population densities of the United States, whereas the Atlantic provinces are geographically separated from the heartland of Canada.

GREAT LAKES AND ST. LAWRENCE LOWLAND OF QUEBEC AND ONTARIO

LANDFORMS   The most important lowlands in Canada lie between Lakes Huron, Erie, and Ontario and along the St. Lawrence River. Physiographically, these lowlands have landforms similar to those of the Central Lowlands of the American states south of the Great Lakes. There are also many similarities in the cultural landscape.

The eastern section of the St. Lawrence Lowland, which is mainly in southern Quebec, is much flatter than the western area. The Quebec lowlands were once the bottom of an arm of the sea which extended into North America when the land was depressed at the end of the Ice Age. The chief relief features are the line of Monteregian hills which jut out from the plain east of Mount Royal.

The southern Ontario part of the lowlands is more rolling. The Niagara escarpment rises several hundred feet above the southwest side of Lake Ontario. The Niagara River tumbles over it in scenic Niagara Falls, which have slowly eaten a gorge southward into the escarpment wall. The ridge swings around the west end of Lake Ontario, rising above Hamilton, and extends northward to Bruce Peninsula, west of Georgian Bay. The east-facing escarpment has been crowned by several hundreds of feet of glacial debris north of London, and the resulting rolling upland is the highest part of southwestern Ontario.

CLIMATE Southwestern Ontario has the highest monthly mean summer temperatures of eastern Canada. Many days in the summer will record maximum temperatures above 90°F. The average frost-free period is the second longest in Canada. The flat southwestern corner of Ontario has 175 days without frosts; sections near the lakes have 150 days; and the whole area of the lowlands has at least 125 frost-free days. Because of the long frost-free season of southwestern Ontario, crops can be grown there that are not found in the rest of eastern Canada.

Winters are mild in southwestern Ontario, resembling those of eastern New York State. Severe cold, below zero, is felt only on a few occasions during the usual winter. Average temperatures decrease to the northeast, where the lowlands of Quebec have a January mean of about 10°F. Cold spells, when temperatures drop to −20 or to −30°F, are possible in most winters there. About one-half of the Canadian population, living in southern Ontario and Quebec, experience winter conditions little different from those of the Northeastern United States.

Annual precipitation is fairly evenly distributed seasonally. As in the rest of eastern Canada, annual amounts decrease from east to west, the Quebec lowlands receiving about 40 inches, and southwestern Ontario about 30 inches.

RESOURCES AND ECONOMIC DEVELOPMENT Although manufacturing is the basis of the population concentration and urban development of the Great Lakes and St. Lawrence Lowland, behind it is a well-developed, prosperous agriculture. Much of the region was settled and forest clearing was well begun by about 1850; most of the good land was occupied and cultivated by 1900. With favorable level to rolling topography, a long frost-free period, and sufficient precipitation, a diversified agriculture developed. The urban population increased as a result of manufacturing, and agriculture had the further advantage of a large local market.

Quebec lowland farms are good examples of a mixed-farming economy, with an emphasis on dairying. Most of the land is used for hay, pasture, and oats, but farms may also raise other grains and potatoes. Behind many long, narrow farms lies the woodlot, from which maple syrup and sugar are obtained each spring, and pulpwood may be harvested. The Quebec "habitant" loves his land and cares for it well. His family is generally large, and the farm is meant to supply much of their food. Their main income is derived from the sale of wood products, livestock, or dairy produce. Near the large cities, as in other parts of North America, dairying and truck gardening have become the major agricultural occupations.

Southern Ontario has a greater diversity of agricultural production, and tends to have more cash crops than does Quebec. Over most of the lowlands dairying is the major agricultural occupation. Large dairy barns and circular silos dot the rural landscape. Very little of the original hardwood forest remains. Within southern Ontario are three regions which are somewhat different from the typical hay-pasture-dairy economy. The southwestern part of the province has a climatic advantage over the rest of the lowlands, and can ripen crops two to four weeks earlier. Because corn is a major crop, the area may be considered a part of the North American Corn Belt. Winter wheat is grown in rotation, and soybeans have become a significant crop. Much of Canada's canning vegetable crop is produced there for large canning companies. In land use, this region looks quite similar to many parts of Ohio.

The sandy soils of the central north shore of Lake Erie are Canada's chief tobacco belt. The region supplies about 90 per cent of the country's tobacco and has a surplus for export. Farms are generally small, having an average of about 30 acres in tobacco, but they also raise hay and feed grains. Many of the farmers were Central European immigrants who entered Canada after World War I, working as tenant farmers until they could save enough money to buy their own farms.

The north side of Niagara Peninsula, lying between Lakes Erie and Ontario, is one of Canada's three major fruit areas. At the base of the Niagara escarpment miles of well-kept orchards and vineyards cover the fertile lowlands east of Hamilton. The area is Canada's main source of peaches and grapes, and produces more than half of Canada's pears, cherries, and plums.

Mining is relatively unimportant in the Ontario and Quebec lowlands. The region is underlain by flat-lying sedimentary rocks, dipping gently to the west. Very large reserves of salt are mined from under southwestern Ontario and eastern Michigan. Some of the earliest petroleum wells in North America came into production near Sarnia, Ontario, and the region still produces a little oil and natural gas. Limestone is quarried at several places across the lowlands, and is used for the chemical and fertilizer industries as well as for building material. Although in many of the cities of the lowlands industries are based on mineral resources, these come mainly from the Shield regions of northern Ontario and Quebec rather than from local deposits.

The economic development of southern Quebec and Ontario has been greatly aided by the Great Lakes and St. Lawrence River system, which is a transportation artery and a source of electrical power. The Great Lakes themselves are used by a large fleet of long lake freighters that carry mainly iron ore and wheat down the lakes during the nine-month navigation season. The return journey to the Duluth-Superior or Port Arthur–Fort William ports may bring some coal or many manufactured products. To Canada, the Great Lakes transport route is important in bringing wheat from the southern Prairie Provinces to the flour mills of southern Ontario and Quebec, or to the east-coast grain elevators for export shipment by ocean cargo ships. Because the lake freighters are designed to fit the canal locks, and are not suitable for ocean travel, prairie wheat is carried as far as the eastern ports of Montreal, Sorel, or Quebec and other smaller lower St. Lawrence ports.

The only breaks in through navigation of the Great Lakes are the rapids at Sault Ste. Marie and Niagara Falls. Both of these hazards are bypassed by wide, 30-feet-deep canals. With the opening in 1958 of the St. Lawrence Seaway, with its new locks and canals, and the dredging of the channels in the Detroit and St. Clair Rivers, the Great Lakes became open to ocean liners, providing they were not larger than the canal locks. Although the overseas traffic to Toronto and Hamilton on Lake Ontario was increased, the bulk of the ocean carriers went to American ports on Lakes Erie and Michigan. By making the St. Lawrence River navigable west of Montreal, however, the Seaway made it possible for high-quality iron ore from Quebec-Labrador to move upstream to steel mills of the Lake Erie region.

The Great Lakes–St. Lawrence system is a major source of electric power for parts of the Canadian lowlands. The chief developed sites in southern Ontario are at Niagara Falls and at Cornwall. In both places the power of these international rivers is shared with New York State. Southern Quebec also uses the great volume of the St. Lawrence to produce electric power at Beauharnois, near Montreal. Each of these power plants produces more than 2 million horsepower annually; their electric-power output is thus comparable to that of Hoover or Grand Coulee Dams in the United States.

The lowlands of southern Ontario and Quebec produce about three-quarters of the value of manufacturing in Canada, and the largest share of this industry is in Ontario. This region is, therefore, similar to the heavy manufacturing belt that lies south of the Great Lakes in the United States. Most cities produce a wide range of consumer manufactured goods, similar to the industries of nearby American Midwest cities. In addition, some cities are well known for particular manufactures because they produce the biggest percentage of the Canadian output. These manufactures include iron and steel (Hamilton), automobiles (the Windsor and Toronto region), clothing (Montreal), shoes (Quebec), petroleum refining and chemicals (Sarnia), rubber goods (Kitchener), cereals and machinery (London), nonferous smelting and refining (Montreal), electri-

cal goods and agricultural machinery (Toronto), and wood pulp and paper (Three Rivers). Canadian manufacturing plants resemble those south of the border, and in fact, many Canadian industries are the branch plants of large American companies.

Many Canadian manufactures are protected by tariffs, which keep out foreign imports; nevertheless, manufactured goods, mainly from the United States, constitute the largest item among Canadian imports. Although some raw materials are imported, the bulk of the natural resources upon which the industries of the southern cities depend come from the Canadian Shield region to the north.

POPULATION In the Great Lakes and St. Lawrence Lowland live about half of the population of Canada. Thirty-five of the 62 cities in Canada, each containing more than 30,000 people, are in the region. Greater Montreal, with a population of 2 million, has more people than all of British Columbia. Greater Toronto, also with about 2 million persons, has more inhabitants than the three Maritime provinces. Other cities are scattered across the lowlands. Many of them are located on the

Figure 5-8 City of Quebec, Quebec, the heart of French Canada. (Courtesy of Canadian Government Travel Bureau.)

Great Lakes or the St. Lawrence River, having grown from original settlements along this route, but many Ontario cities are found away from the lakes, where they have excellent road and rail connections. The cities are spaced fairly evenly apart, indicating the relative effect of the surrounding agricultural hinterland upon urban growth. In Ontario and Quebec about 75 per cent of the population live in urban centers. As in the Eastern United States, the large cities are growing rapidly, and "suburban sprawl" is a problem for city planners. Just as the cities from Boston to Washington are merging together, so is the region at the west end of Lake Ontario becoming a large urban complex, growing outward from Toronto, Hamilton, Brantford, Kitchener, and St. Catharines.

CANADIAN SHIELD

LANDFORMS The Canadian Shield is underlain by hard, worn-down rocks of Precambrian geological age which are some of the oldest known on earth. These "roots of mountains" are now mainly rocky, knobby hills, making a fairly level skyline. The region has many rivers, most of which have rapids, and is dotted by myriads of lakes of irregular shape and size.

The Shield extends in a huge semicircle around Hudson Bay. The eastern section has been upwarped in northern Labrador, where alpine peaks and glaciated ridges rise sharply above a fiorded coastline to altitudes of 4,000 to 5,000 feet. Elevations decrease to the south, where the southern rim of the Shield rises steeply 1,000 to 2,000 feet above the gulf and estuary of the St. Lawrence River.

Eastward in Ontario the Shield's southern edge has altitudes of 1,500 feet. The north shore of Lake Superior is steep, rocky, and indented with many sheltered harbors. Because the drainage divide is close to the Great Lakes, the longest rivers flow northward to shallow, cold Hudson Bay. East of Great Slave and Great Bear Lakes the knobby, rock hills again become characteristic, with altitudes of about 1,500 feet. The longest rivers tumble eastward to broad, poorly drained lowlands west of Hudson Bay.

Within the large area of the Shield are lowlands which form distinct physiographic subregions. Two of these, for example, are the Clay Belt and the Lake St. John lowlands. The former was created during the wane of the last Ice Age, when large, glacial Lake Ojibway formed in front of the ice. After the lake finally drained to the north, a gently undulating plain of about 30 million acres covered the old rocks of the Shield. The region was known as the Clay Belt early in this century, before soil surveys were made, and the name has remained, although it is known that clay soils are not common; most of the soils are sandy and there is much peat. Only part of this area is potentially arable, owing to a short frost-free period, the prevalence of poor sandy soils, and inadequate drainage. Although these two important lowlands contain a large share of the population of the Shield region, most of the residents are engaged in some occupation other than farming.

CLIMATE The climate of the Canadian Shield is almost that of Canada since the Shield covers such a large area. The section northwest of Hudson Bay is the coldest part of mainland Canada, having January average monthly temperatures of $-25°F$. Cold, high-pressure air masses may stagnate over this region for many days, and minimum temperatures may drop below $-50°F$. Only the southeastern part of the Shield, from southern Labrador to Lake Superior, has a January average above zero. Although winters are cold,

Figure 5-9 The Canadian Shield from the eastern boundary of the Mackenzie Valley. This view, taken near Yellowknife, Northwest Territories, shows the stunted forest, low rocky hills, and many small lakes that are characteristic of the Shield. (Courtesy of R.C.A.F.)

they do not prevent work from continuing in the mines and forests. Summer temperatures are warmest in the valleys of the southern sections of the Shield, into which warm air masses from the Great Lakes region may penetrate. The Ottawa and Saguenay River valleys have July monthly averages above 65°F, and maxima may rise into the 90s. The northern sections of the Shield, east and west of the cold water of Hudson Bay, have an Arctic climate, no month averaging above 50°F. Most of the southern Shield has 100 days or more free of frosts on the average, but local regions north of Lake Superior appear to be frost pockets where the average frost-free season is less than two months.

Precipitation decreases to the west and north. Southern Labrador and the north shore of the Gulf of St. Lawrence receive about 40 inches of annual precipitation, much of which is snow. The snowy areas of the southern Shield, just north of the population centers of the Quebec lowlands, have become popular for winter sports and resorts. The Northwest Territories receive only 10 inches of precipitation, because much of the cold air that passes over the region contains very little moisture, and there are few topographic barriers to cause the air to rise and cool in summer.

RESOURCES AND ECONOMIC DEVELOPMENT Much of the population in the Shield is engaged in the extractive industries of mining or forestry. Because there are no large consuming centers within the Shield region, the raw materials are transported to the industrial cities to the south.

The Shield is Canada's "storehouse of minerals," upon which, as it is explored and mapped geologically, the optimistic, expanding economy of Canada largely depends. The ancient hard rocks have experienced widespread mineralization, and thousands of centuries of erosion have now exposed many deposits. Only a few minerals of the Shield were exploited early in this century, and new mines are still mainly on the outer edges of the region. A wide range of minerals are now being mined, and roads and railroads have penetrated into the rugged area to bring out the ores. Numerous new place names have appeared on the map of Canada, denoting well-planned, modern communities, very different from the mining boom towns of the last century.

In the eastern section of the Shield a large deposit of high-grade iron ore came into production in 1954. Extending across the Labrador (Newfoundland)-Quebec boundary, the long, narrow belt of iron-bearing rocks contains a reserve of at least 500 million tons of high-quality ore. The deposit became significant because of the approaching depletion of the high-grade Mesabi ores of the United States. Once the large deposit of iron was explored and a railway built to bring out the ore, it became economic to develop other lower-grade ores in the region. Branch rail lines were built and a new railroad and port were constructed west of Seven Islands, thus opening up Canada's leading iron-producing area. Ore is shipped from the Gulf of St. Lawrence ports to the Lake Erie steel mills, to Eastern United States mills, and to northwestern Europe. To the eastward, also near the Gulf of St. Lawrence, North America's largest deposit of titanium came into production in 1950. The ore is processed at Sorel, near Montreal, where there is plentiful electric power.

The oldest mining district is in the central part of the Shield. Copper-nickel ores were being mined at Sudbury in the last century, and Canada's largest gold mines were discovered near the Clay Belt early in this century. Although dozens of gold mines across the Shield have been discovered, have produced, and then have disappeared, the big producers in the cities of Timmins, Larder Lake, and Kirkland Lake still remain. Eastward in Quebec, gold and copper mines support the cities of Noranda and Val d'Or, opened in the 1930s, and the mining frontier has extended still farther to the northeast, where new railroads bring out base metal ores from Chibougamau and Mattagami.

North of Georgian Bay, at Sudbury, several mines account for more than half of the world's supply of nickel; the mines are also Canada's main source of copper, a by-product of the nickel ore. The region produces a large share of the world's platinum and palladium. The brown and barren rock hills around Sudbury, devoid of vegetation because of the fumes from the smelters, make the city one of the less attractive mining centers. Canada's dominance of world nickel production was further emphasized in 1954, when new deposits were discovered at Lynn Lake in northwestern Manitoba, and in 1960, when still another new city, Thompson, grew up near nickel mines in central Manitoba.

The Lake Superior region in the United States was noted for its iron ore, but it was not until the 1940s that high-grade iron ores were mined on the Canadian side of the lake. When ore was discovered beneath the ice of Steep Rock Lake, the lake was drained so that the ore could be mined at the surface in large open pits. This ore is moved by rail to Port Arthur and is transported down the Great Lakes in long lake freighters. West of Sudbury, Canada's largest uranium mines were opened in the early 1950s. A planned city, Elliott Lake, with modern housing, apartments, shopping centers, and curving streets, rose out of the coniferous forests, amid the many lakes and rocky hills of the Shield.

The northwestern part of the Shield was scantily prospected before 1940. The oldest mines, producing copper-gold-zinc, were at Flin Flon, on the south edge of the Shield and directly on the Manitoba-Saskatchewan boundary. The community was given new life when more mines were opened in the region in the late 1950s. Uranium City, north of Lake Athabasca, began producing uranium in 1953, but its importance declined when Elliott Lake deposits were discovered, closer to the market in the United States.

Much of the southern part of the Shield is densely forested, but northward, where the climate is more severe in summer, the trees become smaller and less numerous. This Boreal (Northern Coniferous) Forest is Canada's chief source of pulpwood logs, and also supplies the cities of Ontario and Quebec with lumber. Quebec, with the largest area of Shield forest, produces 50 per cent of Canada's pulp, and Ontario, 30 per cent. Numerous large and modern pulp and paper mills are scattered throughout the southern Shield, often situated at the mouths of rivers down

which logs may be floated and which may afford great available water power. These mills are turning the forests into the newsprint paper that often ranks as Canada's most valuable export, going mainly to the United States. It has been estimated that three out of every five newspapers in the world are printed on Canadian newsprint paper.

Mills are located on the north shore of the St. Lawrence estuary, throughout the Saguenay and Lake St. John lowlands, up the St. Maurice River valley, in the Ottawa River valley, and along the north shore of Lake Superior. Within the Shield only a few of the northward-flowing rivers that have rail transport are utilized. The western part of the Shield, although well forested on its southern edges, is little utilized as yet because it is farther from markets in the Northeastern United States. Although the pulp mills employ relatively few people, the winter cutting of pulpwood is a major source of income for many persons throughout the Shield and is supplemental income for many subsistence farmers.

The Canadian Shield has the greatest amount of developed and potential water power of any physiographic region of

Figure 5-10 The pulp and paper mill at Kapuskasing, Northern Ontario. Logs are floated downstream on the river or brought in by railroad and road. Employees of the mill live along the curving streets of a planned town in the background. Beyond lies the forested plain of the Ontario Clay Belt. (Courtesy of Ontario Department of Travel and Publicity.)

Canada. Its large size and a number of physical advantages account for the water-power resources. Precipitation is adequate throughout the southern sections, a good percentage being snowfall which becomes available in spring runoff. The poorly drained surface of the Shield, with its innumerable, interlocking lakes, supplies excellent reservoirs. The southward-flowing rivers have a notable drop, or fall line, where they spill over the edge of the Shield to the Great Lakes or St. Lawrence Lowland. To these natural advantages must be added the factor of location with regard to the population concentrations of eastern Canada and the power demands of the industries of the St. Lawrence Lowland.

Almost half of the developed water power of Canada is in Quebec, which produces more than 13 million horsepower. The largest single area of developed power in Canada, producing 4 million horsepower, is in the Saguenay Valley. The dams and power plants in the region supply the aluminum plant at Arvida and also several pulp and paper mills. Other concentrations of developed power are along the Manicouagan, Outardes, Betsiamites (Bersimis), St. Maurice, and Ottawa River valleys. Each valley produces about 2 million horsepower from several large dams, and long transmission lines carry the power to the cities of southern Quebec. One of the reasons why it was possible for the economy of Quebec and Ontario to change from an agriculture-dominated to a modern industrial base was the continued availability of relatively cheap power from the rivers of the Shield. The Shield sections of Manitoba and Saskatchewan have many potential power sites but less development, because the mining and pulp industries are not found to the same extent as in Ontario and Quebec. The largest power plants are on the Winnipeg and Nelson Rivers. As Canadian industries and settlement push northward into the Shield, one of the major advantages is the almost unlimited supply of well-dispersed hydroelectric power.

Agricultural settlement has been of less significance in the developing economy of the Shield region. Subsistence farmers moved into the Clay Belt and Lake St. John region in the early part of this century. Most of the Shield communities grew up as mining or forestry centers, but around these, where the character of the land permitted, agriculture sometimes developed. In Quebec, settlement was more compact, centering in parish villages where the community life and the presence of facilities have encouraged the hardy French-Canadian pioneers to remain in the region.

The Shield region has few areas of level to rolling topography, good soils, and favorable climate. These physical requirements are found mainly in some of the former glacial lake bottoms in the southern part of the Shield. The Clay Belt, therefore, has the largest area of potential agricultural land, only a small part of which is occupied. The exact amount of possible agricultural land is not yet known; there may be between 5 and 10 million acres. Because Canada has a surplus of food-producing land closer to the large urban markets, many of the favorable land areas of the level parts of the Shield probably may be best utilized for the production of forests.

POPULATION   Many parts of the Shield are completely unoccupied, and some sections are inhabited by only a few hundred migratory Indians who still follow a hunting and trapping life. Rural population tends to be rather sparse, whereas a high percentage of the settlement is found in urban centers. Since most of the cities are new, they have a pleasant, clean appearance. Stores are modern, and homes are neat and well built. There is little of the frontier character in Shield cities, although they are the "new North" for eastern Canada. These towns and cities are all located along the few major transport lines. Most of the settlements are supported by the extractive industries of mining and forestry, but other towns are transportation hubs or supply centers, or are situated at water-power sites. There are the mining centers of Sudbury, Timmins, and Kirkland Lake, and the transportation cities of Port Arthur–Fort William, Sault Ste. Marie, and North Bay. The largest group of settlements in the Quebec Shield are in the Saguenay–Lake St. John lowlands, and include Chicoutimi, Kenogami, Jonquiere, and Arvida.

The St. Maurice Valley has the industrial city of Shawinigan located on the fall line at the edge of the Shield.

The Shield is "the North" to most eastern Canadians. Much of the construction related to Canada's expanding resource development is taking place there. New mining towns dot the once empty land of lakes and rocky hills; pulp mills harvest the almost endless crop of coniferous forests; new power plants and dams have tamed the wild rivers; farm clearing is slowly pushing back the forests near some of the cities; and clear lakes and cool forests are attracting thousands of summer tourists and visitors from the crowded cities of southern Canada and the nearby United States. Just as Canadians moved westward at the turn of the century, now they are looking northward—toward the riches of the Canadian Shield.

Figure 5-11 The regions of western Canada are largely the results of physical factors, among which the mountain influence is dominant.

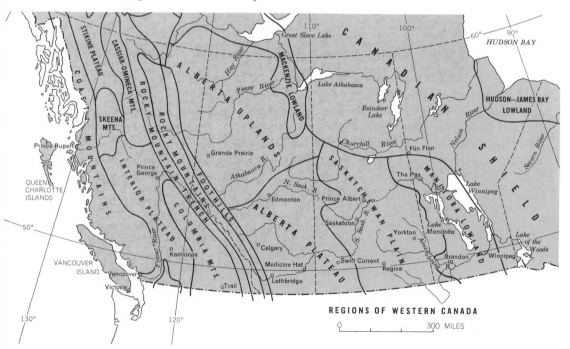

REGIONS OF WESTERN CANADA

INTERIOR PLAINS

LANDFORMS   Although the Interior Plains are frequently dismissed with the word, "flat," several physiographic features break the monotony of the flat areas. Three landform regions across the southern plains increase in elevation from east to west from about 800 feet above sea level near Lake Winnipeg, to above 4,000 feet altitude in the Rocky Mountain Foothills.

The Manitoba lowlands coincide generally with the area covered by ancient glacial Lake Agassiz. The Red River meanders slowly across the deep clay deposits of the former lake bottom. To the northwest a series of old gravel and sand beachlines rise toward an abrupt escarpment which forms the western boundary of the lowlands. Much of the lowlands is still occupied by the three large lakes of southern Manitoba, and the area between the lakes has thinner and stonier soils than the rich farmland of the Red River plain. To the west the gently rolling Saskatchewan plain has some extremely flat areas, such as the former glacial lake area which is now the Regina plain. The northern half of the plain is forested, and numerous lakes have good stocks of fish.

The topography of the Alberta plateau is level to rolling, like that of the Saskatchewan plains, but altitudes are higher. There is no marked escarpment boundary between the two regions. Greater dissection is found in Alberta, where the rivers have cut down 100 to 200 feet into the glacial drift and sedimentary bedrock. Above the plateau rise hills of more resistant rock, such as the Cypress Hills (4,700 feet). To the north the Alberta uplands have more hills than the southern plateau. Drainage is to the northeast, through the Athabasca, Peace, and Hay Rivers toward the Arctic Ocean. The northern part of Alberta is well forested, but lake cover is not as common as in northern Saskatchewan.

CLIMATE   Summer temperatures have little variation over the large area of the Interior Plains. The southern sections have July average monthly temperatures of 66 to 68°F. These averages are similar to those of the Great Lakes region but may not remind one that the searing hot days of the prairies are modified by cool nights. The Red River plain of Manitoba and the land along the South Saskatchewan River in southern Alberta have the longest frost-free period of 120 days, permitting these regions to raise a wide variety of crops. Most of the grassland regions across the Interior Plains have an average frost-free period of more than 100 days, which is generally sufficient for the maturing of grain.

The distribution pattern of winter average monthly temperatures shows a decrease from southwest to northeast. Southwestern Alberta, warmed by occasional chinook winds, has a January average of 10°F. In general, the winter weather conditions of clear, cold days and occasional blizzards are similar to those experienced in the adjoining American states of Montana and North Dakota.

The Interior Plains receive very little annual precipitation, and the amount varies widely from year to year. The highest annual precipitation of 20 inches falls upon southern Manitoba and along the Foothills of southwestern Alberta. Precipitation decreases toward the central plains to a minimum average of about 12 inches along the South Saskatchewan River. Seasonal distribution is more important to agriculture than annual precipitation, and in most areas about 80 per cent falls during the six summer months from April to October.

RESOURCES AND ECONOMIC DEVELOPMENT

Agriculture has been the major occupation of people on the Interior Plains. Although there is a general relationship between vegetation regions, soil zones, and agricultural economies on the Plains, these relationships are breaking down as a result of changing agricultural techniques and practices. Prairie agriculture has become more diversified and can no longer be classified simply as a grain economy.

Cattle ranching is the characteristic form of land use across the brown soils of southwestern Saskatchewan and southeastern Alberta. Although these areas have an adequate frost-free period, precipitation of about 12 inches is marginal for agriculture, particularly when several years may receive below-average rainfall. Ranches may cover 10,000 to 15,000 acres, not all of which, however, is productive grassland. Ranching, including some sheep ranches, is also carried on in the southern Foothills, southwest of Calgary. Although beef cattle are significant across the empty miles of semiarid grasslands, much greater numbers of cattle are supported in the mixed-farming and feed-grain regions near Edmonton and Winnipeg.

Irrigation is making the dry grassland region productive. The common method of irrigation is by small dugouts or earthen dams, which hold groundwater in the valleys and depressions and are useful for stock watering. The large dams and irrigation projects, mainly in southern Alberta, are extending cultivation into lands formerly little used. Sugar beets, alfalfa, and vegetables, the main irrigated crops, support an increasing density of rural population. It is estimated that about 3 million acres could be irrigated in the southern Prairie Provinces, of which about 1 million acres are now served by irrigation projects. Compared with the 60 million acres under cultivation, including fallow, in the region, irrigation acreage remains a small percentage of the total farmland.

Hard spring wheat has been the dominant crop on the dark brown soils, sometimes covering 70 per cent of the cultivated acreage. These large, rectangular wheat fields cover much of south central Saskatchewan. Prairie wheat production is essentially a one-crop economy, the continuation of which is made possible by additions of chemical fertilizers. As a result of mechanization, farms are increasing in size, and at the same time rural farm population is declining. Because neighbors are far apart in this flat, lonesome region, where farms may cover a full section of 640 acres, many farmers have moved to the towns, where they live during the winter. Depending upon weather conditions of the particular summer, the wheat region may produce 400 to 600 million bushels annually. Because little is consumed within the sparsely populated Prairie provinces, the region is one of the world's important food-surplus areas.

The black-soil zone has smaller amounts of wheat and more feed grains for increasing numbers of livestock. Precipitation is more effective in the black-soil zone, as is indicated by the parkland vegetation of tall grasses and trees. The soil is deep and naturally fertile. Farmhouses are not so far apart as in the wheat regions, and barns for the livestock are characteristic of the rural landscape. Numerous small villages, with one or two blocks of wooden stores, are dispersed at fairly regular intervals throughout this region of mixed-farming economy.

The gray soils of the forested area of the Prairie Provinces are being penetrated

Figure 5-12   Hard Alberta wheat ripening under a September sun. (Courtesy of H. Pollard.)

slowly. Poorer soils, time and cost of clearing, and lack of transportation have all been factors in delaying settlement. The northern fringe of agriculture trends northwestward across the Interior Plains from Lake Winnipeg to the Peace River area of British Columbia. Land use generally emphasizes feed-grain and pasture production, and some legume seed. The line marking the northern limit of agricultural settlement was fairly well defined by about 1940, and only a little new clearing occurred in the next twenty years. The northern fringe is therefore well-established agriculture with permanent buildings; it has little of the pioneer atmosphere of forty years ago.

The sedimentary rocks of the Plains yield types of minerals different from the old hard rocks of the Shield. Petroleum and natural gas are the most spectacular of the mineral resources. Although several small fields had been discovered near Calgary prior to World War II, the first big fields were found in the Edmonton area in 1947–1948. Soon separate pipelines brought this oil and natural gas to southern Ontario and southern British Columbia and the adjoining Northwest states. Although a small petrochemical industry grew up at Edmonton and a great deal of sulfur became available by extraction from the natural gas, the large amount of power and fuel has not yet

attracted industries away from the industrial heartland of southern Ontario.

Exploration for petroleum and natural gas fields continues; new fields have been discovered to the west and northwest of Edmonton and across southern Saskatchewan. Known reserves of more than 4 billion barrels of petroleum assure production for many years for a Canadian and export market. Further reserves are available to the north in the Athabasca Tar Sands. These sands, which cover about 20,000 square miles along the Athabasca River around Fort McMurray, contain a petroleum reserve estimated at about 200 billion barrels—about equal to the world's present known reserves of liquid petroleum. Although the petroleum has been separated from the sand experimentally, large-scale production awaits better marketing conditions.

Southern Alberta and Saskatchewan have coal reserves of 75 billion tons, chiefly of bituminous grade. Production is minor, however, because the coal is too far from the markets of southern Ontario and locally can hardly compete with petroleum and natural gas. The discovery of large deposits of potash beneath southern Saskatchewan may balance a declining coal-mining economy.

Because of the availability of local power sources, the character of the Plains region is changing from a dominant agri-

cultural economy to one in which manufacturing is more significant. Although
industries related to petroleum refining
and natural gas purification are important, the most valuable industries are still
those related to the region's agricultural
production. Meat-packing plants, flour
and feed mills, and butter factories are
still major employers in each of the large
cities.

POPULATION   Despite   expanding   resources, the Interior Plains remain
sparsely populated, and large areas in the
north are empty. Most of the agricultural
regions average 5 to 8 persons per square
mile, and there are only a few large cities.
Winnipeg, with one-third of the people of
Manitoba, is the largest city of the Plains
and has a wide range of manufacturing
industries. Its strategic position in the
center of southern Canada, south of Lake
Winnipeg, brings all east-west transport
lines through it. Edmonton and Calgary
are headquarters of the Alberta oil industry, but also have sound agricultural
hinterlands. Regina and Saskatoon, the
chief cities of Saskatchewan, are supply-
service centers for the grain-growing
plains.

CORDILLERA OF BRITISH
COLUMBIA AND YUKON

LANDFORMS   The Cordilleran mountain
system in British Columbia is compressed
into a width of about 600 miles of spectacular, rugged grandeur. There are high
mountains on the east, rising abruptly
above the plains, plateaus in the central
sections, and another line of mountains
along the fiorded west coast.

The Rocky Mountains are the eastern
range of the Cordillera; they form a continuous wall of sharp peaks and ridges
broken by only a few passes. Some of the

most spectacular mountain scenery in
North America is found in Banff and
Jasper National Parks in the Rockies.
Several peaks have altitudes of over
10,000 feet, the highest being Mt. Robson
(12,972 feet). The Rocky Mountains decrease in altitude northward and terminate in the broad plain of the Liard River
in northeastern British Columbia. Another mountain system, the Mackenzie
Mountains, an offset to the northeast,
arcs along the Yukon–Northwest Territories boundary, and still another range
rises above the Mackenzie River delta
and extends westward along the Arctic
coast to become the Brooks Range of
Alaska.

The western boundary of the Rocky
Mountains   is   the   Rocky   Mountain
Trench, one of this continent's outstanding
topographic features. The Trench is a linear, flat-bottomed valley some 1,200 miles
in length, extending from south of Flathead Lake, Montana, to the Liard Valley
of southern Yukon. Although the northern
part of this long valley is little used, it may
some day be a significant through-route
extending   southeast-northwest   through
the mountain masses of the Cordillera.

West of the Trench lie two high mountain systems that are distinct from the
Rockies.   In   the   south   the   Columbia
Mountain system consists of four linear,
sharp-crested ranges, and to the north,
the slightly lower, more rounded, Cassiar-
Omineca Mountains extend into Yukon
Territory. The Interior Plateau of British
Columbia is narrow and entrenched by
the Fraser and Thompson Rivers to the
south, but broadens into a rolling upland
to the north. The Yukon Plateau, about
2,000 feet above sea level, is incised by
broad, flat-bottomed valleys and ringed
by high mountains on the southwest, east,
and north. The ice-capped St. Elias Mountains   to   the   southwest   rise   above   the

Figure 5-13 The Rocky Mountain Trench is a 1,200-mile-long trough in the Cordillera. In the picture the Trench is occupied by the Fraser River flowing northward. The wall of the Rocky Mountains rises on the right (east) and the Cariboo Mountains of the Columbia System on the left. (Courtesy of Government of British Columbia.)

Alaska coast and are crowned by the highest mountain in Canada, Mt. Logan (19,850 feet).

The Coast Mountains rise in rows of jagged peaks in southwestern British Columbia. Several peaks are above 9,000 feet (Mt. Waddington, 13,260 feet), and tower over an indented, fiorded coast,

fronted by a forested raised-terrace foreland. The Coast Mountains are less of a wall to the north, where they are broken by the Skeena, Nass, and Stikine Rivers, but there are more extensive ice fields on the northern ranges. The Insular Mountains are submerged ranges off the west coast of British Columbia in Vancouver

Island and the Queen Charlotte Islands. This mountain system continues northward in the many rugged islands off the panhandle of Alaska.

CLIMATE Because the Cordillera of British Columbia and Yukon has an area equal to that of the Western and Pacific Coast states, a wide variety of climates can be expected. Climates range from that of the mildest part of Canada in the winter, in southwestern British Columbia, to the cold Arctic Coast of northern Yukon Territory. The area has the wettest station in Canada, on western Vancouver Island, where an average annual precipitation of 250 inches has been recorded, and it has the driest station in southern Canada only 250 miles eastward in the Interior Plateau.

Winters are mild on the coast, averaging about 35°F in January, but cold temperatures are common inland, where the Interior Plateau and linear valleys are open to cold air masses from the north. The marine influence maintains cool summers in the coastal strip, but the southern-interior valleys can become quite hot. Although summers are slightly cooler in the central and northern valleys there are no wide regional differences like those that exist in winter. In summer temperature varies more noticeably with altitude than with latitude.

Winter precipitation is heavy on the exposed west coast, which is struck by storms from the North Pacific. Most coastal stations average 100 inches or more of rainfall annually. A dry summer is characteristic of the southern coastal sections which come under the protective high-pressure ridges from northern California. Because of the rain-shadow effect of the Coast Mountains, interior British Columbia and Yukon receive little precipitation, except on the western slopes of mountains.

RESOURCES AND ECONOMIC DEVELOPMENT
Forestry is the most valuable industry of the Cordilleran region. The mild, wet climate of the coast section has endowed the area with some of the world's largest trees. The lumber economy which characterizes Washington and Oregon extends northward into British Columbia. The forests of Douglas fir, western cedar, and hemlock are rapidly being cut, making the region one of the world's major sources of export lumber. Prior to 1940 most of the industry and its large sawmills were concentrated on eastern Vancouver Island and the southwestern coast near the Fraser River. By 1960, however, almost half of the provincial lumber was being cut from the smaller trees of the interior forests, north of Kamloops and around Prince George. In the meantime a pulp and paper industry expanded on the coast, partially using former waste material from the lumber industry and thus forming part of an integrated forest economy. Many of the coastal forest products move by water transport to the Eastern United States, whereas the interior lumber is shipped to the Prairies and eastern Canada by rail.

Mining is characteristic of most mountainous areas, and the Canadian Cordillera has revealed some of its mineralization. At Kimberley, in southeastern British Columbia, one of the world's largest lead-zinc-silver mines has produced as much as 10 per cent of the world's lead. Concentrates from this big mine are transported by rail to the smelter and refinery at Trail, on the Columbia River, near hydroelectric power. Other mines in the southeast produce a variety of base metals for the Trail smelter. Copper and iron are the major minerals of southwestern British Columbia, both produced for export to Japan.

The famous Klondike gold rush of 1898 was the reason for the establishment of

Yukon Territory in the Canadian Northwest. Goldseekers moved northward along the Inside Passage steamer route to Skagway, Alaska, and climbed through passes in the Coast Mountains to reach the headwaters of the Yukon River. Within a decade, however, most of the easily accessible gold had been found in the Dawson City region, and the boom was over. Although gold-seeking dredges still operate along the Klondike River and tributaries, greater mineral wealth comes from rich silver-lead deposits near Mayo. The building of the wartime Alaska Highway across southern Yukon, and a later Canadian government road north to Mayo and Dawson, opened up new areas for prospecting. One of the results was an asbestos mine in northern British Columbia and Canada's largest tungsten mine in southeastern Yukon.

Although fishing is the reason for many small coastal settlements, most of the canneries have concentrated near the mouth of the Fraser River. As in the Panhandle of Alaska, several species of salmon are the most valuable fish. Starting in midsummer in Alaska, and by late summer in southern British Columbia, the salmon arrive off the river mouths to begin their migration upstream to spawning grounds. The Nass, Skeena, and particularly the Fraser, which has the largest drainage basin, are the chief salmon rivers. The increased use of packer vessels which transfer fish from the specialized fishing boats has caused the closing of many coastal canneries, and the processing industry has increased in importance near the world-shipping facilities of Vancouver.

Halibut fishing ranks second to salmon. The halibut fishery is shared with the United States, although the fish are caught in winter around the Canadian Queen Charlotte Islands. The American fishing fleet uses Seattle as a base; Canadian vessels come from Vancouver or Prince Rupert. Whereas most salmon is marketed in canned form, halibut is sold either as fresh or frozen fish.

Water power is abundant. It is not surprising that British Columbia, a mountainous province with heavy rainfall on the coast, should have a potential water power larger than that of the state of Washington. Because rainfall is seasonal and many of the coastal rivers are short, storage of water is everywhere a major problem. Much of the developed power is in southwestern British Columbia, where most of the people and industries are concentrated, but potential power sites are well scattered throughout the province. Near the central west coast, the headwaters of the Nechako, a tributary of the Fraser River, were dammed and diverted through the Coast Mountains by tunnel, to produce hydroelectric power for a large aluminum smelter built at tidewater at Kitimat. Similar diversions of the Yukon River headwaters to the heads of coastal fiords are possible in northwestern British Columbia and Panhandle Alaska, but action has been delayed by the political problems related to international use of this water. Similar political controversies complicated the development of storage, or power, dams on the headwaters of the Columbia River in southeastern British Columbia. Such storage of Canadian water would increase power generation at hydroplants downstream on the Columbia River in the state of Washington, but treaty agreement as to the use of, and payment for, this international water was delayed by Canada. In the meantime, the province of British Columbia began the development of the water power of the Peace River in northeastern British Columbia.

Agriculture is confined to the narrow valleys; less than 1 per cent of British Columbia is under cultivation, and probably less than 5 per cent is arable for future agriculture. Half of the cultivated land is in the southwest, across the Fraser River delta and along the east coast of Vancouver Island. In the southern interior the Okanagan Valley uses irrigation to produce most of Canada's apricots and more than half of its apples, some of which are exported. This narrow valley ranks second to the Niagara Peninsula of Ontario as Canada's other source of cherries, peaches, and pears. The largest areas of level to rolling land and potential arable land are across the railway belt of central British Columbia, centering on Prince George, and in the well-established grain farms of the Peace River area east of the Rockies. Both of these regions, however, have problems of a short frost-free season.

Agriculture was carried on in the valleys of Yukon Territory during the gold-rush days at the turn of the century. It declined in importance, however, following the decrease in population when gold production declined. Gardening is still common in each of the small settlements, and vegetables grow well during the long hours of summer daylight.

POPULATION   British Columbia's population increase, by percentage, has been among the highest in the Canadian provinces, like the population influx to the Western states of the United States. Most people have concentrated in the southwestern corner, where they enjoy a mild climate and can utilize good agricultural land, nearby forest resources, fisheries, and some excellent ports. Half of the province's 1.7 million people (1963) are

Figure 5-14   Looking north over Vancouver, British Columbia. The agricultural lands of the Fraser River delta are in the foreground. The city is in the center, and the sheltered harbor is in the upper right. (Courtesy of Government of British Columbia.)

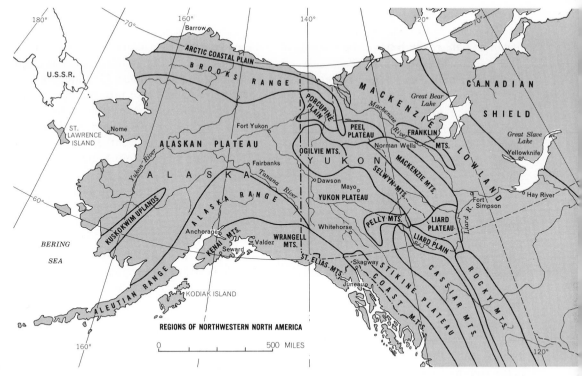

Figure 5-15   The rough topography of the Yukon Territory and Alaska tends to make many elongated regions of relatively small areas. Such topography is a hindrance to the development of transportation.

in the Greater Vancouver area, which includes New Westminster on the Fraser River. The group of cities produce a wide range of manufactured products, of which those related to wood are most valuable. The second city of the province, and the capital, is Victoria on southern Vancouver Island. Interior cities are smaller, and their urban functions are mainly related to one particular local resource.

Although the Yukon Territory had 30,000 people at the turn of the century, the population was down to about 5,000 in 1940. Almost one-half of the present population of about 14,000 is located in or near the crossroads town and Army base of Whitehorse, on the Alaska Highway and at the head of the rail from Skag-

way, Alaska. The historic mining center of Dawson is almost a ghost town with a population of less than 1,000.

NORTHWEST TERRITORIES

LANDFORMS   Because the area of the Northwest Territories is one-third of Canada, one might expect to find a variety of landforms (Figure 5-15). The Territories have consisted of three administrative districts, but the federal government plans to raise the status of Mackenzie District to that of a separate Territory. This new Territory will include the Mackenzie River valley, which now has most of the settlements. The Mackenzie lowlands consist of a flat, poorly drained plain of glacial deposition, into which the wide Mackenzie River has cut down about 100 to 200 feet. The bare rocky hills of the Canadian Shield rise steeply on the east side of Great Bear and Great Slave Lakes. West and northwest of Hudson Bay poorly drained, lake-dotted lowlands, with a mixture of water-laid and glacial-drift deposits, extend inland, mantling or subduing the rocky hills of the Canadian Shield.

The Arctic Islands have no uniformity of landforms. The upwarped, eroded edge of eastern Baffin Island rises to ice-capped peaks of 7,000 to 8,000 feet, and similar altitudes, the highest of eastern North America, are reported in the linear, folded mountains of northern Ellesmere Island. To the westward some of the islands are barren plateaus which sometimes rise directly from the sea. In the central Arctic Islands flat, lake-covered lowlands rise a few hundred feet above sloping ancient beach ridges. The western and northwestern islands are hilly, but altitudes seldom exceed 2,000 feet.

CLIMATE   Although the Northwest Territories are cold in winter, there are wide differences in summer conditions. The Mackenzie River valley is in the subarctic climatic zone, with relatively short but warm summers, whereas the rest of the Territories have an Arctic climate, with no summers. Although winters are cold in both climate regions, the coldest monthly averages are northwest of Hudson Bay on the mainland, and in the far northern islands. The greatest extremes of cold are recorded in the subarctic Mackenzie Valley, where −60 to −70°F are known in many winters. At the coastal weather stations the Arctic Islands are moderated by the cold water around them and have no recorded temperatures below −63°F.

In summer the subarctic Mackenzie Valley warms up; its July monthly averages of 60°F are equal to those experienced much farther south in the Clay Belt of Ontario and Quebec. Daytime temperatures frequently rise into the 80s. In the Arctic region to the northeast, however, July averages remain under 50°F. Although the coastal weather stations may be receiving twenty-four hours of daylight in early July, they are usually cooled by the ice floes which are still melting in the channels of the Arctic Islands. Most of the Territories receive less than 10 inches of annual precipitation. Weather stations on the far-northern islands have recorded the lowest annual precipitation figures in Canada, several stations having under 5 inches.

Ice conditions greatly influence accessibility. Sea ice freezes along the shores of the Canadian mainland and Arctic Islands in early September in the north, and by about early November around Hudson Bay. The region is then closed to sea transport, and planes cannot land on the lakes until the ice thickens. Harbor ice begins to break up in late June in Hudson Bay, and progressively northward until some of the northern islands have open water by early August. Air photos indicate that the sea ice around the northwestern islands remains throughout the whole summer, despite the continuous daylight during June and July.

RESOURCES AND ECONOMIC ACTIVITIES   Most of the developed resources of the Northwest Territories and the future potential are in the Mackenzie River valley. Trading posts were established along the Mackenzie River in the nineteenth century, and fur trapping became the basic livelihood of the native Indian population. Although trapping is still significant to the Indians, mining supports many of the white inhabitants. Yellowknife, on the rocky shore of Great Slave Lake, is the largest town in Mackenzie District and is a gold-mining community. A lead-zinc deposit is being developed near Pine Point, south of Great Slave Lake. Petroleum is the only mineral of significance produced from the Mackenzie lowland region. Many of the wells are capped, and present production at Norman Wells supplies only the small local market of the Mackenzie Valley.

Other resources of the Territories are less significant in the Canadian economy, but may play a greater role in future development. There are agricultural lands of limited quality in many parts of the Mackenzie River valley, but cultivated land totals only a few hundred acres. Soils frequently need drainage and are troubled by permafrost near the surface. At present the land is not being settled while better land is still available farther south in Canada.

Commercial fishing started in Great Slave Lake in 1946, and a large but controlled harvest of lake trout and whitefish is taken out each year. Fish are caught in both summer and winter (through holes in the ice) and shipped in refrigerated transport to southern Canadian cities and to the Midwest United States.

Towns such as Yellowknife, Inuvik, and Hay River have modern frame homes and the usual urban facilities and services, but other settlements are small villages, with a fur-trading store and the homes of government officials—police, weather observers, and radio operators.

The Arctic region in northeastern Canada is located east and west of Hudson Bay, and includes all the Arctic Islands. There are few developed resources and a very limited resource potential. In this treeless region all lumber for houses must be imported. There is no agriculture; the scour of glacial ice left behind bare rock

Figure 5-16 The jagged peaks of the Mackenzie Mountains separate Yukon Territory and Mackenzie District, Northwest Territories. The ranges are very wide and are a difficult barrier to overland travel. (Courtesy of R.C.A.F.)

ridges, and soils in the valleys are mainly sands and gravels containing little organic matter. Although Hudson Bay appears to have no fish in significant numbers, some of the small streams have high-quality Arctic char, a kind of salmon, which is exported by Eskimo cooperative fishing groups.

Mineral resources are the hope for the future. The region has a great deal of bare rock exposed at the surface, and much of it is the same type of old Precambrian rocks which are mineralized in many places in southern parts of the Shield. Although mineralization has been reported from several locations in Arctic Canada, the nickel mine at Rankin Inlet, on the west side of Hudson Bay, was the only one to be developed. The northwestern Arctic Islands are underlain by sedimentary rock basins which may have an oil potential. The main exported resource of the Arctic region has been white fox furs. The Arctic, or white, fox, one of the few furbearers living north of the tree line, is trapped by Eskimos. Since fur production fluctuates greatly from year to year, the federal government has encouraged the production of handicrafts, which have become a major source of Eskimo income.

POPULATION   All but a few hundred of the 10,000 white inhabitants of the Northwest Territories live in the Mackenzie River valley. The native inhabitants of the Territories are Indians and Eskimos. The tree line, which marks a climatic line dividing Arctic from subarctic, is also a cultural line separating Indians and Eskimos. Eskimos live north of the tree line across the mainland of Arctic Canada, including northern Quebec and Labrador, and inhabit the coasts of the southern group of Arctic Islands. They number about 11,000 persons, and are wards of the federal government.

Wide differences in the level of culture and in the acceptance of white civilization are found among Eskimos. Those living near the delta mouth of the Mackenzie River are modern, well-equipped trap-

Figure 5-17 An Eskimo summer camp consists of tents on the rocky beach at Cape Dorset, Baffin Island. The canvas tents are obtained from the trader; each holds one family. (Courtesy of J. L. Robinson.)

pers, and a few of them herd reindeer; other Eskimos are wage earners at air bases like that at Frobisher Bay. Some Eskimos, for example, those in the interior of the Central Arctic near Boothia peninsula, still live chiefly off the caribou on the land and the seals of the sea as their forefathers used to do.

GREENLAND

The Danish county of Greenland is the largest of the Arctic Islands off the mainland of North America. Its area of about 840,000 square miles is equal to all of the Northeastern and Great Lakes states from New England to Nebraska, or is as large as Mexico. Greenland is only 12 miles from Ellesmere Island, the northeastern Canadian island, and is inhabited by the same Eskimo stocks that migrated across northern Canada, reaching Greenland more than one thousand years ago. Greenland became of significance to the world in the modern air age. Its geographic position in the north central part of the North Atlantic Ocean placed the ice-covered island on the Great Circle air routes between Scandinavia and central North America.

LANDFORMS

About 82 per cent of Greenland is covered by a thick icecap. Alpine ridges and sharp peaks of high mountains rise abruptly above the sea along the fiorded, indented, west and east coasts, reaching altitudes of 6,000 feet on the west and 10,000 feet on the east. Behind the old Precambrian rock mountains, and frequently spilling through and around them in beautiful, twisting glaciers, lies the Greenland icecap. It fills an interior basin, the surface of which has two flattened domes arching above the coastal mountains to altitudes of about 10,000 feet. Because soundings indicate that the icecap is about 10,000 feet thick in the north central section, the land base of northern Greenland may be below sea level and may consist of two or more islands. The thickness of the ice over southern Greenland is about 6,000 feet. Although icebergs break off from Greenland glaciers in many places around the coast, the greatest number enter the sea in Melville Bay, in the northern section of the west coast.

The largest areas of low to rolling land are in northern Greenland. These lake-covered lowlands are ice-free, since precipitation is apparently not sufficient to result in an accumulation of snow. The other major ice-free section, where most Greenlanders and Danes live, is on the southwest and west central coast.

CLIMATE

Greenland has an Arctic climate, because of its northerly latitude and the cooling effect of the large mass of ice. In addition, the coasts of east and north Greenland are bathed by cold, ice-covered water discharging from the Arctic Ocean. In contrast, however, the southwestern coast has warmer water offshore, derived from the North Atlantic Drift (Gulf Stream), which moderates the climate. Some harbors of the southwest remain ice-free throughout the winter, and in the summer the small valleys become warm enough for vegetables to grow in the open, and many sheep and some goats are grazed. With such comparatively favorable climatic conditions, it is not surprising that most of the population live in the sheltered subarctic valleys of the southwestern coast.

The northward-moving current off the southwest coast warmed noticeably after about 1930. This increase in temperature is probably related to the general warming of the Arctic regions that became apparent after 1920. To the Greenlander the warmer waters have brought increasing numbers of northward-migrating codfish, which have become the basis of a new fishing industry.

RESOURCES AND ECONOMIC ACTIVITIES

Modern Greenlanders have changed greatly from their Eskimo forefathers who depended upon seals, white whales, walrus, and narwhales for food. Many Greenlanders are commercial fishermen or work on fishing vessels that come from Denmark. Fishing is carried on fairly close to shore because of their small boats; the kayak has almost disappeared and has been replaced by motorboats and fishing cutters. Shrimp fishing grounds were located during World War II, and canned shrimp is now a major export of Greenland.

A thousand years ago Norse settlers attempted agriculture in the valleys of southwestern Greenland; in recent years agriculture has revived, particularly in the Julianehaab district. There are as many sheep as there are people in Greenland, and a surplus of meat and wool for export; there are a few head of cattle and many chickens. Vegetables and grasses grow well. However, much food is still imported from Denmark.

Greenland's mountains may contain minerals, but little is known about the detailed geology. Although mineralization has been reported from several places, only two products, cryolite and lead, have proved valuable enough for development. The government-controlled mine at Ivigtut, in the southwest, has been the world's major source of the very strategic mineral, cryolite, which is used in the production of

Figure 5-18 The old settlement of Narssaq, Greenland. The winter water duct for the slaughterhouse is shown near the foot of the mountain. (Courtesy of Danish Information Office.)

aluminum. Lead is mined on the inhospitable east coast, north of Scoresby Sound. Greenland also produces coal for local needs from Disko Island.

The large area of Greenland has only about 30,000 people. Most of the inhabitants, though of Eskimo origin, have a strong mixture of Danish blood and now call themselves Greenlanders. Most people live in small villages, usually near the open southwest coast for the sake of sealing and fishing, but occasionally at the heads of the fiords. Godthaab, with a population of 3,000, is the largest settlement and the main administrative center. Frederikshaab is a fishing port, and Egedesminde is a local commercial settlement.

Two smaller settlements of more primi-

tive peoples are located outside of the main concentration on the west coast. To the northwest, around Thule, are Eskimo hunters who are quite similar to some of the Eskimos of the Canadian Arctic. They are cut off from the rest of settled Greenland by the icecap which occupies the coastal area along Melville Bay, but are near a large American air base and research station. East Greenland has had a few Eskimo inhabitants from time to time, but the area is poorly endowed with game resources and is icebound most of the year. Resettlement of the Angmagssalik region, south of the central area, and at Scoresbysund, was successful, and east Greenland now has about 1,500 persons. The north and northeast coasts of Greenland are unoccupied.

IN PERSPECTIVE

NORTHERN NORTH AMERICA, LAND OF PROGRESS

North America, north of the coterminous United States, is a vast extent of land, in general only sparsely populated. Its area is over 1.3 times that of the continent of Europe, but the region has only about 4 per cent of the population of Europe although the two land masses are in approximately the same latitudes.

Canada is a nation of great potential. Vast plains areas, when used more intensively, will produce much larger grain and pasture crops. Range lands that are now scarcely used will, in the future, become sources of large meat supplies. In general, the mineral wealth of Canada is undeveloped; some of the area has not been explored in detail. One of the world's largest forest areas extends across the northern part of the provinces and the southern part of the territories. Undeveloped power sites offer great future possibilities for producing hydroelectric power.

In spite of its northern location and climatic handicaps, Canada is potentially one of the world's great industrial as well as agricultural nations.

The Canadian–United States boundary is the longest common boundary line between two nations in the world. These two nations have lived as neighbors for more than 150 years without resorting to war, and today there are no military forts along their boundaries. Many problems have arisen that were not easy to settle, and yet the good judgment of the respective governments has triumphed, and the bonds of peace have not been broken. Future relations between Canada and the United States should be characterized by mutual respect, understanding, and increased cooperation. In the world of today Canada and the United States can prove that peace is not an impossible ideal.

Greenland, the world's largest island, is largely ice-covered. Its small native population has been protected and governed wisely by Denmark. Under present conditions the future development of the island can only continue the present trend.

All parts of northern North America have been fortunate in their political development. Canada, Denmark, and the United States work together in harmony and for the mutual benefit of all.

SELECTED REFERENCES

The Canada Year Book, Bureau of Statistics, Department of Trade and Commerce, Ottawa.

The Canada Year Book, *issued annually, is the standard source of factual and statistical information about Canada. In addition to annual production statistics, each issue has several special articles on current Canadian developments. A condensed, and semipopular, version of the* Year Book, The Canadian Handbook, *is also issued annually.*

Putnam, D. F. (ed.): *Canadian Regions*, J. M. Dent & Sons (Canada), Ltd., Don Mills, Ontario, 1956.

This standard text for geography courses on Canada in Canadian universities is organized by provinces. The "regions" discussed are all smaller than the provincial units. The text is an excellent source of information on the physical geography patterns in Canada.

Somme, A.: *A Geography of Norden*, Oslo, 1960. *Chapter 8, p. 140, of this text deals with Greenland, and is one of the best, recent sources on the Danish island. A bibliography at the end of the text refers to further information.*

Taylor, G.: *Canada: A Study of Cool Continental Environments*, Methuen & Co., Ltd., Toronto, 1950.

This text is out of date for factual information related to recent resource developments in Canada, but is recommended for interesting, provocative reading. Dr. Taylor stresses the compelling environmental influences which have operated in Canadian settlement history. The organization is through a study of twenty "natural" regions.

Tomkins, G. S., and T. L. Hills: *Canada: A Regional Geography*, W. J. Gage Limited, Scarborough, Ontario, 1962.

This text is recommended for use in high schools, and will be of value to students planning to become geography teachers. The "regions" of Canada are the same as those discussed in this chapter. The exercises and work assignments at the end of each chapter are different and good.

chapter 6
MIDDLE AMERICA

Figure 6-1   The outstanding topographic feature of Middle America is the mountain back-bone with its associated volcanoes. The coastal plains, with the exception of the Yucatan Peninsula, are usually narrow. The larger cities are located in the higher valleys or on the plateaus where the climate is more suitable for comfortable living.

THE LOCATION OF MIDDLE AMERICA HAS favored close relationships between that area and the United States. The United States buys a large majority of the region's products and supplies the greatest part of its imports. Middle American countries are important exporters of sugar, coffee, tobacco, bananas, and tropical fruits, as well as petroleum, antimony, silver, and other minerals, and in turn they buy textiles, petroleum products, automobiles, machinery, and a host of other goods. The region is increasingly attractive to tourists. On islands and mainland guests find interesting scenery, sun and warmth during winter months, and the opportunity of becoming acquainted with varied cultures and ways of life very different from those of the United States. In some countries modern hotels and amusement places have been built to attract a wealthy clientele. Economical accommodations are also available, especially outside the major resort areas. Mexico, the Virgin Islands, Jamaica, Puerto Rico, and the Bahamas are among the countries that derive a substantial income from tourists and other visitors.

The peoples of Middle America include American Indians, of both pure and mixed blood, Spanish, English, French, Dutch, and other Europeans. In particular mainland localities and on many Caribbean islands, Negroes and mulattoes predominate. Over 220,000 people from India live in Trinidad.

In the seventeenth and eighteenth centuries European powers fought great naval battles in the Caribbean region. Caribbean waters were crossed by the galleons carrying treasure to Spain, and the buccaneers who lurked in the region had Port Royal, Jamaica, and certain of the Bahama Islands among their home ports. During the colonial period, New Englanders traded with the Caribbean islands, exchanging dried fish, salt, and wood products for sugar, molasses, and rum. In the days before artificial refrigeration, ice cut on the lakes of wintry New England was eagerly welcomed by the tropical sugar planters.

During the nineteenth century men from the United States had many and varied connections with Middle America. The Gold Rush to California took some gold hunters over the Panama and Nicaragua routes. American soldiers of fortune helped in, and caused, insurrections in Cuba, Mexico, and Central America. More significant was economic penetration of the area by miners, sugar planters, banana growers, and other enterprising persons. After 1898, as a result of the Spanish-American War, Cuba became independent, and Spain ceded Puerto Rico to the United States. In the early years of this century the digging of the Panama Canal and the purchase of the Virgin Islands from Denmark were events of special importance to this country. Recently, the establishment of a communist government in Cuba has caused great concern.

Middle America has a land area approximately one-third of that of the United States. It comprises Mexico, the Central American countries, and the islands of the West Indies. Included are twelve independent nations, and colonies or possessions of the United Kingdom, France, Netherlands, and the United States. Environmental, racial, and cultural contrasts are tremendous, both within and among these major political divisions, yet elements of similarity are sufficient to give a geographic unity to the area as a whole.

PHYSICAL SETTING
RELIEF FEATURES

The dominant surface feature of Middle America is the highland backbone and its associated volcanoes. Bordering coastal lowlands are usually narrow. A major exception is the low, featureless plain of the Yucatan Peninsula, which is related geologically to flat areas underlain by limestone in Cuba, Florida, and the Bahamas. Inland from this peninsula, the northwest-southeast trending structures of the Mexican highlands bend eastward through southern Mexico, Guatemala, Honduras, and northern Nicaragua, to dip under the Caribbean and reappear in the Greater Antilles. A second range extends to the southeast through Central America and into northwestern Colombia, where it is separated from the Andean system by the lowlands of the Atrato River.

Three interoceanic passes breach the highlands. One crosses the 130-mile-wide Mexican Isthmus of Tehuantepec at a maximum elevation of 800 feet. A second is part of a structural depression running diagonally through Nicaragua from Greytown to the Gulf of Fonseca. It follows the Rio San Juan to Lake Nicaragua, which has an elevation of a little over 100 feet above the Pacific only 17 miles away. The third route is followed by the Panama Canal. All three breaches, as well as the Atrato lowlands of Colombia, have been crossing places since colonial times, but the Panama route has been the most important. There is another possible route through Honduras. Enlarging and deepening the present Panama Canal to sea level is also being considered.

Mexico north of Tehuantepec is essentially a plateau, bordered on the west by the wide and rugged Sierra Madre Occidental, with peaks over 12,000 feet high, and on the east by the lower, more easily traversed Sierra Madre Oriental. The plateau surface is broken by mesas, mountain ranges, and alluvium-filled basins. It is highest, 5,000 to 9,000 feet, in the south, where it terminates along the 19th parallel in an area of volcanic mountains and ash-filled basins. In this area lofty volcanic

Figure 6-2   Mexico has many colorful towns and small cities. Halfway between Mexico City and Acapulco is the town of Taxco, famous for its silver industry.

cones such as Orizaba, 18,851 feet, Popocatepetl, 17,716 feet, and Iztaccihuatl, 17,342 feet, rise above the general level. South of the volcanic rim are the Balsas Valley and the Sierra Madre del Sur. These can respectively be related structurally to the synclinorium (huge downfold) of the Gulf of California and rugged Baja California to the north, as well as to the Central Valley of Chiapas and the Sierra Madre de Chiapas to the east.

Between the lowlands of Tehuantepec and those of Nicaragua, highland elevations are greatest on the Pacific side. There, volcanic debris and lava largely obscure the underlying structures and form a plateaulike highland with ash-filled basins nestling among volcanic cones. With the exception of British Honduras, each country has mountain peaks approximating 6,000 feet or higher. The most lofty exceed 13,000 feet in Guatemala and 11,000 feet in Costa Rica. In Costa Rica, the Meseta Central, an ash-filled basin, is 3,000 to 4,000 feet above sea level.

In the Greater Antilles one line of highlands may be traced from mountainous Puerto Rico westward, through the Cordillera Central of the Dominican Republic, the northern peninsula of Haiti, the Sierra Maestra of southeastern Cuba, and the Cayman Islands, to southern British Honduras. Another group extends through the southern peninsula of Haiti, the Blue Mountains of Jamaica, and the Swan and Bay Islands to the mainland. The highest elevation in the West Indies, 10,417 feet, is in the Dominican Republic.

The Lesser Antilles, except Barbados, can be divided into high and low islands. The high islands are mountainous, being the tops of volcanic peaks which in some cases are still actively building or emerg-ing from the sea. Fringing deposits of coral limestone often form reefs and raised terraces. The low islands are relatively level and are generally of coral formation, covering submerged mountain peaks. Barbados was formed by the upturning of sedimentary strata, largely limestone.

CLIMATE

There are five main types of climate, each with characteristic associated vegetation and human activity (Figure 6-3). South from near the Tropic of Cancer, the trade winds blow from an easterly direction, and temperatures at sea level are high all year. In this area rainfall differences on windward and leeward slopes, together with the decrease of temperature with increased elevation and exposure to the sea, provide the principal basis for climatic differences. The climate on the east and northeast

Figure 6-3   Note the influence of the trade winds and topography upon the climatic types. In general, the rainy tropical climates are on the northern and eastern sides of the land masses, but the steppes and deserts are in the northwestern and interior part of the area.

sides of the high islands and the mainland is classed as rainy tropical; that on the west and southwest sides, wet-and-dry tropical; elevations above 2,500 feet are of the tropical highland type. North of the Tropic of Cancer, in northern Mexico, the degree of rainfall deficiency becomes the basis of classification; the climate is largely tropical steppe or tropical desert.

One of the principal weather problems confronting Middle America is the hurricane, which is an annual hazard from late August to November. Usually the area most affected is the northern half of the West Indies. Occasionally, however, these storms strike along the east coast of Mexico.

RAINY TROPICAL   The rainy tropical lands are hot, humid, and rainy all year. Rain is usually heaviest from May to November when precipitation normally brought by the trade winds is supplemented by convectional showers accompanying the northward shift of the doldrums. Such places are regions of selva (broadleaf-evergreen rain forest), generally sparsely populated by subsistence farmers and gatherers of forest products, but locally more densely occupied because of banana and cacao plantations.

WET-AND-DRY TROPICAL   Areas having a distinct dry season during the winter months, when the rain-shadow effect of the highlands athwart the trade winds is greatest, are classed as wet-and-dry tropical climates. Summer rain is convectional in origin. Where precipitation is heavier, the vegetation is semideciduous or scrub forest; savanna grassland prevails where precipitation is lighter. Along the Pacific coast there are patches of rain forest as far north as Guatemala. In such places the summer rainfall is heavy enough to compensate for the dry season. Areas with wet-and-dry tropical climate are some-

what more favorable for human occupation than rainy tropical ones, and therefore are generally more densely peopled. Cattle grazing and raising sugar cane are important activities.

TROPICAL HIGHLAND   Climates in the highlands vary greatly within short distances because of differences in elevation, orientation of slope to the sun, and rain-bringing winds. Summer rain and winter drought are characteristic, although slopes on the east side have the year-round precipitation of the adjacent rainy tropical lowlands. Vegetation, as a consequence, is also varied. Rain forests clothe the wetter, east-facing exposures, whereas the seasonally dry western parts have a scrub forest or grassland cover. Mixed forests, pine forests, or evergreen-oak forests occupy higher lands.

In highlands, several altitudinal temperature zones are commonly recognized. The lowest, called *tierra caliente,* lying below 2,500 feet elevation, usually has either rainy tropical or wet-and-dry tropical climate. Above this zone and up to 6,000 or 7,000 feet is *tierra templada,* with average annual temperatures of 60 to 75°F. This is the coffee zone. In Mexico and Central America, except in Nicaragua and Panama, it is the zone of greatest population concentration. Higher still is *tierra fría,* extending to the tree line at a height between 11,000 and 13,000 feet. Only Mexico, Guatemala, and western Panama have areas of any size in *tierra fría;* Mexico City lies in the lower part of this temperature zone. Alpine pastures, above the tree line, are largely limited to Mexico, and this country alone has peaks extending above the snow line, located at an elevation of approximately 15,000 feet.

TROPICAL STEPPE AND DESERT   Northwestern Mexico is desert or steppe land. Near the California border there is a little precipita-

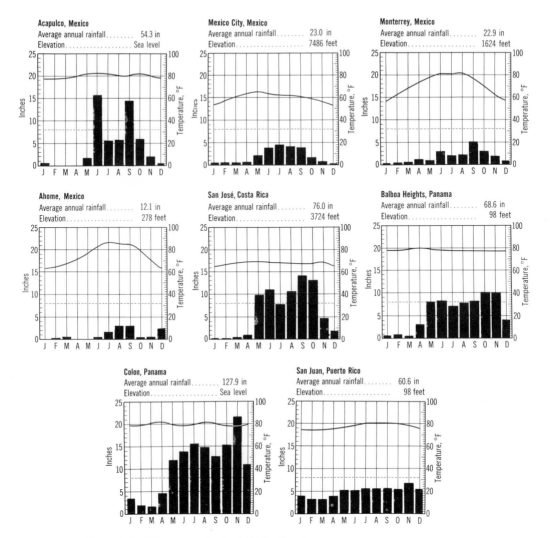

Figure 6-4   Climate graphs for Middle America.

tion from winter storms; this is the only exception to the characteristic summer maximum of rainfall in Middle America. The desert in the lower, northern part of interior Mexico is explained by the dry prevailing winds and mountains to the east and west. Higher surrounding lands with steppe climate, especially to the south, commonly receive more rain, or the rain is more efficient because of lower temperatures. The sparsely populated desert and steppe areas are used mostly for grazing; irrigation farming, especially of cotton or other cash crops, is locally significant.

POPULATION

In Mexico and Central America the racial and cultural mixtures are Indian-Spanish, but in the West Indies they are Negro-European. In both areas colored or mixed races predominate, and in many sections Occidental culture is but a veneer over an Indian or Negro base. Only the small upper class, normally white or near-white, lives ordinarily in an essentially European manner. Native life and culture, however, are being modified by increasing contact with the people of the United States.

In the mainland countries, mestizo people are most numerous, except in Guatemala, where nearly two-thirds are pure Indian, and in Costa Rica, where over one-half are white. Nowhere else do Caucasians make up more than one-sixth of the population. Negroes are most common in Panama and in the Caribbean lowlands of Costa Rica, Nicaragua, and Honduras. Most of the Negroes migrated to the area during the present century to aid in construction of the Panama Canal and to work on banana plantations.

In the West Indian islands, however, there are few mestizos and almost no Indians. Negroes and mulattoes are dominant, except in Puerto Rico and Cuba, where possibly two-thirds of the people can be classified as white. In the other islands the percentage of white people is much lower. In some it is less than 1 per cent.

To the Spaniards, the Indians represented wealth, sometimes in the form of gold and silver which the Indians had accumulated, but always in the form of labor to be exploited and incidentally Christianized. The valley of Mexico and the highland basins of Guatemala were most densely occupied and were the centers of the highest cultural development before the Spanish arrived. Indians there were well-disciplined, sedentary farmers accustomed to hard labor. Although many perished, most managed to survive under their new Spanish masters; hence Negro slaves were not needed. The more densely inhabited areas of pre-Columbian times are thus the most heavily peopled today;

and also, the greater was the proportion of Indians to incoming Spanish, the more Indian is the present population.

In the West Indies, however, the Indians, though fairly numerous, were unaccustomed to hard, steady labor. Rounded up and enslaved to work the plantations and mines of the larger islands—gold was found in Hispaniola within a month after the establishment of the first Spanish settlement—these half-wild beings quickly died or were killed when they rebelled against their masters. They succumbed also to newly introduced European diseases. Almost at once, importation of African slaves was necessary. Cuba, Hispaniola, and Puerto Rico became outfitting points through which passed the manpower and culture of Spain to the farthest ends of the empire. The history of these islands explains the near-absence of Indian blood, the larger proportions of white blood, and the presence of Spanish institutions and language. The Republic of Haiti is an exception. Its language today is French, and the race and culture largely Negro, because it became French in 1697 and almost all whites were slaughtered or driven out by revolting slaves between 1790 and 1791.

The smaller islands were never effectively occupied by the Spaniards. During the seventeenth and eighteenth centuries they became pawns of war because they were held in high esteem as sugar colonies. To grow sugar cane, many Negro slaves but only a few white overseers were needed. Consequently, the population became almost entirely black, and the official language, law, and religion were that of the respective mother country.

Population density in the Caribbean ranges from 1,397 per square mile in Barbados, the Western Hemisphere's most densely settled rural area, to expanses with practically no inhabitants (Figure 6-5). Population is commonly in clusters

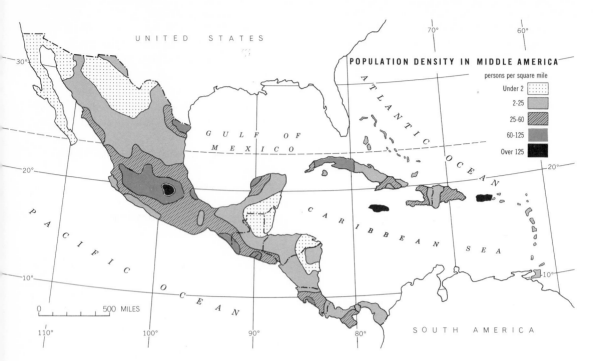

Figure 6-5 Most of the people of Middle America live in the highland valleys or on the plateaus. Note the great density of population in Puerto Rico, the western half of Cuba, and around Mexico City.

separated by sparsely settled lands. In each cluster is an urban core, the focus of economic and social activities. The rural people commonly dwell in villages rather than in dispersed farmsteads. In each mainland country, except El Salvador, are large, thinly occupied areas. Political boundaries usually fall through such lands and bear little relation to natural divisions.

Since much of the unused land is at present submarginal for farming, the rapid expansion of population is a serious problem. Between 1950 and 1960 the number of people in Central America and Mexico increased some 33 per cent, the highest rate in any major world region. Growth in the Caribbean islands was also large. If a country's population increment is 1 per cent annually, it must reinvest 2 to 5 per cent of its yearly in-

come in productive equipment just to continue the current living level. When it is remembered that most Middle American populations are increasing not 1 per cent, but 3 to 4 per cent per year, and that present low living levels must be greatly increased if the people's aspirations are to be satisfied, the magnitude of the problem becomes more apparent.

ECONOMIC DEVELOPMENT

AGRICULTURE

Although mining has long been locally important, forest products are gathered, and in some places industrialization has begun, agriculture remains the principal means of livelihood in all Middle America. Much of the land is still in large holdings, either the great feudal-type haciendas inherited from the Spanish, or the newer, foreign-owned commercial plantations. Whether they are landless workers for day wages or tenants on large holdings, small farmers working their own land, squatters with no legal claims to the plots they till, or dwellers on the communal farms of Mexico, most people have a low level of living. Poverty, poor health, and malnutrition are ever-present problems. The great majority exist mainly by subsistence farming. Although some farmers by skill and irrigation have improved their living conditions, many live almost as did their Indian or Negro ancestors.

Agricultural methods are usually primitive and crop yields low. The best land is in the hands of the large landholders, who use it for cash crops. The small farmers, who produce food almost exclusively for home consumption, are relegated to areas of poorer soil and steeper slopes. Caribbean America is an old land; yet the frontier attitude of wasteful exploitation of resources, both natural and human, still persists. Fortunately an awakening is taking place.

TRANSPORTATION AND TRADE

Land transportation associated with each population cluster is oriented toward the sea. Only the capitals of Mexico, Guatemala, and El Salvador are connected by rail, but all the capitals, except Tegucigalpa, have railroads to the sea. All also have highways to the Pacific, but except from Mexico City and Panama City, roads to the Atlantic are few. The Pan-American Highway is now completed through Central America, but not yet across the Panama-Colombia boundary. External contact has thus been largely by water, although the recent high development of

air-transport facilities has made communication much less difficult.

Exports are mostly raw materials; imports are manufactured goods. Individual countries depend heavily on one or two export crops. A widening of agricultural activities to produce a greater variety of products both for sale abroad and for home use in place of imports is much needed, and import substitution to be obtained by expansion of manufacturing is also desirable. Scarcity of capital, of mineral and power resources, and of workers trained in the necessary technical, clerical, and managerial skills are all drawbacks to industrialization; but the small size of the political units, and thus of domestic markets, is a particularly significant obstacle. Enlarging the market, to support industries that would be uneconomical when dependent on sales in a single country, is a major objective of recent moves to establish a Central American common market.

MEXICO

Mexico shows as great a diversity of physical environment, race, and culture as one might expect to find in several different countries (Figure 6-6). The 37 million people are probably 30 per cent Indian and over 60 per cent mestizo. The official language, law, and religion are of Spanish origin, yet some 4.1 million Mexicans speak one of the more than 50 Indian tongues in use, and over one-half of these people can speak no Spanish.

Although industrialization has been rapid, Mexico's problem—how to raise the standard of living—remains essentially agrarian. Fifty-eight per cent of the gainfully employed are in agriculture which is largely subsistence in character, even though commercial agriculture has

Figure 6-6   Mexico, like the United States, is divided into a series of political units called states. Each state has its capital. Mexico City, the national capital, is not in any state, but is in a federal district.

developed so that its exports are more valuable than those of minerals. Village life is the rule. Fewer than 10 per cent of the population dwell on isolated farmsteads, less than 45 per cent in centers of over 2,500 people.

Actually, the natural endowment for agriculture is rather poor. More than half of the area is too dry to cultivate; additional amounts are too rough, or are excessively hot and wet, and possess only poor soils. Only about 10 per cent of Mexico's surface is cultivated—a little over one acre per capita (Table 6-1). Moreover, because of soil erosion and misuse, primitive tillage methods, poor seed, drought, and frost damage, yields per acre are commonly low.

Crops of a wide variety are grown, but maize, cotton, sugar cane, and wheat together account for over one-half of the total by value; maize alone, for 25 per cent. Maize, with beans, chile, and occasionally meat for supplements, is the people's staple diet, along with pulque, a native drink which is consumed in some parts of the country. Unfortunately, the lands naturally capable of producing the heaviest yields of maize do not coincide with the centers of denser population. Although over half of the cultivated land is in this grain, Mexico must import substantial amounts to meet her needs.

As late as 1930, 78 per cent of all agricultural land was controlled by 2 per cent of the owners. Today, however, large estates are mostly a thing of the past. The government has expropriated such holdings and from them has created *ejidos* in accordance with laws growing out of the revolution which began in 1910. *Ejidos* are agrarian communities that hold the land in common, although the cropland may be worked either by individuals or on a cooperative basis.

Since the land is now distributed on an equitable basis, further progress must be made in increasing crop yields and the acreage tilled. About 1 acre of cropland in 8 is now irrigated, and further ambitious governmental reclamation and conservation projects are under way. An estimated three-fifths or more of the potentially arable land is already in use, but almost one-half of this is fallowed

each year. The problem is the more difficult since an exceptionally high birth rate increases population by about 1 million annually. (In a recent year there were 47 births and 12 deaths per 1,000 population.)

Like most Latin-American countries, Mexico has a central core of dense settlement, with scattered smaller populous districts and sparsely occupied outlying areas. For comparative purposes the political units of Mexico may be grouped into five divisions: Central Mexico, the Gulf Coast, the North, the North Pacific, and the South Pacific. Facts concerning land area, land use, and population in these divisions are shown in Tables 6-1 and 6-2.

TABLE 6-1 LAND UTILIZATION IN MEXICO

Division	Land area, thousands of hectares	Per cent					
		Farms	Crops	Pasture	Forest	Other productive noncultivated	All other*
North Pacific	41,219	45.3	5.0	27.4	8.2	0.9	58.5
North	80,093	87.9	5.8	49.2	21.0	6.0	18.0
Central	28,065	69.2	22.4	28.1	12.7	0.7	36.1
Gulf Coast	23,704	85.8	14.4	15.8	36.9	8.9	24.0
South Pacific	23,308	71.4	14.9	21.6	27.4	1.2	34.9
Nation	196,389	74.1	10.1	34.3	19.8	4.0	31.8

* Unproductive land in farms and land not in farms.

Source: "Mexico," *Anuario Estadístico de los Estados Unidos Mexicanos, 1954,* Dirección General de Estadística, Ciudad de México, 1956.

TABLE 6-2 POPULATION AND AREA OF DIVISIONS

Division	Population, hundred thousands, 1960	Increase 1950–1960, %	National population, %	Approximate area, sq. mi.	National area, %	Population per sq. mi.
Central	17.0	36.3	49.0	106,586	14	159.2
Gulf Coast	4.0	32.0	11.7	91,713	12	44.2
North	6.8	31.6	19.7	309,002	41	22.0
North Pacific	2.6	48.4	7.4	159,247	21	16.1
South Pacific	4.2	26.1	12.2	92,003	12	46.1
Nation	34.6	34.3	100.0	758,551	100	45.6

Source: Based on preliminary figures of the 1960 Census furnished by the Mexican Embassy, Washington, D.C.

Figure 6-7   The regions of Mexico are the product of both physical and cultural influences. The intensity of land utilization varies greatly from region to region.

REGIONS

CENTRAL   This region is the heart of the nation. Although the area occupies only one-seventh of the country, about one-half of the population live in it. It is also the region of greatest industrial development. In addition there are important mineral resources, and three of the four top-ranking cities, including Mexico, D.F., the largest, are located on the Central Plateau.

At least two advanced civilizations flourished in Central Mexico before the Spanish conquest. The influence of one, that of the Toltecs, was greatest between A.D. 600 and 1200. The ruins of their capital, Teotihuacán, 28 miles northeast of Mexico City, together with the great pyra-

mids of the Sun and the Moon, built by a pre-Aztec people, are a prime tourist attraction. The Toltecs absorbed many Mayan cultural traits, which they passed on to the Aztecs who arrived later. The Aztecs belonged to the same linguistic group and probably originated in the same section of the arid north. They established their capital, Tenochtitlán, on the present site of Mexico City, about 1325, and ruled over a large surrounding area. Conquest of the Aztecs in 1521 by Cortés and 600 Spaniards is one of history's great military feats.

Central Mexico includes the mountains and basins at the higher and more humid southern end of the Mexican plateau, volcanic cones which rise majestically above the general level, and the deep-cut valleys along the plateau's southern margin. The population is concentrated in the basins where the land is level, the soils usually fertile, and the temperatures cool and healthful. In general, winters are mild with occasional frosts and infrequent snow, and summers are relatively cool. There is usually enough rain, 20 to 40 inches annually, to support agriculture, although irrigation is often practiced. Recognizing that temperatures vary with altitude and rainfall with exposure, the climate of Mexico City, 7,486 feet above sea level, can be considered fairly typical of that of Central Mexico.

Although the region is Mexico's leading agricultural area, less than one-fourth of Central Mexico is cultivated. More land is in pasture, and more still is nonproductive, too dry, or on eroded slopes long since deforested to supply firewood and charcoal. Maize and beans are the leading crops. Considerable wheat is produced and also sugar cane in lower, warmer places like Morelos. Drier areas near the larger population centers are commonly devoted to the maguey plant. From its juice is fermented pulque, the national drink of the poorer classes. Fruit, vegetables, and flowers in large quantities are supplied to the Mexico City market from the famous so-called floating gardens of Lake Xochimilco nearby. There is also a notable development of dairying tributary to Mexico City, although most milk and much meat consumed in rural areas are from goats.

Mexico City is not only the national capital and the focus of the economic, social, and cultural life of the nation, but the fourth largest city in Latin America, with nearly 3 million inhabitants. Included within its rectangular pattern are numerous parks and plazas, attractive suburbs, and buildings ranging from colonial-age structures to ultramodern, multistoried apartments and office buildings. The location on the drained bed of part of Lake Texcoco has created a prob-

Figure 6-8 Aerial view of the principal business district of Mexico City. Note the wide boulevards and modern business buildings.

lem for the city. Under the weight of streets and buildings, surface levels have subsided, in places as much as 16 feet, as ground water was pumped from the wells driven into the soft subsoil to provide the city's water supply. Consequently, the level of the storm sewers in relation to the Gran Canal del Desaque, completed in 1900 to drain the basin north through a tunnel in the mountains to the Rio Pánuco, is such that during the rainy season considerable areas are commonly flooded.

Mexico City is the nation's leading manufacturing center. Mexican manufacturing is typically light industry, producing consumer goods from domestic raw materials. The bulk of the industrial activity in the capital is concerned with textiles, clothing, food products, beverages, furniture, tobacco goods, shoes, paper, chemicals, ceramic wares, and lighter metal products. Handicraft industries, practiced in the home or in small shops, are common here as elsewhere in the nation.

Figure 6-9 Pottery is one of the main industries in Guadalajara. The artistic and colorful designs of the articles turned out are considered among the best of their kind.

The capital is also the focus for Mexico's excellent network of air transportation, its 13,000 miles of railroad, and its 29,000 miles of all-weather road. Consequently, the capital is the major center for tourism, the republic's largest single source of dollar income. Many tourists travel to Mexico City over the Pan-American Highway, which was opened from Laredo, Texas, in 1936, and has since been completed into Panama. The total length of the highway in Mexico is 1,745 miles.

Other cities of particular note in Central Mexico are Guadalajara, second largest city of the republic and an important transportation and commercial center; Puebla, the fourth largest city and the leading cotton-textile manufacturing center; Pachuca, the world's most important silver-mining community; and Cuernavaca, a tourist paradise. Manzanillo is Mexico's chief Pacific port because of its railroad connection with the interior. Taxco, a small colonial town, long famed for silversmithing, is just outside the division.

GULF COAST The Gulf Coast region has a level surface and a hot, rainy climate. Much of the land is covered with rain forests. In the state of Veracruz, however, the coastal lowlands, which are often swampy and have considerable areas of savanna, are backed by the forested eastern slopes of the Sierra Madre Oriental which lie in the *tierra templada*. Still higher towers snow-capped Orizaba, one of North America's highest peaks. Precipitation is especially heavy and causes a dense forest cover in the lowlands of the Isthmus of Tehuantepec, the state of Tabasco, and the southern part of Campeche. Less rain, a distinct dry season, and rapid drainage into the underlying limestone account for the scrub forest vegetation in the northwestern part of the Yucatan Peninsula.

Although the Gulf Coast region ranks high in output of agricultural products, it still has left undeveloped many of the agricultural resources of the nation. Much of the coffee of Mexico, the world's third-largest producer, is from this zone. Banana exports, largely from the Gulf Coast area, which exceeded 14 million stems in 1937, have now dropped to less than 3 million stems annually. Maize yields are higher and more dependable than elsewhere in the nation, and the grasslands, though tropical, support many cattle. From the forests of the Isthmus of Tehuantepec and those extending south into the Yucatan Peninsula, is gathered much of the world's chicle. Over half of the world's henequen is grown in Yucatan. The annual yield of over 150,000 tons of fiber was once largely exported to the United States for the manufacture of binder twine and cordage, but today most of it is fabricated in Mexico, and much is consumed there. Within the Gulf Coast region is located the largest reclamation and power project ever undertaken in Mexico, a 200-million-dollar endeavor on the Rio Papaloapan.

The principal oil fields of Mexico are located in the Gulf Coast area. Since the first commercial-oil discovery was made west of Tampico in 1901, the cumulative production of petroleum within the country has been greater than that in any other nation except the United States, Venezuela, and the Soviet Union. Peak output was reached in 1921, when over 193 million barrels were exported. Fields are largely in three Gulf Coast areas, contiguous to Tampico, south of Tuxpan, and inland from Coatzacoalcos (Puerto Mexico). Present annual production of about 90 million barrels is in approximate net balance with yearly national consump-tion. The petroleum industry is a government monopoly. Tampico is the important petroleum-producing and refining center as well as one of the principal ports. Production of sulfur in the Isthmus of Tehuantepec area has skyrocketed to over 1 million tons annually since 1954, placing Mexico second only to the United States in output.

Population is largely centered in small communities. Rural population is densest on the temperate slopes of the Sierra Madre Oriental, focusing on such towns as Jalapa and Orizaba, both centers of cotton manufacturing. Veracruz is a major port on the Gulf of Mexico. It is the principal shipping, trading, and processing center in a fertile reclaimed agricultural area. Coatzacoalcos is the Gulf side terminal of a railroad, never very important economically, which was built across the Isthmus of Tehuantepec in 1907. Mérida is the commercial and manufacturing center for the henequen area of the Yucatan Peninsula.

The Yucatan area is famous for its Maya ruins. The "New Empire" of the Mayas flourished in this area between A.D. 800 and 1400. When the Spanish arrived, however, the cities were in ruins and their populations dispersed. The Maya culture, in some ways higher than that of the contemporary European civilization, was a mother culture which contributed much, through the Toltec, to Aztec civilization.

THE NORTH   In this thinly populated semi-arid to arid region, winters are cool and summers warm to hot. The surface is largely plateau, but also included is much of the Sierra Madre Occidental, the northern part of the Sierra Madre Oriental, and a segment of the Gulf Coast plain. Basin floors are lowest and level land most extensive nearer the Rio Grande. Large areas have interior drainage. Steppe grass or desert shrub prevails, though higher mountains may be wooded. The Sierra Madre Occidental has valuable pine forests.

The major land use is grazing. Because of lack of moisture, the carrying capacity of pastures is low. Crops must almost always be irrigated. The principal commercial crop is cotton. Over one-fourth of the nation's annual yield of nearly 2 million bales is produced on *ejidos* in the Laguna district around Torreón, the second largest city of the north. Production is also significant in Chihuahua and has increased spectacularly around Matamoros on the lower Rio Grande. Upstream the huge multipurpose Falcon Dam was dedicated in 1953 as part of an ambitious international water-conservancy project. The North as a whole is also the leading wheat-producing section of the republic.

The chief wealth of the region lies in its mineral resources. Chihuahua, Zacatecas, and Durango are three of the nation's five leading mining states. Mexico is the leading producer of silver, is commonly second in lead, and among the first ten in the production of molybdenum, antimony, mercury, zinc, and gold. Lead, zinc, silver, copper, and gold together total some 85 per cent of the annual value of minerals produced, exclusive of petroleum.

A good-grade bituminous coal, mined at Sabinas in Coahuila, and iron ore from Durango are brought together in Monterrey, making this city the only iron and steel center of consequence in Middle America. Monterrey is second only to Mexico City as an industrial city and is the nation's third largest urban community. The border towns of Ciudad Juárez, Piedras Negras, Nuevo Laredo, and Matamoros are much visited by tourists from the United States. Each is a port of entry connected by railroad and highway with the Mexican capital far to the south.

NORTH PACIFIC Since it is too dry, too rough, or too isolated for development,

Figure 6-10 A goatherd on road to Chichen-Itzá. This part of the limestone plain of Yucatan is checkered with stone wall–enclosed fields of henequen, brush pasture, and idle brushlands containing temporary clearings that produce maize and other subsistence crops. (Courtesy of Paul C. Morrison.)

Figure 6-11   Along the Mexico City–Nogales Highway west of Guadalajara in Jalisco. Note the dry, eroded, brush-covered slopes used only for pasture, if used at all, and the patches of maize on alluvial flats. (Courtesy of Mexican Embassy.)

even for a grazing industry, over half of the North Pacific area is nonproductive. Population density is lower than in any of the other divisions. Settlement is focused where water is available for irrigation, in scattered mining camps and in the border towns of Tijuana, Mexicali, and Nogales.

Sugar cane and wheat are crops of general consequence. The state of Nayarit is Mexico's primary tobacco-growing area, the Yaqui Valley in southern Sonora its leading center of rice cultivation, and the Mexican Imperial Valley oasis, one of the places where the United States and Mexico are in dispute over water rights, its largest long-staple cotton producer. The region's isolation from Central Mexico was partly remedied in 1948 by the completion of a railroad southeast from Mexicali to a junction with the Nogales to Mexico City line. This improvement has helped make possible a fuller development of the Colorado delta area. Copper mines, especially at Cananea in Sonora and Santa Rosalía in Baja California, are foremost in output of this metal in the republic. Tuna caught off the North Pacific coast accounts for much of the value of the nation's fisheries products.

SOUTH PACIFIC Separated from Central Mexico by the deep Balsas Valley, the South Pacific area is largely a highland region composed of narrow, flat-topped divides and steep-sided valleys. A strip of coastal plain, the Tehuantepec lowlands, and a flat-floored valley in central Chiapas provide the most extensive areas of level land. Since most of the surface is well watered, there are valuable forests. In places where rainfall is light, however, as in interior Oaxaca, irrigation must be practiced.

Isolation is the dominant fact in the life

Figure 6-12 A tender brings passengers to Acapulco from a liner anchored in the bay. Acapulco is a favored resort for many tourists from the United States. (Courtesy of P. and O. —Orient Lines.)

of the region. As a result, even mining is relatively unimportant, although mineralization is believed to be great. Set apart from the main currents of Mexican life, most inhabitants lead a primitive subsistence existence; yet with improved transportation, considerable areas, now unused, may become productive.

The region has no large cities; Oaxaca is the principal center. Acapulco, today an internationally renowned resort and in colonial times the principal Pacific port, has a much better harbor than Manzanillo, but few ships now call there because its connection with Mexico City is by a motor road only. Exports of the South Pacific—coffee, bananas, and forest products—leave mostly through the Atlantic port of Coatzacoalcos.

PROGRESS IN MEXICO

Both the Mexican government and private interests are making strong efforts to improve the economy of the country. Big, new, luxury hotels help to attract tourists

TABLE 6-3 CENTRAL AMERICA

Country	Area, sq. mi.	Population, thousands	Population per sq. mi.	Chief exports
Guatemala	42,042	3,759	89	Coffee, bananas, cotton, chicle, abacá
El Salvador	7,722	2,613	338	Coffee, cotton, balsam, sesame
Honduras	43,227	1,887	44	Bananas, silver, gold, timber, coffee
Nicaragua	57,143	1,450	25	Cotton, coffee, gold, timber, cattle
Costa Rica	19,690	1,150	58	Coffee, bananas, cacao, abacá
Panama	28,576*	1,066*	37	Bananas, cacao, shrimp, sugar
British Honduras	8,867	90	10	Mahogany, pine, chicle, citrus fruit and juice

* Excludes Canal Zone.

Source: *The Statesman's Year Book*, St. Martin's Press, Inc., New York, 1961.

to Mexico City and other centers, and tourism is an important source of income. Great improvements have been made in education, from village schools to the National University of Mexico, famed for its ultramodern buildings. The government is assisting agriculture by reclamation, land subdivision, and instruction in improved farming methods. Manufacturing has expanded, especially in such light industries as cotton, rayon and woolen textiles, and tobacco processing. Although iron and steel are produced at Monterrey, where coal and ore from local sources are used, the output supplies only part of the national needs and could well be increased. Most of the principal Mexican cities have made rapid material gains with the development of industry and trade, and with improvements in transportation, education, and construction. As a close neighbor to the United States, Mexico naturally has more trade with this country than with any other. Gradually even the people of rural villages are learning about developments in the outside world, and throughout Mexico the people are in process of changing from a primitive way of life to a culture that will make them a part of the modern world.

CENTRAL AMERICA

Six independent countries and a British colony, British Honduras, are included in Central America (Figure 6-13). All the countries are relatively small, especially when compared with the other countries of the Western Hemisphere. Nicaragua, the largest, is slightly smaller than Michigan, and El Salvador, the smallest, is only a little larger than Maryland. Guatemala has the greatest total population, but El Salvador has the highest population density.

GUATEMALA

Guatemala is the most Indian of the Caribbean nations, for more than half of its people are pure Indian, and most of the rest are more Indian than white. It is also the most populous Central American country and the one with the largest external trade. Yet 75 per cent of the area is forest or brushland and less than 15 per cent is cropped.

The northern third of Guatemala, in Petén, is a jungle-covered southward extension of the limestone plain of Yucatan. Artifacts and stone ruins indicate a once dense Maya population, but today only a few primitive Indians live in the area. Chicle and other forest products are exported.

The middle third of the country is a moderately populated region of steep-sided ridges and deep valleys with east-west trends. The valleys widen into rainy, alluvial plains along the Gulf of Honduras. Most thickly peopled is the Cobán area, which has an elevation of 2,000 to 5,000 feet and produces coffee. Population is also fairly dense in the lower Motagua Valley, site of older banana plantations and more recently of plantings of abacá. Both neighborhoods have notable Maya ruins. Puerto Barrios is the main port and a terminus of the interocean railroad which extends to the Pacific port of San José. The railway also connects with lines extending to Mexico and El Salvador.

Today, most Guatemalans live, just as when the Spanish arrived, in the fertile, volcano-studded, highland part of the southern third of the nation. These subtropical and temperate elevations of 2,000 to 8,000 feet have 35 to 50 inches of precipitation annually, with a rainy season from April to November. Where uncleared, oak and pine forests thrive. Most

Figure 6-13 *Central America and the West Indies include eleven independent countries in addition to territories controlled by European nations and the United States.*

of the coffee, which comprises about 70 per cent of the nation's exports, is produced here, especially between the Mexican border and Guatemala City, Central America's largest urban center. Much more land, however, is in subsistence crops. Mountain scenery, Indians following their traditional way of life, colorful markets, beautiful Lake Atitlán, and the ruins of Antigua, the colonial capital destroyed by an earthquake in 1773, are attractions to the tourists who arrive by air, by sea, and over the Pan-American Highway.

A sparsely tenanted, hot, malarial coastal plain, 20 to 30 miles wide, borders the Pacific. In this part of the nation, cattle ranches occupy tracts of savanna grass; much of the nation's sugar cane is grown here, and banana plantations have become more extensive than those on the Carib-

bean. Nearly three-fourths of the 8 million stems of bananas cut annually are raised along the Pacific coast, mostly under irrigation.

EL SALVADOR

Almost no part of El Salvador is unoccupied; it is the smallest and most densely populated Central American nation. Population is greatest in the highlands, which run lengthwise through the country and have a general elevation of 1,500 to 4,000 feet. Only the loftiest of the volcanic peaks extend into *tierra fría*. San Salvador, the capital, at an elevation of 2,240 feet, enjoys comfortable average monthly temperatures that range from 71 to 76°F. The annual precipitation averages 68 inches, with a dry season from January to May.

Although some gold and silver are produced, both mining and manufacturing are limited. Thirty per cent of the surface is cultivated; one-half of the rest is in pasture. Coffee, mainly produced on small and medium-sized farms, dominates the economic life of the nation. Grown in the highlands, it normally comprises over 60 per cent of the exports. Maize, however, a food crop, occupies more land. Cotton grown on the narrow coastal lowlands is a second agricultural export, while the world's supply of balsam of Peru, a pharmaceutical gum, is gathered from wild trees along the coast between Acajutla and La Libertad. A railroad runs the length of the country and joins with the Guatemalan system.

HONDURAS

Bananas account for about one-half of the value of the yearly exports of Honduras. The country, formerly the world's largest shipper of this crop, is now second to Ecuador. Production has recently been about 20 million stems annually, but reduction from somewhat higher past peak yields is attributable to damage by sigatoka disease. Most of the plantations are owned by large fruit companies, use Negro labor, and are located on the hot, rain-drenched Caribbean coastal plain. Puerto Cortés, Tela, and La Ceiba are banana ports. The only railroads in Honduras are those built in connection with the banana industry.

Most of Honduras is mountainous and forested. Forests near the Caribbean are tropical and still contain treasures of mahogany, lignum vitae, and Spanish cedar. Pine and oak forests, with considerable park land, of value for expanding the cattle industry, cover higher surfaces. Because of a paucity of rich soils (recent volcanic action is lacking), a pronounced dry season, and poor roads, agriculture in the highlands is mainly limited to subsistence crops. The Copán area is known for the ruins of an ancient Maya capital. Most Hondurans live in the western half of the country; large areas in the east are not fully explored and are inhabited only by a few primitive Indians. In the mountains there are mines producing gold, silver, and lead. Tegucigalpa, the capital and principal commercial and industrial center of the country, is located in a high mountain valley.

NICARAGUA

Nicaragua is the most sparsely populated of any Central American country, and competes with Honduras for having the least foreign trade. Only 6 per cent of its surface is cultivated, and but little more is grazed. Except for a few mining camps and small seaside settlements along the flat, swampy Caribbean shore, the rough, forested, inaccessible eastern half of the country has few people. Banana production, focused on Puerto Cabezas, is of small consequence.

The country is unusual in that many of its people live in the *tierra caliente*. Population is densest in the lake region, especially between Managua and Granada. Here, much of the cotton, the most valuable export, is produced. Settlement is also fairly dense in the highlands to the northeast of the lakes, as in the coffee area of Matagalpa. Most coffee, however, is produced southwest of Managua, the capital. Cattle, raised in grasslands, especially those east of Lake Nicaragua, enter foreign trade both as live animals and as hides. The presence of a possible interoceanic canal route has already been mentioned. A treaty made in 1916 gives the United States exclusive rights to construct and control such a canal.

COSTA RICA

Costa Rica has the largest white population, and is the most democratic and most literate of the Central American republics; more than the others, it is a land of small proprietary farms. Yet, nearly two-thirds of the surface is forested and sparsely populated, if populated at all. Coffee accounts for about 50 per cent, bananas for 30 per cent, and cacao for 10 per cent of the annual exports.

Population is concentrated in the fertile and temperate Meseta Central, where most of the people are white or near-white. In this area is located the attractive capital, San José, and three others of the nation's largest cities. The Meseta Central is the chief producer of Costa Rica's fine-flavored coffee. Large amounts of maize, sugar cane, beans, potatoes, fruit, and vegetables are grown for local consumption. There are also substantial grazing and dairy industries.

In the Caribbean Lowlands, settlement is of consequence only along the main line and branches of the Puerto Limón–San José railroad. The world's first large-scale commercial production of bananas was established in these lowlands. Peak exports, in 1913, totaled over 11 million stems. Today, because of Panama disease, the plantations are all abandoned, and the limited export of bananas from the east coast comes from small temporary plantings. Meanwhile, much of Costa Rica's 40,000 acres of cacao has been established in the Caribbean Lowlands, and during World War II there were also plantings of some 10,000 acres in abacá. In addition, Negroes, who constitute most of the lowland population, grow considerable food for domestic use.

The banana plantations are now along the Pacific coast where they have been in operation since 1938. Annual exports of some 10 million stems usually place Costa Rica third or fourth in world shipments. Golfito and Quepos are the leading banana ports. The plantations must be irrigated during the dry season, and are sprayed to prevent sigatoka damage. It is significant, however, that over 12,000 acres of bananas in the Quepos division have already been abandoned because of Panama disease and have been replaced by African oil palm, cacao, pasture, and trial plantings of mahogany and teak. Workers on the plantations are largely from Guanacaste. This northwestern province is a scrub forest and grassland area of cattle ranches and cereal production, with a moderately dense mestizo population.

PANAMA AND THE CANAL ZONE

First traversed by Balboa, who discovered the Pacific in 1513, Panama has since been most significant as an interoceanic pass route. Over the "Old Gold Road" was portaged much of colonial South America's wealth. United States interest in the crossing expanded during the California Gold Rush of 1849. In 1855 American capital completed the transisthmian railroad, but interest then waned. A French attempt to dig a canal between 1880 and 1889 failed because of yellow fever and mismanagement. When the Spanish-American War broke out in 1898, and it took the battleship *Oregon* two months to travel the 13,000 miles from the Pacific to the Atlantic, need for a canal became evident to the United States.

In 1903, when Panama revolted against Colombian rule, the United States quickly recognized the new nation. By the treaty then concluded, the United States gained the right to build, operate, and defend the canal, and to have jurisdiction in perpetuity over the 10-mile-wide Canal Zone. The Zone has a land area of 362 square miles and a population, including those in the ports of Balboa and Cristobal, of approximately 50,000. The Panama Canal was completed in 1914. It is 50 miles long and has three sets of lift locks on each side of the summit elevation of 85 feet in Gatun Lake. On the Atlantic side three locks are at Gatun; on the Pacific side one is at Pedro Miguel and two at Miraflores. Its value to the United States as a wartime facility is, of course, inestimable. In addition it has greatly aided the expansion of American intercoastal commerce and trade between the east coast of the United States and the west coast of South America and eastern Asia. Bulky raw materials constitute the Pacific to Atlantic cargo, manufactured goods, most of the cargo moving in the opposite direction.

The Republic of Panama itself is divided into two parts by the Canal Zone. To the east, much of the rough, rainy, malarial, selva-covered land, with maximum elevations of about 4,000 feet, is almost unoccupied except for the San Blas Indians along the Caribbean littoral. To the west, on the Caribbean side of the mountain backbone, precipitation is very heavy, and the rain forest is thinly peopled. On the Pacific side, where rainfall is less and more seasonal, there is considerable savanna vegetation. In this area live most of Panama's population other than nearly 30 per cent who reside in Panama City and Colón. The completed Panamanian section of the Pan-American Highway loosely ties this population together. The transisthmian highway between Colón and Panama City was constructed during World War II.

Over three-fourths of Panama remains in forests, the source of cabinet woods and other tree products. Cattle, yielding hides for export, graze much of the

Figure 6-14 A passenger steamer proceeding through the Panama Canal. Note the topography of the area and the density of vegetation. (Courtesy of P. and O.—Orient Lines.)

remaining surface. Only about 6 per cent of the land is cultivated. Rice is the leading subsistence crop. Bananas, of which 10 to 12 million stems are shipped annually, are mostly produced on the Pacific side near Costa Rica and move out through Puerto Armuelles. The old banana area in the Bocas del Toro region on the Caribbean is now significant for its plantations of cacao, abacá, and coconuts.

BRITISH HONDURAS

The Crown Colony of British Honduras is the least important part of Central America. The coastal area is a low, flat, tropical land having many swamps and vast jungles. Inland in the south, elevations increase and form a series of low ridges; in the interior are some areas of savanna. The economy of the country is dependent upon its forests. Mahogany, cedar, chicle, and rosewood, sugar and prepared fruits are the principal exports; alligator skins are also exported. Cotton goods, petroleum, and hardware are the chief imports. Much of the foreign trade is carried on with the United States. Racially the people are mainly a mixture of Negro and Indian, and only about 4 per cent are European. Belize is the capital and chief city.

WEST INDIES

Geographically, the West Indies comprise three island groups, the Bahamas, the Greater Antilles, and the Lesser Antilles. Included are the independent countries of Cuba, Haiti, the Dominican Republic, Jamaica, Trinidad, and Tobago; and various islands associated politically with the United States, the United Kingdom, France, and the Netherlands.

CUBA

Nearly 80 per cent of Cuba's exports are sugar and other sugar-cane derivatives; the island is the world's largest sugar exporter. The industry employs about one-third of the nation's workers directly and uses nearly two-thirds of its cultivated land. Stress on this and other cash crops is so great that insufficient food is grown for home consumption. Sugar, either directly or indirectly, accounts for about two-thirds of the national income. Even slight variations in the quantity or price of sugar marketed are quickly reflected in the nation's well-being.

The above, written before the establishment of Castro's dictatorship in 1959, is still essentially true, although there have been some major changes. The sugar industry, once dominated by large companies and foreign capital, has been expropriated and is state-operated. Closed off from its former principal market, the United States, where Cuban sugar received preferential tariff and quota treatment and sold at a higher price than on the world market, trade has shifted to the Communist nations, especially Russia and China. Reported export of 7 million tons of sugar in 1961, after the United States

TABLE 6-4   WEST INDIES

Political division	Area, sq. mi.	Population, thousands	Population per sq. mi.
Cuba	44,218	6,743	152
Haiti	10,714	3,505	327
Dominican Republic	18,816	3,014	160
Puerto Rico	3,435	2,353	685
Virgin Islands (U.S.)	133	32	241
Bahama Islands	4,400	103	23
Barbados	166	232	1,397
Jamaica	4,677	1,620	346
Leeward Islands	356	123	345
Trinidad and Tobago	1,980	826	417
Windward Islands	825	315	382
Netherlands Antilles	371	195	526
Guadeloupe and dependencies	687	270	393
Martinique	425	275	647

Source: Center of Latin-American Studies: *Statistical Abstract of Latin America, 1961,* University of California Press, Los Angeles, Calif., 1961.

had severed relations, was much in excess of the 1950–1959 average of 5.6 million tons. This did not result in a rise of living level, however, because the price received was lower than before, and payment was largely in the form of armaments. Instead, there were critical shortages of food and consumers' goods on the island.

Sugar production reached an all-time high of 7.9 million tons in 1952, but much more than this amount could be produced. Cuba is nearly as large as the rest of the West Indies combined, and only one-quarter is hilly or mountainous; yet less than 20 per cent is cultivated. Soils, derived from the limestone underlying half or more of the surface, are particularly productive of cane. The frost-free climate, with a dry season to raise sugar content, the easily cleared palm-savanna vegetation, and the numerous excellent harbors are other advantages.

The famous cigar tobaccos are mostly grown on small farms in central and western Cuba. About half of each crop has normally been exported. Bananas from Oriente, grapefruit from the Isle of Pines, and pineapples and avocados from the Havana area are other traditional exports. Although considerable land is now unused that could supply most of the foods, except wheat, that have been imported in the past, recent efforts to increase home production have apparently failed.

Cuba mines some copper and nickel, and has regularly been the second largest Latin-American producer of manganese, but the once sizable output of iron ore has more recently been negligible. Over half of the country's people live in cities. Havana has 1.3 million residents. Tourists from the United States formerly spent large sums on the island, but today they go elsewhere, and the removal of their patronage adds to Cuba's financial prob-

lems. Its government, because it considers itself the leader of Communist revolution in the Western Hemisphere, has become a threat to world peace.

HAITI

The French-speaking Negro nation of Haiti occupies the western third of Hispaniola. Approximately 75 per cent of the surface is mountainous. The Cul-de-Sac plain extending east from the capital, Port-au-Prince, is so dry that irrigation is necessary. About 90 per cent of the Haitians are rural dwellers who work thousands of small subsistence farms by primitive hoe and machete methods. Evidence of the old French plantations has been largely obliterated. Population pressure—the density of over 327 per square mile—has pushed agriculture into the mountains, where often only shifting cultivation is possible. This results in deforestation, serious soil erosion, and impoverishment. Coffee is the leading cash crop, some of it growing semiwild.

DOMINICAN REPUBLIC

Differences of language, culture, race, and a lower population density separate the Dominican Republic, which occupies the eastern two-thirds of Hispaniola, from Haiti. Language and culture are Spanish. About 10 per cent of the 3 million people are Caucasian, an equal number Negro, and the rest mulatto. Population density is 160 per square mile.

The sparsely peopled Cordillera Central splits the country from east to west. A northern lowland, the Cibao, except for its drier western end, is a heavily inhabited and productive region of small farms. There is a second concentration of population on the southern coastal plain. Territory to the west of the capital, Santo

Domingo (Ciudad Trujillo), which is semiarid and must be irrigated, is a center of sugar production by a few large land-holders and associated tenants and small farmers. Sugar constitutes nearly 75 per cent of the nation's exports. Cacao, coffee, leaf tobacco, beef, and live cattle are also exported.

UNITED STATES DEPENDENCIES

PUERTO RICO   Self-government in the Commonwealth of Puerto Rico, taken over from Spain in 1898, is now practically complete. The island's biggest problem is too many people and too little land. Population density is 685 per square mile. Although 75 per cent of the area is mountainous and irrigation is necessary along most of the south coast, nearly one-half of the surface is tilled. This is less than ½ acre per capita, and opportunities for extending cultivation are small. Much food must be imported, especially since one-third of the cropped land produces sugar which makes up 21 per cent of the exports.

Vigorous efforts are being made to improve the level of living. The Land Law of 1941, providing for enforcement of a 500-acre limitation on land ownership, has resulted in the division of large holdings into thousands of smaller properties. Efforts begun in 1947 to attract new industry have been highly successful. A Tax Holiday Act gave new industry blanket tax exemption until 1959. Other attractions to industry have been financial assistance, cheap hydroelectric power, plentiful and cheap labor, a sizable local market, and good access to foreign markets. San Juan is the leading manufacturing center, the capital, and the largest city.

National income from manufacturing now exceeds that from agriculture by 60 per cent, although agricultural earnings are as large as in the past. Textiles and garments have displaced sugar and sugar products as the leading class of exports, and shipments of machinery and other fabricated goods have expanded remarkably. Income from a booming tourist trade helps to balance the usually large excess of imports over exports, as do also remittances from Puerto Ricans working in the United States and expenditures by the Federal government on the island. Per capita income, $115 in 1940, reached $621 in 1961, second only to that in oil-rich Venezuela in all Latin America.

VIRGIN ISLANDS   The Virgin Islands include St. Thomas, St. Croix, and St. John, along with some 50 islets and rocks that are mostly uninhabited. They were purchased from Denmark in 1917 to obtain the site for a naval base at Charlotte Amalie on St. Thomas, and to prevent Germany from gaining title to them. Both the population and the economic importance of the islands have declined, although small amounts of sugar and rum are produced and there is some tourist trade.

BRITISH WEST INDIES

Six groups of West Indian islands—the Bahamas, Barbados, Jamaica and dependencies, the Leeward Islands that include the British Virgin Islands, Trinidad and Tobago, and most of the Windward Islands—were until recently directly controlled by the United Kingdom. In 1958, except for the Bahamas and the British Virgins, the islands were united into a short-lived dominion in the British Commonwealth of Nations. Because of sectionalism, however, first Jamaica and then Trinidad broke away. Both became independent nations in August, 1962, but remained in the Commonwealth. Barbados and the seven islands of the Leeward and Windward groups are again colonies, but consideration is being given to forming the eight into a new West Indies Federation. The Caymen Islands and the Turks and Caicos Islands, former dependencies of Jamaica, are also at present separate colonies. There is no proposal to change this status. Only Trinidad and Jamaica have much importance to the world at large.

TRINIDAD   Trinidad is a junction point for international air and steamship lines and an entrepôt for a large surrounding area. Its cosmopolitan population is over one-third East Indian, descendants of indentured laborers brought in to work sugar plantations after Negro slaves were freed in 1838. Only 3 per cent of the people are white. Trinidad's annual production of more than 40 million barrels of petroleum is especially significant. Oil and oil products constitute roughly 80 per cent of its annual exports. The principal fields are in the southwestern peninsula. The famous lake of natural asphalt, located in the northeast part of this peninsula, now produces only a small part of the world's supply.

Three parallel west-east ranges of low mountains or hills cross Trinidad in the

Figure 6-15   Spraying cacao trees against witches'-broom disease. Note the cacao pods connected to the tree trunk. (Courtesy of United Fruit Company.)

north, center, and south; the highest point, 3,085 feet, is in the north. Between the ranges are undulating lowlands. About 45 per cent of the surface has been cleared of the original rain forest. Most of the people reside on the drier west side of the island, where wage workers on large estates produce most of the leading crop, sugar cane. Cacao, the colony's second crop, is produced in the east, where rainfall of 100 inches is twice that in the sugar area. Because of attacks of witches'-broom disease, however, cacao production has declined greatly from the time when Trinidad was one of the world's main sources of the commodity. Port of Spain, with its deep harbor, is the business and administrative center of the island. Near here the United States maintains a large naval base, the only World War II base still retained of those established on the Bahamas, Jamaica, St. Lucia, Antigua, and Trinidad under terms of an agreement made with the United Kingdom in 1940.

Tobago, an island twenty-two miles northwest of Trinidad, was first amalgamated with Trinidad by the British in 1888 to form a colony under a single control. Trinidad and Tobago now form the nation of the same name, with Port of Spain as the capital. Physically Tobago has several good anchorages for small ships. The island is crossed by a low ridge rising to 1,800 feet. Parts of the interior are covered by virgin forests of hardwoods. Tobago is becoming noted as a tourist attraction. Passengers to and from the island usually enter and exit through Port of Spain.

JAMAICA   Jamaica is largely an upraised, highly eroded plateau of coral limestone rock with the Blue Mountains of hard resistant rock rising to a top height of

7,402 feet in the east. Only 15 per cent of the surface of 4,450 square miles is level, and not much more is tilled. Coastal plains are widest on the drier south side of the island; rainfall is heaviest, 150 to 200 inches, on the northeastern Blue Mountain slopes. Less than 1 per cent of the people are white. Kingston is the capital. In addition to income from agriculture, Jamaican balances are increased by money sent home by laborers who have gone abroad, and by the expenditures of tourists at Montego Bay, Kingston, and other resorts.

Sugar, so important in early days, is again the most valuable crop. Jamaica was once the world's largest producer of bananas, shipping over 24 million stems one year, but because of plant diseases exports have declined to about 5 million stems annually. Crops of Blue Mountain coffee and of coconuts have also declined. Three aluminum companies, two from the United States and one Canadian, control extensive bauxite deposits. Large-scale shipments begun in 1953 have made Jamaica the leading source of this raw material.

BARBADOS AND OTHER BRITISH ISLANDS   On only 166 square miles, Barbados has 232,000 people, a population density of 1,436 persons per square mile. The staple product is sugar, with molasses and rum as by-products. There is some commercial fishing. The chief city is Bridgetown. Antigua is the largest of the Leeward Islands, which include St. Kitts, Nevis, Montserrat, and the British Virgins. The Windward Islands consist of Grenada, St. Vincent, the Grenadines, St. Lucia, and Dominica. Cacao, nutmegs, mace, bananas, arrowroot starch, lime juice, vanilla, coconut products, and cotton are exported. Some rum is manufactured. The

Bahamas off southern Florida are chiefly known for their resorts and fishing. Nassau is the principal port.

NETHERLANDS WEST INDIES

The six islands owned by the Netherlands are divided into two groups, 500 miles apart, and are governed from Willemstad (Wellemstadon) on Curaçao. The northern group consists of small islets of no consequence. The southern group is important only because of the great oil refineries on Aruba and Curaçao. One refinery on Aruba, established in 1929, reportedly has a capacity of 500,000 barrels daily and is the largest in the world. Refineries on Curaçao, established in 1917, can refine 275,000 barrels of crude oil daily. The petroleum for refining comes mainly from Venezuela, with some imports from Colombia. Aruba has 70 square miles of area and 53,200 people; Curaçao, 210 square miles and 123,689 people.

FRENCH WEST INDIES

The French West Indies include Guadeloupe, its five dependencies, and Martinique.

GUADELOUPE   This island has 583 square miles of area and 265,000 inhabitants. Its two parts are separated by a mangrove swamp. The high, rugged, western part reaches a maximum elevation of 4,867 feet and oddly enough is known as Basse Terre (lowland). The smaller eastern part has a surface less than 400 feet high and is called Grande Terre (great land). Sugar and rum produced on plantations of Grande Terre and bananas, coffee, and vanilla grown on smaller farms on Basse Terre are the leading cash crops. Sugar

cane is the principal crop in terms of area occupied, value, and number of people employed in its production and harvest. The crop is grown on the rolling volcanic soils of Basse Terre and the relatively flat and low limestone soils of Grande Terre. Banana production, the second crop in importance, is located largely on the southern and lower mountain slopes of Basse Terre. Pointe-à-Pitre and Basse Terre, the capital, are the principal cities and ports of the island.

MARTINIQUE   Slightly smaller than Guadeloupe but more populous, Martinique is a mountainous island, culminating in the north in Mt. Pelée, 4,428 feet high. This volcanic peak erupted May 8, 1902, destroying the island's principal town, St. Pierre, and 40,000 people. Fort-de-France is now the largest city. Precipitation varies from over 200 inches on the windward exposures with year-round rain, to as little as 41 inches on the southwest coast where there is a January-to-April dry period. Over one-third of the island is cultivated. Bananas account for almost one-half of the value of exports and sugar, canned pineapples, and rum for most of the rest.

IN PERSPECTIVE

MIDDLE AMERICA, LAND OF TOO MANY AND TOO LITTLE

Middle America is of great importance to the United States because of its location and because its resources are used to supplement those of our country. Mexico, the largest and most populous nation in the region, is a leader in inter-American relations and is also a major field for trade and investment by the people of the United States. The country reaches its maximum width along its northern border where it adjoins the United States. Except for cotton, most of the exports of Mexico are marketed in the United States.

Central America and the West Indies are so easy to reach by sea and air routes that the majority of their trade is also with the United States, and with the exception of Cuba they are increasingly popular with tourists. Except in the highlands, most parts of Middle America have tropical climates. The agricultural products of these tropical regions are in demand in the United States, which imports coffee, cane sugar, henequen, bananas, cigar tobacco, fruit juices, cacao, and spices from the area. Mahogany and chicle are among the natural forest products exported.

The United States has made large investments in Middle America, particularly in banana and sugar plantations and in the mining industry. Airlines, railroads, public utilities, factories, and resort hotels are other fields for investment.

Besides Mexico, Middle America is divided into a large number of independent countries and dependencies, and at times in the past the governments of some of these have left much to be desired. Today, however, most countries of Middle America are making strong efforts to improve living conditions and opportunities for their people. In many places, new mills and factories give jobs to many who previously never worked in industry. Experimental work is being done on many phases of agriculture, such as pest control, seed selection, use of fertilizers, irrigation, and mechanization. Such experiments will result in improvement in crop yields and incomes for many people.

Although revolutions do occur and dictators are not unknown, most elections now are by ballots, not bullets. Middle America is making striking progress in political stability, education, industriali-

zation, construction of highways, improvement of agriculture, and altered attitudes toward others. These and other changes now in the making will cause readjustments and lasting benefits in ways of life for most people throughout the region, especially if health and living standards continue to improve and communism does not spread from Cuba.

SELECTED REFERENCES

Augelli, John P.: "The Rimland-Mainland Concept of Culture Areas in Middle America." *Annals of the Association of American Geographers,* vol. 52, pp. 119–129, June, 1962.

A proposal of a generalized scheme of culture-area classification to facilitate understanding of the complexity resulting from the existence in Middle America of a "somewhat different composite of people, habitat, and cultural orientation in almost every island and mainland nucleus of settlement."

Center of Latin-American Studies: *Statistical Abstract of Latin America, 1961,* Center of Latin-American Studies, University of California, Los Angeles, Calif., 1961.

A handy annual compilation of data from many diverse sources, planned to be a ready reference and to facilitate comparison of statistical information between the various Latin-American countries and the United States and Canada.

Hoy, Don R.: "Changing Agricultural Land Use on Guadeloupe, French West Indies," *Annals of the Association of American Geographers,* vol. 52, no. 4, pp. 441–454, December, 1962.

A discussion about changing land utilization on the largest island of the Lesser Antilles especially as related to changing cultural conditions.

Jones, Clarence F., and Paul C. Morrison: "Evolution of the Banana Industry of Costa Rica," *Economic Geography,* vol. 28, pp. 1–19, January, 1952.

Too much dependence upon one or two cash crops

for foreign exchange has long been a major flaw of most Middle American economies. This detailed study of the changing nature of a plantation industry in a single country is representative of the characteristics of much commercial agriculture elsewhere in the tropics.

Morrison, Paul C.: *Middle America, Land of Too Many and Too Little,* Professional Paper no. 21, National Council for Geographic Education, Norman, Okla., 1961.

The population growth rate in mainland Middle America is the highest in any major world division. This paper touches many of the facets of the basic problem of rapid population increase, one of the great issues of contemporary times, particularly as they apply to the Middle American area.

Pearson, Ross: "The Jamaica Bauxite Indus-try," *Journal of Geography,* vol. 56, pp. 377–385, November, 1957.

An account of the development of bauxite mining in a country that has recently become the world's largest producer and exporter of this important ore. Elsewhere in Middle America, except in Mexico and Trinidad, mineral exploitation is presently of little significance.

Winnie, William W., Jr.: "The Papaloapan Project: An Experiment in Tropical Development," *Economic Geography,* vol. 34, pp. 227–248, July, 1958.

A case study of a huge, TVA-like, government-sponsored, multipurpose reclamation and settlement project of the kind becoming more and more common as a means of economic development in both underdeveloped and advanced nations, regardless of their political system.

chapter 7

SOUTH AMERICA

VENEZUELA

BRITISH GUIANA
SURINAM
FRENCH GUIANA

Rio Orinoco

COLOMBIA

Guiana Highlands

ECUADOR

Rio Negro

Amazon River

ANDEAN Mountains

PERU

Rio Madeira

BRAZIL

Rio São Francisco

MATO GROSSO

Altiplano

BOLIVIA

Rio Paraguay

Brazilian Highlands

Atacama Desert

ANDEAN MOUNTAINS

Gran Chaco

PARAGUAY

Rio Paraná

ARGENTINA

URUGUAY

CHILE

Pampa

Rio de la Plata

Rio Colorado

Patagonia

*Figure 7-1 Mountains domi-
nate the landforms of western
South America, plains and plateaus the broad areas to the
east. The coastal plain of western South America is very narrow, in many places less than 5
miles wide.*

COFFEE, BANANAS, SHEEP, CATTLE, petroleum, iron ore, bauxite, and copper, with a host of other commodities, continue to be today, as they have been for decades, the bases of international trade between South America's nations and their industrialized neighbors facing the North Atlantic. The harvests from the fields, the products of the livestock industries, and the minerals from the earth's crust all give employment to people, and earn revenue for industries and nations alike. On the continued output and marketing of these commodities depends the livelihood of millions of families. Western Europe and North America constitute a growing market for these commodities and in return rely on the peoples and nations that produce them for their own exports.

South America's nations are caught up in the storms of economic and social transition. For some nations change moves swiftly; for others it has hardly begun. Country by country, the continent is experiencing the dislocations of peoples, social and political groups, and economies. As the older traditions are being eroded or swept aside, new patterns emerge, reflected in the distribution of people, land and resource utilization, and expansion of lines of communication across the continent. For every nation the trend is away from complete dependence on other nations for manufactures, as each nation is striving for self-sufficiency. This is a revolution of hopes, but it has not altered substantially the basic patterns of international commerce.

The cultural ties between the countries of South America and the lands of their heritage—Spain and Portugal—retain life and reality after more than a century and a half of political separation and independence. In Brazil, Portuguese is the official language of the people; everywhere else, except in the three Guianas in the northeast, Spanish is the official language. Nowhere is the cultural heritage better exemplified than in Roman Catholicism, the religious faith of most of the people. The social order, the pattern of property ownership and division of land into large estates, and the affinity of many of the nations to authoritarian government attest to the firm planting of an Iberian way of life in South America.

Although these ties remain, they have been modified locally by isolation, the rise of provincial customs, and contact with strong indigenous cultures. Since independence was attained early in the nineteenth century, entirely different and sometimes contradictory relationships have arisen through contacts with the scientific and economic concepts and the social philosophies prevalent in Western Europe and North America. The early bonds of commerce, trade, and investment with Northern Hemisphere trade partners created new institutions and spurred the emergence of economic and social goals often in conflict with the feudal Luso-Hispanic heritage of the continent. In this era of the twentieth century, the nations are now faced with rapidly growing populations, who benefit already from the miracles of modern science in their lives, but who have not yet assimilated completely the knowledge and skills necessary to attain the new goals they have set for themselves. How to realize these goals and utilize the resources of the people, the natural environment, and the rich cultural heritage without undue turbulence and still maintain a framework of democracy, is the great challenge of each nation of South America today.

A parallel goal is to raise yields of agricultural commodities from the variety of climates, soils, and terrain with which each nation is endowed. Another is to

Figure 7-2   South America is divided into ten independent countries and the three Guianas, each of which is controlled by a European country.

increase the production of metals and other minerals from the storehouse of the continent for use within each nation, as well as for export. The development of more stable governments will help in solving such crucial problems as land tenure, education and assimilation of the "awaking" Indian groups, and the securing of better world markets. The attainment of these goals will augur well for improved living standards for the people of South America, without the loss of overseas markets, still so essential to the economies of every nation.

South America is characterized by spectacular conditions and contrasts—the hot, steamy, tropical forests, deserts where rainfall is unknown, the highest mountains outside of Asia, the mighty expanse of river plains, and the material poverty of societies rich in heritage and tradition. As a major continent, South America's area is small by comparison with North America, Africa, or Asia. Considerably smaller, and fortunately so, is its population of 136 million. One nation—Brazil— occupies almost one-half of the area and contains almost one-half of the entire population of the continent. Argentina occupies another one-third, and the balance is shared by eight other nations and three tiny European dependencies. Metallic ores are richest in Peru and Bolivia; petroleum is concentrated in Venezuela; developed plantations are largely in Brazil and Colombia; and the mid-latitude farm regions of fertile soils are largely in Argentina. Yet in total, South America does have its share of the world's resources, and the problem is one of political and economic organization and skill rather than of niggardly environment. During two centuries these peoples have not been able to organize their economies by their own efforts; a large infusion of capital investment and political-economic knowl-

edge is a necessary prelude to progress. Let us hope that it can come from the Western democracies.

PHYSICAL SETTING

South America has an area of nearly 7 million square miles and is nearly twice the size of the United States. The continent is situated southeast of North America and reaches beyond the equator far into the Southern Hemisphere. The meridians of New York or Miami intersect the extreme western margin of Peru. The eastern continental cities of Rio de Janeiro and Buenos Aires are thus much closer to the capitals of Western Europe and west Africa than to the United States.

From the isthmus of Panama the continent stretches southward for over 5,000 miles to the cold, stormy coasts of Tierra del Fuego. South America attains its greatest breadth, almost 3,000 miles, from northern Peru to the bulge of eastern Brazil in the equatorial zone just south of the equator. Nearly 76 per cent of the continental land area is tropical in climate and vegetation. Beyond 35° south latitude, the continent tapers southward farther than either Africa or Australia and enters the mid-latitude and subarctic climate zones.

RELIEF FEATURES

The Andean Cordillera is the largest continuous mountain chain in the world (Figure 7-2). As the outstanding landform feature of South America, the mountain system is second only to the Himalayas in altitude. The Andean Cordillera extends from the island archipelagoes north from Tierra del Fuego to the Caribbean. Approaching the Caribbean, the ranges turn eastward as the backbone of the north coast, only to disappear in the Atlantic beyond Trinidad.

In the south the Andean Cordillera is low, with crests averaging 5,000 feet. The Cordillera rises to peaks of 20,000 feet or more in middle Chile and western Argentina, maintaining this altitude to northern Peru. The highest peak in the Western Hemisphere, Mount Aconcagua, rises to 22,835 feet, standing amidst its solitary snowfields and glaciers northeast of Santiago, Chile, in western Argentina. The high Cordillera divides into two ranges in northern Chile, supporting lofty plateaus, or altiplanos, with altitudes of 12,000 to 14,000 feet as they traverse Bolivia and southern Peru. In Bolivia and Peru the ranges merge into a broad system that is incised deeply on the east by Amazon tributaries. The system narrows across Ecuador and contains ten basins, before it thrusts northward into Colombia. In southern Colombia the ranges separate, extending north as three smaller cordillera. The broader eastern arm of the system also supports several highland basins.

The Caribbean margin north of the Andean Cordillera is dominated by the Magdalena River basin, the Maracaibo lowlands, and outliers of the mountains. Flanked on the west by narrow coastal lowlands and plains in the north, the western slopes of the Cordillera drop precipitously into the Pacific in its middle section. To the south the Cordillera is paralleled by a lower coastal range and longitudinal valley. In the extreme south of Chile, the valley has been invaded by the ocean, forming a lengthy archipelago. Along its eastern flanks, the Andean Cordillera faces the three great river basins of South America that are fed by rivers rising on its slopes.

South America has three major inland river basins—the Orinoco, the Amazon,

Figure 7-3   The Andes of southern Argentina are noted for their rugged beauty. Many lakes mirror the snow-lined mountain peaks. (Courtesy of Argentine Embassy.)

and the Paraguay-Paraná. The rivers and their tributaries occupy large basins that reach the Atlantic in widely separated places. The river plains and associated lowlands are situated within the tropical and subtropical climates of the continent.

The Orinoco River system is fed by tributaries rising in the Andes and the Guiana plateau. It flows in a great semicircle from south to northeast across Colombia and Venezuela before its muddy waters enter the sea. The Orinoco plain, or llanos, is low and gently rolling, with

Figure 7-4 Angel Falls, located in the Guiana Highlands of Venezuela, is the world's highest waterfall, 3,212 feet. (Courtesy of Hamilton Wright.)

large areas that are nearly flat. During the rainy seasons these flat areas are covered by floodwaters over hundreds of square miles.

The Amazon is the grandest spectacle in South America. With its tributaries, it drains at least 40 per cent of the continent. The Amazon itself rises within 150 miles of the Pacific in Peru, to flow 4,000

miles to the Atlantic through a wilderness of rain forest. With its multitude of tributaries, each one a river of consequence, the Amazon occupies hot, steamy, lowlands that seldom rise more than 1,000 feet above sea level. The river basin is 800 miles wide at its widest but narrows to 20 miles where it passes between the Guiana plateau and the Brazilian highlands on its journey to the ocean.

A low tableland extends westward from the Brazilian highlands to divide the watersheds of the Amazon to the north from the basin of the Paraguay-Paraná system to the south. The Paraguay-Paraná system, with its large tributaries, drains the southern portion of the Brazilian highlands and the eastern slopes of the Andean Cordillera as it crosses the Gran Chaco, the third of the great lowlands of South America. The Chaco merges imperceptibly with the Pampas of Argentina and Uruguay as the system enters the estuary of the Rio de la Plata and the Atlantic.

The plateau of Patagonia occupies the extreme southern segment of the continent south of the Argentine Pampa. The plateau rises to altitudes of more than 2,500 feet where it stands between the sub-Andean depression at the foot of the Andean Cordillera and the Atlantic. It has a rolling surface, through which mountain-fed streams have cut canyons to the clifted, rugged coast.

The eastern margin of South America is marked by the Guiana plateau north of the Amazon channel and the vast Brazilian highlands that occupy almost one-quarter of the continent. The Guiana plateau has a rolling surface of rounded hills with broad tablelands, and is intersected by several short mountain ranges. One small river in the plateau pitches over the edge of a high mesa to form Angel Falls, a drop of 3,212 feet, perhaps the highest waterfall in the world. The Guiana plateau has been important for diamonds and gold, and today produces large amounts of iron ore.

The Brazilian highlands are the largest and most important of the eastern plateaus. The highlands rise along a steep escarpment a few miles inland from the Atlantic to altitudes of 1,000 to 3,000 feet, and descend by steplike terraces to the valley of the Amazon in the north and the Paraguay-Paraná River basins in the south and the west. The edge of the escarpment, the Serra do Mar, overlooks narrow, discontinuous lowlands along the coast. The plateau surface is rolling, with numerous areas of steep hills and several isolated ranges of low mountains that do not exceed 9,000 feet. In the west the surface is moderately elevated and rolling, interrupted by areas of swamps and marshes. Much of the plateau is suitable for agricultural purposes, although little land is tilled in the far interior.

Rivers rise in the highlands near the crest of the Serra do Mar a few miles from the Atlantic, only to turn westward and flow inland to the Paraná or north to the Amazon tributaries. The Rio São Francisco, the Rio Doce, and the Rio Paraíba have cut through the mountains directly to the ocean. For centuries the Brazilian plateau has been known for its wealth of minerals—gold, diamonds, and semiprecious stones, such as topaz and aquamarine. In recent decades, its great stores of iron ore, manganese, and base metals have become important in the mineral economy of Brazil.

CLIMATE AND VEGETATION

South America has the largest area of wet equatorial climate found on a continent (Figure 7-5). Yet most of the continent's population lives within the tropical highlands and subtropical areas. The altitude of the Andean Cordillera and the Brazilian plateau offset significantly the otherwise hot temperatures that would befall these areas, and the great latitudinal extent of the southern part of South America provides another notable area of mid-latitude climate favoring settlement.

The northern part of the continent lies across the equator. Temperatures are warm to hot over much of the continent most of the year. Only the elevations of the highlands and the amount and seasonality of precipitation give variety to the climatic pattern. Since the southern part of South America falls within the mid-latitudes, it enjoys a distinct seasonality in both temperature and precipitation that gives it a true summer and winter.

WET EQUATORIAL The wet equatorial climate of South America dominates the Amazon basin and the trade-wind coasts to the northeast and southeast and in Pacific Colombia. In this hot and humid region rainfall is possible almost every day of the year. Temperatures will average 80°F, but will seldom exceed 90°F month by month. Rainfall will average 60 inches yearly, increasing to 80 inches or more upslope on the highlands and coastal littorals.

Although the lateritic topsoils of the wet equatorial climate are usually badly leached of plant nutrients, the deeper soils will support a thick selva of luxuriant broadleaf, evergreen forest. The forest consists of tall hardwoods and some softwoods, with a tremendous number of species. The trees are cloaked with a multitude of vines clinging to the trunks and branches from the rather open forest floor to the treetops. Only low shrubs and bushes occupy the openings between the trees. Along the rivers that penetrate through the thick forest, the sunlight seeks

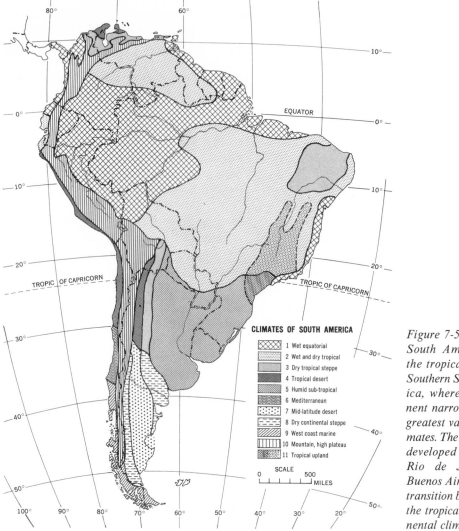

Figure 7-5 Much of South America is in the tropical climates. Southern South America, where the continent narrows, has the greatest variety of climates. The most highly developed area, from Rio de Janeiro to Buenos Aires, is in the transition belt between the tropical and continental climates.

CLIMATES OF SOUTH AMERICA

1 Wet equatorial
2 Wet and dry tropical
3 Dry tropical steppe
4 Tropical desert
5 Humid sub-tropical
6 Mediterranean
7 Mid-latitude desert
8 Dry continental steppe
9 West coast marine
10 Mountain, high plateau
11 Tropical upland

SCALE

0   500
| | | | | MILES

out the forest floor, and a riot of jungle palms and shrubs fills in between the trees.

WET-AND-DRY TROPICAL On the poleward margins of the wet equatorial climate, rainfall declines in amount and is distributed during the year so that a distinct dry season occurs when the sun is low in the heavens. North of the Amazon region, the Orinoco lowlands and the

northern third of the Guiana highlands experience this climate type. It has a distinct low-sun drought that lasts from November through March, followed by rainfall of 30 to 50 inches during the high-sun rainy season. South of the Amazon lowlands, in the Southern Hemisphere, the extensive areas of west central Brazil and the Gran Chaco have high-sun precipitation during December to April, followed by low-sun drought from May to October. Since the Chaco extends farther poleward than the Orinoco basin, its southern margin has cooler temperatures during the low-sun period, with frost as a major possibility. The better-watered savannas close to the Amazonian rain forests have large numbers of trees, interrupted by grassland openings in the drier or poorly drained areas. As rainfall amounts decrease and the dry season becomes prolonged, broken woodland with tall grasses gives way to shorter grasses with trees limited to stream courses or to low areas where sufficient moisture is present. Over many of the savannas, rainfall is so scant and evaporation during the year so effective that little moisture remains even to support short grasses.

SEMIARID GRASSLANDS Away from the wet-and-dry tropical climates, seasonal rainfall finally may become so small in amount, less than 18 inches, and so variable from year to year that the environment can support little more than a cover of short grasses with occasional clumps of xerophytic shrubs. The semiarid grasslands are generally narrow belts of transition between the savannas and the desertlike regions of South America. Although they are small in area, their significance is great. During the high-sun season, rainfall will fluctuate between 10 and 20 inches, and is erratic, sometimes coming as violent, sudden downpours that result in flooding. In the tropical steppes, however, the temperatures are so high that all available moisture is evaporated rapidly from the land. The foreland of the Cordillera de Mérida in Venezuela, the western slopes of the Andean Cordillera in the *tierra templada* except in western Colombia, and the *sertões* of northeast Brazil are dominated by this climate type.

The semiarid steppe also is found where temperatures are cooler, either because of altitude or seasonal variations. The high altiplanos of Peru, Bolivia, and extreme northwestern Argentina are semiarid temperate steppes, with cooler temperatures generally and even less precipitation during the year. From the Puna de Atacama in northern Argentina, skirting the western deserts at the foot of the mountains, a tremendous area of semiarid grassland with intermediate climate dominates the tableland of Patagonia. Although this zone is sometimes almost too dry to be classified as a steppe, it is mild enough in temperature, especially in the south, to support short grasses.

None of the steppe lands are so crucial or important to large population concentrations as is the semiarid tropical steppe in northeast Brazil. Covering 250,000

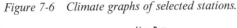

Figure 7-6 Climate graphs of selected stations.

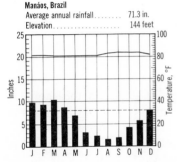
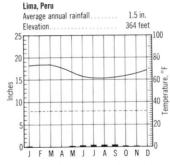
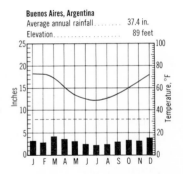

square miles and harboring 25 million people, this vast area occupies the eastern bulge of Brazil. In few other areas is the rainfall more erratic from year to year or the vegetation more nearly desertlike in appearance. Overgrazing of livestock has cleared much of the natural grass cover; it has been replaced with thorny shrubs and other useless xerophytic types.

DESERT   Western South America, from northern Peru to La Serena in Chile, embraces a desert backed by the Andean Cordillera. The Peruvian coastal desert and Atacama desert in northern Chile are among the driest areas on earth. Iquique, northern Chile, has received little rainfall since European settlement of the continent. Other areas to the north in Peru have heavy coastal fog that moistens the land and permits some shrubs to exist near the coast. For the most part, however, the desert is barren, dominated by drifting sand and barren rock surfaces. Water from melting snows and from rainfall on the higher Cordillera slopes finds its way to the Pacific in alternately wet and dry braided channels. In Peru the streams have been diverted into districts where irrigation agriculture is important. The desert extends up the slopes to about 5,000 feet in Peru, and virtually to the Cordillera crests in Chile.

In western Argentina a narrow desert region follows the foot of the Andes south to Patagonia. Lying in a rain shadow where the land is sheltered from the moisture-bearing winds from the Pacific, this barren region has no settlements except near streams that rise in the snow-fields of the Andes or where there is water from artesian wells.

MEDITERRANEAN   Middle Chile occupies a small segment of western South America from 30° to 38° south latitude and enjoys a climate similar to that of southern California. During the rainy winters the temperatures are usually mild, but vary with the southern frontal storms that sweep in from the Pacific. On the other hand, the summers are quite dry, with temperatures more like those of the desert areas to the north. Temperatures range from 68°F for the warmest months to 48°F during the winter, from May to September. Usually, total rainfall is greater in the subhumid south, 40 inches, than in the semiarid north, 10 to 12 inches, nearer the Atacama. In addition to the frontal storms from the Pacific, air masses from the ocean are forced to rise up and over the Andes, cooling and giving up precipitation as they do so.

The vegetation of middle Chile resembles closely the vegetation types of California, whence many of the trees, shrubs, and grasses have been introduced. Plant life is adjusted to the wet-dry cycle and consists mostly of grasses, drought-resistant shrubs, and thorny bush similar to the chaparral of California. Broad-leaved trees, cedar, and the introduced eucalyptus are found in better-watered areas and wherever irrigation is possible.

MARINE WEST COAST   In southern Chile the dry season becomes shorter and finally terminates as rainfall increases in amount and is distributed more evenly during the year. The frontal storms carried along in the "roaring forties" persist all year round and carry large amounts of precipitation inland. Pushing inland, the air masses are forced to rise and are cooled, giving up nearly continuous and heavy precipitation. The summers are chilled by the persistent cover of cloud and mist, and the winters are quite cold, with snow blanketing the mountain slopes to the shore. A veil of fog hangs continually over the island archipelagoes. Precipitation averages 80 inches but may reach over 150 inches in windward headlands or on exposed mountain slopes. The islands and fiorded coastline are covered with thick stands of Chilean pine in the north and beech, aspen, fir, and spruce in the south.

HUMID SUBTROPICAL   The humid subtropical climate is second only to the highland climate in the numbers of people who dwell and gain a livelihood in a single area. It is situated in the southeastern segment of the continent, approximately between 25° and 40° south latitude. In South America, the humid subtropical climate extends farther equatorward than the comparable climate type in the United States, and is shut off from frontal storms during the summer. The humid subtropical climate is more strongly marine-influenced; thus its winters are milder and marked by frequent invasions of frontal storms from the south. The admirable climate conditions and fine soils that prevail over the land in this region support natural grasslands and pine forests. The grasslands, or pampas, have proved unusually suited to the introduction of European agricultural systems. In the summer temperatures will average 68°F and in the winters 55°F, varying somewhat from southern Brazil to Bahia Blanca in Argentina. Precipitation is heavier in the winter, ranging between 40 inches in the eastern pampa to 22 inches on the drier margins in the interior.

TROPICAL HIGHLAND   The variety of climates on the mountainsides and valleys of the highlands are quite similar to those present throughout the highlands of tropical Middle America. But the major climate zones occur at lower altitudes on the mountains nearer the equator, while the greater latitudinal length of the Cordillera causes the lower zones—the *tierra caliente* and *tierra templada*—to disappear entirely south of 35° south latitude.

Prevailing easterly trade winds cause the east-facing slopes to be quite rainy, whereas western slopes, in general, lie in a rain shadow and are considerably drier. Exposed headlands will receive large amounts of precipitation, but slopes facing them across valleys may lie in a local rain shadow and be quite dry. Each valley and slope will thus have its own individual microclimate, perhaps quite different from that of the surrounding slopes.

Near the equator, the *tierra caliente* dominates slopes to about 3,000 feet, where it gives way to the *tierra templada* that extends to about 7,000 feet. Above 7,000 feet, the *tierra fria* continues to the paramos at 9,500 to 10,000 feet. The paramos reach the snow line at 11,500 to 12,000 feet, beyond which snowfields and glaciers are found.

The vegetation types present in each of these climate zones depend on the amount of precipitation. Usually, the *tierra caliente* will reflect the vegetation and climate of the surrounding lowlands. On the eastern slopes of the Andes, in the Brazilian highlands, and on the Guiana plateau, the lower slopes in the *tierra caliente* continue the tropical forests of the lowlands. The tropical species of trees and other vegetation give way gradually to subtropical species in the *tierra templada,* and to temperate species in the *tierra fria.* The drier western slopes of the Andean Cordillera are completely devoid of trees to the upper limits of the *tierra templada,* where some forests appear and reach into the *tierra fria.* Grasslands cover the slopes beyond the tree line, and alpine vegetation dwindles out in the colder, remote uplands of barren rock and snow toward the crests of the mountains.

ECONOMIC DEVELOPMENT

The majority of the people of South America are still tied very closely to the land (Figure 7-7). Although the growth of

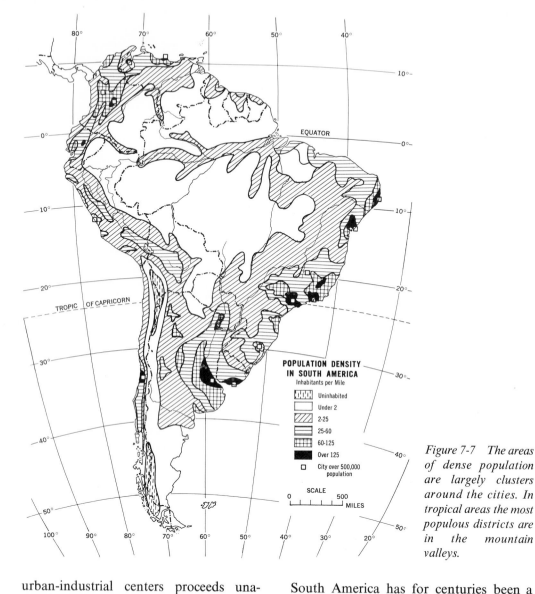

POPULATION DENSITY
IN SOUTH AMERICA
Inhabitants per Mile

	Uninhabited
	Under 2
	2-25
	25-60
	60-125
	Over 125
□	City over 500,000 population

SCALE

0   500
MILES

Figure 7-7 The areas of dense population are largely clusters around the cities. In tropical areas the most populous districts are in the mountain valleys.

urban-industrial centers proceeds unabated, and medium-sized cities are beginning to experience the tide of migration from the countryside that has already flooded the great cities, it is the farmer, tenant, farm laborer, and rancher who provide the food staples for the cities and the major export commodities of nearly all the countries on which the national economies of several nations depend.

South America has for centuries been a provisioner of tropical agricultural products and temperate grains and livestock commodities of worldwide significance. To the exports of the colonial era—gold, silver, indigo, brazilwood, natural rubber, sugar, and coffee—carried by the wooden-hulled ships of centuries past, have been added cargoes of bananas, wheat, corn, wool, mutton, and beef, filling the holds of great ships that ply the ocean lanes between the continent and Europe and North America. The climatic and seasonal differences of South America are implicit in the development of commerce with Northern Hemisphere markets and the foundation of commercial agriculture today. The roles of the individual countries differ strikingly. But the output of export commodities should increase substantially in decades ahead as domestic and international markets for these essential agricultural products expand.

AGRICULTURE

Agriculture is in a critical state throughout most of the countries of South America, because two types of agriculture exist side by side. The one harvests the commercial export commodities; the other provides the day-to-day needs of millions of families who dwell on the land and eke out a marginal existence. Sometimes side by side, sometimes inextricably interrelated, sometimes completely apart from each other, these divergent systems prevail and must be understood clearly to appreciate the severe difficulties facing the nations and their peoples.

The traditional commercial landholding is in the form of a plantation, referred to in some places as the hacienda, fazenda, *estancia,* or *fundo.* The older types of plantations were owned usually by a family who received the land as a royal grant and passed it on intact generation after generation. Newer types of plantations have been purchased in recent decades either by new owners or corporate enterprises. The owners hire laborers to work the land, or rent land to them by sharing the income from crops they produce. In centuries past, slavery and forced Indian labor were socially approved and widely used. These lands have been used rather efficiently

when cultivated, especially in recent decades, to produce export commodities. The introduction of modern techniques and machinery has been found necessary to assure good harvests. Not all of the land is utilized, however, and in many places, because of the lack of markets for commodities or the shortage of field laborers, the land is underdeveloped; it is held as capital awaiting development or for personal prestige.

In sharp contrast, tiny plots of poorer land, often on slopes and mountainsides, are tilled by the farmers, who may or may not own the land. In accordance with the economic practices of the previous Indian societies, the land given over to the Indian populations was held communally in trust, first by the Church and later by the individual governments. Using primitive farm methods that have changed little since the Inca Empire or seventeenth-century Spain and Portugal, these subsistence farmers work the soil today to provide food for their families and graze small flocks on the poor pastures on mountain slopes, in valleys and basins, or on the plains. Occasionally for wages, formerly by coercion, the peasant farmers work on the plantations, where they are guided in the cultivation and harvest of the commercial crop or in the care of livestock. While hardly the best techniques are used on the plantation, those practiced by the small farmer on his own land are even more destructive of the soil.

The great inequality in land distribution is a major challenge to the economic and social structures of every South American country. The problem is simply that if the land were to be distributed equally, the production on the plantation of the commercial crops indispensable to the very existence of several countries would decline or nearly cease. The small farmers would apply to the land the primitive, destructive farming techniques that they have inherited and would ruin much of the land. Meanwhile more and more of the commercial land must be shifted to the production of food staples for the growing populations of the cities, and the output of the vital export commodities is leveling. How to sustain expanded production of export commodities and to provide the cities with enough food, at the same time that land distribution and rural education programs progress, is the challenge that staggers the imagination. Yet projects are under way.

MANUFACTURING

In the cities, the development of manufacturing industries to supply the domestic market at home with consumer items and the growth of heavy industry in countries whose markets can support them keynote a major change in South America. Modern manufacturing, except in Argentina, is a development of the past forty years. As recently as 1950, every nation relied on revenue earned by the export abroad of mineral and agricultural commodities to purchase the larger share of the needs of its people. Since then Brazil, Chile, and Colombia have joined Argentina in managing to supply from their own factories a wide variety of consumer needs such as clothing, shoes, foodstuffs, small appliances, and simple chemical products. Brazil and Chile pioneered in integrated iron and steel industries, followed by Colombia, Argentina, Peru, and Venezuela. The products from these industries have multiplied job opportunities for those who are skilled in various subsidiary industries and have increased the number and variety of goods available.

These industries, however, are not as efficient as those in Western Europe or North America that provide quantities of import manufactures. To protect the home industries it has been necessary to raise tariff walls, license corporations, and restrict certain classes of items. At the same time, large-scale factories producing goods on a mass-production basis do not employ the numbers of unskilled people who are swarming to the cities, responding to the good news of a better life elsewhere.

TRANSPORTATION

Within each country and across South America land transportation is still more a feat of accomplishment than a fact of everyday life. Only the Argentine Pampa, east central Brazil, and central Chile have anything approaching an integrated network of highways and railroads. Railroad construction faced the nearly insuperable hurdles of the mountains and sparsely settled tropical lowlands, and was limited to service lines leading to commercial agricultural areas and mining camps.

The past four decades, however, have witnessed the construction of thousands of miles of all-weather and hard-surfaced highways. Today it is the highway, traversed by trucks, buses, and automobiles, that gives promise of better assembly to raw materials, circulation of people, distribution of manufactures, and spread of education. Of the older means of inland transportation, only the navigable Amazon, Rio de la Plata, lower Paraná, and the lower Orinoco show improved prospects for the future. Even the tributaries of the rivers, including those of the Amazon and Magdalena, are slowly declining in importance as faster or more efficient avenues of transport are developed.

THE CARIBBEAN COUNTRIES

The independent countries of Venezuela and Colombia and the three dependencies, commonly referred to as the Guianas, are called the Caribbean countries of

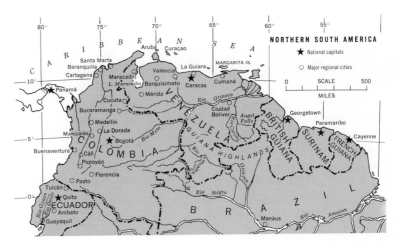

Figure 7-8 Northern South America is dominated by the Andes Mountains and the Guiana highlands with the llanos separating the two areas.

South America (Figure 7-8). Except for a small part of southeastern Colombia, the entire area is north of the equator. Venezuela is the only independent South American country that has no territory in the Southern Hemisphere. Large areas in all these countries are sparsely settled and generally undeveloped. Each has highlands and lowlands in a topographical pattern that greatly influences the activities of the people; but in Colombia and Venezuela the highlands offset, to some extent, the climatic disadvantages of the low-latitude tropics. The Caribbean countries are well situated for world trade because their northward-facing coast is near, and pointed toward, the principal world-trade lanes, those leading to the United States and northwestern Europe. The Caribbean countries are areas of great potential.

VENEZUELA

Black gold has flowed from beneath Lake Maracaibo since the fabulous petroleum fields of Venezuela were opened in the 1920s. Before the advent of petroleum, coffee and cacao, along with cattle and hides, provided the economic base of Venezuela, then a poor Caribbean nation.

Today petroleum and iron ore exports provide the revenue essential to the life and vitality of the nation. Although the farms and ranches of Venezuela employ 40 per cent of the working force of the country, the output of the very commodities that were so important in the country's earlier history is lagging. Agriculture has failed to progress with the rest of the economy, and Venezuela sometimes finds it difficult to provide many necessary food staples. For a nation rich from royalties from petroleum and iron ore, this is indeed a paradoxical situation.

Thousands of people seeking better opportunity have been drawn to the oil fields, to the cities, and recently to the iron districts of the Caroní Valley. Behind them they have left their fields and herds untended, with no one to take their places. Many small farms have been abandoned, and the large haciendas find it increasingly difficult to recruit dependable, skilled field hands. The migrants arrive in the cities and mining centers only to discover that they lack the technical skills necessary for employment and are stranded, living on government aid.

REGIONS   The Andean Cordillera extends along the Caribbean fringe of Venezuela for 600 miles and embraces about 12 per cent of the area and three-quarters of the people of the country. The Cordillera separates the Maracaibo lowlands from the vast lowlands to the south occupied by the Orinoco River. Beyond the Orinoco is the Guiana plateau, shared by Venezuela with Brazil and the Guianas. The sparsely populated Orinoco lowlands and the Guiana plateau include nearly four-fifths of the country. The Andean highlands have all the large cities except Maracaibo and a few coastal ports, most of the agriculture, and a very large proportion of the manufacturing of the nation.

The Maracaibo lowlands, with their large petroleum production, are the greatest source of Venezuela's wealth. Surrounded on three sides by highlands, the region is nearly shut off from the moderating influence of the Caribbean trade winds. With their high temperatures and constant humidity, the lowlands have one of the most unpleasant climates in South America. The Maracaibo Lake plain is

Figure 7-9 The Lake Maracaibo area of Venezuela is one of the principal oil-producing regions of the world. (Courtesy of Hamilton Wright.)

broader on the west, but the petroleum fields are along the eastern shore. Until recently, a sandbar across the channel limited traffic to shallow-bottomed lighters and tankers entering the lake at high tide. A deep channel has now been dredged, and larger tankers have access to the oil terminals on the eastern shore. Maracaibo, a modern, tropical city, is the center of the petroleum industry and is the second largest urban center in Venezuela.

The coastal oil fields produce more than 1 million barrels of petroleum daily. Over one-half of the 4,400 producing wells are offshore in the shallow waters of the lake. Venezuela ranks among the three leading world producers and exporters of petroleum, and for many years exported more petroleum than any other country. Over two-thirds of the entire national production is concentrated in the petroleum fields around Lake Maracaibo. Petroleum and its derivatives provide about 90 per cent in value of the country's exports.

Aruba and Curaçao, two islands of the Netherlands Antilles, are important to the economies of Venezuela and Colombia. On Aruba and Curaçao are petroleum refineries which process Venezuelan and Colombian oil that is sent to Western European and North American markets. In each country refineries provide most of the domestic requirements for petroleum products.

Aside from petroleum, the Maracaibo lowlands are of small importance. Cacao, sugar cane, coffee, and some livestock come from the highlands and plains that surround the basin to Maracaibo City for export. However, pioneer settlement is under way in the south, where the new branch of the Pan-American Highway cuts through the wilderness of the rain forest.

The Cordillera de Mérida rises as a great arch from the Maracaibo lowlands and Orinoco basin to the only snow-covered peaks in Venezuela at 15,000 feet. The people of the Cordillera live in population clusters between 2,500 and 6,000 feet in elevation in the upper *tierra caliente* and lower *tierra templada.* Coffee is the major crop from the tree-shaded slopes and valleys. The Cordillera is the chief coffee region and a major cacao region of Venezuela. Mérida and other communities in the highland basins and valleys have a more temperate climate than the lower tropical slopes. Lying in the *tierra templada,* they were among the first centers of settlement, where much of the land was divided into large estates. Between 7,500 and 10,000 feet, the basins and mountain slopes are covered with fields of wheat, barley, and potatoes, and cattle forage on the temperate grasses. Sheep graze the higher pastures of the paramos. Everywhere below 6,000 feet, corn occupies most of the cultivated land and provides the principal food staple, with beans, cassava, bananas, and other subsistence crops.

North of the Cordillera is the low Segovia plateau. It is highly dissected and dominated by a harsh, dry climate that favors only scattered grazing of cattle and goats; farming is restricted to a few valleys where the population is clustered about the streams.

The coastal ranges and eastern highlands include the densely settled Valencia basin and the Caracas Valley, with their urban centers and smaller valleys and basins in between. Caracas, the capital, is the fastest-growing metropolis of northern South America. A modern city, with tall buildings and tree-lined boulevards, it is the financial and industrial center of Venezuela.

A series of basins and valleys lie in a

Figure 7-10 Aerial view of Caracas, Venezuela. The city is located in a level area surrounded by mountains. (Courtesy of Hamilton Wright.)

trough between the two paralleling mountain ranges that comprise the coastal ranges. From the Caribbean, the coastal ranges rise abruptly to altitudes of 7,000 to 9,000 feet. As the most important agricultural district of the country, the Valencia basin produces sugar cane, cotton, rice, corn, and beans from the commercial plantations, and coffee and cacao from the slopes. Earlier in the century the Caracas Valley was equally important, but agriculture has declined before the invasion into the former farming districts of suburban Caracas. To replace the food supply lost from the Caracas Valley, emphasis was shifted to the Tuy River valley in the *tierra caliente,* just south of Caracas. On the mountain slopes in the *tierra templada* around the basins and valleys, coffee and cacao remain important. The other commercial crops include tobacco and sisal, which are used within the country. Beans, cassava, and rice are the important food staples.

The elevations of the coastal ranges, particularly the Caracas Valley and Valencia basin, are great enough to alleviate the extreme heat of the Caribbean shore. Valencia is at an elevation of 1,500 feet, and Caracas is 3,000 feet above sea level. Situated only 8 airline miles from its port at La Guaira, Caracas was for centuries nearly cut off from the outside world by the steep slopes of the north coastal range and the articulated valleys that the old road and railway followed inland. Today, the modern *Autopista* from the coast covers the distance and altitude in only 20 miles, a trip of a few minutes.

The eastern highlands have numerous small population centers, among which Cumana is notable as the oldest permanent European settlement in South America, and as a port for cacao, coffee, cotton, and livestock products of the region. Barcelona also serves as a port for petroleum from the eastern Venezuelan fields and for cattle driven to packing plants in the port.

The Orinoco lowlands include a large river watershed that incorporates much of eastern Colombia. Nearly 1,000 miles long and averaging 200 miles in width, the lowlands stretch from the Andean Cordillera on the west and north to the Guiana plateau in the south. Even though they have seen remarkable development recently in industrial growth, pioneer settlement, and improved animal husbandry, the lowlands remain very sparsely settled.

The Orinoco River plain is flat and interrupted by occasional rolling hills until it rises against the Cordillera de Mérida and the coastal ranges as a series of piedmont terraces. The wet-and-dry climate brings heavy rainfall during the hot, high-sun season. The downpours are so great that vast areas of the plain are flooded. Grasses will grow in thick luxuriance, but will be unavailable to cattle that have been moved by ranchers to protected uplands. With the onset of the warm, dry season, the grasses will ripen and dry out, becoming almost inedible and of little value to cattle. Insect pests and diseases plague the animals at all times. The cattle seldom fatten properly, but still walk to markets at river towns, in the highland basins, or along the coast. They produce low-quality beef, and usually are of value for their hides only.

Two factors are altering the character of the Orinoco lowlands. Pioneering efforts by the Venezuelan government have opened new lands to farming on the south-facing piedmont slopes. With irrigation waters from the mountains available plus good soils, the warm climate favors commercial production of basic food staples in short supply in the highland cities. The settlers have been selected carefully and trained in modern farming methods. Another type of settlement near Calabozo in the central lowlands depends for water on a large reservoir that collects water in the wet season for irrigating pastures as well as field crops. The objective is the development of a modern cattle district that is self-sufficient in most food staples. Both experiments have proved so successful that others are planned.

The second factor of importance has been the exploitation of minerals in the Orinoco lowlands and the neighboring Guiana plateau. Almost one-third of Venezuela's oil comes from the eastern fields that extend some 50 miles north of the river and westward from the Orinoco delta for over 300 miles. Moreover, the lower Orinoco plain is experiencing the impact of iron ore exploitation in the Caroní River district just south of the Orinoco. Below Ciudad Bolivar, river ports and several industrial communities are rising and changing the outlook of the region.

The Guiana plateau is hilly, with large areas of tableland edged by precipitous escarpments. The hot temperatures and large amount of rainfall favor a tropical forest cover interrupted occasionally by open grasslands. The plateau has scant population; most of the people are Indians living in the forested wilderness. Agriculture is patch farming in forest clearings of tropical subsistence crops. The region probably has a wealth of undiscovered minerals, as the discoveries of iron ore in Venezuela, bauxite in the Guianas, and manganese in Brazil attest. Gold and diamonds have been recovered for centuries and are still taken from tiny placer mines worked by hand in the sands and gravels of the streams issuing from the plateau.

Iron ore is the most important mineral produced and is the second export of Venezuela. Very large deposits of high-grade hematite with an iron content of 50 to 70 per cent are being mined. Subsidiaries of two United States corporations are exploiting the huge reserves at the rate of over 20 million tons a year. To aid in shipping the ore, the muddy Orinoco has been dredged to San Felix, where ocean vessels may enter to take on the ore. Mining is done in open cuts, and the ore is transported to the river ports, from which it is shipped in ore carriers to tidewater steel mills near Baltimore and Philadelphia. A steel mill with a capacity of 140,000 tons is in operation at Puerto Ordaz, a new industrial city created to house the plant. The Caroní River has been impounded to provide hydroelectricity for both the steel mill and the mining camps. Coal from mines near Barcelona is shipped to Puerto Ordaz, where it is treated to provide coke suitable for the furnaces.

FOREIGN TRADE   Venezuela's per capita foreign trade is the greatest of the Latin-American countries, and is exceeded in total trade only by that of Brazil and Argentina. Petroleum and derivatives account for 93 per cent of the total exports, in value more than 1 billion dollars annually. Iron ore now accounts for almost 5 per cent of the exports. From revenue earned by these sales Venezuela obtains the money to purchase goods in foreign countries. Almost two-thirds of Venezuela's imports originate in the United States. From the United States come imports of industrial machinery, automobiles and trucks, other metal products, textiles, chemicals, medicines, and many other items. Demand from the oil fields and the cities, especially Caracas, accounts for large imports of foodstuffs which help to keep the cost of living very high.

COLOMBIA

Having coasts on both the Pacific and Caribbean, Colombia enjoys a unique position in South America. With an area of 440,000 square miles, it ranks fourth in size. The population of 15 million causes Colombia to rank third among the nations of the continent in number of people. Rugged arms of the Andean Cordillera cut across the country and divide it into several regions, separating the lowlands of the Pacific coast, the Caribbean river plains, and the eastern rain forests and llanos. Several highland areas in the tropical zone favored settlement, but the nearly insurmountable terrain acted as a barrier to surface communication and isolated almost completely one population cluster from another. Only with the advent of air transport and the construction of modern highways in recent decades have the major population centers been tied together effectively. The shadow of early isolation still hovers over the political and economic thinking of the country.

REGIONS   The tremendous diversity of landforms and climates of Colombia results in several major regions. The Caribbean Lowlands in the north incorporate the river systems of the Magdalena and its tributaries and the islandlike outlier—the Santa Marta highlands. The Andean Cordillera that divides the country is bordered by lowlands and low mountains on the Pacific and is sliced by river valleys that traverse the country from their headwaters in the south to the Caribbean Lowlands. The eastern arm of the Andean Cordillera thrusts across Colombia into Venezuela, where it carries the system eastward to the Atlantic. Thus the Cordillera stands as a bulwark overlooking the hot, tropical rain forest of the Amazon to the south and the llanos and Orinoco tributaries to the east.

The Caribbean Lowlands of Colombia encompass several of the most highly developed tropical grazing districts of South America. The wet-and-dry savanna climate affords adequate rainfall in the high-sun period to support good tropical grasses, many of which have been introduced and are more nourishing to cattle than the native grasses. Improved livestock such as the zebu breed of India has supplanted the older *criollo* (Spanish longhorn) breeds still common in the llanos and Orinoco lowlands. Moreover, irrigation from the waters of the Sinú, the Magdalena, and other rivers has brought a harvest of fine crops of sugar cane, rice, cotton, corn, beans, tobacco, and food staples. The western piedmont slopes of the Santa Marta highlands were among the first banana plantation districts of the Caribbean; now disease has cut heavily

Figure 7-11   Llanos of eastern Colombia. (Courtesy of Standard Oil Company of New Jersey.)

into the plantings. The older cities of Cartegena and Santa Marta have been important since the days of pirates and the glory of the Spanish Main. Today, Barranquilla, a functional, modern city, dominates the economy and captures most of the Magdalena River trade from the interior highlands.

The middle Magdalena basin is the center of Colombia's petroleum industry. Originally developed by foreign capital, the industry is now shared with a government-owned enterprise. From the interior and the Cúcuta lowlands where there are other oil fields, pipelines carry petroleum to Mamonal near Cartegena for export.

The Pacific slopes of the Andes are hot, wet, and cloaked with clouds and tropical forests that limit settlement and make economic activity a challenge. Nonetheless, the port of Buenaventura has achieved unusual prominence since it became the most accessible seaport for the coffee crop when highways and railroads were constructed to the coast. At least two-thirds of the country's coffee—from Antioquia, the distant eastern Cordillera, and the Cauca Valley—is shipped to overseas markets through the port. Other than a few scattered subsistence settlements along streams in the forests and the placer mining of platinum and gold from the sands and gravels of the Atrato and other rivers, the region remains remote and forbidding.

The Cauca Valley rests between the arms of the Andes. Shut off by the mountains from the moisture-bearing air masses of the Pacific, the Cauca Valley and Antioquia to the north stand intermediate between the *tierra caliente* of the Pacific and Caribbean Lowlands and the *tierra templada.* The Cauca Valley Corporation, modeled after the Tennessee Valley Authority, is transforming the farming and ranching activities in the valley. With its economic hub at Cali, the irrigated valley floor is a major producer of sugar cane, rice, cotton, and a host of food staples. The entire valley benefits from the multipurpose development of the Cauca watershed—the regulated flow of river waters, a plentiful supply of hydroelectricity, and the wise utilization of soils. The mountain slopes of the western and central Cordillera, which face each other across the valley, have many small *fincas,* or family-sized farms, producing coffee and cacao. The valley is also well known for its important herds of quality cattle, and sustains a major dairying industry.

To the south of the Cauca Valley lie the southern highlands, where the three major Cordillera separate as they enter Colombia. In the highlands, tiny family farms scattered over the basins and valleys in the *tierra fría* give moderate to low yields of wheat, barley, potatoes, and other food products. The provincial cities of Pasto and Popayan reflect the primitive nature of life in a region that still clings to colorful handicraft and workshop industries.

North of the Cauca Valley is Antioquia and its prosperous, modern metropolis, Medellin. A few population concentrations in Latin America are cores from which pioneer settlement has migrated voluntarily into unoccupied lands. From Antioquia colonies have pushed forward vigorously, south into the Cauca Valley, across the central Cordillera into the Magdalena Valley, and north into the margins of the Caribbean Lowlands. As independent farmers, they have carried with them the coffee culture that today serves as the economic base not only of Antioquia, but of Colombia as well. More than coffee is produced; cacao, sugar cane, potatoes, dairy products, and many other crops help to support the people of the region, and to provide for the needs of surrounding regions of Colombia. Medellin has one of the finest medium-sized industrial establishments in South America. Textiles and wearing apparel, in particular, have a national market.

The Magdalena Valley, east of the Cauca Valley and Antioquia, is flanked by the central and eastern Cordillera. The volcanic soils of the mountain slopes and the climate of the *tierra templada* that so abundantly favor coffee and cacao in Antioquia are also present here. The valley floor of the Magdalena is closer to sea level and drier than its neighbor to the west. Dry tropical grasslands of the valley floor support lower-grade cattle. However, by channeling the river waters to irrigation projects, major yields of rice, cotton, sugar cane, beans, and corn supply many of the needs of the country.

The eastern Cordillera is much broader than the other ranges and includes numerous highland basins and valleys that have long favored settlement. The largest and most important of these is the Sabana de Bogotá, with the nation's capital. Situated in the *tierra fría,* these extensive basins are producers of numerous food staples. The excellent grasses of the basins support fine beef herds and the most important dairying region in northern South America. Though much of the land is still farmed below capacity and the small farmers must cling to the tiny patches on hillsides, important progress has been made to raise the level of yields and to mechanize production on large haciendas in the basins and valleys. The northern third of the Cordillera is at a lower elevation, in the *tierra templada,* and sends tropical beverage crops and tobacco to markets in Bucaramanga.

Bogotá is both the political and intellectual capital of Colombia. In recent years, however, with the establishment of the iron and steel industry near supplies of iron ore and coal at Paz de Rio in the highlands northeast of the capital, Bogotá has developed an industrial base worthy of note. It is from mines near Bogotá that the world's major supply of emeralds find their circuitous way into world markets.

The eastern lowlands or llanos of Venezuela continue south into Colombia where *criollo* cattle roam the tropical grasslands and encounter the same hazards of flooding and disease that plague those to the north. Southward, across a low divide formed by outliers of the Guiana plateau, wooded areas appear and gradually merge into tropical forests, as rainfall increases and the dry season present in the llanos disappears completely. Only scattered tribes of forest Indians and a few trading stations are located in the wilderness. Forest products such as balata, natural rubber, and medicinal barks are collected. There is a lumbering industry, but the removal of tropical cabinet woods through the rain forest and down the Amazon is slow and difficult.

TRANSPORTATION   The creation of an adequate surface transportation system across seemingly insurmountable barriers has wrought a change in the political and economic intercourse of Colombia's otherwise isolated population centers. Modern highways can be traversed by automobiles and trucks from the Caribbean shore at Santa Marta or Cartegena through the eastern Cordillera or Cauca Valley, south along routes of the Pan-American Highway into Ecuador. A railroad, completed in 1961, extends from Santa Marta to Salgar, opening the Magdalena Valley to easier travel and transportation between the coast and industrial centers in the interior. Shifting channels and sandbars clogging the Magdalena River below La Dorada, the head of navigation, have nearly terminated a century of passenger travel on the once colorful, though lengthy, passage on paddle-wheel steamers to Barranquilla and the north coast. Air travel has proved a boon to people.

FOREIGN TRADE   The base of Colombia's foreign trade is mostly coffee, which is sent mainly to the United States. Over 65 per cent of the country's imports and 80 per cent of its exports are with the United States. Colombia's mountain-grown coffees, like those of Central America, are more carefully harvested and prepared than are the Brazilian coffees. They bring 3 to 5 cents more per pound in world markets. Petroleum is second in value among exports, but is declining as more of the product must be used at home. Other exports include bananas, gold, hides, and emeralds.

The country's imports, like those of most other South American countries, reflect the economic change in progress. Heavy industrial machinery for new manufacturing plants, automobiles, railroad equipment, and temperate grains, to supplement national production, are important. A substantial source of income is the tourist industry, particularly from winter Caribbean tours that stop over at the beautiful old colonial cities of the Caribbean shore.

THE GUIANAS

The three Guianas—British, French, and Dutch (Surinam)—remain political dependencies of the United Kingdom, France, and the Netherlands. Only British Guiana has achieved a considerable measure of internal self-government, in preparation for eventual independence. Surinam is incorporated with the Kingdom of the Netherlands, and French Guiana is an overseas department of the French Republic. Although these dependencies have been ruled by European nations for over 350 years, they remain undeveloped and sparsely populated. Of the approximately 1 million people who live in the Guianas, about 650,000 live in British Guiana, 250,000 in Surinam, and 30,000 in the French colony.

The narrow coastal plain, originally too swampy for dense forest growth but capable of being drained, provided a satisfactory area for settlement. A few miles inland, the Guiana plateau rises from the coastal plain to elevations of 9,000 feet. As in Venezuela and Brazil, the upland is blanketed by a dense tropical forest. The monsoonal tendency along the northeast coast amplifies the already high rainfall, and the discomfort of heat and humidity creates an exceptionally unpleasant and monotonous environment.

Though the coast was skirted by Spanish and Portuguese ships of discovery in the sixteenth century, the first permanent settlement was made by the Dutch about a century later. The dense forest, almost impassable swamps, and difficult climate discouraged the early discoverers. The Dutch, and later the British, drained the swamps and began growing the highly lucrative crop of sugar cane. Since labor was scarce, as in the Antilles, Negro slaves were introduced from Africa; but the experiment proved a failure since they escaped into the thick forests. The labor problem was solved by bringing in workers from India and the East Indies. Descendants of the early escapees, the "Bush Negroes," pursue subsistence farming on tiny clearings in settlements scattered throughout the tropical wilderness.

There is considerable similarity between British Guiana and Surinam. The overall population density is among the lowest in South America; yet in settled districts, small as they may be, densities are very high. In these two dependencies the leading crops are sugar cane and rice. The cane is grown chiefly for markets in Western Europe, and rice, the staple food of the Asiatics, is second in acreage. Other crops include cacao, coconuts, cassava, yams, and tropical fruits. There are few Europeans and practically no indigenous Indians in either dependency. The Europeans live in the capitals at Georgetown and Paramaribo, the principal cities and ports of their respective countries.

Perhaps the greatest boon to the otherwise weak economies of Surinam and British Guiana has been the discovery and exploitation of bauxite, in which the two dependencies are leading world producers. Though some of the ore is washed and concentrated locally, all is exported; the United States and Canada are major importers. Other minerals include gold and diamonds, panned from placers as they are in Venezuela.

French Guiana has a small population and area and a weak economy. With scant population, the total area of cultivated land does not exceed a few thousand acres. The capital, Cayenne, has only about 15,000 people and ships few commodities abroad.

WESTERN SOUTH AMERICA

In the Andes of Ecuador, Peru, and Bolivia, on gentle slopes at high elevations, Indians have dwelt for thousands of years (Figure 7-12). It was on the high, cool plateaus of the central Andes that the Spanish first became established in South America, selecting this region because of its mineral wealth and the considerable supply of native labor. Despite more than four centuries of occupation, the Spanish methods of development of the land and other resources were only partially successful. The modern prosperity of Colombia and Venezuela has not been attained by most of the Indians living on the high plateaus of the central Andes.

Chile, the fourth country of western South America, extends southward from Peru and Bolivia for about 2,600 miles, a distance as long as from Lake of the Woods to Panama, or from southernmost Alaska to Mexico City. South of Bolivia the Andes narrow, first to a series of parallel ridges and then to one tremendous range, a continuation of the Sierra Occidental. A large majority of the 6 million people in Chile live in a long valley, some 50 miles inland from the ocean, which lies between a low coastal range and the mighty Andes.

ECUADOR

Ecuador, the second smallest country in South America, has large neighbors to the north and south. It lies on both sides of the equator, backed up against the Andean Cordillera. Two areas are conducive to settlement: the highland basins that are walled in between the crests of the Cordillera and the watershed of the Guayas and Daule Rivers opening on the seaport of Guayaquil.

REGIONS   Across Ecuador, from north to south, the Andean Cordillera is pocketed with ten basins and a multitude of valleys at elevations of 7,000 to 10,000 feet. The Cordillera separates the hilly Pacific lowlands on the west from the eastern valleys and slopes that descend to the Amazon.

The Pacific lowlands of Ecuador form a transition from the rainy tropical forests that continue south from Colombia and the warm, semiarid grasslands and deserts that extend south into Peru. From the

Figure 7-12 Activities in the four western countries of South America are greatly influenced by the Andes. The only large plains areas are in eastern Peru and Bolivia.

Figure 7-13 Quito, the capital of Ecuador, is situated in a high mountain basin almost on the equator. (Courtesy of Pan American Airways.)

Gulf of Guayaquil northward, tropical forests in the *tierra caliente* hug the river valleys and lower mountain slopes, and in the north spread over rolling hills and low, dissected mountains that are crossed by rivers rising in the Andean Cordillera. Settlement is sparse, and only the hinterland of Esmeraldas, the smaller port of San Lorenzo, and a few subsistence communities have any agriculture. Tropical crops of cacao and bananas are grown in the *tierra caliente.* Coffee and fruits from pioneer settlements are sent to the coastal ports from settlements in the *tierra templada.* Otherwise, collecting forest products and hat weaving from local palm fibers are the local means of livelihood.

West of Guayaquil is the dry Santa Elena peninsula, whose shore is bathed by the cold Humboldt Current. Air masses cooled by the cold waters carry little moisture to the peninsula, and what does

fall follows the wet-and-dry regimes, with brief showers during the high-sun seasons. The cold waters harbor a bountiful supply of fish. A small oil field supplies local refineries, which produce enough petroleum for the country. Oil products are shipped by pipeline to Guayaquil. Where water is available from hill lands further inland, irrigated sugar cane and subsistence crops are grown. The settlement at Salinas is one of numerous small fishing villages along the coast, and is also a delightful recreation area for people from Guayaquil who wish to escape the rigors of heat and humidity, or for people from Quito who wish to escape the rigors of cold and altitude.

Guayaquil guards the head of a sizable river network. Hills of the coastal lowlands stand to the west, and the gentle piedmont slopes of the Andes rise to the east. The fertility of fine alluvial soils is renewed by seasonal flooding. The land is cultivated intensively and supports a dense population. Plantation crops of rice from the lowlands and cacao, coffee, and bananas provide the nation's leading exports. Foreign and domestic plantation owners export bananas from several small ports that open onto the gulf. The south coastal lowlands are dry, and cattle graze over the natural grasslands. Irrigation is practiced where mountain-fed streams cross the plain. Guayaquil is the largest city of Ecuador. It is becoming a modern, commercial center and seaport that has, to some extent, overcome the limitations of climate and the handicaps of disease that once clouded its future.

The cool highland basins, from 7,000 to 10,000 feet in elevation, contain almost two-thirds of Ecuador's population. The distribution of races is unlike that of the Pacific lowlands, in that most of the highland people are Indians, whereas mestizo and European peoples dwell in the cities.

The capital, Quito, is in this area. The northern basins and valleys lie at lower elevations, extending from the *tierra fría* into the *tierra templada*. Here subsistence crops of corn, wheat, potatoes, and barley are important, together with subtropical crops of sugar cane, fruits, and vegetables. The soils are derived from volcanic ash and are productive, especially when irrigated. The basin of Quito and the central basins are grain and vegetable producers, supplying the day-to-day needs of families and sending food staples to the cities. Although there are many large haciendas divided into farms that are rented to tenant farmers, much of the land is held communally by the Indian settlements. Field methods are very simple; the pointed stick and hoe are the most common farm tools. South of Quito, the basins are used more frequently for grazing, since there is less flat land and the climate is generally drier. But the basic subsistence grains are found everywhere. Cattle, sheep, and goats pasture on the slopes, cattle being the most important. The basins are linked together by the Pan-American Highway that enters the country from Ipiales in Colombia and traverses the basins south to Peru. The railroad line from the highlands joins the northern and central basins to follow an incredible, breathtaking descent to Guayaquil and the river plains.

The sheer altitude of the basins so offsets their equatorial location that temperatures are quite cool to cold, making them less than satisfactory for human comfort at nearly all times during the year. Quito is situated in one of the larger basins at 9,350 feet above sea level. Although it is just a few miles south of the equator, frost can be expected and snow may fall during the two low-sun periods each year. Towering majestically above the basins and valleys of the Andean Cordillera are several snow-clad volcanic cones exceeding 19,000 to 20,000 feet. The symmetry and grandeur of Cotopaxi and Chimborazo dominate the horizon as they overlook the basins and guard entry and exit to the highlands.

Eastern Ecuador, beyond the crests of the Andean Cordillera, slopes toward the low Amazon basin. Though attempts at pioneer settlement on the forested slopes have been made, the slopes and rain forests of the lowlands remain sparsely settled. Since access is difficult and fraught with hazards, the region is unimportant to a nation whose transportation system has not yet overcome the barriers of the land.

FOREIGN TRADE Ecuador is a producer of tropical agricultural commodities; bananas, rice, cacao, and coffee are the leading exports. The only products of the highlands to enter into world trade are small amounts of copper, gold, silver, and wool.

PERU

The great empire of the Incas, whose political center was at Cuzco, and whose mantle of authority encompassed Indian communities as far north as Colombia, across Bolivia, and south into Chile, occupied the southern highlands of Peru, the center of the impressive pre-Columbian civilization. Well disciplined by their culture, the Incas developed remarkable agricultural and irrigation systems and constructed temples and dwellings that represent feats of engineering and architecture. The Spanish conquistadores were able to substitute themselves in the system of totalitarian rule by the Incas. Seeking gold, the Spanish directed the labors of the Inca peoples away from agriculture, which fell into disuse and decay, and turned instead to the search and accumulation of precious metals from the mines of southern Peru and Bolivia.

Figure 7-14   Peruvian Indians dressed in their traditional garb. Note how barren these mountains near Cuzco are. (Courtesy of Pan American Airways.)

Though the culture of the Indians was submerged, it was not obliterated. Today the highland Indians usually speak the Quechua and Aymara tongues of their ancestors, rather than Spanish. A knowledge of their background is essential as we approach the problems, paradoxes, and cultural provincialism of the Indian communities in the highlands of Peru and Bolivia. The significance of the Indian population today becomes quite apparent when we remember that in Peru and Ecuador about two-thirds of each nation's population live in the highlands, even a higher percentage in Bolivia, and that they are Indian peoples.

REGIONS   As in Ecuador, the Andean Cordillera of Peru separates the Pacific lowlands from the eastern slopes and the Amazon lowlands. The Pacific lowlands, the broad Andean Cordillera—called the Sierra in Peru—and the Montaña of greater Amazonia occupy more than ½ million square miles, making Peru the third largest country in South America.

The Pacific lowlands of Peru are a coastal desert. Although the desert plain may reach a width of 100 miles before it rises into the Sierra, in most places the lowlands are less than 10 miles wide. In places they disappear entirely as clifted headlands and spurs of the mountains break across the lowlands to the Pacific. Fifty streams, fed seasonally by melting snow and rainfall from the Sierra, cross the Peruvian coastal desert. These waters are the lifeblood of tiny valley oases that form strips of green in a region essentially rainless. Peru's desert oases are among the most productive agricultural districts of the country. They provide cotton and sugar, the two leading agricultural export commodities, and manage to supply many of the necessary food staples to the large urban-industrial centers of Lima and its seaport, Callao, as well as to cities in the petroleum fields of the north. With better water resources and more efficient farming methods, the northern oases produce rice, sugar cane, and cotton. The middle oases along the coast, including the productive Rimac Valley, where Lima is situated, produce cotton, sugar cane, and vegetable crops. Irrigated alfalfa supports a modern dairy industry near the capital. The small, drier oases of the south grow subsistence crops and grapes for wine.

Offshore, the cold waters of the Humboldt Current are rich in marine life that sustains an abundant supply of fish. The fish catch supports a major fishing industry, and the fish are also the chief food for millions of birds that nest on tiny islands and peninsulas along the coast. Where the birds nest, guano (a rich natural fertilizer) accumulates. Once more important to the irrigated oasis agriculture than it is today, the guano industry is being replaced slowly by a synthetic nitrogen–fertilizer industry.

At the northern end of the Pacific lowlands in the Talara area are three fairly important oil fields. With the increase in domestic use of oil products, the export of petroleum has leveled.

As the primate city of Peru, Lima and its nearby port city of Callao stand unrivaled and centralize every major aspect of urban life in the country. The port city, 8 miles from the capital, is linked to Lima by a broad, modern highway, along which many new commercial and industrial establishments are situated. Lima has a centrally located position near the coast, and has easy access to the principal corridor to the interior through which supplies move inland and mineral wealth moves out. Lima also has adequate access to the interior by airline. The Pan-American Highway reaches the length of the country south to Chile, seeking out every oasis, including the Rimac Valley and Lima, along its route. The good agricultural hinterland, the fine port at Callao, and the coastal highway have contributed to Lima's emergence as the largest city of western South America.

The Andean Cordillera is only 150 miles wide at the Ecuador border but broadens to almost 450 miles across Chile and Bolivia further south. The Sierra of Peru is composed of three ranges: The western Cordillera is the barricade along the Pacific; the central Cordillera is less definite, but follows the sturdy eastern Cordillera that surveys the Amazon Basin from its crest as it swings southeast. Between the principal ranges are several major highland plateaus (*punas*) that lie in the *tierra fría* and paramos. In the Sierra live two-thirds of the people of Peru, of whom the vast majority are Indian.

Highland agriculture clings to steep slopes and occupies the valleys and basins

Figure 7-15 Main oil lines leading to the refinery located in Talara, Peru. Note the dryness of the area. (Courtesy of Standard Oil Company of New Jersey.)

to elevations of 14,000 feet and beyond. The people have added little to their knowledge of agriculture since the early years of the Spanish conquest. They utilize little more than the stick and hoe in planting the food staples so vital to their existence and in harvesting them from the stony, nutrient-robbed soils that have been worked for centuries. Tiny properties, communal Indian lands, or parcels of large estates may be grazed when in fallow, but when under cultivation they yield meager harvests of wheat and barley at lower altitudes and quinoa (Indian barley) on higher slopes. The potato and related tubers will grow in most cultivated areas. Livestock add to the pitiful livelihood of the Peruvian Indian communities. Llamas and alpacas—native to the Andes—and sheep give wool, which is woven laboriously into blankets and clothing to help stifle the cold. Cattle are found on the lower slopes and better-grassed valleys. Nearly barren slopes with clumps of bunch grass and xerophytic growth are barely maintained by the 22 to 40 inches of rainfall that is at the same time indispensable to the field crops. Deep, almost desertlike valleys and canyons isolate segments of the highlands. Cuzco, the regional center of the highlands, reflects the massive architectural achievements of the ancient Inca civilization and is today one of the four major clusters of settlement in Peru's Sierra. Arequipa, situated on the western slopes, is a marketplace for many of the livestock products from the highlands. In view of the harsh nature of the terrain, the severity of the climate, and the general oppressiveness of the Sierra environment, it is difficult to understand why most of the people of Peru choose to live in the highlands.

The Montaña, east of the Andean Cordillera on the slopes and in the lowlands, covers one-half of the area of Peru that has some prospect of development but remains virtually unoccupied. Down the grassy slopes of the eastern Cordillera low shrubs merge gradually with subtropical and finally tropical broadleaf forests in the hot, humid lowlands and river plains. Several tributaries of the Amazon, the Huallaga, Ucayali, Urubamba, and upper Amazon (Marañon in Peru), have sheared deep clefts into the eastern Sierra and afford valleys and piedmonts suitable for some settlement. Several pioneer settlements on the valley slopes send coffee, cacao, and sugar cane across the Sierra to Lima via highways. Otherwise, most of the people live along the Amazon tributaries. Iquitos is the major city in this inhospitable environment. Situated at the head of river navigation, some 2,000 miles from the Atlantic, this city of 75,000 serves as a collecting center for products of the rain forest.

MINERALS   The mines of Peru that were worked before the Spanish conquest continue to provide valuable amounts of gold and silver; but today the plentiful base metals are more important. Copper, lead, and zinc are produced in mines sometimes above 14,000 feet in elevation as at Cerro de Pasco near Lima. But new mining districts for copper have been opened in the south near Toquepala. The small steel mill at Chimbote is supplied with iron ore from mines near Marcona and with bituminous coal that is mined in the Sierra.

FOREIGN TRADE   Products of the mineral industries are Peru's leading exports, amounting to 40 per cent of the exports in most years. Cotton and sugar account for another 40 per cent. The United States is Peru's leading customer, but the total export trade with Western Europe and other South American nations, Chile in particular, is much greater. Peru imports industrial machinery, equipment, automobiles, trucks, and foodstuffs. The country's major trade partners are the United States and Western European nations.

BOLIVIA

The population core of Bolivia, in the cold, dry altiplano, is surrounded by the walls of the Andean Cordillera. The people are cut off, as is the nation, from access to the Pacific by topographic and political boundaries. In view of its area, Bolivia's population appears small, since the country is almost as large as Colombia. The Indian community and the pattern of land use in the highlands of Bolivia differ very little from those found in highland Peru. At least two-thirds of the Bolivian people are wholly or partly of Indian heritage and live at high elevations in the plateaus and basins between the Andes. The high plateau, or altiplano, lies between the western Cordillera that continues south from Peru into Chile and the central and eastern Cordillera that continues south into Argentina. To the east, the deeply dissected slopes and valleys of the Cordillera give way to the river plains of Amazonian tributaries in the north. A low divide of hill lands separates the Amazon watershed from the Paraná-Paraguay lowlands occupied by the Gran Chaco and the Pilcomayo River.

REGIONS   The western Cordillera and the two merged ranges of the central and eastern Cordillera support the more than 12,000-foot-high plateau, or altiplano. Above the altiplano, the snow-crested Cordillera rises beyond 20,000 feet. The western range is very dry with little snow on its crests as it extends from the dry Pacific lowlands of Chile to the altiplano. The Cordillera to the east blocks the southeast trade winds but does capture a considerable amount of moisture on its north and east-facing slopes. Thus the altiplano, which stands above the tree line in the cold paramos, is a dry, bleak, grassland. In the fields and mines at these high elevations oxygen is so sparse that only the barrel-chested highland Indian is capable of exerting himself without experiencing shortness of breath. The altiplano is about 60 miles wide and 500 miles long, with spurs of the Cordillera cutting the plateau into basins. The southern part of the altiplano is a desert, with salt plains and the salt Lake Poopó, that receives overflow from Lake Titicaca to the north via the Rio Desaguadero. The northern part of the plateau, near the capital at La Paz and around Lake Titicaca, is the most heavily populated area of the highlands. Since rainfall is somewhat more plentiful, coming during the high-sun season, an agricultural community similar to highland Peru has been able to subsist. Tilled fields and hill terrace farms grow potatoes, barley, and quinoa.

Herders tend flocks of llamas, alpacas, sheep, and burros on the slopes.

La Paz, at an elevation of 12,000 feet, is situated at the base of the eastern ranges in a steep-walled canyon nearly 1,500 feet below the level of the surrounding altiplano. It is the *de facto* capital of Bolivia, although Sucre, located to the south in an east-facing valley in the *tierra templada,* is officially so designated. The northern margin of the altiplano, including the city of La Paz, has a population of nearly 1 million persons. Linked by rail to Antofagasta in Chile, and by rail and steamship service across Lake Titicaca to Peru, and by rail and road to Cochabamba on the eastern slopes, La Paz has been able to maintain its primacy. The wealth of the highlands does not spring from the poverty-stricken farms and barren pasturelands of the bleak, cold altiplano, but rather from the storehouse of metals found in the surrounding Andes. The central Cordillera from La Paz south to Oruru is pocketed with mines which were worked even before the Europeans entered the continent. Formerly gold and silver, today tin, copper, lead, silver, zinc, antimony, and tungsten are important. Several of the settlements such as Corocoro, Oruru, and Potosí exist only for mining; every item needed by the miners and the industry is brought into the highland desert.

Bolivia faces a tremendous challenge, since two-thirds of its people live in the altiplano on only one-tenth of the land area of the country. The mining industries are now owned by the government and are heavily subsidized. In recent years ore and metal output, especially tin, has declined sharply. The highland agricultural communities have changed only in minor respects since the political and social changes instituted by the revolutions of the early 1950s. The people dwelling in the altiplano are not able to fulfill their own everyday needs of food, fuel, or manufactures; yet they are the majority of the Bolivian population. The Indian of the altiplano is tied to his habitat, and no amount of persuasion or promise of a better life, greater income, or opportunity seems to be able to wean him away from the desolation or suffering of the highlands he calls his home.

Beyond the eastern crests, the Andean Cordillera slopes to the greater interior lowlands of the continent. The river valleys and slopes in the *tierra templada* are remarkably blessed with rainfall, and in many places quite good soils are found on the underdeveloped frontier of Bolivia. The forested slopes of the mountains are indented deeply with fertile valleys in the *tierra caliente,* whose streams carry snowmelt and runoff to Amazon tributaries to the north and to the Pilcomayo watershed to the south. The valley farms are producers of wheat, corn, and other food staples and are the breadbasket of the altiplano. They also send cacao, coffee, sugar, fruit, grains, and the narcotic coca leaf, chewed by the highland Indian to alleviate the highland rigors of cold and hunger, from Cochabamba and other cities along the slopes to the cities of the altiplano. Lumber and firewood, so essential in the ever-cold highlands, are cut from the coniferous forests of the upper slopes and the hardwood forests of the *tierra templada.* Cattle are driven on the hoof or are flown to the highland markets. Only a few scattered pioneer settlements follow the rail lines across the eastern hill lands to Brazil. The eastern hill lands, along with the tropical forests to the north and the Chaco to the south, have not improved greatly during the past decade. Along the foot of the Andean Cordillera in the south are several small petroleum fields, especially near Tarija.

Oil is shipped by pipeline across the Andes through Cochabamba to Arica in Chile. Cochabamba is second in population and the principal commercial center in the east.

TRANSPORTATION   The major handicap to Bolivian development is the lack of an effective surface transportation system. Railroads descend precipitous slopes slowly and are limited in the volume of goods they can carry. Highways are merely trails, except for the La Paz–Cochabamba road. Even airplanes find access to airports at high altitudes very difficult.

CHILE

Chile extends southward from Peru along the Pacific shore for over 2,600 miles, over half the length of the continent. Although its length is great, the country attains a maximum width of only 300 miles from the Pacific across the low coastal range, the longitudinal valley, and the Andean Cordillera to the snow-clad political boundaries with its eastern neighbors. The length of the country from the subtropical deserts of the Atacama to the chilled waters and grasslands of Tierra del Fuego creates striking climatic contrasts. In much the same fashion, the coastal ranges, the longitudinal valley, and the Andean Cordillera which run the length of each region add a second interesting dimension to the climate divisions arising from the increasing distance of the country from the equator.

REGIONS   The Andean Cordillera, extending the length of the country and demarcating the political boundaries with Bolivia and Argentina, forms one of the major regions of Chile. The other regions, according to latitudinal position from north to south are: the Atacama desert, Mediterranean Chile, and the marine west coast of south Chile.

The Atacama continues the dry, desolate, and barren landscape of Peru southward to the vicinity of La Serena, where rainfall amounts to about 10 inches yearly. The desert of north Chile is reputedly the driest in the world. The extreme dryness has preserved deposits of sodium nitrate, the chief product of the Atacama. In the longitudinal valley, between the coastal ranges and the Andes, this soluble salt is found in layers near the surface, where it is mined and processed for export through the coastal port of Antofagasta. Chile is the leading world producer of natural nitrate, which constitutes one of its leading exports, and is also the outstanding producer of iodine, an important by-product. Large amounts of borax and salt also come from desert mining operations. The arduous climatic conditions require that all necessities to sustain the workers and the mining facilities must be shipped in, including water. The water is carried by pipelines from reservoirs in the high Cordillera. Near Coquimbo in the south, high-grade iron ore is mined from rich deposits at El Tofo. Developed by a United States corporation, the iron ore supplies Chile's iron and steel mill at Huachipato near Concepcíon, and is also exported to the eastern United States through the Panama Canal.

The international boundary follows the Andean Cordillera. Mighty peaks, including Aconcagua, rise to nearly 23,000 feet and descend to elevations of 5,000 feet or less from north to south behind the desert and the major regions of Chile. The mountains are extremely rugged and very scenic. Although they are sparsely settled, the mountains provide the leading export and source of revenue for the country. Rich in copper, iron, cobalt, gold, zinc,

and other metals, the great deposits have been developed by two United States corporations. Usually Chile ranks second to the United States in copper production; in a recent year, copper provided nearly two-thirds of the value of the country's exports. The three principal mining districts, all situated on the western slopes of the Cordillera, are Chuquicamata, El Salvador, and El Teniente. Chuquicamata has a fabulous history, and has the distinction of being the largest single copper-mining camp in the world. To develop these rich deposits in the remote, barren wastes of the mountain desert, hundreds of millions of dollars have been spent on equipment, housing, electric power, and transportation. Hydroelectric stations constructed in the high mountain valleys provide electricity, and this power is supplemented by diesel electric stations using imported fuel oil. Every year thousands of tons of food staples, expensive machinery, and other necessities are shipped in at great cost to support the workers in their homes and to maintain the operation of the mines and reduction facilities.

Mediterranean Chile is located from La Serena south to Valdivia, in the area where winter (May to October) concentrated precipitation increases appreciably from 10 inches to over 40 inches. The seasonality of temperature becomes quite evident, especially in the central valley, some 1,500 feet above sea level, lying between the coastal ranges and the Andean Cordillera.

During the summer dry season (November to April), melting snowfields and glaciers in the Cordillera supply water for irrigation from mountain streams that cross the valley and coastal ranges to the Pacific. Over the uncultivated mountain slopes and hills that divide the valley into smaller basins, there is dry shrub vegeta-

Figure 7-16   Many wheat fields in the Andes are sectioned off by stone walls. (Courtesy of Hamilton Wright.)

tion similar to that of southern California. In this particularly delightful climate live nearly 90 per cent of the Chilean people, who pursue farming activities on the good soils of the central valley and manufacturing activities in the large number of medium-sized cities in the valley and along the coast. Most of the cultivated land is still held in large estates and is not fully utilized; much of the land remains unused seasonally. Simple farm methods and inefficient use of the land have thus contributed to the lag in agricultural production. Where Chile was once an exporter of foodstuffs, the country is now forced to rely on imports of grains and other food staples. The estates are producers of winter wheat, but much of the land is kept seasonally in improved pasture grasses, such as alfalfa, that support dairy and beef herds. Table grapes thrive

in the mild climate, and Chilean wines have an international reputation. The small farms are important producers of corn, beans, potatoes, and tobacco. To the south, where temperatures are cooler and the winter season is more pronounced, wheat, barley, corn, and potatoes become much more important, as are the hardier fruits—apples and pears. Significant efforts are being made to achieve a more equitable distribution of the rich agricultural land of the central valley. Land ownership is still concentrated in large estates, but government expropriation with reasonable compensation is providing land for farmers who are capable of using it to advantage to increase the national agricultural output.

Santiago, the capital, its seaport Valparaiso, and the nearby resort at Viña del Mar comprise the largest concentration of people in Chile. Santiago is about 50 miles inland from the Pacific and is situated on a broad plain at the foot of the snow-crested Andes. Centrally located between the north and south extremities of the country, the capital is the distributing and trading center of the central valley and dominates the industrial, commercial, and cultural life of the country. Valparaiso and Callao in Peru share the distinction of being the two leading ports of western South America. In addition to being a trade and manufacturing center, Valparaiso is the terminus of the trans-Andean route to Buenos Aires, and is also a leading fishing center.

The marine west-coast climate dominates Chile south of the Rio Bio-Bio, where the winters become more rigorous and the mild summers are merely seasons of less rainfall. During the year rainfall may average 100 inches or more along the coast, increasing to torrential amounts on the islands in the archipelago and the Andean slopes inland. Between Concepción and Puerto Montt, the central valley has been cleared of much of the natural forest cover for agriculture. The longitudinal railway, with lateral lines to coastal ports, extends from near the Peruvian border south through Santiago to terminate at Puerto Montt.

In the lowlands along the coast, as at Valdivia and in the central valley, nearly a million people depend primarily on agriculture for their livelihood. Root crops such as potatoes together with wheat, barley, rye, and lush pasture grasses yield heavily. Cattle are grazed on the valley pastures, and sheep and goats on hills and lower mountain slopes. As settlement progresses into the forest lands, Chilean pine and other conifers are providing raw materials for lumber and pulp industries.

The grand archipelago of south Chile sweeps in an arc from Chiloe Island south of Puerto Montt for nearly 1,500 miles to the cold, bleak, and stormy island of Tierra del Fuego. The forbidding coast is the habitat of the Araucanian Indians, who have retreated before the advance of European civilization. The rain-soaked, fog-cloaked coast is indented deeply by giant fiords, with mountain glaciers reaching to the sea. Far-south Chile, across the low Andean Cordillera facing the Atlantic, is protected from the heavy rainfall and has numerous grassy plains that support sheep herds numbering in the tens of thousands. The sheep thrive and produce fleeces of superior size and quality. The wool clip is marketed through Punta Arenas, facing on the Strait of Magellan, the inland passage.

FOREIGN TRADE With the opening of the Panama Canal, Chile's mineral industry entered world commerce in volume for the first time. Only the production of the unique nitrate deposits in the north had provided sizable exports prior to that time. The policy of encouraging foreign investments for the development of the mineral deposits has hastened their exploitation, established important trade relationships, and contributed revenue to the national economy.

Copper, nitrates, iodine, iron ore, and other minerals constitute over 95 per cent of Chile's exports; wool, mutton, and lumber are also notable. Most of Chile's foreign commerce is with Western Europe. The country's imports consist of a wide variety of manufactured goods, machinery, automobiles, and agricultural commodities.

SOUTHEASTERN SOUTH AMERICA

The agricultural riches of the Argentine and Uruguayan Pampas, the industries of cities fringing the Rio de la Plata, and the affluence and cosmopolitan atmosphere of

Figure 7-17 Southern South America is the best-developed part of the continent agriculturally. The Pampa is a world leader in the production of wheat and meat.

Buenos Aires and Montevideo present an astonishing contrast with the more provincial nations and capitals of Andean South America (Figure 7-17). One finds it difficult to believe that these nations are among the most recently settled areas of the continent. The mild, mid-latitude climate, well-watered during the year, and the large stretches of flatland with good soils have favored both livestock ranching and farming. Growing markets in Europe for food staples during the late nineteenth and early twentieth centuries and the

immigration of tens of thousands of Europeans from Spain, Italy, and other lands, who came equipped with capital and modern farm methods, spurred the emergence of commercial agriculture. The native Indian population was sparse, except in Paraguay, and was reduced as it was in North America. Rail lines and, later, highways spread the benefits of European civilization across the land. Without an avenue to the sea, isolated Paraguay still retains its provincial character and Guarani Indian culture, modified by contact with Europeans. Facing the Rio de la Plata, the metropolis of Buenos Aires, the Argentine cities to the north, together with Montevideo, are continental leaders in commerce, modern transportation, and education, and are among the first in manufacturing.

ARGENTINA

Since the middle of the last century, the Argentine nation has advanced quickly and is one of the three most prosperous nations of Latin America. The wealth and prosperity of Argentina have come from the remarkable combination of excellent climate, fine soils, an extensive cultivable area, and a willing and technologically equipped people. Foreign capital has played a leading role in the country's development. British and French capital constructed the railways and provided electric power; United States capital built meat-packing plants and grain elevators. Though capital from overseas is still welcome, the Argentines themselves have assumed the major role in the operation and expansion of transportation and industry.

Since Argentina stretches from the Tropic of Capricorn in the north to the Strait of Magellan in the south, and extends from the Andean Cordillera and rain-shadow deserts of the west to the well-watered Pampa fringing the Atlantic on the east, the country may be divided into several regions: the humid Pampa, Mesopotamia, the Chaco, the western deserts and oases, and Patagonia. Of these, the humid Pampa is by far the most important. Most of the people, most of the industry, and most of the agriculture are situated in the Pampa.

REGIONS   The Pampa encompasses almost ¼ million square miles and stretches from

Buenos Aires, south and west for over 300 miles. Few areas of this size have been so favorably endowed by nature for farming or livestock ranching. Among its assets are the nearly level land, broken only by a few isolated ranges in the south, the fine, mellow, nearly stone-free soils, and an admirable subtropical climate hardly excelled for agriculture. The summers are warm; rainfall is plentiful and is usually reliable, though occasional droughts do occur. The winters are mild at Buenos Aires, but snow may occur, and snow is common to the south at Bahia Blanca.

The humid Pampa is the center of the cattle *estancia* in the better-watered east, and the dry Pampa in the west includes the grain-producing fertile crescent. Nowhere in the greater Pampa is less than one-half of the land used for pasture. South and east of Buenos Aires the low relief of the land and the heavier rainfall support excellent planted alfalfa grasses and fine herds of cattle. Since the marketing of Argentine beef in European markets began, pure-bred stock has been imported,

Figure 7-18   Cattle ranch on the Pampa. Notice the windmill, the vast extent of level land, and the close resemblance of the area to the ranch land of the Western United States. (Courtesy of Argentine Embassy.)

and excellent domestic Argentine breeds have been perfected. The eastern Pampa is fenced into very large pastures of 100 to 5,000 acres, where the combination of excellent planted forage and year-round grazing fattens steers for market a year younger than do the native pasture grasses. Almost one-third of Argentina's sheep are in the Pampa, and mutton and wool are important national exports.

Westward from the pastoral district, farming becomes evident, though the grazing industries continue in importance. Corn, wheat, barley, oats, and flax are notable cash grains raised in addition to alfalfa. In the northwest Pampa, near Rosario, corn is the chief crop, used to fatten swine as well as for export. To the south, flax and wheat gain the ascendancy in the drier fertile crescent where the growing season is shorter. Flaxseed is raised primarily to recover the linseed oil so important to paint industries. The wheat lands of the western Pampa extend as a vast crescent nearly 600 miles from Santa Fe south to Bahia Blanca in southern Buenos Aires province. Wheat constitutes the single most valuable export commodity of Argentina. The wheat crescent lies on the western margin of the Pampa, where rainfall is insufficient for other crops. Wheat farming is gradually shifting to the south, away from competition with corn and flax. Most of the Argentine wheat is planted and harvested by using modern farm machinery, in contrast to the methods used in the grain districts in western and northern South America. Alfalfa and beef cattle are also significant in the crescent as they are everywhere in the Pampa. Near Buenos Aires a major dairying and market-garden zone, some 50 miles wide, sends fresh vegetables, fruits, and fresh milk to the capital.

All Argentina focuses on the Pampa and the federal capital. Buenos Aires, with its 6 million people, and the adjoining Pampa region contain over two-thirds of the nation's population. Argentina has a distinctly cosmopolitan population almost entirely of European origin. The capital and other leading cities, such as Rosario, Santa Fe, La Plata, Córdoba, and Tucuman, reflect this strong heritage.

Buenos Aires is a splendid and attractive city, the largest in Latin America and among the ten largest in the world. In the heart of the city, close to the port and commercial houses, tree-lined boulevards run between government buildings, banking institutions, fashionable shopping districts, theaters, and beautiful waterfront parks. Buenos Aires and the cities facing the Paraná and Rio de la Plata constitute one of the three manufacturing districts of Latin America. The limited resource base of the nation formerly limited manufacturing to consumer goods. But today heavy industry, including a modern steel mill, and petrochemical plants are supplying one of the largest national markets in Latin America. Rosario, located north of the capital, is the leading exporter of corn, beef, and flax. It too is developing major industries. Santa Fe is an inland port and distribution center; La Plata, to the east of the capital, is especially important as a meat-packing center. Córdoba, located inland on the margin of the Pampa, is a cultural and commercial center that has become the automotive capital of Argentina.

North of Buenos Aires between the Paraná and Uruguay Rivers, rainfall becomes more plentiful, the winters are milder, and the summers are both longer and warmer. This is the Argentine Mesopotamia. Bordered by river plains, the center of the region is a rolling hill land. Many of the river and valley bottoms are swampy, tree-covered areas. The higher land is grassland favorable for pasture.

Figure 7-19 Buenos Aires, the capital of Argentina, is one of the largest cities in the world south of the equator. This aerial view of the principal business district shows many tall buildings, wide streets, and several methods of transportation. (Courtesy of Argentine Embassy.)

In the southern part of the Argentine Mesopotamia, Pampa agriculture holds sway and wheat, barley, flax, and alfalfa are the important crops. Agriculture is accompanied by an important livestock industry. Though the livestock do not have the fine quality of Pampa cattle, they are valuable for beef and hides. The northern districts are grazed by sheep. In the far north, fine stands of Paraná pine forests supply a small lumbering industry. Yerba maté, an American tea, is taken from forest stands and from small plantations. At the border with Brazil and Paraguay, the Paraná River plummets over the edge of the Brazilian plateau to emerge as the magnificent Iguassú Falls, higher and broader than Niagara Falls. A tourist attraction of the first order, these falls have tremendous potential for hydroelectric development sometime in the future.

The Gran Chaco of South America, a region of forest and grasslands, extends southward into subtropical Argentina. The warm to hot temperatures are complemented by a wet-and-dry–precipitation pattern. Scrub forests and grasslands afford poor range for the scattered herds of low-grade cattle. From the forests of the Chaco comes the quebracho tree, whose wood is very hard and serves as fence posts and railroad ties; the most valuable product from the tree, however, is the tannin obtained from the wood. Mills for processing the products are located generally along the rivers, which are rust-colored for miles downstream.

Since the early part of the century, areas cleared of the forest have become Argentina's cotton belt. High-grade cotton harvested in the Chaco is shipped by riverboat south to the textile mills of Pampa cities. Settlers are pushing into the Chaco from the south, where improved herds of cattle and sugar cane production are taking over much of the land.

The western oases and desert of Argentina are located between the Pampa and the Andean Cordillera. Nearly one-fourth of the Argentine people are here clustered in settlements wherever water is available for irrigation from streams rising in the mountains or from wells. These oasis settlements play an important role in the agriculture and livestock industries of the country. The northern oases including Jujuy, Salta, and Tucuman are the principal sugar districts of the country, producing more than half of the national output. Besides sugar cane, citrus fruits, vegetables, and tobacco are grown. The middle oases, focusing on Mendoza, are smaller and suffer generally from water shortages. The largest of the middle oases, Mendoza, has an adequate water supply and raises large amounts of grapes for wine, in addition to alfalfa and grains. The alfalfa is used to pasture and fatten the herds of cattle that range across the dry grasslands before they are sent to markets in the east. The southern oases extend into northern Patagonia and are much cooler than those to the north. They, too, are important for alfalfa and grazing, as well as for a variety of fruits, including apples and pears, that enter the export market.

The vast, windswept Patagonian plateau stretches from the crests of the Andean Cordillera to the Atlantic shore, and from the Rio Negro south to Tierra del Fuego. The sub-Andean depression parallels the foot of the Andes from Lake Nahuel-Haupi south through the island of Tierra del Fuego. Deep valleys and canyons traverse the plateau where rivers fed by western mountain streams have cut their way to the ocean. The depression is interrupted only by the forested lower slopes of the foothills and the charming lakes district. As a major region encompassing one-third of the country. Patagonia is at the same time one of the most sparsely peopled areas of Argentina. Located in the southern extremity of the continent south of 40° south latitude, the region is cool, dry, and dominated almost constantly by strong winds from the mountains or from the sea.

Spectacular mountain landscapes, deep blue lakes, and cool summer temperatures followed by winters with plentiful snowfall create an ideal year-round resort area near San Carlos de Bariloche on Lake Nahuel-Haupi. The famous National Park affords boating, fishing, and skiing in a magnificent setting. The forest cover on the slopes stands as a great resource, only now being developed.

Figure 7-20 Patagonia is noted for its large estancias, which send fine fleeces and wool to market each year. (Courtesy of Argentine Embassy.)

Sheltered from the strong, sand-laden winds by the deep river valleys in the north, opening in the south onto the lush grassy plains, the large *estancias* send fine fleeces and wool of the best quality to small ports along the coast. Over one-quarter of Argentina's sheep graze across this difficult region, and supply one-half of the country's export of wool, making the country second only to Australia in world production.

PETROLEUM Although Argentina has produced some petroleum for many decades, the development and recently accelerated exploitation of the fields centering on Comodoro Rivadavia has made the country nearly self-sufficient. Natural gas from districts north of Jujuy and petroleum from Mendoza, Neuquen, and Comodoro Rivadavia in particular have ushered in a new period in the use of the resource base of Argentina.

TRANSPORTATION Argentina's railroads and highway facilities are among the most extensive in South America. In the late nineteenth century farming and livestock industries moved inland along the frontier of the Pampa, followed by a wave of railroad construction equaled only by the highway-building programs of the first decades of the twentieth century. Unimpeded by natural barriers present in the Andean countries, modern railroads and highways radiating from Buenos Aires and the river ports on the Paraná spread across the Pampa linking every city and town to the coast. From the corners of the Pampa and surrounding regions, the products of field and pasture—wheat, corn, flax, and barley, beef cattle, sheep, and hogs—move quickly to the port cities for processing, then on to markets in the cities or overseas.

URUGUAY

Uruguay, the smallest independent nation of South America, is wedged into the southeast corner of the continent between the two largest nations. The Pampas extend from Argentina across Uruguay and into south Brazil. Except for a small, rugged upland in the extreme north, Uruguay has an undulating to rolling surface subjected to a strikingly uniform land use throughout. Quite unlike Argentina or Brazil, in which large areas separate population centers and vast segments of the national territories lie unused or useless, virtually every square mile of Uruguay is productive and contributes to the livelihood of the nation. In a country that has few resources other than its land, farming and grazing are naturally the foremost human activities.

Sheep range the natural grasses that are fenced into areas of 100 to 5,000 acres on large haciendas, and from their clip comes the most important export of the country. The sheep ranges are found usually north of Montevideo and away from the lowlands of the Uruguay River and Rio de la Plata, where farming is more important. Together with the sheep, fine herds of Hereford cattle are fattened on the grasses before they are shipped south to packing plants in Montevideo or along the Uruguay River. In recent years the number of cattle has declined, while the overseas markets for wool and mutton have held firm.

A typical Uruguayan landscape resembles the Argentine Pampa, except that natural grasses, rather than alfalfa, provide the forage for sheep and cattle. Small frame houses, the homes of the cattlemen, are surrounded by trees to protect them against the winds that sweep inland from the Atlantic throughout the year. Since grazing can proceed all year in the mild climate, no shelter or stored feed is required, and there are only a few outbuildings. Trails and paths radiate from the clusters of dwellings across the large, fenced pastures, following rows of trees that mark property lines and give respite from the winds of the sea.

In the south and west, crop farming is especially important to Uruguay's economy, though production may be small by comparison with Argentina. Every endeavor is being made to stimulate increased harvests of wheat, corn, barley, and flax, for the breadgrains are needed at home and flax is a valuable export commodity. The expanding farming is encroaching on lands used formerly to fatten and finish cattle before they were shipped to packing plants in Montevideo. The continued growth of farming has contributed to the diminishing of herds of cattle and the reduction of a major export commodity.

Montevideo is the hub of Uruguay's universe; in it live nearly one-third of all Uruguayans, and it is the commercial, social, economic, cultural, and political center of the nation. Moreover, Montevideo is fast becoming a manufacturing center worthy of mention. The metropolis is the seaport and chief meat-packing center for the leading export industry. The climate is mild in the summer, surpassed in its salubrity only by the delightful climate of Punta del Este, the nearby resort center. Winters are equally mild, though cooler and marked by frontal storms that push in from the South Atlantic.

Though its population is increasing rather slowly for Latin America, Uruguay is nonetheless already feeling the pinch in the drive for exports and the need also to supply grains to its people. Uruguayans enjoy a remarkably high standard of living in comparison with other Latin-American nations. To sustain both a high level of exports and provide an adequate food supply without sacrificing the good living standards achieved already is the nation's challenge. More efficient use of the land for crops and livestock indicates that the challenge can be met.

PARAGUAY

Hundreds of miles from the Atlantic, with no direct route to the sea, Paraguay shares with Bolivia the handicaps of isolation and an undeveloped economy. Yet the rather mild climate and fertile soils of well-watered eastern Paraguay indicate good natural endowment for this nation of the Guarani Indian and the mestizo. Paraguay has the smallest population of any of the independent nations of South America. The dual culture of the large population of full-blooded Indians and city-dwelling mestizos recognizes the Guarani tongue as well as the Spanish as official languages of the country.

Flowing from north to south, the Paraguay River divides the country into two major regions—the Paraguayan Chaco to the west and the eastern river plains and uplands. Most of the western Chaco is flat, with a distinct wet-and-dry climate during the year. Temperatures are so hot that they may become almost unbearable during the summer, and near desertlike conditions prevail in some districts. When the rainy season begins, temperatures moderate, but torrents of rain inundate tremendous segments of the land. Herds of very low-grade cattle, valuable only for their hides, graze over the scattered patches of grass and through the dry, scrub forest. With scant population, only the quebracho tree, taken from the broken woodlands near the Paraguay rivers, produces any additional income for the people.

The eastern plains are likewise rather sparsely settled, except for the triangle of population clusters extending from Asunción, the capital, through Villa Rica and Encarnacíon on the Paraná River and the floodplains of the Paraguay and Paraná Rivers that form the south and west boundaries of the country. Forests have been leveled and fields of cotton, rice, and wheat planted wherever the slope or climate favors the crops. Near Villa Rica settlements of Europeans produce tobacco and grapes for wine. Citrus fruits, especially oranges, are also harvested for export. In the settled area and near the Paraguay River north of Asunción, are numerous large cattle ranches. A good number of the cattle are of improved breeds or the zebu that has been acclimated to the warm, subtropical climate. Though meat and hides are the chief exports, cotton also holds a primary position in foreign trade. Yerba maté, the national beverage, is brewed from the powdered leaves of the maté tree (an American holly), which grows in many parts of the eastern forests in the uplands. Timber and some coffee are sent to markets from the eastern uplands.

Asunción is both the capital and the river port of Paraguay. When water is high, riverboats loaded with cargoes of commodities make the exciting, though long and dangerous journey to Argentine ports, where the exports of Paraguay find their way to the channels of world commerce.

THE UNITED STATES OF BRAZIL

One-half of the continent is occupied by Brazil, and one-half of the people of South America are Brazilians, whose heritage is Portugal and whose language is Portuguese (Figure 7-21). Brazil is the fifth largest of the world's nations and one of the fifteen largest in population—a youthful nation to be recognized among the powers of the world. The Treaty of Tordesillas, in 1494, assigned the western part of South America to Spain and the eastern to Portugal. Although little was known of the eastern part of the continent, the Portuguese implanted their culture on what has emerged as the giant of South America, a land of resources and industry.

The greatest number of Brazilians live and work in the states of Rio de Janeiro, São Paulo, and southern Minas Gerais, in the east central region of the country. Enjoying the highest living standards, the rural and urban centers of the region have the most modern agriculture and manufacturing establishments of Brazil. Arrayed about this core of settlement, to the northeast, the north, west, and south are the other regions and population cores of this gigantic nation, separated from each other by hundreds of miles of scant population and near-wilderness. Only recently (1960), the political capital of Brazil has been relocated away from the former capital at Rio de Janeiro and thrust into the sparsely settled region at Brasília. Yet for the time being, the effective political force remains in Rio de Janeiro.

A tropical giant, Brazil has little of its national territory lying to the south in the subtropical climate of the South American Pampa. Only the vast highlands that spread over the eastern third of the country offset the otherwise hot, tropical geographic location and afford zones of settlement that have favored agriculture. The Brazilian highlands have also proved to be a storehouse of minerals vital to the life of the nation. Strangely, the luxuriant forests of the wet Amazon, which once controlled the life of the nation with their production of rubber, and the dry

EQUATOR

EASTERN BRAZIL

★ National capitals

○ Major regional cities

SCALE

0   500

MILES

TROPIC OF CAPRICORN

Figure 7-21 Brazil is the largest country in South America and one of the five largest nations in the world. Eastern Brazil has no high mountains but does have a great variety of landforms.

northeast, which was first settled and was the seat of the early sugar plantations, are today burdens that weigh heavily on the prosperous agricultural and industrial economy of east central Brazil.

EAST CENTRAL BRAZIL

São Paulo and Rio de Janeiro, two of the largest metropolises of the continent, the great coffee fazendas and sugar planta-

tions, the largest iron and steel industry, and the largest diversified manufacturing base of South America are concentrated in east central Brazil. All these are situated within 300 miles of the Atlantic Ocean.

The state of São Paulo is notable not only for the largest city of the country, but also for its location where the great coffee fazendas begin, the plantations that extend south into Paraná state, west across the Paraná River into eastern

Matto Grosso state, and even into southern Minas Gerais state. Coffee is the biggest industry of the country. Brazil is the world's largest coffee producer, and coffee accounts for over two-thirds of the value of all Brazilian exports. Brazil's coffee is sold principally to the United States, and it helps forge a strong community of interest between the two nations.

The coffee fazenda is a large plantationlike unit that usually has been divided into separate farms, each placed in the care of a tenant farmer. Although each farm has space set aside for food crops and a homestead, most of the land is planted in coffee trees by the owner. The coffee trees are set out in groves about 15 feet apart, and later are trimmed so that the red coffee berries may be harvested easily. Most Brazilian coffees are not selectively harvested. Once each year the crop is taken, and the berries, after being hulled to recover the coffee beans, are dried, sorted, selected, sacked, and shipped in bags to the seaports. The world's coffee port is Santos, on the narrow lowlands below the escarpment of the Serra do Mar and São Paulo. The railroad or highway trip of the coffee beans is difficult, traversing the 35 miles from São Paulo City, 2,680 feet above, to the sea-level plain below. The construction of railroads and highways across the Serra do Mar challenged the genius of foreign and Brazilian engineers alike, but the gap has been bridged.

A rare combination of terrain, soils, and climate has remarkably favored the coffee culture and the diversified agricultural economy of the entire region. The altitude of the highlands, broken along the east by the high escarpment, or wall, of the Serra do Mar that rises suddenly and precipitously from the ocean or narrow coastal lowlands, offsets significantly the otherwise hot temperatures. The southeast trade winds carry moisture-bearing winds inland during the year, giving only a less rainy season to the region. During much of the year cloud cover protects the coffee trees from the harsh, tropical sun. Without the deep, rich terra rossa soils, derived from the lava base that spreads over the highland in the south, coffee cultivation and agriculture in general would be limited. Growing of coffee is confined largely to the low plateau, mostly between 1,500 and 3,000 feet, where elevation keeps the air temperatures mild, while the tropical location precludes killing frosts.

Coffee is "king." But São Paulo state, the Paraíba Valley near Rio de Janeiro, and southern Minas Gerais are also the national leaders in the production of sugar cane, cotton, rice, and other staples. Modern farming methods, the increasing use of agricultural machinery, and fertilizers have hastened growth and pushed the region into leadership in commodity production. Dairy and beef herds graze in planted pastures on adequate natural grasses. That farming and livestock industries of the first order are necessary is quite clear, since they must support the millions of people who live and work in the metropolitan areas of São Paulo, Rio de Janeiro, Belo Horizonte, and the large number of smaller communities.

The leading cities do not stand as isolated islands of population as they frequently do in western South America. They are surrounded by sizable industrial and service cities that contribute substantially to the agricultural hinterlands and supply the urban-industrial centers with both raw materials and the greatest market for goods on the continent. São Paulo, with over 3 million inhabitants, is the business and manufacturing center of Brazil. Though its prosperity is derived chiefly from coffee, the alert *Paulistas* are well aware of the "boom-and-bust" history of Brazil and are constantly trying to

Figure 7-22   Copacabana Beach, Rio de Janeiro, Brazil. (Courtesy of Brazilian Government Trade Bureau.)

introduce new crops and new industries. The former capital, Rio de Janeiro, now in Guanabarra state, is also a leading manufacturing center. But it is better known as the cultural and political center of Brazil, the leading port, and a recreation center of international fame.

The state of Minas Gerais has been important for centuries for the exploitation of several rich mineral deposits. The state is the source of almost all the gold mined in Brazil as well as of diamonds of value as industrial stones. However, the much larger and more abundant deposits of iron ore, manganese, and base metals have eclipsed the original mining activities. In the rolling hill land and low mountains east of Belo Horizonte near

Itabira are iron ore deposits of high-grade hematite without impurities in harmful amounts, which rank among the finest yet discovered in the world. While much of the ore is utilized principally in iron and steel industries at Itabira or Volta Redonda, relatively little of the ore enters the export market. The ore for Volta Redonda, the national steel industry located in the Paraíba Valley north of Rio de Janeiro, is sent by rail to the coastal port of Vitória, where it is carried by ore ships to the south. There it is transshipped once again inland to the steel plant. The high costs of the overland haul and ocean transshipment make the ore expensive. Coal for the steel mill is mined in south Brazil near Tubarão, and is shipped northward to the port, where it too is shipped to the mill to be treated and mixed with imported coals of coking quality. Volta Redonda is the largest integrated steel mill in Latin America.

NORTHEAST BRAZIL

The Portuguese colony in the New World was first settled along the northeast coast of modern Brazil. *Capitaincies,* large land grants or patents, extended inland along the coast and were important from the outset. They were the first centers of sugar-cane culture in the Americas. The several small states extending inland, with ports that are now state capitals, attest to the lingering impact of the early settlement pattern. The narrow coastal lowlands, backed by an escarpment as in the south, were planted and harvested first by the few Indians, then by Negro slaves who were needed to work in the cane fields. Few crops have responded more rapidly to the rise and fall in prices or to the expansion and contraction of plantations than has the sugar culture of the northeast. In an effort to decrease the dependence of the region on sugar, the production of plantation cotton, cacao, and bananas was introduced into the lowlands.

In the lowlands and foothills of the highlands behind the bay at Salvador, the largest and most important cacao district in the Western Hemisphere has been developed. The Brazilian cacao crop provides usually about three-quarters of the South American crop and 15 per cent of the total world supply. Only the newly independent West African nations produce more.

The critical problem faced by the agricultural economy of the northeast is that other regions in Brazil or in other nations have been able to produce the same commodities in large quantities, of better quality, or at lower prices. The older plantations, using outmoded methods, cannot compete effectively, and much of their land falls into disuse. Thousands of laborers are left without jobs and migrate into the dry interior, where they barely eke out a livelihood. The unpredictable droughts that befall the interior of Brazil's northeast drive families, bearing what possessions they can carry out of the region, to the coastal cities where they subsist on food provided by the government. Nevertheless, the population of the northeast has increased steadily even in the face of adversity. Hardships and poverty seemingly beyond the endurance of the people are seldom dispelled even by leaving behind the barrenness of the bleak landscape in their pilgrimages in search of sustenance. The northeast of Brazil is the poorhouse of the nation and one of the most economically depressed regions in the entire Western Hemisphere.

The interior of the northeast is dry and hot. The calamity of drought is equaled by the devastation of water when, as happens on occasion, tremendous downpours cause flooding. For some reason not yet precisely understood by meteorologists, the trade winds fail to carry rainfall into the region, and the highly variable yearly rainfall averages only 25 inches. The tropical rain forests of the coast disappear quickly beyond the escarpment, and grasslands, thorn bush, and cacti become common. In rainy years, about two out of seven, herds of cattle do well and crops flourish; in the years of rainfall deficiency, crops wither, and the herds of livestock waste away. Large reservoirs constructed to catch and hold water for irrigation usually stand dry and empty. When there is water, the crops—cotton, beans, rice, maize, and alfalfa—give fairly high yields, and in wet years they satisfy the very small needs of the subsistence farmer and rancher. But in dry years the land is parched, crops die, and people and livestock starve.

SOUTH BRAZIL

South Brazil embraces the northern margin of the Pampa, the southern edge of the Brazilian highlands, narrow river plains in the west, and an equally narrow coastal plain along the Atlantic. Climatically, south Brazil resembles Uruguay, but in the highlands and in the interior temperatures are cooler, and frost, even snow, may occur with some regularity. Most of the highlands and much of the lowlands were originally forested. Pioneer settlement pushing inland from the coast has cleared ribbons of the land leading into the interior and placed it into farming. Settlement by a dominant European population has progressed slowly but steadily. The small, family-sized farm is the principal economic unit, quite in contrast to the giant fazendas and plantations of the regions to the north. Farming has proved to be prosperous and is pursued with vigor. The small farms produce wheat, barley, corn, and other grains together with potatoes. In a few places along the western rivers and the eastern coastal lowlands, rice cultivation is important, and in warmer areas cotton is a leading crop. On the open pampas cattle ranching has become important as it is in both Argentina and Uruguay; as yet, pastures occupy most of the land, and cattle and sheep provide most of the income. Porto Alegre, the chief city, which lies near the northern edge of Lagõa dos Patos, is the leading port and also the state capital of Rio Grande do Sul, the most powerful state in the south. Inland, population clusters quickly become dispersed and densities decline as the frontier is reached. The three principal cities in south Brazil—Porto Alegre, Florianopolis, and Curitiba—are local service and commercial centers, supporting some industry as well as serving as state capitals. The rich forests of paraná pine are of prime importance in providing lumber for building materials and pulp and cellulose for paper and chemical industries; unfortunately, the wood is used widely for charcoal and firewood in a region and nation short of fuels. In spite of the danger of frost, the coffee frontier has been pushed south into northern Paraná state, and coffee is being grown in a marginal climate as older coffee lands become exhausted or are shifted to other commercial crops in São Paulo state.

INTERIOR PLATEAU AND PLAINS

The interior uplands of Brazil are a westward extension of the coastal highlands across the center of South America. Sheared on the north and south by rivers and their tributaries that flow north to the Amazon or south to the Paraguay and Paraná Rivers, the low plateau surface is a rolling hill land with numerous cliff-bordered tablelands. Farther to the west are extensive plains. More than one-third of Brazil's national territory is encompassed by the plateau and plains and contains only a fraction of the country's population.

To the capital of Brazil, which was moved into the sparsely populated frontier region in 1960, Brazilians migrate only with the greatest reluctance. Situated on a high plateau, very near the headwaters of two rivers flowing north and south, Brasília, a magnificent city of beautiful symmetry and daring and of symbolic architecture, has risen in hope that the Brazilian spirit will look inland from the coast to a future of occupying the virtually uninhabited interior. The elevation of the upland moderates the tropical temperatures, giving relief from the very great heat. Besides, the wet-and-dry, high- and low-sun periods give a seasonality to temperatures as well as to rainfall. The higher eastern segment of the plateau, north of São Paulo state, though warm throughout the year, is marked with daily and seasonal variations. Thunderstorms and occasional frontal storms pushing inland from the Atlantic bring 30 to 50 inches of rainfall yearly, concentrated generally in the high-sun period. It is hardly sufficient to affect adversely the soils through excessive leaching or to promote a dense forest cover.

Brazilians are reluctant to leave the coast and move inland, and thus, after centuries of pioneering efforts, the land is still in the early stages of frontier development. Ranging through the open woodlands and tropical grasslands, cattle herds provide most of the income. From remote and isolated corners of the interior hides and skins and sun-dried beef are still shipped to eastern markets. But west of São Paulo state, in southern Matto

Grosso, herds of cattle move quickly to urban markets across new roads and railroads. The use of zebu cattle and breeds developed in Brazil has raised the quality of beef animals. Even the coffee culture of São Paulo has crossed the Paraná River. West of Minas Gerais, toward Goiás and the new capital at Brasília, commercial farming and livestock ranching have made substantial progress in a short time. The most important single change that has occurred is the construction of modern highways, the bridging of the Paraná River, and the construction of hydroelectric stations to provide power along the pioneer fringe.

AMAZONIA

Over a million square miles, constituting another one-third of Brazil, are blanketed by the forests and grasslands of the vast Amazon Basin, the largest single rain forest in the world. Yet Amazonia is the most sparsely settled region of Brazil, with fewer than 2 million people. The basin is flat to gently undulating throughout, and only in a few places stands higher than 600 feet above sea level. The climate is monotonous, constantly warm, humid, and rainy. Lying in the *tierra caliente* and away from the sea, no moderation of temperature occurs during the day or significantly from season to season. The trade winds sweep across the highlands from the east and carry moisture that gives between 70 and 100 inches of rainfall during the year. Violent thunderstorms breach the quiet of the forests and dump tremendous volumes of water on the land. The Amazon Basin, however, does for the most part experience a less rainy season during the low-sun periods. At Manaus, one of the older population clusters located on the Amazon near the confluence with the Rio Negro, the average temperature for the warmest month, October, is 83°F, while for the least warm month, April, it is 80°F.

The abundance of rainfall and the warm temperatures support the largest equatorial forest in the world. The trees are tall, often reaching heights of 100 to 150 feet. Their crowns intermingle, forming a canopy, and close out the sunlight from the forest floor. A multitude of lianas and other vines grow among them high above the ground, and the tangle of leafy branches and lianas casts a dense shade on the forest floor, so that bushes and other low growth are often absent. Of the hundreds of species of trees that may be found in every square mile of the forest, only the rubber tree has been widely exploited. The Amazon Basin is the original home of the *Hevea brasiliensis,* the tree from which natural rubber is obtained. The rubber industry has long languished, and today Brazil obtains most of its rubber from synthetics produced at São Paulo.

Only a few land animals live in the tropical forest, and most of these live partly in the trees. Birds and monkeys provide food for several species of large cats and snakes, which also live mostly in the trees. Insects and spiders, here in great numbers, attain gigantic size. All are troublesome, and some are dangerous.

Since the rivers are still the principal means of surface transportation into the rain forests, settlements are scattered along the Amazon and its tributaries. Today the rain forests are quite unproductive. Forest gatherers still bring gums, nuts, and woods to the river settlements for trade, but the rubber trade has ceased to be of any significance. As elsewhere in Brazil, a long era of quiet is coming to an end. A highway from northeast Brazil already reaches to Belem, the once isolated seaport of the Amazon accessible only by ship or by air. Manaus, although it lies 1,500 miles up the Amazon, may be reached by oceangoing vessels because of the great depth of the river. Already a road under construction from Brasília is pushing slowly through the forest wilderness toward the south bank of the river. Near Manaus, jute is being grown successfully by a colony of Japanese, and rice and other food staples are being produced.

The great undeveloped resource of the Amazon is its forest, capable of yielding a considerable amount of lumber, and possibly pulpwood. The valuable species are rather few and scattered among a larger forest of useless types. The timbers must be dried in the forest for several years before they will float, and another problem involves getting the timbers out of the dense forest growth. The Amazon Basin remains an enigma to modern man, for it probably will not bloom, as some believe, into a rich agricultural region that will support millions. On the other hand, its promise is much better than at present. Perhaps the further discovery and exploitation of petroleum may improve the economy somewhat, but at the present time the rather infertile soils and few people ensure that no great changes will come in the near future.

IN PERSPECTIVE

SOUTH AMERICA, AN AREA TO BE DEVELOPED

South America is favored by having at least as much cultivable land as the neighboring continent of Africa and also considerable areas suitable for settlement in highlands near the equator. Moreover, the continent is much more evenly and reliably watered than either Africa or Australia and thus has superior agricultural

possibilities. The population of 136 million, a comparatively small number for a continent the size of South America, and the significant areas of agricultural land and mineral reserves of some potential are fortunate circumstances. Unlike the millions of people who crowd the Orient, or who show the cultural and linguistic diversity of both the Orient and Africa, the people of South America speak two major languages and have an essentially Iberian culture. Long and favorable commercial and cultural ties with northwestern Europe and North America have brought new ideas and an acceptance of new technology in the lives of millions of people. South America was settled by great numbers of Europeans from Spain, Portugal, Italy, Germany, and other parts of the continent. They have accepted the Latin languages and culture and have pursued successfully the assimilation of these by millions of Amerindian and Negro peoples.

There remain notable areas of sparsely settled land that may be placed into more productive use. In addition, many of the lands already under cultivation can be used more intensively and efficiently. The tropical forests, long a barrier to economic development, can be harnessed for productive purposes through improved technology. Already domestic industries of impressive size are situated in some countries. Though base metals are plentiful, the problem of fuel remains unresolved. That manufacturing may thrive and prosper in South America, there is no longer any doubt.

The two-century-long epoch of massive transatlantic migration has ended. Therefore the peopling of the unoccupied lands and the techniques used to make them productive of food and other agricultural and livestock commodities depend on the peoples and leadership of the nations themselves. If the inexperienced are permitted to carry forward their destructive practices and capture the frontier, the land will be laid waste. On the other hand, if care and instruction are provided and if guidance follows the opening of new lands to farming and settlement, there are no serious difficulties ahead for South America. Perhaps the most critical problem clouding the future of the continent is the question of how the land will be owned. Will the ownership patterns of the past be perpetuated, with land incorporated into large estates and concentrated in the hands of the few, or will the land be divided into family-sized farms that can produce on a commercial basis? Perhaps there is still another, as yet unrecognized, solution; the core areas from which frontiers have already developed in Colombia, Chile, Argentina, and Brazil should continue to open new areas to settlement. Yet unsolved social, economic, and demographic problems of dangerous proportions continue to overshadow such areas as Brazil's northeast and the Bolivian-Peruvian highlands. In every instance, one great weakness of South America's nations is the inability to provide sufficient food for the burgeoning urban and rural populations.

SELECTED REFERENCES

Dyer, Donald R.: "Population of the Quechua Region of Peru," *Geographical Review*, vol. 52, pp. 337–345, July, 1962.

The outstanding problem in South America's Andean provinces concerns the Indian populations. They comprise communities and societies often completely apart from the rest of their respective nations. Where and why these cultural groups live in the highlands, how they eke out a meager livelihood, and what prospects the future holds for them in the arduous highland environment are subjects explored in this article.

James, Preston E.: *Latin America,* 3d ed., The Odyssey Press, Inc., New York, 1959.

An outstanding general text and reference work in the Latin-American field. This text presents a balanced regional coverage and an authoritative overall view of the Latin-American area.

Platt, Robert S.: "Brazilian Capitals and Frontiers: Part I," *Journal of Geography*, vol. 53, pp. 369–375, December, 1954. "Brazilian Capitals and Frontiers: Part II," *Journal of Geography*, vol. 54, pp. 5–17, January, 1955.

These fine articles are written for students and teachers of geography as well as for scholars. They approach the colossus of South America with understanding and take the reader into the heart of Brazil and South America. Perceptive comments on a future that has already unfolded along the Brazilian frontiers lend greater authority to suggestions of possibilities in the longer view.

Shurz, William L.: *Brazil, the Infinite Country,* E. P. Dutton & Co., Inc., New York, 1961.

This survey, written by an historian, encompasses the people, the cultural contrasts and frictions, and the historical-geographic unfolding of Brazil. Though written in a popular form, it will serve as an admirable primer to the giant of the continent.

Wagley, Charles: *Amazon Town: A Study of Man in the Tropics,* The Macmillan Company, New York, 1953.

A wilderness city serves as the microcosm of a tropical universe in this anthropological and sociological study of the vast Amazonian region. Amazonia spreads into many nations, and the life, habitats, and occupations of the people and their problems emphasize for the student and reader the barrier that has prevented the penetration of civilization into this tropical forest land.

White, C. Langdon: *Whither South America: Population and Natural Resources,* Professional Paper no. 22, National Council for Geographic Education, Norman, Okla., 1961.

A concise statement of the principal problems of South America—the rapid increase in population, the varied distribution of material resources, and potential manufacturing.

Part II   THE OLD WORLD

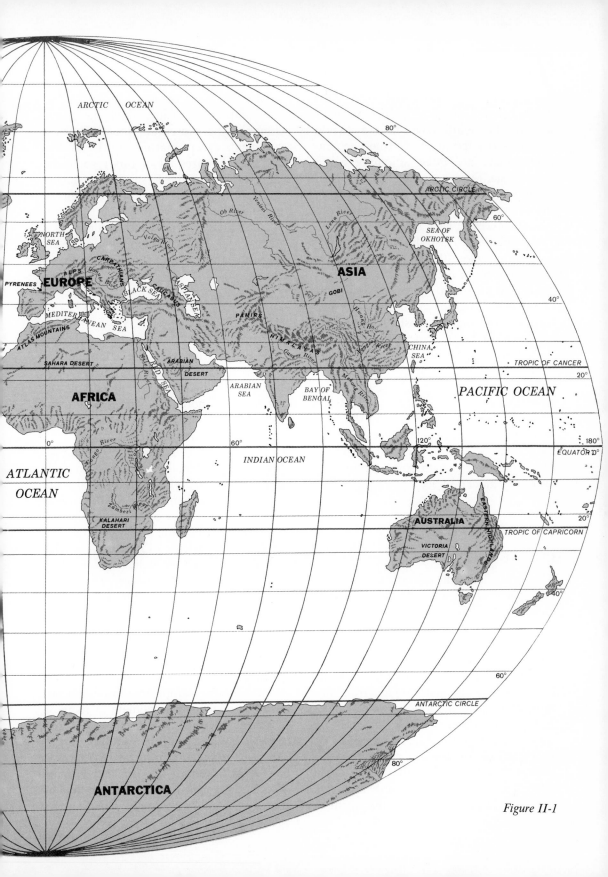

Figure II-1

THE LAND MASSES OF THE EASTERN Hemisphere extend from well north of the Arctic Circle to south of the equator halfway to the South Pole. In the "world island"—so referred to by some geographers—there are three adjoining continents: Asia, Europe, and Africa. The continent of Australia has been isolated from the others for millions of years; numerous islands, however, have served as a partial bridge between Australia and Asia. All Eurasia and more than half of Africa are situated north of the equator; Australia is entirely to the south. From the standpoint of physical geography, Europe and Asia form one continent, Eurasia, with Europe essentially a large western peninsula of Asia. Eurasia's separation into two continents is justified on racial, cultural, and historical grounds.

Antarctica is divided between the Eastern and Western Hemispheres but for descriptive convenience is discussed with the former. So far as is known, it consists of a high plateau with some mountains, all nearly hidden by ice.

PHYSICAL SETTING

CLIMATE

The great land masses of the Eastern Hemisphere have areas of every type of climate known except the polar icecap. Location chiefly determines the types of climate present in the separate continents. Africa, bisected by the equator and extending only about 35 degrees to the north or south, has climates ranging from the rainy tropical to the Mediterranean type. Europe, situated in middle latitudes to the west of the largest continent, has climates characteristic of the intermediate zone between the tropics and the Arctic. Only a small area near the Caspian Sea is arid, though a large part toward the north is

tundra and subpolar continental. As a whole, Europe is the most favored of all continents climatically. Asia has every climatic type present in the Old World continents except marine west coast; Europe monopolizes all of this type in the northern half of the Eastern Hemisphere. Australia has the same range of climatic types as the southern half of Africa, but unfortunately much of the continent is a trade-wind desert. Tasmania and New Zealand are in the marine west-coast climate.

RELIEF FEATURES

Major relief features in the Eastern Hemisphere are varied and include lowlands or plains, plateaus, old, worn-down mountains, and young, rugged mountains. In general, the shorelines of Eurasia are extremely irregular when compared with those of Africa and Australia.

The lowlands of Eurasia are very important since on them live more than one-half of the world's population. Many of the plains are underlain by seams of coal and have become the site of great manufacturing centers. Petroleum also occurs in some of the lowlands; for example, those near the Persian Gulf are believed to contain the world's largest oil reserves. The largest lowlands extend across Eurasia. Only a few low mountains and plateaus rise above the surface of this vast plain, and except in the Pacific borderlands these are not difficult for man to cross. A large population lives on the plain especially from Western Europe to central Siberia. Because of the severe climate in its most northerly part near the Arctic Ocean and widespread aridity in the southern part in Asia, the population in those two areas is small. In Southern and Eastern Europe and in Asia, the plains are smaller than in the north and are usually separated by mountains or other highlands. Some, like the Alföld in Hungary and Szechwan in China, are of a basin character; many are river lowlands like the Po, Ganges, and Yangtze Valleys. Coastal plains are common, although generally rather narrow, and include those of Portugal, Israel, Malabar in western India, and the quite small ones in Japan. Often, these various sorts of lowlands in southern Eurasia are small; they have, nevertheless, the highest population density of the entire region and contain most of the large cities.

In Africa the coastal fringe along the Mediterranean Sea and the irrigated Nile Valley are well populated, as are parts of the Sudan region. In contrast, the large but hot and humid Congo Basin, much of the Guinea coast, and the tropical lowlands of eastern Africa have attracted comparatively few people. In tropical Africa, the highlands usually have more inhabitants than the adjacent lowlands, largely because of the cooler climate.

Although Australia has extensive plains, those in the central and western parts of the continent are so arid that the population is small; much of the desert is uninhabited. The humid lowlands on the east, southeast, and southwest portions contain most of the country's population but are too small in area to support great numbers of people.

Old mountains, with rounded summits, are characteristic of northern Ireland, Scotland, Scandinavia, southern Germany, much of east central China, parts of Siberia, and some areas in southeastern Australia and Tasmania. In many of the old mountain areas the gentler slopes are tilled and thus support a fairly dense population. The steeper land, used for grazing and forestry, has few inhabitants. Frequently, mining is an important industry.

Young, rugged mountains, such as the Atlas in Africa, the Pyrenees, Alps, Apennines, Balkans, Carpathians, and Pindus in Europe, and the Lebanon and Taurus in Asia, nearly surround the Mediterranean Sea. Other groups of young mountains, curving eastward from the Black Sea area, include the Caucasus, Elburz, Karakorum, Kunlun, Nan Shan, and Himalayas. The upfolded ranges continue southeast through Burma, Thailand, and the Malay Peninsula into the volcano-studded islands of the East Indies. Off Eastern Asia, southward from the Kamchatka Peninsula, are the mountainous islands of Japan, Taiwan, and the Philippines. Much of New Zealand also has rugged, mountainous topography.

Plateaus are numerous in Eurasia, with Tibet surpassing all others. This type of highland is especially common in the southern part of the continent and forms the main mass of several peninsulas. Among the plateaus are those of Iberia, Turkey, Arabia, Iran, Afghanistan, Deccan (India), and Yunnan in southwest China. Most of Africa south of the Sahara consists of plateaus, with Ethiopia rising high above the rest.

PEOPLE OF THE OLD WORLD

Representatives of all the major races of mankind reside in the Eastern Hemisphere. Probably the original home of man was somewhere in Asia. The Caucasian peoples are classified into several groups, among which are the Indians of Hindustan and Pakistan, the Semites of North Africa and Southwest Asia, the Nordics of Northwest Europe, the Alpine type in Central Europe, and the Slavs to the east and southeast. The primitive Ainus of Japan are also included in the white race. The so-called Mongolians are found in China, Japan, and Central Asia. The

Malays are natives of Burma, the Malay Peninsula, Indonesia, the Philippines, and other island groups. Negroes and Negroid peoples live in Africa south of the Sahara, in New Guinea, in isolated portions of Southeast Asia, and in islands as far east as Fiji. Originally they were the inhabitants of Australia. Polynesians are a mixed race living on Pacific islands from New Zealand to Hawaii; the Malagasy of Madagascar are related to the Polynesians. The Hamites of the Sudan and Ethiopia are another example of mixed ancestry. Since racial characteristics are fused through intermarriage, it is difficult to describe a typical Englishman, German, Frenchman, Korean, or a representative of many other peoples who are loosely grouped together.

GEOGRAPHIC SITUATIONS

EUROPE

Europe has the most irregular coastline of any continent. It consists of several large peninsulas—Balkan, Italian, Iberian (Spain and Portugal), Brittany, Jutland (Denmark), Scandinavia—and many smaller ones. Great Britain, Ireland, Sicily, Sardinia, and numerous other islands adjoin the mainland. Iceland and Spitsbergen are distant outliers. Between the peninsulas, major islands, and the mainland are many straits and seas. Some seas, like the Mediterranean, Tyrrhenian, Adriatic, Aegean, and Black, as well as the North and Baltic, are nearly landlocked.

There are three great physical-relief regions in Europe: (1) the Northwestern Highlands in Scandinavia and Scotland, (2) the Central Lowlands in northern France, Netherlands, northern Germany, and adjacent areas, and (3) the Southern Uplands of mountains, plateaus, basins, and peninsulas in Spain, Switzerland, Italy, and the Balkan countries. The variety of surface forms and areas within the major region gives rise to a large number of environments, each with its typical industries or occupations. The most extensive lowland plain on earth extends, with few interruptions, from the North Sea across northern Eurasia to eastern Siberia. Densely populated in Europe, the plain supports few people in northern Siberia.

The bulk of Europe's population is crowded onto its plains. The largest of these is the North European Plain, which extends from northwest France across the Low Countries, northern Germany, and Poland into the U.S.S.R. Most of the European part of the Soviet Union is included in this plain. In Central and Southern Europe many small plains, valleys, and basins are interspersed between the hills and mountains; they are common in England, southern Germany, France, Italy, and in the southeast from the Carpathians to Greece. The plains have easy routes for railways and highways, generally favorable conditions for agriculture, and convenient sites for cities. Many have navigable rivers. The Alps, Pyrenees, and Scandinavian mountains are formidable barriers, but in general, the mountain systems are relatively easy to cross, as compared with ranges like the Andes or Himalayas.

As a result of the deep penetration of the continent by marginal seas, ocean transport has easy access to all Western Europe. Ocean ports are within a few hundred miles of nearly all parts of the Continent. In addition, navigable rivers and canals bring cheap water transport to localities far inland. No other continent equals Europe in accessibility. Although the Mediterranean shore is girt by mountains, breaks in the barrier allow access to the hinterland. Among these breaks are the Gap of Carcassonne to Bordeaux, the Rhone Valley, the Brenner and other passes from the Adriatic, the route from Salonika up the Vardar Valley, and the Dardanelles. The longest railroad tunnels in the world, the Simplon, 12.5 miles, and the St. Gotthard, 9.25 miles, pierce the Alps and connect the Po Valley with the Rhineland and northern lowlands. Shores of the North and Baltic Seas, however, are usually low and often swampy. Some of these lowlands have been reclaimed for agricultural use by the building of dikes.

Europe has many natural resources. For energy there is coal, petroleum, and water power. There are extensive forests and considerable grazing areas. Iron ore and bauxite are abundant, and many other important minerals are in ample supply. In addition to using resources of local origin, heavy consumption by both population and industry necessitates large imports of many materials and goods.

The value of Europe's imports greatly exceeds that of its exports. The difference is made up by money spent by tourists and foreign residents, and such invisible exports as interest on investments abroad, money sent home by emigrants, profits on insurance and ships carrying goods for other nations, commissions on sales, services, and management outside the Continent, and income earned abroad by writers, artists, musicians, lecturers, and other workers. In general, Europeans go abroad to work; visitors pay for living and travel on the Continent. After World War II, the United States gave or lent European countries large quantities of goods and much money.

ASIA

The largest of the continents, Asia, has over half of the world's population; it supports more than 1 billion people.

Large, fertile lowlands, with abundant water from rainfall or irrigation, and continuous or long growing seasons make possible two to four crops a year. Most Asiatics consume little meat, and many are vegetarians. In China, where animal food is used, the sources are mainly swine and poultry, both of which gain much in weight compared with their food supply— in part materials that would otherwise be wasted. Furthermore, custom encourages a high birth rate, and standards of living are usually far below those of the United States and Canada.

Although Asia thus supports a teeming population, the continent has vast deserts, high, frigid plateaus, the greatest mountains on earth, and frozen tundras— areas that have few, if any, inhabitants. The enormous size of Asia and the highland barriers handicap transportation; in the midst of the continent, an area larger than the United States is without railroads. Deserts dominate from Arabia through Iran and Tibet into Turkestan and Mongolia. From the Caspian Sea, the lowlands to the east are also desert. Except for concentrated areas reclaimed by irrigation, the land is left to roving nomadic herders. The entire northern coast of Siberia is open to navigation for only a few weeks each year, and small use can be made of the Lena, Ob, and Yenisei Rivers because they are tributary to the Arctic. Smaller plains are common, especially those associated with rivers, for example, the Sung-hua and Liao Ho plains of Manchuria, the Yellow Plain of the Hwang Ho and Yangtze in China, the Ganges and Indus lowlands, and Mesopotamia. Coastal lowlands also occur but are often narrow.

Plateaus are such numerous and important features in Asia that it might be called a continent of plateaus. The greatest are those in the interior which are centered in

Tibet, with smaller plateaus in Mongolia, Gobi, Turkestan, western China, Afghanistan, and Iran. Peninsular plateaus in Turkey, Arabia, and the Deccan of India are noteworthy.

Double sets of mighty mountain ranges cross Southern Asia from Turkey to China. The ranges spreading out from the Pamirs, called the "roof of the world," in western Tibet are the Hindu Kush to the southwest, the Karakorum and Himalayas to the south and southeast, the Altyn Tagh and Kunlun to the east, and the Altai and Tien Shan to the north.

Like Europe, Asia has several protruding peninsulas, and to the east and southeast the ocean is filled with islands, large and small. The chief peninsulas are Anatolia (Turkey), Arabia, India, Malay, Shantung (in China), Korea, and Kamchatka. On the south, the Red Sea and Persian Gulf are connected with the Indian Ocean. To the east are the Yellow Sea and the Sea of Japan, guarded by the Japanese islands, and farther north the Sea of Okhotsk and the Bering Sea. To the southeast, the Philippines and Indonesia are a mixture of islands and seas. The inland Caspian Sea is the largest lake in the world.

The natural vegetation, soils, and land utilization are closely related to the climatic regions. Vast softwood forests cover much of Siberia. Teak and other hardwoods come from the tropical monsoon regions. A great variety of native plants occur, many of which have been domesticated. Asia is the original home of more cultivated crops and domestic livestock than any other continent.

Besides resources based on agriculture and grazing, Asia has minerals, fisheries, and water power. In minerals, it is rich in petroleum, possibly having more than any other continent. There is much coal in China and considerable in India, Japan, Vietnam, and Siberia. Many metals are produced. Fisheries are most important off the northeast coast, but are valuable both in the cold Arctic and the warm Indian Oceans. The greatest development of water power has been in Japan, where industrialization is most advanced. Asia has large rivers that descend thousands of feet from their mountain sources to the plains, among them the Yangtze, Indus, and Brahmaputra. In the future, great dams will develop the power that will be needed when China, India, and Pakistan become important manufacturing regions.

AFRICA

On the basis of the culture and history of its peoples, Africa can be divided into the Mediterranean lands that are closely related to Europe and Asia and into central and southern Africa. The Sahara is the natural zone of separation. Most of the two-thirds of Africa south of the Sahara is a plateau that usually breaks steeply toward the oceans. The resulting rapids and falls in the lower courses of rivers make them unnavigable. The upper Nile flows through the swampy Sudd, where papyrus and other water vegetation has choked the channels and prevented water travel. Penetration to the interior was so difficult in the past that until after the middle of the nineteenth century much of Africa was unknown; it was a blank on the map and was frequently called the "dark continent." When industrialization comes to Africa, the Congo, Niger, and other large, swift rivers will become great sources of power; the continent exceeds North America in its potential water power. Plateau lands in Africa are preferred places for living, especially by Europeans, because of their relative coolness compared with the lowlands.

As yet, most African resources are little developed, but the old rocks have important deposits of minerals. Iron, copper, gold, uranium, diamonds, and many others are mined; coal is mined in South Africa. Petroleum has been discovered in Tunis and Algeria. Products of the tropical forests, wool and hides from the grasslands, cotton, rubber, cacao, and vegetable oils from the plantations are among the developed resources.

The smooth coastline of the continent is indented by few harbors. The Gulf of Guinea, off the west central coast, is broad and open to the Atlantic Ocean. North of Africa is the Mediterranean Sea and northeast the Red Sea—each enclosed by land except for a narrow strait. Madagascar, in the Indian Ocean, is the only large island, being the third largest in the world.

AUSTRALIA

Australia, the smallest of the continents, can be divided into three physical divisions, the Eastern Highlands, the East Central Lowlands, which extend north-south across the continent, and Western Australia. Because of the highlands along the eastern edge of the continent and the continental location within the trade-wind belt, most of the western and central parts are desert. Within much of this arid area the drainage systems are poorly defined, or uncoordinated, and have no outlets to the sea.

The area just east of the Eastern Highlands is the area of greatest population and highest population density. West of the mountains, population decreases rapidly with decreasing rainfall. Near the coast are the largest cities, commercial and industrial centers, and the most productive farms. The large sheep stations are either in southeastern Australia, between the farm lands and the deserts, or in the southwestern part of western Australia and southwest Queensland. North of the Tropic of Capricorn in the northern and northeastern part of Queensland and the northern part of the Northern Territory, cattle predominate and are numerous near the east, southeast, and southwest coasts.

Broad, curving indentations mark the coast—the Great Australian Bight on the south and the Gulf of Carpentaria on the north. Harbors are few and the coastline is generally smooth. Tasmania is the only important island.

chapter **8**

NORTHWESTERN AND
CENTRAL EUROPE

Figure 8-1   Northwestern and Central Europe is an area of contrasting topography ranging from the Alps of Switzerland to the polders of the Netherlands. Strategic straits such as Dover, Skaggerak, and Kattegat separate islands from the mainland and peninsulas from each other. The largest plains area is in northern Germany.

IREL

LOFOTEN ISLANDS

KJOLEN MOUNTAINS

GULF OF BOTHNIA

FINLAND

Central Lake Region

THE FAROES

NORWAY

Interior
Highlands

SWEDEN

SHETLAND
ISLANDS

ORKNEY
ISLANDS

SKAGERAK

KATTEGAT

Smaland
Highlands

Northern Highlands

SCOTLAND

Eastern
Lowlands

Central
Lowlands

NORTH SEA

DENMARK

THERN
ND

UNITED

Lake District

PENNINES

KINGDOM

NETHERLANDS

WALES

ENGLAND

English Lowlands

Thames River

Sandy Coastal Fringe

Polder Lands

North European Plain

Elbe River

STRAIT OF DOVER

Interior Plains

Ruhr River

ENGLISH
CHANNEL

wall

Interior
Uplands

Rhine River

EAST
GERMANY

BELGIUM

LUXEMBOURG

Seine River

Ardennes
Plateau
and
Vosges

Central
Highlands

Loire River

Northern
Lowlands

WEST
GERMANY

Danube River

FRANCE

Alpine
Foreland

Aquitaine
Basin

Central Plateau

ALPS

ALPS

AUSTRIA

Garonne River

MASSIF
CENTRAL

Rhone River

FRENCH ALPS

SWITZERLAND

PYRENEES

*E*UROPE MIRACULOUSLY ROSE FROM THE depths of World War II to a state of economic health, productive power, and political stature which must be seriously reckoned with in today's world. Individually, the countries of Northwestern and Central Europe have declined relatively in world significance partly as a result of the loss of direct political control over overseas territories and partly because of the economic growth of countries in other areas, particularly the United States and the U.S.S.R. However, the world impact of this small geographical area, both past and present, has been of immeasurable importance. Its location, the diversity and number of its people, its resources, advanced culture, contributions to science and technology, tremendous agricultural and industrial productiveness, and dominant position in world trade make this small continent of prime concern to every world inhabitant. Excluding the U.S.S.R., Europe contains 16 per cent of the people on only 3.5 per cent of the world land area.

IMPORTANCE OF NORTHWESTERN AND CENTRAL EUROPE

Marked political fragmentation, a dominant characteristic of Northwestern and Central Europe for the past century, indicated the deep desire of diverse peoples to have sovereignty over their own affairs. This tendency has been partially offset in the post–World War II period by regional groupings of nations for economic, trade, defense, and political reasons. The ultimate may be the formation of a federated Europe, but the area currently possesses political units ranging in size from France with 212,737 square miles to tiny Liechtenstein with 61 square miles (Table 8-1).

Western Europe was the home of modern Western civilization including the mechanized-industrial type of economy.

From each country people and ideas have penetrated into far corners of the earth. The industrial revolution germinated here, grew rapidly, and spread to other parts of the world. Large industrial cities and complexes replaced rural areas and today dominate much of West Central Europe, with the German Ruhr and the English Midlands as outstanding examples.

Europe's proportion of the world's industrial production decreased from 68 per cent in 1870 to 25 per cent in 1948. Prewar European industrial output was one-third greater than that of the United States; by 1948, as a result of the war and rapid growth in the United States, it was more than one-fourth less. The gap has been narrowed, however, as Europe's industrial production doubled from 1947 to 1955, and increased by an additional 35 per cent in the 1955 to 1962 period.

The densely populated, coal-rich, industrial core of England, Benelux (Belgium, Netherlands, Luxembourg), northern France, and West Germany is surrounded by areas where agriculture, forestry, fishing, and mining produce raw materials of importance. Nevertheless, the area is heavily deficient in food, petroleum, and many other items and must rely on imports to supplement local production. Thus, Western Europe has become the focus of world trade routes and well-developed land-transportation facilities vital to commercial relations with neighboring countries. Trade deficits are offset by such things as earnings of merchant marines, foreign investments, insurance, and spending by numerous tourists.

LOCATION AND SHAPE

Northwestern and Central Europe, as here defined, includes 1,055,215 square miles or 56 per cent of Europe (excluding the U.S.S.R.). The 15 countries and princi-

TABLE 8-1   POPULATION AND AREA OF NORTHWESTERN AND CENTRAL EUROPEAN COUNTRIES, 1961

Country	Date	Population, thousands	Area, nearest thousand sq. mi.	Average density per sq. mi.
United Kingdom	1961	52,673	94	560
England		43,431	50	863
Channel Islands		104	75§	1,386
Isle of Man		48	211§	227
Northern Ireland		1,420	5	207
Scotland		5,178	30	170
Wales		2,641	8	329
Republic of Ireland				
(Eire)	1961	2,815	27	104
Norway*	1961	3,615	125	29
Sweden	1961	7,526	174	43
Denmark†	1961	4,599	17	274
Finland	1961	4,497	130	34
Iceland	1961	178	40	4
Belgium	1961	9,204	12	772
Netherlands	1961	11,532	12	916
Luxembourg	1961	316	1	325
France	1961	45,876	213	214
Germany				
East Germany	1961	17,188	42	407
West Germany‡	1961	54,108	96	573
Austria	1961	7,071	32	217
Switzerland	1961	5,455	16	332
Liechtenstein	1961	16	61§	262

* Does not include Svalbard (24,000 sq. mi.).
† Does not include the Faroe Islands or Greenland.
‡ Includes West Berlin.
§ Square miles.

Source: *The Statesman's Yearbook*, 1962–1963, St Martin's Press, New York, 1963; and *Major Political Entities of the World*, U.S. Department of State, Mar. 7, 1962.

palities would cover about one-third of the United States. The distance from northern Norway to southern France measures 2,125 miles, equivalent to the distance from Chicago to Los Angeles. Small countries have the advantage of unity, compactness, and ease of exchange of goods and ideas but usually lack sufficient domestic resources on which to base an economy without heavy reliance upon imports.

The strategic buffer-zone location between the two world powers, the United States and the U.S.S.R., is useful in peace but not in war. The central location in the land hemisphere facilitates world trade, especially as Western Europe faces three major water bodies, the Arctic Ocean, the Atlantic Ocean, and the Mediterranean Sea.

No other comparable world area has such disrupted coastlines and irregularly shaped countries. The North Sea, Baltic Sea, English Channel, and Bay of Biscay cause major separations and indentations. The peninsulas of Scandinavia, Jutland, Brittany, as well as several smaller ones, add to the irregularity, as do the numerous islands, ranging in size from Great Britain and Iceland to tiny skerries along the Norwegian coast. Norway and Scotland exhibit highly fiorded coasts.

PHYSICAL SETTING

RELIEF FEATURES

Western Europe has a very complex physical structure. East of the Carpathian Mountains and the Vistula River is the stable Russian platform. West of this platform, repeated elevation and depression of the land with folding and erosion has left mountains, plateaus, hills, and plains in close proximity.

HIGHLANDS The highlands found in Scandinavia, northern Scotland, and Ireland are composed of very old, hard rocks that have been repeatedly uplifted and eroded. Moreover, huge ice sheets during the Glacial Period sculptured, scoured, and smoothed the topography. The fiorded coastline of Norway, with some fiords reaching 120 miles inland, and the rounded highlands of northern Scotland demonstrate the great erosive power of the ice. Most of Norway is a high, glaciated plateau averaging between 4,000 and 5,000 feet. The Scandinavian highlands drop sharply to the west but gradually to the Baltic. These highlands include northern Finland and the southern Swedish highlands. Soils are generally infertile. Valleys and adjoining lowlands possess limited arable land. Timber and water power are abundant, especially in Scandinavia.

Mountains and plateaus in West Central Europe, although geologically younger than the Scandinavian highlands, have been eroded for so long that their relief is one of rounded maturity. Such remnants, called "the central highlands," extend from the southern uplands of Ireland to the highlands of central Germany and include southwest England, Brittany, the Central Plateau of France, the Ardennes, and the Vosges. These uplands consist of hard, resistant rock with considerable relief and poor soil. Adjacent basins and lowlands contain more recent soils of higher agricultural value. The metallic ores and coal measures which are associated with these highlands form the basis of major industrial regions. Agriculture is limited, but grazing and forestry are locally significant.

The Alpine System, a complex combination of young folded mountains with associated forelands and intermontane structural basins and plains, dominates Switzerland, Austria, and the eastern borderlands of France. The Alps average 12,000 feet, with higher sharp peaks, such as Mt. Blanc, 15,781 feet. Valleys are narrow, steep, and rocky. The south slope of the Alps is abrupt but the north slope is gradual. The Alps, because of their east-west orientation, are not a major climatic barrier to the marine westerly winds. Despite the high altitudes, numerous passes and tunnels allow remarkably easy north-south communication between the Mediterranean Basin and Northwestern and Central Europe.

The Pyrenees Mountains extend between the Bay of Biscay and the Mediterranean Sea. Like the Alps, they are young folded mountains and form a considerable barrier between France and Spain.

LOWLANDS Fortunately, Northwestern and Central Europe contains considerable areas of lowland. The great European Plain extends from southeastern England, through western and northern France, Belgium, Netherlands, Denmark, north Germany, Poland, and on into the Soviet Union. It is narrow in the west and widens

Figure 8-2 Rugged mountains, such as the Bernese Alps, dominate three-fourths of Switzerland. (Courtesy of G. Muller.)

in the east. Generally, it is level; rolling to hilly topography occurs, but elevations rarely rise to 500 feet above sea level. Much of the existing relief is a result of continental glaciation, and ridges of glacial debris (moraines) border the Baltic in north Germany and Denmark. Outcrops of slightly folded beds of shale, chalk, and limestone, called "downs" or "scarp and vale," give relief to southern England and

Figure 8-3 The Finnish lake country near Sovonlinnia. Note the rounded glacial topography, the abundant forest cover, and the clearings on the better soils along the lake edges. (Courtesy of Legation of Finland.)

northern France. Sand, gravel, and silt of glacial origin cover most of the remaining lowland area; in central Germany there are fertile wind-deposited soils called "loess."

Lowlands border also the Baltic Sea and the Gulf of Bothnia in Sweden and Finland. Generally, southern Sweden and southern Finland are less than 500 feet above sea level, with numerous lakes, swamps, and glacial ridges. The Baltic lowlands are underlain by very old crystalline rocks, except for the fertile sedimentary plains of Skåne in the extreme southern tip of Sweden. Soils are usually thin with scattered deposits of fertile marine clay.

RIVERS The Alps and associated mountains are the source of the major rivers of Central Europe. Large north-flowing rivers, such as the Oder draining into the Baltic, and the Elbe and Rhine draining into the North Sea, are rapid and of value for water power near their sources, but become broad and sluggish in crossing the European Plain. France has three major west- or northwest-flowing rivers in the Seine, Loire, and Garonne; the Rhone empties into the Mediterranean. A system of interconnecting canals and rivers gives Western Europe the best inland water-transportation network in the world. The British Isles have numerous short rivers, the longest being the Thames and Shannon. Scandinavian rivers draining to the Atlantic are short and rapid; those entering the Baltic are longer, with slower flow. Finland and the Netherlands are handicapped by considerable poorly drained land.

CLIMATE

Reliability of climate, the keynote of Northwestern and Central Europe, fosters agricultural development and other hu-

man activities. Temperatures are far more moderate than those of similar latitudes in eastern North America or interior Eurasia (Figure 8-4). Only the rigorous climates of the higher mountains and the exposed coastal areas with heavy rainfall are unsuitable to crops. Barley and rye are grown beyond 70° north latitude in Norway, farther north than on any other continent.

Mild winters, cool to warm summers, small temperature ranges for the latitude, and well-distributed precipitation typify the climate. Position on the western side of a large land mass, prevailing westerly winds off the warm North Atlantic, flowing inland without land barriers, and the prevalence of cyclonic influences are largely responsible for these conditions.

The movement of storms from west to east results in frequent weather changes of temperature, wind, and precipitation. The cyclonic influence is especially strong in the winter.

MARINE WEST COAST The British Isles, the western fringes of Continental Europe, and southern Iceland are dominated by marine influences. Mild winters, cool summers, evenly distributed precipitation, and damp, cloudy conditions are characteristic. In January, the 32°F isotherm runs virtually north-south along the Norwegian coast and then trends northwest-southeast through mainland Europe. The adjoining water moderates the summer temperatures; the long days are warm but rarely hot. The annual temperature range averages between 15 and 30°F. The frost-free period is 180 days or more except in the highlands.

Slightly greater amounts of precipitation are normally received in the winter half-year; spring months are generally the driest. Annual precipitation varies from less than 25 inches in the plains of southeastern England to nearly 200 inches on

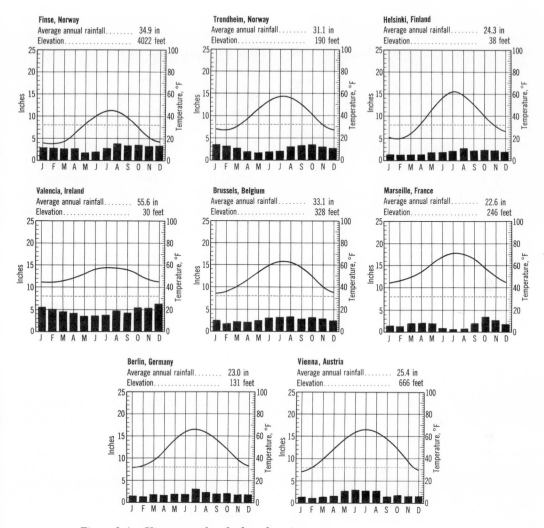

Figure 8-4   Climate graphs of selected stations.

the exposed peaks of Ben Nevis in Scotland and Snowdon in Wales.

TRANSITIONAL CLIMATE OF CENTRAL EUROPE
The climate of Central Europe is transitional between marine Western and continental Eastern Europe. The annual temperature range increases and precipitation decreases eastward with greater distance from the Atlantic, the source of moisture. Northeast winds from Siberia bring low winter temperatures and snow for four or five months in eastern Germany, eastern Norway, Sweden, Austria, and Switzerland. Though the North and Baltic Seas rarely freeze, the tributary rivers and harbors are icebound. The average is 32 days at Lübeck and 61 days at Stettin. Precipitation decreases eastward from marine Europe, and averages 22 to 26 inches annually with a spring and summer maximum.

HUMID   CONTINENTAL   Finland,   northern

Sweden, and parts of Norway have a humid continental climate with short, warm summers and long, severe winters. This area is partially blocked from the moderating oceanic winds by the Scandinavian highlands. Finland is dominated in winter by cold northeast winds from Siberia. Coniferous forests grow well, but the short growing season limits agriculture primarily to hardy crops.

MEDITERRANEAN Southern France experiences the climate typical of the lands bordering the Mediterranean Sea, having hot, dry summers and mild, rainy winters. In summer, a zone of high atmospheric pressure extending over the Mediterranean Sea results in stable conditions. In winter, a southward migration of the paths, followed by cyclonic storms, brings rains to the area. Winter is the natural growing season as the summers are too dry except for drought-resistant crops and vegetation.

TUNDRA AND HIGH ALTITUDE The Alps, Scandinavian highlands, and other highland areas of Northwestern and Central Europe exhibit great climatic zonation and extremes typical of mountainous areas. The Alps form a divide between the climates of Mediterranean and Central Europe.

NATURAL VEGETATION AND SOILS

Natural vegetation and soils in Europe are related closely to the varied relief, subsurface rock structures, and climatic conditions. Man's intensive utilization of the land has greatly disrupted the original natural patterns of Western Europe, especially the pattern of vegetation. Rapid soil changes, because of glaciation or type of parent rock, result in much less uniform belts of soil than in Eastern Europe.

Nevertheless, the distribution of certain broad associations of native vegetation and soils can be identified (Table 8-2).

DIVERSITY OF CULTURES AND LANGUAGES

The thirteen political units (besides Luxembourg and Liechtenstein) indicate the tremendous diversity of peoples, languages, and cultures in this area. Each country, no matter how small, has developed a national identity and traditions peculiar to its individual culture. In most cases, the country has its own language, within which several dialects may have evolved because of separation by water bodies or land barriers. Switzerland has four and Belgium and Finland each have two language and ethnic groups.

Various races of people are found in Northwestern and Central Europe, but language and cultural rather than racial differences form the basis for nationalistic desires and territorial problems. Germanic, Celtic, and Romanic languages predominate; the Asiatic-derived Finnish and Lapp languages are found in the north. This diversity of languages, dialects, customs, and traditions is a major barrier to the much talked of "United States of Western Europe."

The European area was once divided into a few great empires: French, German, Austro-Hungarian, and Russian. During the nineteenth and twentieth centuries, a great nationalistic movement spread across Europe, fed by the democratic ideas of equality, fraternity, and liberty generated during the French Revolution. Many nations achieved independence as the great empires were divided, and some nations attempted and failed to dominate Europe by aggressive warfare.

Economic difficulties brought on by two

TABLE 8-2 PRINCIPAL VEGETATION AND SOIL CHARACTERISTICS

Vegetation	Soil
Tundra Moss, lichens, and low bushes. Dwarf birch, larch, spruce, and sphagnum-peat bogs on southern fringe.	Tundra Subsoil permanently frozen, acid, lacking humus. Surface swampy and waterlogged in summer. Little or no agriculture.
Taiga Cedar, larch, pine, fir, and spruce, common coniferous species. Some deciduous aspen, birch, and alder.	Podsol Ashen gray color, highly leached, acid, low in humus. Limited agriculture.
Mixed coniferous and deciduous Transitional between coniferous and deciduous in north and oak, beech, hickory association in south. Largely cleared for agriculture.	Podsolic and brown Transitional. Gray to brown in color. Brown soils less leached, higher in humus, less acid, with better structure than podsolic. Productive if heavily fertilized and carefully managed.
Mediterranean Drought-resistant types such as olive, cork oak, cypress, and scrubby evergreen. Deciduous at higher elevations. Shrub and bush growth common.	Mixed Varies, depending upon parent material and amount of rainfall and leaching. Alluvial, high-iron-content (red), and volcanic soils common. Lowland soils productive, especially where irrigated.
Mountain and moor Vertical zonations with Alpine grasslands in the Alps, Pyrenees, and Norway. Moor (heather) found in highlands of British Isles and Scandinavia.	Highland Thin, rocky, and infertile. Dark brown soils in Alpine grasslands. Grazing and forestry developed.

world wars, common trade problems, the loss of colonies by Western European powers, and joint defense efforts have resulted in the development of various economic and political unions. Belgium, Netherlands, and Luxembourg entered into an economic (customs) agreement called the "Benelux Union" immediately following World War II. In 1953 the Schuman Plan (European Coal and Steel Community) for pooling steel and coal in six Western European nations was initiated to attempt to offset by unification and cooperation the raw-material deficiencies and market disadvantages of small nations. This evolved into the Common Market Treaty, signed in Rome in 1957, which creates a customs union of Benelux, France, West Germany, and Italy. The objective is a large single market of 180 million, in which trade barriers will be gradually removed over a fifteen-year period, and free movement of goods, labor, capital, and services will eventually occur. The treaty also directs that the economic policy of the six countries be coordinated and common policies applied over broad sectors of the economy. The Euratom Treaty, aimed at the peaceful use of nuclear energy, was signed by the six nations at the same time. It seems inevitable that England will join the Common Market and that many other European countries will associate with it in some way. To counter the Common Market, seven other European nations formed the European Free Trade Association. An even broader grouping of nations in the Atlantic Community including the United States is being considered. Various organizations with political and collective security implications have also been formed, such as the Council of Europe and NATO (Table 8-3). The success of these attempts would be an important step toward the unification of Western Europe. Any federal movement faces the tremendous obstacles of strong nationalistic and self-sufficiency movements, but significant progress has been made.

POPULATION DISTRIBUTIONS AND PRESENT STAGE OF ECONOMIC DEVELOPMENT

A belt of extremely dense population extends from central and southern England across the English Channel to include northern France, Benelux, the Rhine Valley, and the contact zone between the highlands and lowlands in Germany (Figure 8-5). This is one of the most intensely urbanized and industrialized regions in the world. More than 70 per cent of the population of Great Britain live in cities of over 10,000. Netherlands

TABLE 8-3   MEMBERSHIP OF EUROPEAN ORGANIZATIONS

Euratom	OEEC[3]	Common Market (EEC)[7]	European Coal and Steel Community[4]	NATO[5]	EFTA[6]
Austria[2]	X[1]				X
Belgium[2]	X	X	X	X	
Denmark[2]	X			X	X
Eire[2]	X				X
Finland[2]					X
France[2]	X	X	X	X	
Germany (West)[2]	X	X	X	X	
Greece	X			X	
Iceland[2]	X			X	
Italy	X	X	X	X	
Luxembourg[2]	X	X	X	X	
Netherlands[2]	X	X	X	X	
Norway[2]	X			X	X
Portugal	X			X	X
Sweden[2]	X				X
Switzerland[2]	X				X
Turkey	X			X	
United Kingdom[2]	X			X	X

[1] X indicates members or proposed members.
[2] Political units in Northwestern and Central Europe.
[3] Organization for European Economic Cooperation.
[4] Also known as the Schuman Plan.
[5] North Atlantic Treaty Organization.
[6] European Free Trade Association.
[7] European Economic Community.

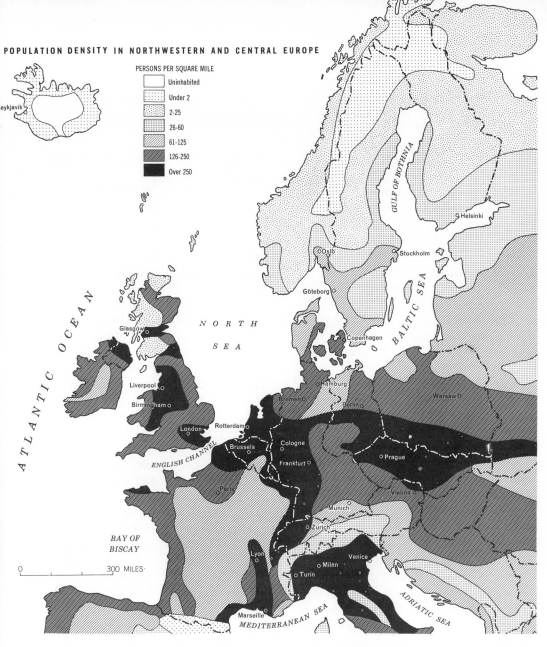

POPULATION DENSITY IN NORTHWESTERN AND CENTRAL EUROPE

PERSONS PER SQUARE MILE

Uninhabited
Under 2
2-25
26-60
61-125
126-250
Over 250

Figure 8-5   Note the great density of population in the central part of the region and the low density in the northern areas. Belgium and the Netherlands are two of the most densely populated nations in the world.

has the highest average population density of any industrialized world nation—916 persons per square mile. If Australia and New Zealand were as densely settled, for instance, they would contain the entire world's population. The Scottish Low- lands, South Wales, eastern Denmark, the northern tip of Ireland, the Swiss Plateau, the Danube Valley of Austria, and the Rhone Valley of France are also densely populated areas.

Surrounding the industrial and commercial cities are thickly peopled and intensively developed agricultural areas. In many instances handicaps such as infertile, sandy, and swampy soil have been overcome by heavy fertilization and scientific farming practices. Pasture, hay, cereal grains, and root crops predominate. Almost all agricultural produce is marketed locally except in Netherlands and Denmark.

Most of the area is characterized by deficiencies of food and surpluses of industrial products. This situation, and the need for considerable imports of industrial raw materials, makes Northwestern Europe foremost in world trade. Commercial development is aided by excellent ports, large merchant marines, and good inland-transportation facilities.

Access to minerals associated with the highlands of Central and Northern Europe, especially coal and iron, favors industry. Although Great Britain, Belgium, and Germany have large coal supplies, each imports some coal as well as nearly all of the petroleum consumed. The Netherlands has large reserves of petroleum and natural gas. Low-quality iron ore is available in France, Luxembourg, and Great Britain. Sweden is an abundant producer of high-quality iron ore. France has a large output of bauxite for aluminum production, and France and Germany have potash. Pyrites, copper, silver, lead, and zinc are found but in insufficient quantities. Water power is significant in Scandinavia and mountainous Central Europe.

Many peripheral areas of Northwestern and Central Europe are sparsely populated but significant for certain raw materials. They are generally regions of poor soils, rough topography, and severe climate. Fish, forest, and mineral resources, notably iron ore in Sweden, are vital to

Europe. Much of the agriculture is subsistence in nature, but grazing and dairying are locally highly developed.

SCANDINAVIAN COUNTRIES AND FINLAND (NORDEN)

The northern countries (Norden), loosely referred to as Scandinavia, are of increasingly strategic importance in Europe. The five countries of Norway, Sweden, Denmark, Finland, and Iceland have a great deal in common; yet each shows individuality (Figure 8-6). As a result of past association, cultures and traditions are in part similar. Except for the Finns and Lapps, racial and language similarities exist, and the majority of the people stem from the characteristically blond Nordic stock. All the countries are socialist democracies, although monarchs still reign in Denmark, Norway, and Sweden. The Lutheran religion is strongly predominant. Illiteracy is practically nonexistent.

Physical similarities also are numerous. With the exception of Denmark and the southernmost tip of Sweden, old, resistant rocks are characteristic, and the entire area has been glaciated. Iceland and Norway still possess sizable permanent glaciers. Soils, with a few exceptions, are generally infertile. With long and indented coastlines, fishing and commercial development loom high in importance. The Atlantic slopes of the Scandinavian Peninsula are rugged, abrupt, and fiorded; the Baltic slopes are gradual, southern Sweden, southern Finland, and all of Denmark being relatively flat. Population is concentrated in the seaward peripheries of the countries.

The severe climate expected in these high latitudes is offset by the prevailing westerly winds off the warm North Atlan-

Figure 8-6   Scandinavia is an area of peninsulas, indented coastlines, and islands. Note the narrow coastal regions and the dominance of mountains on the Scandinavian Peninsula.

The following labels appear on the map:

NORWEGIAN SEA
LOFOTEN ISLANDS
ARCTIC CIRCLE
Tromso
Kirkenes
Narvik
Kiruna
Trondheim
JÄMTLAND
Aalesund
Bergen
Stavanger
Kristiansand
SKAGERAK
KATTEGAT
Oslo
Lake Väner
Lake Vätter
Göteborg
Uppsala
Stockholm
AALAND ISLANDS
Turku
Helsinki
GULF OF FINLAND
GULF OF BOTHNIA
BALTIC SEA
GOTTLAND ISLAND
ÖLAND ISLAND
BORNHOLM ISLAND
Copenhagen
Malmo

NORWAY · SWEDEN · FINLAND · DENMARK

REGIONS OF SCANDINAVIA

NORWAY
1 North Norway
2 Trondheim
3 Western and Southern fringe
4 Southeastern lowlands
5 Interior highlands

SWEDEN
6 Skåne
7 Småland
8 Central lowlands and Bothnian fringe
9 Northern highlands

DENMARK
10 Western Denmark
11 Eastern Denmark

FINLAND
12 Lapland
13 Central lake region
14 Baltic littoral

—·—·— Political boundary
— — — Regional boundary

0   200 MILES

TABLE 8-4   ANNUAL TEMPERATURE RANGE

Station	Jan. average, °F	July average, °F	Annual temperature range, °F
Bergen	34	58	24
Oslo	24	63	39
Helsinki	21	62	42

tic. This oceanic influence is strongest during the winter, as is evidenced by the 32°F isotherm paralleling the entire Norwegian coast, which is ice-free the year round. Annual temperature ranges increase eastward (Table 8-4). Summer days are long but rather cool. Precipitation varies from over 60 inches in western Norway to 25 in Finland, and less than 20 in the extreme north.

Agricultural and maritime interests have been foremost in the past, but recently industry (manufacturing) has emerged as the principal segment of the respective economies. All the countries lack coal, and most of the iron ore produced in Sweden and Norway is exported. Local raw materials supply forest products and food-processing industries. Water power is abundant except in Denmark. The combined merchant marines and fishing fleets account for more than 5 per cent of total world trade.

NORWAY

Norway guards more than 13 degrees of latitude or 1,100 miles of Northwestern Continental Europe. If stretched out, the indented coastline would reach more than halfway around the world. The total area of 124,587 square miles includes thousands of offshore islands and skerries (rocky islets).

Rocky and rugged highlands dominate the topography of Norway. Much of the highland surface is plateaulike in character, averaging between 2,000 and 5,000 feet in elevation. Glaciation has rounded the landforms and cut numerous fiords along the west coast, some extending over 100 miles inland. The 3 per cent of arable area is located primarily along the coast and in the flatter southeast.

Forests cover one-fourth of Norway's land area. They occur at elevations below 3,300 feet in the south and 1,000 feet in the north. The best forests are on the eastern slopes of the highlands. About two-thirds of the commercial forest is coniferous Norway spruce and fir, and one-third deciduous trees, with birch dominant.

Norway's lack of coal is partially offset by plentiful hydroelectric power. Abundant precipitation, melting glaciers, negligible freezing, and high stream gradients give Norway more available water power than any other European country. Pyrites (source of sulfur and sulfuric acid) and iron ore, the principal minerals, normally represent three-fourths of the value of ore production. Molybdenum and silver are also mined. Coal is produced on Spitsbergen (Svalbard), a large group of Arctic islands belonging to Norway.

ECONOMIC DEVELOPMENT   Agriculture experiences handicaps of relief, climate, and poor soil, but nevertheless is the occupation upon which one-fifth of the population depend. Dairying and livestock production predominate. Farming often is combined with fishing in the coastal districts and with forestry in the interior. Small farms, 90 per cent owner-operated, and limited merchanization are characteristic. Hay, pasture, cereal grains, and root crops are grown.

The intensified industrial activity after World War II, largely based on abundance of cheap water power, employs one-third of the labor force and contributes nearly

40 per cent of the national production. Processing fish, forest, and food products and manufacturing electrochemical and electrometallurgical goods are leading industries. A large integrated state iron and steel works at Mo-i-Rana produces most of Norway's needs.

Many Norwegians look to the sea for their livelihood. From the waters adjacent to Norway and certain foreign waters are landed over 1.5 million metric tons of fish per year. Norway ranks first in Europe and sixth in the world as a fishing nation. Fish and fish products normally account for 15 per cent of the total value of exports. Herring are caught predominantly south of Trondheimfiord and cod to the north, especially in the Lofoten area. Drastically declining catches of herring and to a certain extent cod are causing shifts in the dependence upon fishing along the coast and are also forcing more emphasis upon larger vessels and distant fishing banks such as West Greenland and Iceland. The whaling fleet, operating largely in Antarctic waters, has encountered severe competition primarily from Japan and the U.S.S.R. and has declined from one-half to one-fifth of the annual world catch.

Norway's merchant marine ranks fourth in the world, behind the United States, Great Britain, and Liberia. About 85 per cent of the merchant fleet is engaged in trade between foreign ports.

REGIONS   North Norway, the area north of the 65th parallel, is largely a thinly populated, narrow, barren, mountainous plateau region with a dissected coastline. Cod fishing is of commercial importance in the Lofoten Island waters; cod are dried and salted, and some are sent southward for further processing. Small-scale enterprises often combined with farming predominate. Since the 1940s, several freezing and fish-packing establishments have been erected as part of a plan to increase economic opportunities in the resource-poor north. Narvik is an important railhead, shipping iron ore from north Sweden. Tromsö is a center of the coastal whaling and Arctic sealing industry. Iron ore is mined near Kirkenes within a few miles of the U.S.S.R. boundary.

The Trondheim depression, surrounding Trondheimfiord, is a fertile dairying area, with hay, oats, barley, and potatoes as the principal crops. Well-forested slopes form the basis of the paper, pulp, and lumber industry. Trondheim is the major commercial and fishing center of the area.

The western and southern fringes area, south of the Trondheim depression, is a fiorded, precipitous, island-dotted coast

TABLE 8-5   SCANDINAVIAN COUNTRIES: LABOR FORCE CATEGORIES BY PER CENT

Occupation	Denmark	Finland	Iceland	Norway	Sweden
Agriculture and fishing	24	46	40	26	20
Mining	—	—	—	1	1
Manufacturing	29	21	20	26	31
Construction	7	6	9	9	8
Electricity, gas, water	—	1	—	1	1
Commerce	14	8	9	11	13
Transport	6	5	8	10	8
Services	20	12	13	16	17
Others	—	1	1	—	1

region, where fishing and farming are important along with scattered industry in the fiord valleys and cities. The population is concentrated on the coastal islands and the fringes of the mainland, along the fiord borders, and in the interior valleys. Farming often is combined with fishing to provide sufficient income. The heavy precipitation, cool temperatures, and rough topography favor hardy fodder crops and dairying. The flat southwest coast is famous for its dairy cattle.

Ålesund is the leading fishing port and herring capital, Kristiansund, the klipfish (dried, salted cod) center, Stavanger a fish-canning center, and Bergen the major port of western Norway. The growth of industry is based on available water power. Kristiansand is an industrial center and port on the south coast.

The southeastern lowlands dominate Norway. Nearly 50 per cent of Norway's 3.8 million people live in Oslo and seven surrounding counties. A larger proportion of rolling but relatively arable land exists here than elsewhere. As usual, dairying predominates. Excellent forests are found on the slopes, and many farmers work in the forests during the long, cold winters. Sawmills and paper and pulp mills are common. Oslo, the capital and largest city, is the industrial, transportation, commercial, and cultural center of all Norway. It has shipbuilding and a variety of manufactures. Electrochemical and electrometallurgical industries, located in smaller cities, utilize large amounts of hydroelectric power. Sandefiord, Tönsberg, and Larvik are bases for the declining Norwegian Antarctic whaling fleet.

The interior highlands are sparsely populated. Some forestry is found on the lower slopes, and cattle are summer-pastured on the grasslands of the upland plateaus. Communications have been constructed with difficulty. Railroads from

Bergen and Trondheim cross the highlands and terminate in Oslo. The northern terminus of the state railroad is Bodö.

TRADE AND PROBLEMS   Norway is normally an exporter of raw materials and an importer of finished goods. About two-thirds of the exports consist of three main types of commodities: processed timber products, fishing and whaling products, and ores and metals. Imports are dominated by foodstuffs, coal, petroleum products, textile raw materials, iron and steel, and machinery. Earnings from the merchant marine, ECA (Economic Cooperation Administration) aid, and self-imposed postwar austerity did much to offset a trade deficit and set the stage for the economic boom Norway is enjoying in the early 1960s. Western European countries and the United States dominate Norway's trade. Both economically and politically Norway is oriented toward the West.

SPITSBERGEN (SVALBARD)   Norway gained control of the strategic Arctic archipelago of Spitsbergen in 1920. Two-thirds of the 24,095 square miles are permanently covered with ice and snow. A branch of the warm North Atlantic Drift keeps the west coast ice-free for a short summer period. Coal is the most valuable resource; during some years nearly 800,000 tons have been exported. The inhabitants, mostly coal miners, number 3,400; about two-thirds of them are Russian. Jan Mayen Island and parts of Antarctica also belong to Norway.

SWEDEN

Sweden, the largest and economically most significant of the Scandinavian countries, is slightly larger than California and ten times the size of Denmark. The population of the country is nearly 8 million. Nearly 90 per cent of the people live in the southern half of Sweden, which has a humid continental climate more favorable for crops than is the subpolar climate of the northern section.

Sweden occupies a central position in the Baltic area. With landlocked northern and western boundaries, its historic orientation has been toward the east although present trade and economic interests are westward. Politically, Sweden stands aloof as a neutral in Northern Europe. This neutrality, begun in 1814 and maintained through two world wars and the postwar period, is due to a considerable extent to Sweden's geographical position in the Baltic and in regard to Finland and the U.S.S.R.

The surface slopes gradually from the mountainous heights along the Norwegian border to the Baltic Sea. The many large rivers that follow this gradient, flowing northwest to southeast, are vital for hydroelectric power development and transportation of logs to coastal sawmills. Sedimentary rocks occur in the southern peninsula of Skåne, but old crystalline rock prevails elsewhere. Soils are generally thin and infertile, except for those in Skåne and certain marine clay soils in the central lowlands.

Only 9 per cent of the total land area is arable, 55 per cent is forested, 3 per cent is permanent pasture, and 33 per cent is wasteland or uncultivated. Inland lakes and rivers cover about 9 per cent of the total area. Despite the northerly latitude, agriculture is aided by a climate moderated by Atlantic and Baltic influences. Glacial scouring was less severe in southern Sweden than in Finland or Norway.

ECONOMIC DEVELOPMENT The principal natural resources of Sweden are forests, iron ore, water power, and soil. Over 50 per cent of the postwar exports are forest products. Pine, spruce, and birch are

Figure 8-7 Shipbuilding in Göteborg, Sweden. The bow of a 10,000-ton freight vessel, having been prewelded, is being swung into place in a modern shipyard. (Courtesy of American Swedish News Exchange.)

the main commercial species. About one-half of the forests are state-owned, and an efficient conservation program is in effect.

Sweden mines one-fourth of the iron ore of Europe, excluding the Soviet Union. The Lapland ores average over 60 per cent metallic content but are high in phosphorus; a large part is exported either via Narvik, Norway, or Luleå, Sweden, and the remainder is utilized by the steel plant at the latter city. The central Swedish (Bergslagen) ore is lower in metallic content but contains less sulfur and phosphorus. Some is exported, some utilized in Sweden's high-quality iron and steel industry. Gold, low-grade coal, and copper are among other minerals found.

Sweden's relief and climate favor water power development. Nearly one-half of the 60 billion kilowatt-hour potential is utilized. Although approximately 80 per cent of the potential is in the northern half of the country, distant from the southern urban and industrial centers, it is being increasingly utilized.

Sweden is nearly self-sufficient in food. Infertile soils are offset by hard work, application of fertilizer, and successful plant breeding. Farming is marginal and allied with forestry in the north but intensive in the favored soils of the south. Over three-fourths of the farms contain less than 25 acres and are not adapted to mechanization.

Industry has increased rapidly since the 1880s and now considerably outranks agriculture as a supporter of Sweden's population. Industrialization is based on high-quality raw materials, abundant water power, technical skill, and the contributions of Swedish inventors, on which 10 per cent of the country's industries are based (Table 8-5).

REGIONS Sweden is divided roughly into two parts by the 60th parallel. The sparsely populated northern area is a source of raw materials from the forests and mines; the south embraces most of the agriculture, commerce, industry, and population. The following regions can be distinguished: Skåne (Scania), Småland highlands, Central lowland and Bothnian fringes, and Northern highlands (Norrland).

Skåne is the most intensely cultivated area of Sweden, containing about 12 per cent of the people on only 2.5 per cent of the area. Ninety per cent of the land is cultivated; wheat and sugar beets are grown in addition to the common Scandinavian crops. Dairying is highly developed. Malmö, with ferry connections to Copenhagen, is the main urban center. The islands of Öland and Gottland are geologically similar and are mostly sheep-grazing and resort areas.

The Småland highlands are a detached portion of the northern highlands. The forested slopes range from 300 to 1,000 feet above sea level. The thin, infertile soil handicaps agriculture. Handicraft industries such as wood working and glass manufacture are common; Jönköping is famous for safety matches.

The Central lowlands and the Bothnian fringes are the agricultural, industrial, and commercial heart of Sweden. The marine clay deposits favor agriculture, especially dairying. Large lakes such as Lake Väner and Lake Vätter cover much of the area. Rolling glacial topography is characteristic, with rougher and poorer soils left in forests.

Metal and wood products are leading industries. Iron ore for the high-quality steel comes from the Bergslagen district. Industrial specialties are found in many smaller centers such as steel in Eskilstuna and textiles in Nörrkoping. Uppsala is a university town, Oxelosund, a shipping point for Bergslagen ore. Numerous wood-processing and export centers are found along the Bothnian coast. Luleå exports Lapland ore and has an iron and steel works.

Stockholm and Göteborg are the major cities of Sweden. Stockholm is the capital, cultural center, and chief Baltic port, and has a variety of manufacturing. Göteborg, with a favored west-coast position, is the principal foreign trade port, and its shipyards are a chief factor in placing Sweden fourth in world shipbuilding. Textiles and metal goods are also manufactured.

The Northern highlands, covering approximately two-thirds of Sweden, are located north of the 60th parallel. The glaciated topography is crossed by numerous large, fast-flowing rivers with headwaters in long, narrow glacial lakes in the upland valleys.

Forestry is the chief occupation. As the spring thaw moves upstream, logs, cut during the winter, are floated to coastal sawmills. Processing of the logs is largely a warm-season activity.

Minerals, especially high-grade iron ore, provide a second mainstay of the northern economy. The Lapland and Bergslagen districts are found in the extreme northern and southern portions of the highlands respectively. Isolation, darkness for nearly six months, and severe winter cold hamper workers and production in the area centering around Kiruna and Gällivare. Iron ore can be shipped only during the warm season from Luleå, but leaves the year round from ice-free Narvik. Boliden is the leading European gold-mining area.

Climate, soils, and relief are handicaps to agriculture. Limited development is found in the valleys and around the edges of the lakes. Jämtland is the Swedish counterpart of the Norwegian Trondheim area. In the north, 10,000 Lapps make a living by grazing 200,000 reindeer.

TRADE AND PROBLEMS Forest products, iron ore, iron and steel, and metal products dominate Swedish exports. Coal, petroleum, metals and machines, and raw materials for industry are major imports. England, Germany, the United States, and Scandinavian neighbors are leading trading partners. Invisible exports such as merchant marine earnings generally offset import excesses.

A major question facing Sweden is the ability to continue the so-called "middle way" economically and politically. Sweden faces trade and economic difficulties especially as her neutrality hampers association in any way with the Common Market.

DENMARK

Denmark consists of the peninsula of Jutland and about 500 islands, mostly in the Baltic, an area less than one-eighth of the size of Norway. Denmark, however, has 1 million more people, with about one-fourth of the 4.8 million total living in metropolitan Copenhagen (København). The average population density reaches 400 per square mile in the fertile eastern islands but drops to 125 in sandy, infertile western Denmark. Approximately 75 per cent of the gently rolling terrain is used for agriculture. The surrounding water and moderating westerly winds result in a mild marine climate with summer temperatures averaging 60° and winter 32°F.

Physically, Denmark is similar to the north German glaciated plains, but culturally it is linked with Scandinavia. The position of Denmark, controlling the narrow water outlets of the Baltic, is highly strategic. Germany occupied this tiny nation during World War II in order to command the Baltic. Russian expansion in the Baltic gives Denmark's position added significance.

ECONOMIC DEVELOPMENT Denmark lacks the mineral, water power, and forest resources of her neighbors; even the soil is not exceptionally fertile. Nevertheless, intensive agriculture is vital to present-day Denmark. Small, carefully tended holdings, when supplemented by considerable imports of protein concentrates and grains, support large numbers of cattle, swine, and poultry. Dairy products, meats, and eggs are leading Danish exports. Quality production is largely a result of the effort made by the highly developed cooperative movement. About 90 per cent of the milk is marketed cooperatively. Postwar economic problems have stemmed from the austerity program in Britain, the major market, and from the difficulty of finding outlets in other Western European countries and the United States.

Agriculture and fishing employ 23 per cent of the working population; industry, which employs about one-third, is increasing. Much of Danish industry consists of processing domestic agricultural goods. Most other industrial raw materials and all power sources must be imported.

REGIONS   Western Denmark, the western two-thirds of the Jutland Peninsula, is a sandy, infertile outwash plain interspersed with subdued old moraine hills (Figure 8-8). Sandy heaths, made productive by great efforts, support grasslands and hardy crops. Poorer areas have been planted with pine trees. Sand dunes, marshes, lagoons, and shallow water are

Figure 8-8   Each year the Danish farmers plow the soil, sow and harvest it. Today tractors pull the plow, and horses are seen less frequently. White sea gulls feed upon the worms and larvae. (Courtesy of Royal Danish Ministry of Foreign Affairs.)

found along the unindented coast. The port of Esbjerg, constructed to carry on trade with England and Western Europe, together with Limfiord and Frederikshavn to the north are fishing centers.

With better agricultural land, many islands, and an indented coastline favoring harbor development, eastern Denmark has the bulk of the population. The area has the disadvantage, however, of a Baltic orientation whereas trade and other interests are mostly with Atlantic nations.

Rolling morainic hills and intervening valleys with fertile clay soil replace the flat, sandy terrain to the west. The highest point reaches only 536 feet. The intensive methods of cultivation, favorable temperature and rainfall conditions, and careful plant breeding result in some of the highest crop yields per acre in the world. Pasture, hay, wheat, sugar and fodder beets, oats, and barley are leading crops. Most of the exports, butter, bacon, cheese, and eggs, originate in this section. The intensive forced feeding of animals based partially on imported feed has been termed factory farming.

Copenhagen dominates the industrial and commercial development not only of eastern Denmark but of the entire country. It is the capital, the cultural and intellectual center, and rivals Stockholm for beauty and charm among North European cities. Shipbuilding, food processing, beer manufacture, margarine (so butter can be exported), textiles, world-famous silverware, porcelain, and china are the chief manufactures. The excellent port of Copenhagen is the headquarters of Denmark's maritime interests and also contains an international free port. Aarhus, Aalborg, and Odense are the only other cities exceeding 100,000 in population. Small fishing ports are common along the coast. The island of Bornholm, located 95 miles east of Copenhagen in the Baltic,

Figure 8-9 Copenhagen, the capital of Denmark, is located on the island of Seeland. New and old buildings share the skyline. (Courtesy of Royal Danish Ministry of Foreign Affairs.)

provides kaolin for the pottery industries, smoked herring, and dairy products.

The Faroe Islands, 230 miles northwest of Scotland, are Danish territory. The 35,000 inhabitants engage primarily in sheep grazing and fishing, along with limited agriculture. In 1948 Denmark granted home rule in all matters pertaining exclusively to the islands.

ICELAND

Iceland, located just south of the Arctic Circle in the North Atlantic, has the smallest total population and lowest density per square mile (3.5) of any European nation with its area. Over 80 per cent of the area is uninhabitable and less than 1 per cent arable. More than two-fifths of the 180,000 inhabitants live in the capital city of Reykjavik.

Iceland is a mountainous island with active volcanoes and hot springs. Over 13 per cent is permanently covered with snow and ice. Limited coastal lowlands have grass vegetation, but trees are rare. The marine location and the North Atlantic Drift combine to give mild winters and cool summers. The average January temperature of Reykjavik is 33°F; the summer mean is 50°.

The waters off Iceland yield abundant cod, herring, coalfish, and ling; the average annual catch is some 600,000 tons or over 3,000 pounds per capita. Fish normally provide over 90 per cent of the exports, and Iceland's prosperity fluctuates with the fish catch and world-market prices for fish. Fishermen from other nations also exploit Icelandic waters. Grazing of sheep and cattle and limited crops of hay, potatoes, and turnips are found on the coastal lowlands. Iceland must import many daily-food and raw-material needs.

Although Iceland is on the great-circle route between the United States and Europe, its significance as an Atlantic air

Figure 8-10   Busy harbor at Reykjavik, Iceland, points up the fact that trade and commerce are larger in Iceland, per capita, than in any other nation. (Courtesy of Icelandic Airlines.)

station for commercial planes is decreasing. The faster, long-range jet planes make most of their flights across the Atlantic nonstop.

FINLAND

One-fifth of the area of Finland is north of the Arctic Circle. Despite this position, the climate is tempered by warm westerly winds. The short, warm summers last from June 1 to September 1. The winters are long, cold, and snowy. Hardy crops, aided by long sunlit days, mature in the three-month growing season.

War destruction and peace treaty concessions resulting from World War II were costly. The 12 per cent (17,780 square miles) of its territory on the east and north which Finland lost to the Soviet Union included its Arctic outlet, 13 per cent of the forest resources, one-third of the installed hydroelectric power, 30 per cent of the fisheries, 11 per cent of gross value of industrial production, the Petsamo nickel mines, and some of its most fertile land. The Porkalla peninsula, a territory of 151 square miles guarding Helsinki, was leased by the Soviets for a period of fifty years but returned in 1955. The U.S.S.R. also demanded a staggering 226.5 million dollars in reparations, to be paid in wood products, cables and ships, and metal goods. To meet these demands, the ship-building industry increased six times, and the metal industry doubled in size, virtually revolutionizing Finland's industrial structure. The debt was paid in September, 1952, despite an annual drain of more than 10 per cent of the national income. In order to find markets for the expanded shipping, metals, and other industries,

Finland has had to continue to look for certain markets in the Eastern bloc nations, since she could not compete in Western markets. Another problem, resulting from the territorial losses, was the resettlement of 420,000 people, one-tenth of the total population.

PHYSICAL SETTING   Finland is a glaciated, old crystalline-rock platform. Only in the northeast and in Lapland does the generally low elevation reach over 650 feet. Glacial scour and deposition left a large number of swamps and lakes (60,000 lakes cover 10 per cent of the area). Coastal lowlands and lake borders have more fertile recent sand and clay deposits but comprise only 9 per cent of the soils.

Finland's most valuable resource is the 56 per cent of area that is productive forest land and provides over 80 per cent of the gross value of exports. There is a variety of minerals, of which copper is the most important. The complete lack of coal and petroleum is partially offset by abundant water power.

ECONOMIC DEVELOPMENT   The population numbers approximately 4.8 million. Over 90 per cent are found in the southern half, mainly on the south and west coastal fringes. Swedish-speaking peoples compose about 8 per cent of the population, located primarily in districts nearest Sweden and in the Åland Islands.

Finland's chief livelihood, supporting 42 per cent of the people, is agriculture and forestry. The Finns produce approximately 98 per cent of their food needs; they normally have dairy surpluses and shortages of cereal and sugar. About 29 per cent of the gainfully employed obtain their livelihood from manufacturing, 7 per cent from commerce, 6 per cent from transportation, and 16 per cent from other

sources. Forests and hydroelectric power are the two major industrial assets. War reparations forced certain industrial developments which with other increases reflect the growing emphasis upon manufacturing throughout Northern Europe.

REGIONS   Lapland, in the northern part of Finland, is a rather rugged area with tundra vegetation in the north and stunted, inaccessible, state-owned forests in the south. The climate is too severe for crops. The chief occupation of the 2,350 Lapp inhabitants is grazing about 100,000 reindeer.

The central lake region is a swamp- and lake-dotted area in which forests are the primary resource. Timber cutting is a winter occupation; the logs are floated out in summer. Dairying is found around the edges of some lakes.

The Baltic littoral, having more favorable clay and silt soils, climate, and acces-

Figure 8-11   Finland's main wealth is 55 million acres of forest. During the winter months as many as 300,000 workers are engaged in felling trees and hauling them to the railroads or floating them down the rivers. (Courtesy of Finnish National Travel Office.)

sibility than the other areas, is the principal agricultural region of Finland. Hay, oats, rye, barley, wheat, and potatoes are grown; but two-thirds of Finland's arable area is used for fodder production, indicating the predominance of dairying. Commercial fishing is found in the southwest and the Åland Islands.

Helsinki, Turku, and Tampere, the chief industrial cities, have access to transportation facilities, forest resources, labor, and imported raw materials. Water power is abundant where streams break through the Salpausselka, a double moraine located to the south of the lake district. Manufactures include wood and paper, metal, food, drink, textiles, chemicals, and tobacco products. About 20 per cent of the industry is located in Helsinki, the capital and the cultural, financial, and university center.

TRADE AND PROBLEMS Finland's postwar trade was dislocated by the burdensome war reparations. Even after completion of payments Finland has had to continue to look eastward for markets for ships, metal, and other products. Forest products dominate the exports, though ships, machinery, and dairy products are also important. Metals and metal products, cereal grains, raw textiles, coal, and petroleum are leading imports. Important in Finland's trade are the United Kingdom, West Germany, the U.S.S.R., other countries of Western Europe, and the United States.

Economically and culturally, Finland faces the West, but politically, though independent, it is within the Soviet sphere of influence. Trade and defense agreements with the U.S.S.R. restrict some relations with the West. Finland's future development depends largely on being able to reconcile these conflicting interests.

BRITISH ISLES

Over 55 million people inhabit the British Isles—about 5,000 islands, of which Great Britain and Ireland are the largest.[1] This relatively small area has played an extremely prominent role in the development of Europe and the world.

Before the fifteenth century the islands were on the periphery of the known world, but more recently they have occupied a central location among the populated land masses. The people were maritime-minded, and the power of England increased as the country secured colonies, developed its manufactures, and expanded its overseas commerce. Excellent harbors along the indented coastline and the inventions of the industrial revolution were significant factors in this expansion. The islands, part of the European platform, are separated from the mainland by the narrow Strait of Dover. This separation allowed the English to spend much of their energy on trade and commerce rather than on wars. World War II showed that the Strait of Dover is no longer a complete barrier in wartime. With the loss of her colonies and the trade threat of economic unions on the continent, the United Kingdom has gradually abandoned its aloofness to developments in the nearby European mainland.

[1] Great Britain includes England, Scotland, and Wales; the United Kingdom includes Great Britain and Northern Ireland.

Figure 8-12 The regions of West Central Europe are the result of cultural activities as well as of the physical environment. Most land is used intensively.

REGIONS OF WEST CENTRAL EUROPE

BENELUX
1. Sandy Coastal Fringe
2. Polder Lands
3. Interior Plains
4. Interior Uplands

FRANCE
5. Massif Central
6. Pyrenees
7. French Alps
8. Brittany and Normandy
9. Ardennes Plateau and Vosges
10. Northern Lowlands
11. Aquitaine Basin
12. Rhone Valley and Mediterranean Coast
13. Corsica

GERMANY
14. Saar
15. North European Plain
16. Central Highlands

17. Ruhr
18. Bavarian Alps and Alpine Foreland
19. Rhine Valley

SWITZERLAND
20. Alps
21. Jura
22. Central Plateau

AUSTRIA
23. Alps
24. Austrian Lowlands

GREAT BRITAIN
25. English Lowlands
26. Wales
27. Cornwall
28. Southern Scottish Uplands and Pennines
29. Lake District
30. Central Scottish Lowlands
31. Grampians and Eastern Lowlands
32. Northern Scottish Highlands

NORTH SEA

IRISH SEA

ENGLISH CHANNEL

CHANNEL ISLANDS

BAY OF BISCAY

EAST GERMANY

WEST GERMANY

FRANCE

SWITZERLAND

LIECHTENSTEIN

AUSTRIA

CORSICA

SARDINIA

MEDITERRANEAN SEA

Belfast
Dublin
Glasgow
Edinburgh
Dundee
Liverpool
Leeds
Manchester
Sheffield
Birmingham
London
Bristol
Southampton
Cherbourg
LeHavre
Rouen
Brest
Rennes
Paris
LeMans
Orleans
Nantes
Bordeaux
Toulouse
Barcelona
Amsterdam
Rotterdam
Duisburg
Dusseldorf
Coblenz
Frankfurt
Saarbrucken
Hamburg
Bremen
Hannover
Berlin
Leipzig
Dresden
Munich
Vienna
Bern
Geneva
Lyons
Marseille
Nice

Land areas less than 1000 feet in elevation
Land areas more than 1000 feet in elevation

0   200 MILES

PHYSICAL SETTING

RELIEF FEATURES Hilly and mountainous terrain dominates the north, west, and southwest of Britain, and undulating downs and plains the south and southeast. The highlands average between 500 and 2,000 feet in elevation. Ben Nevis in the Scottish Highlands, 4,406 feet above sea level, is the highest point. Rounded peaks and deepened valleys are a result of glacial erosion; rocks composing the highlands are mostly old granites and schists. Flanking some of the highlands are valuable coal deposits. Young sediments in the south and east are largely limestone, sandstone, and chalk, which form resistant ridges called downs. Weak chalk and clay underlie the valleys and plains. Recent glacial drift covers all of the British Isles except the Cornwall peninsula and the remainder of southern England.

Most of Ireland is a low, poorly drained glaciated plain rimmed by low mountains.

CLIMATE The marine climate is free from extremes except in the highlands. Summer temperatures range from a July average of 63°F in southeastern England to 55° in northern Scotland and 59° on the west coast of Ireland. The winter tempering by the sea is shown in January averages of 44° in southwest Ireland, 39° in southeast England, and 37°F in northern Scotland.

The annual precipitation ranges from 24 to 55 inches, with generally a slight winter maximum. The exposed and higher western portions have the heaviest precipitation; Valencia in western Ireland averages 55.6 inches per year as compared to 24.5 in London. Eastern districts, in the rain shadow of the highlands, have a summer maximum, largely of convectional origin. The cyclonic influence causes dominantly cloudy, humid, rainy, and often foggy weather, and southern England has a cloud cover seven-tenths of the time.

NATURAL RESOURCES

Soils range from a leached, moderate-fertility type in the rainy western districts to a less leached, more fertile soil in the drier east. The thin, infertile soils of the highlands and limestone escarpments are used mostly for grazing. Glacial soils and those in the clay vales and chalk areas of the southeast are generally good for cultivated crops.

Only 7 per cent of Great Britain is forested—a serious lack in the British economy as most of the forests are not of commercial value. Much of the meager natural vegetation consists of lowland marsh and upland moor of limited value for grazing.

Minerals are the principal natural resources of Great Britain. Coal, the outstanding mineral, accounts for 80 per cent of the mineral output by value. The 200-million-ton annual production is consumed almost entirely domestically, and large imports of petroleum and small increases in water power and nuclear energy are providing the needs of steadily increasing amounts of power. Principal coalfields include those on the flanks of the Pennines, the Northumberland-Durham (Newcastle) fields, and those in South Wales, Cumberland, and the Scottish Lowlands. All are leading industrial districts, although recent manufacturing growth is taking place more along the coast and in London rather than near the coalfields.

Some current British economic problems can be traced to difficulties in the coalfields. Production and exports have steadily decreased, and the output is less than 200 million tons. In the early 1960s coal provided less than 1 per cent of the total value of exports, as compared with 33 per cent in 1913. In some years coal must be imported. Handicaps facing the British coal industry are thin seams, deep mines, dipping and faulted beds, lack of mechanization and modernization, and labor shortages. The industry was nationalized in 1946.

Iron ore, the second mineral, has the low average metallic content of 29 per cent. It is a low phosphorus- and high sulfur-content ore. The principal fields are east of the Pennines. The strong iron and steel industry imports over two-thirds of its need, primarily from North Africa and Sweden. Excluding the U.S.S.R., Britain ranks fourth in European iron ore production.

Nonmetallic minerals such as limestone, chalk, and kaolin are quarried for cement and pottery manufacturing.

Fish abound in the North Sea and adjacent bodies of water. Easy access to nearby banks on the Continental Shelf and the maritime-mindedness of the people have led to the development of a fishing industry ranking second only to that of Norway in Europe excluding the U.S.S.R. Although the catch averages slightly under 1 million metric tons annually, fish exports have decreased, and increasing amounts are imported from various sources. The fishing fleet operates from such ports as Aberdeen, Grimsby, Hull, and Yarmouth.

ECONOMIC DEVELOPMENT

The large population places considerable pressure upon land area to produce food. Nevertheless, before World War II, much land was extensively rather than intensively used. The United Kingdom imported 70 per cent of prewar food needs, including grains and meat products to supplement home production. Land use was intensified during World War II. Immediately after the war, Great Britain produced nearly one-half of its own food requirements. Despite the war and postwar domestic increases in food production, the British are again back to the prewar-level dependency upon imports.

The plow-up campaign increased the acreage devoted to grain crops and to intensive dairy farming. Scientific grassland cultivation and mechanization also increased production; British agriculture is among the most highly mechanized in the world. Agriculture employs nearly 1.1 million people and utilizes 48 of 60 million acres of land in the United Kingdom. In Eire approximately 40 per cent of the working population are engaged in agriculture.

The marked predominance of industry over agriculture is the outstanding feature of the British economy. Manufacturing, accounting for over 33 per cent of civilian workers, employs eight times as many people as agriculture and fishing. Transport and trade activities are another important segment.

Industrial concentrations show marked correlation with the location of coalfields with the exception of London and coastal ports. Industries are often localized as the cotton textile industry is in Lancashire. There has been a definite shift from basic to lighter metal products, and from cotton and wool to rayon, nylon, and other synthetic fibers. In general, the trend has been to utilize Britain's technical skill and ingenuity in making quality consumer goods.

In Ireland, the economy centers primarily upon agricultural pursuits, although industry is increasing, especially in Northern Ireland.

DIVISIONS OF GREAT BRITAIN

SCOTLAND The Northern Highlands, rising 1,000 to 3,000 feet above sea level, are a plateau strongly eroded by water and glaciers. The western portion is high and rugged with a fiorded coast. Agriculture is handicapped by poor soils, excessive precipitation, and rather severe winters. Approximately 95 per cent is sparsely populated moorland utilized for crofting (limited sheep grazing). Local areas specialize in high-quality tweeds based, in part, on imported wool. Grouse and deer hunting and the scenic country attract tourists.

The eastern coastal Lowlands have better soil, less rainfall, and higher summer temperatures. Grass, oats, turnips, and barley are the principal crops. Scottish arable farming is closely associated with raising beef cattle for the English market. Aberdeen, the largest city of nearly 200,000 population, is a cattle market and major fishing port on the North Sea.

The Orkney Islands are low and similar in land utilization to the Scottish east

Figure 8-13 A shepherd and hill sheep in the southern uplands of Scotland. Sheep grazing is suited to the bleak grass-covered slopes. Note the rounded glacial topography. (Courtesy of British Information Services.)

coast. In contrast, the rugged Shetland Islands specialize in sheep grazing. Lerwick is a fishing port.

The Central Scottish Lowlands are one of the major agricultural and industrial regions of the British Isles. On 20 per cent of the area are 80 per cent of the people of Scotland. The Lowlands have recent alluvial and glacial soils and a moderate climate. Approximately two-thirds of the eastern portion is in cereal grains; sheep utilize the pastures and rougher areas. Grass farming, with emphasis upon the breeding and rearing of dairy cattle, dominates in the rainier western portions.

Scotland produces about 12 per cent of the British coal, much of which is of excellent bituminous grade, in the central and east portions of the basin, with some coming from the Ayrshire field in the western part. The iron and steel industry, localized in and around Glasgow, produces one-seventh of the United Kingdom tonnage and depends mainly on imported iron ore.

Glasgow, with over 1 million people, Edinburgh, and Dundee are the three major urban centers of the Central Scottish Lowlands. Glasgow, located on the Clyde River, is the fourth port in the British Isles and a heavy-industry center, specializing in iron and steel, machinery, and chemicals. The famous *Queen Mary* and *Queen Elizabeth* were built in the Clyde River estuary, one of the world's leading shipbuilding centers, which annually provides about one-third of the tonnage constructed in the United Kingdom. Edinburgh, the capital, is a cultural, university, printing and publishing, and light-industry center. Dundee is noted for manufacturing imported jute fiber.

The Southern Scottish Uplands, although smaller and less rugged than the Northern Highlands, are a communications barrier between the Scottish Lowlands and England. The Uplands are dissected by numerous small river valleys. Over 10 per cent of the hill sheep of Great Britain are found here, and a high-quality woolen tweed industry is centered in the Tweed River valley. Cattle grazing, dairying, and crop agriculture have been expanded in the coastal districts, river valleys, and lower slopes.

ENGLAND   The Pennine Chain is a rolling to flat-topped upland averaging between 600 and 2,000 feet in elevation. The western slopes are quite abrupt, but the eastern slopes are more gentle. Lower gaps, separating the several highland blocks, are utilized by major east-west railways or highways. Most of the sparsely populated Pennine Chain is heathland, moorland, and rough pasture.

The Lake District consists of a rugged highland core surrounded by gentle slopes and lowlands. Several deep glacial valleys, occupied by lakes, are a tourist mecca. Dairying is prominent in the lowlands. Extremely heavy rainfall restricts highland agriculture.

A small industrial district is based on the Cumberland coalfield and low-quality iron ore. Barrow is a small iron and steel and shipbuilding center. Carlisle is a rail focus leading into Scotland.

The Isle of Man is located 30 miles west in the Irish Sea. Sheep grazing and tourism employ most of its 50,000 people.

The Cornwall peninsula of southwest England is dominated by several high moors on which sheep are grazed, and the luxuriant lowlands furnish grass for beef and especially dairy cattle. The mild climate of the south coast and protected valleys permits the growth of early flowers and vegetables for the London market. Small fishing villages dot the rugged coast. Considerable china clay is produced for a local pottery industry and for export.

Plymouth is a port of call for passengers and mail steamers. The climate and quaintness of Cornwall, especially of Lands End, make it a popular vacation area.

The English lowlands, which make up approximately three-fourths of England, are less than 500 feet above sea level. The bulk of the topography is undulating to rolling, but some rough hills and downs reach nearly 1,000 feet. This is the agricultural, industrial, and commercial heart of England and the British Isles. The agriculture is similar to the mixed-farm economy of the European plains, and a variety of crops adapted to cool summer temperatures are raised, with considerable emphasis upon grazing. Animal and dairy products are the sources of cash farm income.

Cropland is predominant in the fertile eastern sections of England that have less than 25 inches of rainfall and warm summers. Wheat, barley, oats, and root crops are utilized in the winter fattening of beef cattle. Certain areas specialize in fruits, potatoes, vegetables, and dairy products for the large urban market. Sugar beets are locally important.

The western districts, with wet, cool summers, have extensive rotation grass pastures. Dairying is common, with oats as the major cereal crop. Certain districts ship cattle eastward for fattening; others fatten them locally.

The rougher summits of the chalk downs and limestone escarpments in the south and central portions are generally sheep-grazing areas. The clay soils of the intervening lowlands support wheat, beans, and oats, with turnips and barley on the chalk soils.

England's industrial concentrations occur in or near the coalfields and iron deposits or contact zones between highlands and lowlands. London is the principal exception. The industrial northeast, which is dominated by the iron and steel industry, normally produces about 20 per cent of Great Britain's steel. Coking coal is obtained locally, but over half of the iron ore must be imported to supplement Cleveland Hills and Northampton ore. Iron and steel manufacturing is concentrated in Middlesborough and surrounding Tees River towns. Shipbuilding on the Tyne and Tees River estuaries normally accounts for one-third of the total British tonnage. The fabrication of iron and steel products and chemical industries based partly on local salt, gypsum, and lime are also important. Exports of coal from Newcastle have declined to relative insignificance.

East of the Pennines, industry is based primarily on Yorkshire coal. This field supplies 25 per cent of Great Britain's total and extends over 70 miles in north-south, and 15 to 20 miles in east-west, distance. The northern part of this district specializes in woolen manufacturing and the southern part in high-grade steel products. The woolen industry was originally based on local raw materials and water power, but now a large portion of the wool is imported, and coal supplies most of the power. Soft water for washing the wool is easily available. Leeds and Bradford are the major woolen centers.

Sheffield is the center for high-grade cutlery, hardware, machinery, and other steel products. Some steel is imported from other parts of England or abroad. Sheffield usually accounts for nearly 15 per cent of British steel.

At the southern end of the Pennine Chain is the leading English industrial complex, often referred to as the Midlands or "Black Country." Though these terms characterize the cities, there is much green agricultural land between them. As local iron supplies declined, basic iron and steel production tended to move to coastal areas for import of foreign ore. Some iron and steel is still produced, but industries using steel made elsewhere (such as metal goods, motors, automobiles, and locomotives) are now more important. Birmingham, with a population of over 1.1 million, the major center, manufactures a variety of materials, especially brass, other nonferrous metal products, leather products, clothing, and pottery. Nottingham, Leicester, Stoke-on-Trent, and Coventry are other major urban centers.

Lancashire leads the British Isles in cotton spinning and weaving. Access to nearby coal, early development of water power, plentiful pure water, a mild, moist climate lessening thread breakage, and an advantageous position for the import of foreign cotton were the principal reasons for this localization. Great Britain's and Lancashire's place in world cotton manufacturing has suffered because of foreign competition, antiquated machinery and methods, and competition from synthetic fibers.

Though cotton still dominates, textile machinery, engines, electrical goods, glass, chemicals, leather, and paper are also manufactured in this district's numerous cities totaling 2.5 million people. Liverpool is the third-ranking British port and is connected to Manchester by a deep-water canal.

London, long the world's largest metropolitan district, is rivaled only by New York City and Tokyo. Greater London contains over 8.5 million people, and 10 million or nearly one-fifth of the population of Britain live in the city and surrounding area. Although located 65 miles up the Thames, London is a major world port. It collects, processes, and distributes goods from numerous distant points. London is the single leading industrial center of Great Britain and has a large variety of processing and light industries. It is also a cultural, transportation, financial, and commercial center of British and world importance.

Several port and industrial centers are scattered along England's coast. Hull, a major fishing port, handles much of the North Sea and continental trade. Portsmouth is the great dockyard on the south coast; Southampton is the major passenger port servicing North Atlantic and African areas. The western port of Bristol has access to coal and processes tobacco and cacao.

CHANNEL ISLANDS   The Channel Islands base their economy on early vegetables for the English market, dairying, and tourism. Guernsey, Jersey, Alderney, and Sark, the four chief islands, contain about 100,000 people. The Jersey and Guernsey breeds of dairy cattle originated here.

WALES   Wales consists of a highly dissected central plateau surrounded by narrow coastal lowlands. The highlands culminate in Mt. Snowdon, reaching 3,560 feet. The rugged, isolated character of Wales has handicapped interchange with outside areas and accounts for the persistence of the Welsh language and an intense national feeling.

The grasslands of the excessively rainy highland interior favor sheep grazing. Dairying, along with oats as a major crop, is found on the broader southern coastal lowlands. Small resort towns are located along the northern and western coasts.

The South Wales coalfield supports a densely populated mining, industrial, and exporting region. The extensive coal measures vary in quality from bituminous coal in the east to anthracite in the west. The changeover to oil-burning vessels and the general decline of British coal trade resulted in large-scale prewar unemploy-

ment and poverty in the congested mining valleys. The population has found employment in the expanded steel, food, and chemical industries.

Cardiff and nearby cities account for about one-fifth of the steel of Great Britain. Swansea is a tin-plate center and processes zinc, nickel, and copper.

IRELAND

Since 1921 Ireland has been divided into Northern Ireland and the Republic of Ireland (Eire), which became completely independent of the Commonwealth on April 18, 1949. Eire occupies about five-sixths of the island's 31,840 square miles and has a population of 2,815,000, as compared with 1,412,000 in Northern Ireland. The average population density, however, is 104 people per square mile in agricultural Eire compared with 270 in more industrialized Northern Ireland. Eire is predominantly Roman Catholic, Northern Ireland Protestant.

The long English domination has geared the trade of both areas to that nation—supplying agricultural materials and buying manufactured goods. The protective policy of independent Eire and the continued close political and economic imperial ties of Northern Ireland, however, are causing the economies to become more diverse. As differences grow, unification becomes less likely.

EIRE   Since 1921 Eire has become more self-sufficient by breaking up many large estates, placing greater emphasis upon raising wheat and sugar beets, and increasing industrialization. About one-third of the national income is derived from agriculture and one-fourth from industry. Most industries must be based on agricultural raw materials, for Eire lacks coal and iron. Developments

Figure 8-14   O'Connell Street in Dublin. (Courtesy of Irish Tourist Bureau.)

on the Shannon River provide some water power. One-third of the exports are live animals shipped to England for fattening, and another one-third are manufactured products of recent development. Eggs,

Figure 8-15   Bleaching linen in Northern Ireland. Linen is spread on fields around the factory for bleaching by the moist air and sun. (Courtesy of British Information Services.)

dressed poultry, bacon, butter, ham, tobacco, beer, leather goods, and linen are also exported. About 75 per cent of the export trade and 50 per cent of the import trade are with the United Kingdom. The steadily declining rural population (60 per cent in the last century) is a problem facing Eire.

ULSTER   Northern Ireland, or Ulster, the principal area of industrial development, is dominated by linen and rayon manufacturing and shipbuilding; both are centered in Belfast and vicinity. The linen industry was a natural outgrowth of the local flax raising, a water supply and climate favorable for bleaching, and the large supply of female labor in families of shipyard workers. Considerable flax is now imported. The linen trade employs one-sixth of the working population of Northern Ireland; two-thirds of this number are women. Electronics and aircraft manufacturing are recent additions to the area's products. The shipbuilding operations of Belfast normally account for 10 per cent of the annual tonnage of the United Kingdom. Coal, iron, and steel are easily available from Great Britain.

The value of exports from Northern Ireland is far greater than of those from Eire. Trade is almost entirely with Great Britain. Imports of food, drink, tobacco, other raw materials, and manufactured products usually are greater than the exports; this deficit is offset by income from tourists, investments abroad, and pensions paid from Britain. Industrial materials such as ships and textiles dominate the exports, and over 90 per cent go to Great Britain, some for reexport.

REGIONS OF IRELAND   The central plain is largely the poorly drained basin of the Shannon River, covering most of central

Eire and extending into Ulster. The limestone soil is often covered by glacial debris and peat bogs. Small farms, with considerable area in pasture and meadow, are characteristic, but the amount of cropland decreases westward with the increasing annual rainfall. Livestock and occasional cash crops provide the chief source of income. Sheep raising and fattening, with some cattle raising, is the chief type of farming in the western central plain, mixed crops and livestock in the center, and dairying around Dublin and in Northern Ireland. Dublin (Baile Atha Cliath), the chief industrial city of Eire, is the outlet of the central plain.

The highland rim and associated valleys surround the central plain except on the east. The higher parts are rough, sheep-grazing areas. Dairying is predominant in the ridge-and-valley section of the south and around Belfast. Crop farming is predominant in the southeast and in the valleys of Northern Ireland; oats, potatoes, and turnips are common crops, with flax in the north and barley in the southeast as specialty crops. Animals supply most of the cash income. Fishing is of local importance in the southwest. Cork and Cobh have excellent natural harbors. Shannon is an international airport but is now often bypassed by long-range transatlantic jet airliners.

The coast of Ireland is irregular with many broad bays. The entire island has been glaciated, and the scenery attracts many tourists.

TRADE AND PROBLEMS OF THE BRITISH ISLES

The densely populated and heavily industrialized British Isles are highly dependent upon trade to supply much of their food and considerable quantities of industrial raw materials. British exports are completely dominated by manufactured products, which find worldwide markets. Imports exceed exports in value by some $3 billion, and the gap must be covered by profits from foreign investments, world insurance services, merchant marine earnings, tourism, and other various forms of "invisible" income. Foreign markets are vital to British survival; yet the situation is made difficult by increasing competition, loss of direct control of overseas areas, newly independent countries that were formerly good customers and are now favoring homemade products, regional tariff protection like that of the Common Market, and less dominance of trade with Commonwealth countries.

Food, raw materials for industry such as metals and textile fibers, mineral fuels (particularly petroleum), and semifinished manufactures are the leading imports, with finished manufactures contributing only 12 per cent. Principal exports include machinery, vehicles, other iron and steel products, finished textiles, and chemicals. The exports are 85 per cent manufactured products and represent largely quality items for which technical ability and skill give a competitive edge. The Commonwealth, Western Europe, the United States, the Near East, and Argentina are foremost in British trade. Changes in the direction of trade are taking place, however, as Great Britain's share of the Commonwealth market fell from 58 per cent in 1954 to 44 per cent in 1960. Trade with Western Europe increased 30 per cent from 1955 to 1960—a trend that undoubtedly will continue. As a member of the European Free Trade Association, tariffs between the seven member countries are gradually being decreased. Application for membership in the Common Market is a major indicator that the future of the

British will increasingly be tied with that of Western Europe after several centuries of primarily worldwide and secondarily European interests.

BELGIUM, NETHERLANDS, AND LUXEMBOURG

Belgium, Netherlands, and Luxembourg possess a combined area of nearly 26,000 square miles, slightly larger than that of West Virginia. Within this area live 21.5 million people, nearly half the number found in France, which is eight times larger. The Netherlands, with 916 people per square mile, and Belgium, with 772, are unrivaled in Europe in population density.

The triangle of land occupied by the three countries is wedged between Germany and France. This buffer position is an advantage for peacetime trade but a disadvantage in time of war. The natural funneling of Rhine and West German traffic through Netherlands and Belgium is of tremendous value to their respective economies. The location of the North Sea, whose coastal regions are traffic-generating areas, also aids commercial development. Despite extremely limited natural resources, the industrious inhabitants have made these countries significant for their size in both agricultural and industrial production, although loss of control over large overseas territories has eliminated valuable sources of raw materials.

These countries are often referred to as the Low Countries or Benelux. The first is partially a misnomer, for interior areas, especially in Belgium and Luxembourg, are quite rugged and reach altitudes of 2,000 feet. The Benelux designation developed during World War II, when the governments in exile of these countries decided to form a customs union with the ultimate goal of a free-trade area and a larger market for Benelux products. Subsequently the Benelux countries became key members in the Common Market, which has the same objective for a larger area of Western Europe.

CULTURAL DIFFERENCES

The people of the Netherlands have a common culture and language; they speak the Dutch language, which developed from ancient Frankish or Germanic dialects. The people are thrifty, industrious, strongly nationalistic, and have high educational standards.

The Walloons and Flemings, highly diverse peoples, occupy Belgium. The Walloons, short, dark, and French-speaking, populate the southern industrial portions of the country. The Flemings are of a dominantly tall, fair, Nordic type; they speak Flemish, a Germanic language, and are largely in agricultural and commercial occupations. Both languages are official. The views of the two groups are often dissimilar. The people of Luxembourg show both French and German influences in their language and culture.

NATURAL RESOURCES

For their small size, the Benelux countries have considerable resources, including minerals. Coal is the most prominent in Belgium and Netherlands. The Sambre-Meuse coalfields of Belgium extend into the Limburg province of southern Netherlands. These deposits, especially in Belgium, are deep, faulted, and have thin seams. Mining is difficult and expensive, and the output per man is the lowest in Europe. The Campine field in northern Belgium, though 1,500 to 3,000 feet deep, has thicker seams and greater reserves. The

Netherlands produces 12.5 million and Belgium about 23 million tons of coal and 15 million tons of lignite a year. Luxembourg shares the Lorraine iron-ore field with France and produces about 1.7 million tons of ore annually and 4.1 million tons of steel.

Other minerals include petroleum and salt in the Netherlands. A petroleum field, developed since World War II in northeast Netherlands, produces nearly 2 million metric tons a year, about 25 per cent of the home consumption. Natural gas is also produced. Approximately 60 per cent of the salt produced in eastern Netherlands is exported.

The soil is a major resource in all three countries. Much of it has been reclaimed from the sea. Infertile, sandy soils have been made productive by great effort and ingenuity. Limited forests are found on rougher and sandy soils of the interior.

REGIONS

COASTAL   The sandy coastal fringe area, a narrow belt of sand dunes, separates the interior lowlands from the sea in Belgium and the Netherlands. In northwestern Netherlands it exists as the Frisian Islands. Some of the higher dunes are forested, and sheep graze on the grassy portions. They are commonly utilized for home and town sites such as The Hague ('s Gravenhage), a Dutch government center. The coast has poor harbors, but Ostende and Hoek Van Holland are crossing points to Britain. The Frisian and Zeeland Islands are important for fishing. The excellent sandy beaches are summer resorts.

The polder lands, which form approximately 40 per cent of the Netherlands and nearly 10 per cent of Belgium, are subject to flooding at storm or spring tide levels in the absence of sea and river dikes. Drained and diked lands, called polders, must be constantly drained by the power pumps which have replaced former picturesque windmills. In the Netherlands, 1,285,000 acres have been reclaimed since the thirteenth century, and an additional 549,000 acres are being reclaimed from the shallow Zuider Zee (Yssel Lake), cut off from the sea by a barrier dam in 1932. The completed project will add 7 per cent to the total land area. The flood of 1953, covering one-sixth of the Netherlands, caused the most severe damage in centuries. The dikes were repaired, the land returned to cultivation, and a project called the Delta Scheme was embarked upon to give further protection to the southwest coast.

The polders are often left in grassland, as it is uneconomical to lower the water table sufficiently to grow crops. Dairying is predominant, but on higher ground wheat and fodder crops are grown. Cash crops such as seed potatoes, flax, sugar beets, vegetables, and horticultural crops are raised in the north and southwest. Flower bulbs and vegetables are found inland from the coastal sand region on

Figure 8-16 Dairy cattle grazing on polder land as a ship passes through the North Sea Canal. (Courtesy of Netherlands Information Service.)

clay and peat soils, especially between Haarlem and Leiden. South of The Hague, horticultural crops are extensively grown in greenhouses.

Amsterdam, Rotterdam, and Antwerp (Anvers) are major commercial and industrial cities. Despite their inland locations, rivers and canals give them ocean connections. Antwerp and Rotterdam handle Rhine hinterland trade and transshipments; grain, iron ore, forest products, petroleum, cotton, and oil seeds go upstream, and iron and steel products, coal, and building stones come downstream. A new port facility for Common Market Europe called Europoort is found at the mouth of the Rotterdam waterway. Amsterdam is the capital and the financial and diversified-manufacturing center of the Netherlands.

INTERIOR PLAINS   The interior plains in eastern Netherlands and central Belgium are slightly rolling and sandy. The infertile soils have been improved, and when heavily fertilized, produce potatoes, sugar beets, wheat, oats, barley, and hemp. Rye, buckwheat, forest, and heath are found on the poorer soils. Dairy cattle are common. Coal is mined in the Campine field of Belgium and in the Limburg district of the Netherlands. Brussels (Bruxelles), capital of Belgium, has a population of over 1 million, and is the commercial, transportation, and industrial hub.

INTERIOR UPLANDS   The interior uplands in the extreme southeast of the Netherlands, southeast Belgium, and Luxembourg vary from 300 to 2,000 feet in elevation. The Ardennes proper is a sparsely populated, dissected, infertile plateau with forests and moors, suitable for dairying, but the fertile loam soils of the foreland are densely populated and intensively utilized. Lim-

burg has many orchards and carries on much dairying.

The industry of the Sambre-Meuse Valley and the adjacent province of Limburg in the Netherlands is based on local coal. Iron and steel machinery, zinc smelting, textiles, chemicals, glass, and leather products are principal manufactures in such cities as Liège, Mons, and Charleroi. The Battle of the Bulge was fought in this region during World War II.

ECONOMIC DEVELOPMENT

THE NETHERLANDS   This country is an agricultural and commercial nation, whose industry is increasing in importance. About 20 per cent of the labor force are employed in agriculture, 37 per cent in industry, 24 per cent in trade and transport, and 19 per cent in other occupations. The highest use of fertilizer and the highest average wheat yields per acre in the world indicate how intensive is Netherlands agriculture. Farms are small; 42 per cent are less than 12.5 acres. The land-use percentages are as follows: pasture 36, arable 30, built-up 15, woodland 7, horticulture 3, and wasteland 9. Agricultural products such as vegetables, flowers, bulbs, butter, and cheese are exported. Widespread cooperatives maintain high-quality products; they control a large percentage of the dairy output. Leading industries include shipbuilding, refining of tin and other metals, textiles, chemicals, and leather goods.

Location, trade, skill, experience, and necessity have greatly aided the commercial development, including the important transit trade to and from Germany. Besides agricultural goods, Dutch exports include a wide variety of finished and semifinished goods. Imports include petroleum, coal, timber, iron and steel, and

*Figure 8-17 Grain transship-
ment facilities in the port of
Amsterdam. (Courtesy of Netherlands Information Service.)*

textiles. The merchant marine of nearly
5 million tons ranks seventh in the world.

Lack of resources, loss of income from
now independent Indonesia, decreased
German transit trade, and competition in
the Common Market are major problems. The prosperity of Germany is essential to the Netherlands.

BELGIUM   The economy of Belgium
places greater emphasis upon industry and
less upon agriculture and commerce than
does that of the Netherlands. Heavy industries, such as basic iron and steel,
contrast with the lighter types found in
the Netherlands. Using iron ore from
Luxembourg, France, and elsewhere, Belgium and Luxembourg produce over 11
million tons of steel annually, ranking
seventh among world producers. The
refining of zinc and copper is another leading industry, along with textiles, machinery, and chemicals. One of the world's
densest transportation networks serves
the industrial and commercial centers.
Foodstuffs, iron ore, and other raw materials for industry are prominent imports;
metal products, chemicals, textiles, and
glass are exported.

An earlier liberation than its neighbors
gave postwar Belgium a head start in
recovery. The loss of the Belgian Congo
was an economic blow to the country.
Nearly 40 per cent of the industrial production must be exported to maintain a
prosperous economy. German transit
trade is also important to the welfare of
Belgium.

LUXEMBOURG   The smallest of the Benelux
countries, Luxembourg, a tiny principality, bases its livelihood almost entirely
upon iron and steel. It engages in only
limited forestry and agriculture. Luxembourg has the highest per capita steel production in the world: nearly 12.6 tons
compared to 0.5 ton in the United States
and 0.8 in Belgium. Production totals over
4 million tons annually. Luxembourg has
had an economic union with Belgium
since 1919.

All three Benelux countries are gambling heavily upon the Common Market,
which they hope will offset their small

areas and lack of resources and domestic markets, as well as the tariffs and trade restrictions imposed by others.

FRANCE

France has recovered from war destruction and postwar political instability to take its place again as a key European nation. Rich in the traditions of 2,000 years, this great republic has long been a cultural and artistic center, and more recently industry has grown to outstrip the traditional importance of agriculture. Except for the Soviet Union, France is the largest nation of Europe and one of the best balanced in terms of natural resources. The country and its people are vital to the economies and the defense of all Western European nations.

LOCATION AND SHAPE

The location of France gives it a dual continental and maritime orientation. Though 1,870 miles of coastline face the Atlantic Ocean and the Mediterranean Sea, the strongest links have been with Continental Europe. Possession of the world's second largest overseas empire and eighth largest merchant marine indicates French maritime interests. In the east and south, common land boundaries exist with eight nations. Much of the border follows the barrier-forming ridges of the Pyrenees, French Alps, and Juras, but the northeast is open to areas of dissimilar language and culture.

The area of France, including the island of Corsica, totals 212,737 square miles, nearly twice the size of the British Isles. This relatively large country includes many agricultural and industrial diversities.

The compact shape and natural boundaries, except on the northeast, give France a greater degree of cultural, social, and economic uniformity and national consciousness than most European countries. The large amount of lowland area facilitates north-south and east-west communications and results in few isolated areas.

POPULATION

France's population, stabilized at 40 million since the middle of the nineteenth century, has grown to 46 million largely since World War II. It now leads most European countries in rate of growth, and its birth rate, coupled with longer life expectancy, results in an average excess of 320,000 births over deaths. Because of the large number of old and young people, immigrants, particularly from Italy, have been brought in to help solve the labor problem and maintain the rising level of productivity. The French population, which increased 4 million in a ten-year postwar period, gives every indication of continuing this rate of increase. Of the total population, 56 per cent is urban and 44 per cent rural—another indication of the balance in France. Only the Central Plateau, the Pyrenees, Alps, Juras, and other highlands of the northeast are sparsely populated; yet with 214 people per square mile, France has the lowest average population density among the industrial nations of Western Europe.

The population is remarkably homogeneous although minor regional language-dialect and other cultural differences exist, particularly between the north and the south. Small minority groups are found on French borders, for example, the Basques toward the western end of the Pyrenees. A rather large group in Alsace-Lorraine near the German border are Germanic in language and culture. All but 1 million of the people are Roman Catholics.

PHYSICAL SETTING

RELIEF FEATURES The varied topography of France is relatively simple in structure. Three major landform types exist: (1) areas of old rock such as the Massif Central (Central Plateau), the hills of Brittany and Normandy, the Ardennes, and the Vosges Mountains; (2) the rugged, young, folded mountains represented by the Alps, Juras, and Pyrenees; and (3) the recent deposits in river basins and valleys. Strategic corridors such as the Belfort between the Rhine and Rhone Valleys and that of Verdun between the Rhine and the Paris Basin are among the connecting lowlands.

CLIMATE The varied climates of France are the result of several factors including relief, latitude, and location between the Atlantic Ocean and the Mediterranean Sea. The position of 42° to 51° north latitude and the location on the west coast of Europe places the country in the path of the tempering prevailing westerlies and cyclonic storms. The cities in Table 8-6 illustrate the major climatic differences.

The daily and seasonal temperature ranges and the amount of summer rainfall increase eastward with the lessening sea influences. Paris has a blend of the maritime and transitional climates. The higher mountains generally have heavier precipitation and lower temperatures. These diverse climates give France growing conditions suited to a variety of crops.

NATURAL RESOURCES

MINERALS Among the world's iron ore producers France ranks third, following the United States and the Soviet Union. Over 50 million tons are mined yearly, 90 per cent in the Lorraine district and 10 per cent in the Normandy and East Pyrenees fields. The Lorraine ore averages 30 to 35 per cent metallic content but is self-fluxing. It was not usable, however, until the development of the Thomas-Gilchrist process for reducing high-phosphorus-content ore. The Lorraine ore, occurring on or near the surface in an area 70 by 12 miles, is easily mined. Much smelting is done near the mines as it is uneconomical to ship the low-quality ore long distances. Considerable quantities, however, move freely into Belgium, Luxembourg, and Germany as a result of the Coal and Steel Community. The Normandy ore is of higher quality but is less abundant and less accessible.

The coalfields of France normally supply only two-thirds of the country's needs. Especially significant is the lack of coking-quality coal. Over one-half the 58 million tons mined come from the Sambre-Meuse field near the Belgian border; scattered fields on the fringes of the Massif Central and the lower Loire River valley provide the remainder. The Saar and its coal mines, which produce 16 million tons a year, were lost to Germany by plebiscite on January 1, 1957. Thin and broken

TABLE 8-6   CLIMATIC DIFFERENCES

City	Jan., average °F	July, average °F	Average annual rainfall, in.	Climate
Brest	45	61	30	Marine west coast
Paris	36	65	24	Modified marine
Strasbourg	32	66	27	Transitional
Marseilles	44	72	23	Mediterranean

seams, deep beds, and coal of poorer quality than Germany's cause difficulty in competition. Modernization has taken place to the extent that the coal output per manshift is now among the highest in Europe.

In bauxite production, France ranks fourth in the world and first in Europe except for the U.S.S.R. Bauxite is mined on the southern flanks of the French Alps, near the Spanish border in the Pyrenees, and just west of the Rhone River near the Mediterranean coast. With hydroelectric power available nearby, much is processed into aluminum; some also is exported.

Potash deposits are located near Mulhouse in Alsace. France ranks third, behind Germany and the United States, in world production. Potash is used in the commercial fertilizers vital to the intensive agriculture of Northwestern Europe. Extensive salt deposits in Lorraine are used along with potash in the chemical industry. Petroleum discoveries in southwestern France have greatly increased home production. Natural gas from the southwestern France Lacq field has become significant. Development of atomic power is progressing, and 2.5 million kilowatts are expected from this source by 1970.

OTHER RESOURCES   The water power resources of France are limited primarily to the highlands of the east, central, and southern districts. Of the approximately 72 billion kilowatt hours of electric energy output, about three-fifths is hydroelectricity and two-fifths thermoelectricity.

Forest products are of primary importance in the highland economy. The Alps, Vosges, and Massif Central produce furniture, pit props, and construction timber. Pine trees planted to prevent the migration of sand in the Landes district of southwest France are now a major source of lumber and naval stores (resin, tar, and turpentine). Lumber and wood pulp also are imported.

Fisheries are located in Atlantic and Mediterranean coastal waters. The Brittany coast and the English Channel have the best-developed fishing industry. France ranks fifth among European fishing nations, behind Norway, the United Kingdom, West Germany, and Spain.

The soils of France are productive. The country has large areas of fertile, arable lowlands. Postwar figures show 39 per cent in arable cropland, 24 per cent in meadow and pasture, 21 per cent in forest and woodland, and 16 per cent in other uses. Only one-tenth of France is classified as unproductive.

ECONOMIC DEVELOPMENT

The significance of France in Europe is illustrated by the fact that it accounts for 21 per cent of the value of agricultural output and 18 per cent of the gross national product of Western Europe (excluding the Communist bloc). Agriculture produces 10 per cent of the national income, manufacturing and construction 43 per cent, trade 12 per cent, transportation and communication 6 per cent, and other activities 29 per cent. Industry is handicapped by raw-material deficiencies, especially power, by labor shortages, particularly of young men to man new industries, and by slow modernization of equipment and organizational procedures. By 1961, however, French industrial output had more than doubled prewar levels.

AGRICULTURE   Employment figures indicate the importance of agriculture, since 29 per cent of the working population are farmers, compared with 35 per cent in industry. Agriculture is a vital sector of the French economy, supporting nearly one-fourth of the people. Diversified agri-

Figure 8-18   Picking grapes for wine making in southern France. (Courtesy of French Embassy Press.)

culture predominates, but specialties have developed based on long tradition and highly skilled farm labor. Examples are wine, cheese, fruit, and vegetables. Cash income comes largely from the sale of animals, animal products, and certain crops. Wheat is the single most important crop grown. Olives, cork oak, irrigated fruits, and vegetables are found in the Mediterranean region; corn is peculiar to southern France. Grapes and wine production are widespread over the southern two-thirds of the country, with certain areas of specialization. France is second to Italy in world wine production and first in consumption. The areas of cool, moist climates and rugged topography encourage livestock production and dairying. Crop yields per acre are increasing but are generally lower than in the United Kingdom or Belgium because of poorer soils and agricultural methods. Farms average less than 25 acres and are rather intensively cultivated. Mechanization is increasing rapidly partly to offset the loss of labor to French industry.

INDUSTRY   France ranks behind the United Kingdom and Germany as a European industrial nation. The possession of iron ore and coal is largely responsible for this position despite the necessity of importing between 30 and 40 per cent of the power needed for the economy.

The localization in French industry depends upon access to steam and hydroelectric power, transportation facilities, labor, cheap and skilled, and raw materials, especially iron ore. The bulk of French manufacturing is found east of a line from Calais to Orleans to the mouth of the Rhone River. The following individual areas stand out: (1) the northern area around Lille and the Sambre-Meuse coalfield—wool and linen textiles and iron and steel; (2) the northeast (Alsace and Lorraine)—metallurgy, cotton textiles, and chemicals; (3) metropolitan Paris—diverse manufactured products, with emphasis on quality; (4) the Lyon and St. Étienne district—silk and rayon textiles and metal products; and (5) the lower Loire River valley and Bordeaux—shipbuilding, metal products, and diversified manufacturing. The latter areas received impetus from the dispersion of industry during World War II, but Paris remains unrivaled in importance.

France has a well-developed rail, highway, and inland-waterway transportation system, although there is congestion in Paris because of overdependence upon it as a focal point and distribution center. The Rhone, Loire, Garonne, and Seine Rivers are all navigable and connected by canals.

REGIONS

HIGHLANDS The Massif Central, dominating south central France, averages 3,000 feet above sea level. It is mostly a dissected crystalline rock plateau with some volcanic rock; sedimentary rock is found on the edges and in the lowlands. Except for a few favored valleys, poor soil and a rigorous climate restrict agriculture to hardy crops and grazing. This is the chief rye-growing area of France and contains one-fourth of the cattle and one-fifth of the sheep. The Massif is a barrier to communications within France. St. Étienne is an iron and steel and textile center. Clermont-Ferrand manufactures rubber, textiles, and chemicals, and Limoges is famous for china.

The crest of the Pyrenees, rising to over 9,000 feet, forms the French-Spanish boundary. The inaccessible rugged and infertile slopes are sparsely populated. The climate of the western portion is marine; the eastern is Mediterranean. Grazing of the transhumance type is dominant in the higher grasslands, with some crop agriculture on the lower slopes and in the valleys. Hydroelectric power, iron ore, and bauxite provide the basis of growing electrochemical and electrometallurgical industries.

The French Alps and the Jura Mountains are thinly peopled and play a minor role in France. Cattle and sheep are pastured on alpine grasslands. Small chemical and metallurgical centers utilize part of the large hydroelectric potential. Grenoble is a rail, university, and glove-manufacturing center. The Juras consist of longitudinal valleys and ridges with some peaks reaching over 5,000 feet. Dairying, forestry, and small workshop industries, especially watchmaking, are predominant.

Brittany and Normandy differ from the Massif Central in that their outcrops of crystalline rocks have lower relief, no volcanic material, and a peninsular shape with numerous offshore islands. The hedgerow landscape is characteristic. One-fourth of France's cattle and some sheep are grazed on the interior uplands. There is little land suitable for wheat; thus buckwheat is the major cereal grown on the poor soils. Apple orchards are common, and cider is the usual beverage. More than 2 million tons of iron ore are mined annually, with smelting works in Caen. Laval is a textile and automobile center and Rennes the regional capital.

The narrow Brittany-Normandy coastal strip is densely populated. A rich soil and mild marine climate favor vegetable gardening. Nantes and St. Nazaire are metallurgical and shipbuilding centers, with industries based on Swedish and Spanish iron ore and British coal. Ports and naval bases are located also at Cherbourg, Brest, and Lorient. Brittany has 36 per cent of the country's 600,000 annual tonnage of shipbuilding, Normandy 26 per cent, the Mediterranean coast 17 per cent, the North Sea coast 12 per cent, and the Gironde estuary 7 per cent. Several smaller villages are fishing and resort centers. Part of the Normandy coast is famous for the World War II invasion.

The Lorraine and Ardennes plateaus

and the Vosges Mountains possess a strategic location bordering on Germany. They contain nearly one-half of the iron ore resources of Europe. The iron and steel industry, which is concentrated in Nancy, Metz, and other smaller centers, obtains coking coal from the Ruhr. The Common Market is eliminating the iron ore–coal trade hindrances between France and West Germany. The chemical industry is based on the by-products of iron and steel manufacturing and on local salt and potash deposits. The textile industry also is noteworthy. The Vosges support lumbering, dairying, and paper and cotton-textile manufacturing, based on water power.

The fertile Rhine Valley, a down-dropped block, produces grapes, tobacco, hops, sugar beets, and wheat. Strasbourg, a key rail and water-transportation center on the Rhine, has served as the Council of Europe headquarters since 1949.

LOWLANDS   The northern lowlands include the Paris Basin, Loire and Saone Valleys, and the industrial North. The Paris Basin is the most productive agricultural as well as industrial region of France. It is formed by saucerlike sedimentary rock layers. The outer layers, consisting of a resistant limestone and chalk, form rugged and wooded outcrops. Transportation lines pass through breaks or gaps in the escarpment faces.

Agriculture is intensive, with wheat, oats, sugar beets, flax, vegetables, and fruits the principal crops. Cattle predominate in the more humid west and sheep in the drier, rougher east portion of the northern lowlands. Two important wine areas are found: white wine in the middle Loire Valley and champagne from grapes grown on the warm, south-facing slopes east of Paris.

Paris, with a population of 5 million

people, is the cultural, artistic, and leading manufacturing center, the hub of water and rail traffic, and the first inland or river port of France. Nearly one-fifth of France's population is in the metropolitan district. Industry consists largely of finishing types of manufacturing. Luxury goods, for which Paris is famous, play a relatively minor role as compared with automobile assembly and the electrical, chemical, food-processing, and printing industries.

Lille is the industrial center of northern France. Industry is powered by coal from the Sambre-Meuse field; iron and steel dominate, along with woolen and linen textiles. Rouen, near the mouth of the Seine, is a cotton-milling center and the deepwater port for Paris. Le Havre has transatlantic and transchannel trade and is important for the refining of imported crude oil as well as for being the starting point of a pipeline to Paris. Cherbourg handles the transatlantic liners between France and New York, and Calais is a ferry terminus. Resorts are common along the Channel coast.

The Aquitaine Basin is drained primarily by the Garonne River and its tributaries. The Garonne Valley and the central parts of the basin contain wheat, corn, vineyards, and pastures for cattle grazing. The area has one-fourth of the French vineyards; production of red wines predominates, but poor farming methods and the unreliable precipitation result in low yields. Sheep grazing is a leading activity of the infertile sub-Pyrenean northeast and sandy Landes districts.

Bordeaux is the sixth port and fifth city of France. It is the outlet for wine and many other products including those from the forests of the Landes district. The city also refines petroleum, some from nearby areas. Toulouse controls the narrow gap between the Aquitaine and Mediterranean lowlands. It is an important industrial center, and there is a natural gas field nearby.

The climate of the Mediterranean lowlands and the Rhone Valley results in a distinctive agriculture. West of the Rhone River is the leading vineyard and wine-producing district of France. East of the Rhone, where the topography is rougher and soils are poorer, olives, vineyards, and the grazing of sheep and goats are common. Wheat and early irrigated crops such as citrus fruits, rice, and vegetables occur on the better soils. Flowers for perfume are grown. The Rhone Valley has vineyards on the slopes and crops and cattle grazing in the valley bottom. Mulberry trees for the silk industry are found near Lyon.

The large bauxite deposits form the basis of the aluminum industry and bauxite exports. Marseilles, the second city in France and first in ocean shipping, is the major Mediterranean port. It has a wide range of manufacturing activities, including the processing of tropical materials and petroleum refining. Lyon, strategically located at the confluence of the Rhone and the Saone, utilizes nearby coal and water power for silk and rayon as well as for automobile and other manufacturing. Toulon is a naval base and Nice a Riviera resort town. The Riviera coast, protected from cold north winds by the Alps, has long been a famous resort area.

CORSICA   The island of Corsica, a miniature Massif Central, is located about 100 miles southeast of France in the Mediterranean Sea. Mediterranean climate and agriculture prevail, with pastoral activities most important because of lack of fertile arable land. Tourism is of increasing significance.

EMPIRE

The French overseas empire has dwindled to a few scattered subtropical and tropical areas. Algeria is the most recent country to gain independence after a long, costly war. Certain economic ties still exist with past dependencies, but France is more and more focusing attention on domestic and European areas. Intense interest exists in maintaining control, at least economically, over the Sahara oil fields.

TRADE AND PROBLEMS

The position of France is favorable for trade with Europe and the world. Although minerals and other raw materials are scarce, the high technical skill of the people is reflected in the making of commodities like clothing and art goods for which the country is famous. Raw cotton,

Figure 8-19   Nice, located on the French Riviera, is one of the principal tourist centers of Europe. (Courtesy of French Embassy Press.)

coal, crude petroleum, crude rubber, copper, hides and skins, wool, and wood pulp are raw material imports. Machinery, other manufactured products, foodstuffs, and beverages (coffee and wine) are also imported. Machinery, textiles, clothing, chemicals, automobiles, and products of agriculture including wine are the chief exports. Western European countries and the United States are major trading partners; 38 per cent of the imports and 42 per cent of the exports are with Common Market countries.

France faces many problems, social, political, and economic. Although the birth rate has risen during the postwar period, a preponderance of young and old people exist, with their current manpower implications. Two world wars and wars in Indochina and Algeria within a generation have drained French resources. Frequent governmental crises contributed to political and economic insecurity, and colonial unrest burdened the French treasury. Balanced though the French economy is, there are serious regional disparities. French individualism hampers the rapidity of introduction of modern mass production and distribution techniques. Hence, despite major postwar improvements, French agriculture and industry are insufficiently mechanized. In the past, French capital preferred foreign to domestic investment, and much was expropriated in Communist countries. The French export structure is weak. French industrial specialization, especially in the production of luxury goods, is changing as the country industrializes within Common Market Europe. France is striving to become an atomic power. President de Gaulle is seeking closer economic and political ties with West Germany, Benelux, and Italy and is reluctant to share Continental leadership with the United Kingdom.

GERMANY

Germany is generally recognized as the political and economic key to postwar Europe, especially Western Europe. United in 1871 after a long period of disunity, Germany has twice risen to the status of a major world power in this century and twice has lost that position in a world war. The countries that defeated her in World War II, especially the United States, helped to revitalize West Germany. Recovery has been remarkably rapid since 1948, and this part of Germany has emerged as a major agricultural, industrial, and trading nation. West Germany is cooperating in NATO, the Common Market, and other economic and political plans but still faces the perils of being a major instrument in the cold war between the Communist and Western world. The Allied occupation of Berlin, for instance, and its position within East Germany continue as unsolved issues.

The location of the former Germany in Europe was generally advantageous in peacetime and a liability during war. The central location, transitional between Eastern and Western Europe, offers the following advantages: (1) ease of development of trade relations with nine bordering countries; (2) ease of development of water, rail, and highway routes for east-west and north-south transit traffic; (3) the facilitation of water-borne trade by access to both the North and Baltic Seas and by good harbors; (4) a transitional climate for agricultural development; (5) access to Lorraine and Swedish iron ore vital to German industry; (6) access to Southeastern Europe via the Danube River and rail routes.

Encirclement by possible enemies in wartime is a major disadvantage. Other liabilities are the boundaries with Poland

and France that have been shifted repeatedly in modern times; the fact that the Rhine outlet, vital to the industrial regions of western Germany, is controlled by the Netherlands; and the vulnerable position of the Ruhr and Berlin. The added distance from the Rhine-Ruhr industrial district to north German ports on the Atlantic is a handicap in competition with other Western European ports like Rotterdam and Antwerp.

POSTWAR CHANGES AND PROBLEMS

The postwar boundaries, though not established by treaty, considerably change Germany's size, shape, and resources. Major changes are the loss of all territory east of the Oder-Neisse River line. Included in that territory are some of the best agricultural land, the important Silesian coalfields, and associated industrial districts. Minor Belgian and Netherlands boundary shifts also have been made. The Saar and its important coalfields and industrial development were obtained from France by plebiscite in 1957 and fully integrated into Germany by 1959. The resultant postwar Germany has a more compact shape. The economy is much less self-sufficient in food but still has surpluses of industrial goods as the country retained 93 per cent of the prewar industrial output potential.

Germany, now separated into eastern and western parts, has approximately 75 million people in an area about equal to Minnesota and Wisconsin combined. The population density in West Germany averages over 573 people per square mile; if one considers only arable area, the density reaches nearly 1,300. The densest zone of concentration is found near the contact between the highlands and plains extending from the Ruhr Valley to Dresden. About 70 per cent of the population is urban and 30 per cent rural.

The German ethnic group is numerically the largest in Europe, excluding the Russians. About 15 million ethnic Germans and German nationals have been forced out of East European countries and former German territory now occupied by Czechoslovakia, Poland, and the Soviet Union. The net result is that East and West Germany together have 5 million more people than Germany's prewar population on three-fourths of the former area. Regional differences in dialect, religion, and group character sometimes lead to antagonisms, like that between Prussians and Bavarians.

DIVIDED GERMANY

After World War II, Germany was divided into four zones of occupation. The British, Americans, and French occupied about 94,700 square miles of western Germany which became the Federal Republic of Germany in 1949. In 1955, it became a sovereign state with free and equal partnership in the Western world. Germany participates in NATO, Common Market, and other organizations as a full and equal member. A peace treaty has not been signed, and Allied forces remain as security forces.

Dominantly industrial West Germany has a population of 55 million. It contains only 45 per cent of prewar Germany's arable land and must import one-third of its food requirements, much of which previously came from East Germany. The Ruhr mines most of Germany's hard coal and produces a large share of the 34 million tons of steel and other industrial products. Potash, salt, and limited quantities of iron ore and petroleum are found. Located here are the two leading German ports, Hamburg and Bremen. Production and trade are oriented toward the West.

The Soviet Union occupied about 41,700 square miles of eastern Germany.

In 1949 a Soviet-sponsored puppet Communist government, called the German Democratic Republic, was established. Berlin, 100 miles within Soviet-controlled East Germany, is a focal point of the world struggle between the Communist bloc and the West. After millions of refugees had crossed to the West through Berlin, the escape hatch was closed in 1961 by a concrete wall separating East and West Berlin.

East Germany, with 17 million people, is nearly self-sufficient in food production. It has valuable lignite, potash, and salt deposits, and large chemical and electrical industries. Production and trade are oriented toward Communist Europe. A unified Germany would benefit from the domestic exchange of agricultural, fuel, and industrial products.

The Saar, an area of 991 square miles, contains nearly 1 million people. It was controlled by Germany from 1871 to 1920, by the League of Nations from 1920 to 1935, by Germany from 1935 to 1945, and by France from 1945 to 1956. After the Saarlanders voted for annexation to Germany, it was reunited with that country on January 1, 1957. Coal, the major resource that makes the Saar desirable, is of good quality for steam power but must be mixed with Ruhr coal to produce coke. Easy access to coal and Lorraine iron ore have made the iron and steel industry a natural development. Nearly 4 million tons of steel and 17 million tons of coal are produced annually. Saarbrücken is the leading industrial center.

PHYSICAL SETTING

RELIEF FEATURES   The two general German landform types—in both East and West Germany—are the glaciated lowlands in the north and the highland complex in the south. The northern lowlands, covered with recent unconsolidated glacial deposits, are generally below 600 feet in elevation. The central zone is characterized by the dissected remains of Hercynian mountains, reaching nearly 5,000 feet at their highest point. In the extreme south the rugged Bavarian Alps and their forelands dominate. The Alps average between 6,000 and 7,000 feet; the forelands are lower and strewn with rock debris brought down by the Alpine streams.

CLIMATE   Western and especially northwestern Germany (considered as a whole) has a marine west-coast climate. Eastern Germany has a modified continental type, and the southern portions reflect the altitude and varied relief of the highland areas. The major characteristics of climate for the whole country are cool summers, relatively mild winters, except in highland Germany, and summer maximum precipitation. The marine influence lessens eastward and southward. Most crops raised are suited to cool, moist conditions except the grapes, corn, and tobacco found in sheltered valleys of the south and west.

VEGETATION AND SOILS   The original vegetation cover of both East and West Germany was largely a mixed coniferous and deciduous forest. Forests still cover more than one-fourth of the country, with a greater percentage in the central and southern highland regions and the poorly drained areas of the lowland north. An efficient conservation program, including replantings of cut timber, has been developed. The forests are an important resource for timber, pulp and paper, and locally for wood carvings and toys.

The acid, leached soils that prevail in Germany are generally mediocre to poor except for the loess soils at the southern edge of the North German Plain. Most soils are highly productive only through careful management and fertilization.

Figure 8-20   Ahu Valley in southern Germany. Note the rugged topography and the intensive land use. (Courtesy of German Tourist Information Office.)

RIVERS AND DRAINAGE   Germany has eight river systems, of which the Rhine, Elbe, Oder, and Danube are the most important. These rivers, connected by a system of canals, give Germany one of the best waterway networks in the world. Even precipitation plus the melting snows in the Alps give a fairly steady stream flow although at times traffic is handicapped by low water or ice. Normally, 30 per cent of the total freight traffic is carried on the inland waterways, much of which is on the Rhine. The Oder is now shared by the East Germans and Poles, the latter con-

trolling the outlet; the Elbe, cut by the Iron Curtain, is limited in navigational use.

Poorly drained areas are found principally in the northwest, where glacial lakes are common, and along the North Sea coast.

NATURAL RESOURCES

COAL   Germany's greatest mineral resource is coal, of which all kinds from anthracite to lignite are found. The Ruhr or Westphalian fields are the principal producers of anthracite and bituminous coal, and much of the bituminous coal is of coking quality. Large lignite deposits are important in East Germany. In 1961 West Germany mined 143 million tons of bituminous coal and 96 million tons of lignite, as compared with 3 million tons of bituminous coal and 225 million tons of lignite in East Germany. In addition, West Germany imports considerable coal from the United States and exports 24 million tons of coal and coke to European neighbors deficient in that resource.

IRON ORE   Germany has limited, widely scattered iron ore deposits and must import approximately 60 per cent of its consumption primarily from France and Sweden. The Siegerland deposits south of the Ruhr are the most valuable. Germany benefits from the free flow of iron ore from the French Lorraine fields within the Common Market.

POTASH AND OTHER MINERALS   Between the Weser and Elbe Rivers on the flanks of the Harz Mountains is a 100-square-mile area estimated to contain 20 billion metric tons of potash. Mining areas are split by the Iron Curtain, with West Germany producing 2 million tons of K_2O content or one-quarter of world production. Potash is essential to the commercial fertilizer and chemical industries.

Insufficient quantities of copper, lead, zinc, pyrites, petroleum, and salt are mined. Petroleum production is increasing, however, and about one-third of the West German needs come from fields within the country.

WATER POWER   The highlands, especially the Bavarian Alps, supply considerable water power. Germany ranks sixth among European countries, excluding the U.S.S.R., in hydroelectric production. Its importance to industries, railways, and homes as a source of power is generally overlooked because of the prominence of coal.

ECONOMIC DEVELOPMENT

Germany is favored by a relatively large amount of arable land (Table 8-7). Much of the North German Plain, a number of river valleys and basins in the central and southern regions, and considerable areas on the lower slopes of the highlands can be cultivated.

Despite setbacks by two world wars, the West German economy has boomed to such an extent that the country is the most prosperous and stable industrial power in Western Europe. Industrial-production levels are more than 2½ times prewar levels, partly as a result of United States and other aid but mostly as a result of the ability and industriousness of the German people. The skills of the refugees have aided considerably. Levels in Berlin, however, are much lower. Germany de-

TABLE 8-7   LAND USE OF GERMANY

| | Acres, thousands | Per cent | | | |
		Arable	Meadow and pasture	Forest and woodland	Other
Germany	86,806	39	20	28	13
Western Germany	60,307	35	23	29	13
Eastern Germany	26,499	48	12	27	13

pends on quality, low wage rates, and efficiency rather than mass-production techniques to meet foreign competition, although the Volkswagen automobile is a product of the assembly line. Industry is diversified; both heavy (basic) and light (finished and consumer goods) are represented.

In West Germany, 45 per cent of total production is provided by industry, 33 per cent by services, 8 per cent by government, 7 per cent by construction, and only 7 per cent by agriculture and forestry. West Germany, with a production of about 34 million tons of steel, ranks third in the world. Industry in East Germany is geared to Soviet-sphere needs. The greater emphasis is on agriculture.

German agriculture is characterized by mixed farming, small farms, low income per farm, large families providing labor, and increasing use of machinery. The inherently poor soils necessitate scientific farming and heavy fertilization for high production. Prewar Germany produced about 75 to 80 per cent of its food requirements; now, two-thirds of the needs are grown in West Germany, and East Germany no longer produces surpluses because of droughts, war dislocations of farmers, fertilizer shortages, and lack of response to Communist collectivization of agriculture.

REGIONS

NORTHERN LOWLANDS   The German portion of the Central European Lowlands extends from the Netherlands to the Polish boundaries, with tongues, or lowland bays, protruding southward into the highlands in both West and East Germany. The maximum east-west extent is about 300 miles. Surface materials and relief are largely a result of continental glaciation. The previous drainage system was disrupted, leaving lakes, large areas of bog and marsh, and east-west–oriented glacial valleys that facilitated the building of canals connecting the navigable rivers. The topographical differences can be summarized as follows: (1) a poorly drained outwash plain extending inland from the North Sea; (2) a sandy, heath-covered, outwash area between the Elbe and Weser Rivers; (3) a sand, lake, and forest district east of the Elbe with greater relief due to morainic ridges, and (4) the southern transitional zone, largely loess-covered, bordering on the highlands. Most of the plain is under 300 feet and only rarely reaches over 600 feet.

The agricultural development reflects the differences mentioned above. Dairying and livestock grazing are the predominant uses of the bog, marsh, and sandy heaths

Figure 8-21 Agricultural scene on a Communist farm in East Germany. Note the use of various machines in harvesting and processing the crop. (Courtesy of German Consulate General.)

Figure 8-22 Sheep and farm buildings, Luneburg Heath, Germany. Note the structure of the fence and buildings. (Courtesy of German Tourist Information Office.)

of the northwest, with crop agriculture, especially vegetables and sugar beets, in the artificially drained areas. To the east, crops are increasingly important, with potatoes and rye on the poorer soils and sugar beets and wheat on the better soils. The rougher grasslands are grazed. The more sparsely populated northeast normally produces food surpluses. Forestry and resort activities are significant. The transitional zone to the south is one of the best farming areas in Germany; its dense rural population grows wheat, barley, sugar beets, and fodder crops for stall-fed cattle.

The North Sea coast is much more favorable than the Baltic for ports and trade. Both coasts are sandy and have shallow water offshore. The Baltic, however, is frozen for several months during the winter, and trade is limited largely to the neighboring countries. The North Sea ports, improved by deepened, narrow estuaries, have better access to Atlantic and world trade. Hamburg and Bremen, the leading ports, are located considerable distances up the Elbe and Weser Rivers respectively, with access to rich agricul-

tural and industrial hinterlands. Hamburg, whose population is nearly 2 million, is the first port and second city of Germany. Although its free port attracts considerable trade, Hamburg is handicapped by the Iron Curtain, which bisects the productive Elbe River hinterland 20 miles upstream. Extensive war damage to harbor facilities and the city have been repaired. Hamburg also has engineering, shipbuilding, and other industries. Cuxhaven, Hamburg's outport, is used by large passenger vessels. Bremen, Germany's second port, does not have such a large hinterland but normally has as much ocean traffic. Bremerhaven, Bremen's outport, important for fishing, is the chief German port supplying the Allied forces and industrial West Germany. Wesermüde is another leading German fishing port, and Emden is a small North Sea port.

Berlin, the prewar governmental, cultural, and artistic center, is handicapped by its location deep in Soviet-controlled East Germany, and its unsettled position in the cold war. Its 1960 population of 3.3 million was over 1 million less than in 1939. Of the total, about 2 million are in

West Berlin and 1 million in East Berlin. Varied manufacturing establishments made prewar Berlin the leading German industrial and commercial center and hub of a vast railway and waterway network. Berlin's present Four Power occupation and access routes were agreed to with the intention that Germany would be unified and Berlin again become the capital and focal city. Unification now seems unlikely, and the status of West Berlin is precarious. It is a showcase for the West, a moral obligation, and a thorn for the Communist world. West Berlin produces electric machinery, clothing, and chemicals. At present East Berlin is the capital of Communist East Germany.

CENTRAL HIGHLANDS   A complex of worn-down mountains and dissected plateaus, the central highlands, extends southward from the northern lowlands to the Alpine forelands. The forested or grass-covered highlands are infertile, but the basins and valleys are generally intensively cultivated and grow sugar beets, potatoes, wheat, and other cereals. Many of the slopes are terraced for such crops as the vine and fruit. Livestock is grazed on the poor, rough grasslands.

The populous contact zone between the highlands and the northern lowlands is one of the most intensely developed industrial and agricultural regions of Germany. The minerals of the highlands and the coal along their northern flanks provide the principal basis for industry. The Ruhr coal and the lignite fields near Cologne and Leipzig are the major sources of power. From Hannover to Dresden are a number of prominent industrial towns. Lignite, potash, and salt provide raw materials for the heavy chemical and fertilizer industries in cities on the flanks of the Harz Mountains such as Halle, Stasz-furt (Stassfurt), Magdeburg, and in the

Leipzig area. Lignite is also used in synthetics production to make rubber, plastics, dyestuffs, explosives, and other materials. Textiles, scientific instruments, and watches are among products made in this area. Leipzig, a great commercial and rail center, led in prewar publishing and printing. Dresden, a music and art center, also produces a variety of specialty products such as scientific instruments, china, and optical goods. The latter two cities are in East Germany.

Uranium and other minerals are mined in the Erzgebirge (Ore Mountains). Lumbering, wood carving, and toy and clock making are developed in the Black and Thuringian Forests.

RUHR INDUSTRIAL   The huge industrial complex based on Ruhr coal is one of the outstanding manufacturing concentrations in the world. Nearly 10 million people are found in an area about the size of Delaware, which has a population of 484,000. The Ruhr accounts for over 90 per cent of the anthracite and bituminous coal of West Germany and for over one-half of that mined in all six Common Market countries. It has 80 per cent of the steel output of West Germany; its steel production exceeds that of the United Kingdom. It is a leading manufacturing district for metal products, coke and coal derivatives, machinery, chemicals, and textiles. It was the arsenal of both the Kaiser and Hitler and is a pivotal production area in the East-West struggle as well as in the Common Market.

The following factors favor the development of the Ruhr: (1) the most extensive deposits of excellent coking and other qualities of coal in Europe (130 seams, of which 57 are used, occurring in succession, with the lowest at a depth of 9,000 feet); (2) good water and rail connections for access to raw materials, especially Lorraine and Swedish iron ore, as well as for export of finished products to foreign markets; (3) a location at the junction of the Rhine Valley and east-west rail and water routes along the northern edge of the central highlands; (4) nearby Sieg Valley iron ore; and (5) an abundance of skilled labor.

The Ruhr in the south is hilly and forested, but the relatively level and fertile agricultural north provides about 50 per cent of the area's food needs. Four cities, Essen, Dortmund, Düsseldorf, and Duisburg, have populations of more than 500,000; 14 cities have more than 100,000 people. Urban districts in the north specialize in coal mining and heavy industry such as iron and steel. High-quality metal industries requiring skill and only small amounts of raw materials such as machine tools, motors, springs, and locks are found in the southern hilly district. Located here and in cities west of the Rhine are textile and clothing industries, and chemical, metal, and glass industries are scattered throughout the Ruhr.

Much of the prewar industry was controlled and integrated by huge cartels. During the occupation period, attempts were made to break up and replace the large concerns in an attempt to initiate competition, but they were unsuccessful. The dismantling of plants was stopped, and Ruhr production, a key to the prosperity of West Germany and Western Europe, is again flourishing.

BAVARIAN ALPS   The northern limestone fringe of the Alpine system, the Bavarian Alps, extends in southern Germany from Lake Constance to the Austrian border. Though not so high as the main Alps, they average from 6,000 to 7,000 feet in elevation and are snow-covered most of the year. The Zugspitze, 9,721 feet, is the highest peak. Tourism is a major industry;

the wooded slopes and mountain meadows form the basis of lumbering and pastoral pursuits.

ALPINE FORELANDS   Averaging 1,000 to 3,000 feet above sea level, the Alpine forelands slope northward to the Danube River. They are a relatively level plateau covered with coarse glacial debris. The generally poor soils and swampy areas foster an important dairying industry. The richer soils of the Danube and tributary valleys are most intensively utilized for wheat, barley, oats, and hops and for cattle. Lumbering is developed on the forested slopes.

Munich (München), the third city of Germany, is an art and music center. Industries include breweries, textiles, and electrical and mechanical goods. The city is located at the intersection of the Berlin-Rome and Vienna-Paris routes. Augsburg is of regional importance; Ulm and Regensburg are Danube River ports. Considerable water power is available for industry.

RHINE VALLEY   The Rhine Valley is divided into three sections: the upper rift valley, the central gorge, and the lower plains. The rift valley is a down-dropped block of rock 20 miles wide and 185 miles long, part of which is in France. Except for swampy meadows near the river, the valley floor produces abundant wheat, tobacco, hops, and fruit orchards. Vineyards and pastures occupy terraced lower slopes; the upper slopes are forested. Karlsruhe and Mannheim are strategic transportation centers. Petroleum was discovered in 1952.

The Main and Neckar Valleys are tributary to the rift valley. Fertile, terraced fields and a moderate climate result in agriculture similar to that of the rift valley. Frankfurt, on the Main River, and

Nuremberg (Nürnberg), on a tributary of the Main, are the chief cities of this region. Frankfurt has a major civilian and military airport and is a major industrial city. Stuttgart dominates the Neckar industrial region.

From just west of Mainz to Bonn is the picturesque Rhine gorge. The valley, cut into resistant rock, is barely wide enough in places for a railway and highway on each side of the river, and terraced vineyard slopes are prominent. Bonn is the present capital of West Germany.

North of Bonn, the Rhine enters the flat European Plain. Cologne, with nearly 800,000 inhabitants, has access to large lignite deposits and is a diversified industrial center and important Rhine port. Duisburg-Ruhrort is the chief German Rhine port and the principal river port in Europe. The Rhine, an international artery, carries more traffic than any other European waterway.

TRADE AND PROBLEMS

About one-third of the trade of individual countries of Western Europe is with West Germany. West Germany exports principally coal and coke and manufactured goods—iron and steel, machinery, vehicles, chemicals, textiles, and precision equipment. Principal imports are foodstuffs and industrial raw materials such as petroleum, iron and other ore, coal, cotton, wool, wood pulp, and paper. The trade of West Germany is predominantly with the United States and Western Europe.

East German imports include primarily coal, iron and steel, petroleum products, and agricultural and forest products. Chief exports are brown coal, potash, cement, chemicals, metallic ores, and various consumer goods. Eastern Europe accounts for over three-fourths of East Germany's

Figure 8-23 Rhine River port of Mannheim. (Courtesy of German Tourist Information Office.)

foreign trade. Lack of interchange of East German food for West German coal and manufactured goods handicaps both parts, particularly the East.

Western Europe and the United States dominate West Germany's trade; only 5 per cent of its trade is with Eastern Europe and the U.S.S.R. Although severe competition exists for markets, by the early 1960s West Germany had regained all of its prewar world-trade volume, or about 10 per cent of the whole.

The refugees and expellees, early a problem for postwar West Germany, are now a strength, for their ability and labor are vital to the resurgent economy. Few war ruins are visible in the West German landscape. Labor shortages have replaced unemployment and overpopulation. Despite all obstacles, including the lack of unification, West Germany is the focal point of a peaceful Europe. By the early 1960s great progress had been made in West Germany; business was prosperous, exports were expanding, and the standard of living was higher. This bright picture contrasts markedly with the state of East Germany, controlled by the Communists, where economic conditions are stagnant, and political conditions caused thousands to flee to West Germany before the escape hatches were closed in 1961.

SWITZERLAND

Switzerland is one of the smallest but most continuously successful of European countries. Since 1815 the Swiss have maintained a neutrality policy in their landlocked Central European nation. They have avoided the war destruction and disruption so disastrous in much of Europe and with the return of peace were ready to trade and carry on normal relations.

Figure 8-24   The most famous mountain peak in Europe, the Matterhorn in Switzerland. (Courtesy of Swiss National Tourist Office.)

Switzerland has 5,350,000 people within 15,944 square miles, an area slightly less than that of Denmark. Population is concentrated largely in the Central Plateau areas, as much of Switzerland is too mountainous for settlement.

Switzerland exemplifies how peoples diverse in race, language, and religion can be welded into one nation. It has four official languages, German dialects spoken by 73 per cent in the central and northern districts, French spoken by 21 per cent in the southwest, Italian spoken by 5 per cent on the southern slopes of the Alps, and Romansh, a Latin-derived tongue spoken in a few southeastern districts by 1 per cent of the people. In religion, 58 per cent are Protestant, 41 per cent Catholic, and 1 per cent of other faiths.

The physical resources of Switzerland are limited. Severe climate, poor soil, and great slope limit agricultural development to favored valleys and the Central Plateau. Small, low-quality, poorly located coal deposits, building stone, sand, and clay are the only minerals. Mountains are dominant and occupy over 70 per cent of the total area. They are of major significance for defense; for grazing and dairying partially based on Alpine grasslands; for water power, the greatest natural resource; for channeling profit-earning traffic through Switzerland, since major arteries of communication use the low passes in the Alps and Juras; and for tourism.

ECONOMIC DEVELOPMENT

Since about 1880, industry has emerged as the major segment of the Swiss economy despite almost complete lack of raw materials. Approximately 46 per cent of the working population are engaged in industry, 16 per cent in agricultural enterprises, and 20 per cent in services. Only Belgium and England rival Switzerland in emphasis on manufacturing. Many of the small and scattered enterprises specialize in high-quality goods such as watches and precision instruments. Swiss industries of major importance are engineering and metals, chemicals, watchmaking, and textiles. Greater emphasis is being placed upon machinery and chemicals.

Despite handicaps of soil and relief, the Swiss have developed a rather intensive agriculture. Dairying is dominant, supplemented by the growing of hay and cereal crops. Sugar beets and tobacco, with orchard and vineyard products, are cash crops.

REGIONS

The Alps, the Jura Mountains, and the Central Plateau are the three regions of Switzerland. The rugged Alps cover 60 per cent of the country, with the famed Matterhorn reaching 14,705 feet. Forestry, dairying, and tourism are the major economic activities. Transhumance, the seasonal transfer of animals and caretakers to summer mountain pastures, is practiced.

The Jura Mountains, located on the French boundary, are folded parallel valleys and ridges reaching 5,000 feet. Dairying and forestry are common, with vineyards on south-facing slopes. La Chaux-de-Fonds is a center of the watchmaking industry. Basel, a Rhine port and railway hub, is a chemical, machinery, and silk-manufacturing city.

The glaciated and stream-dissected Central Plateau covers 29 per cent of Switzerland but contains 70 per cent of the people. It is the heart of Swiss economic activity. Elevation varies from 1,300 to 4,600 feet, and the climate is damp and rather severe. Agriculture is intensive, with specialization in dairying. Milk is used in the production of cheese, condensed milk, and chocolate. Other scattered industry is based primarily upon hydroelectric power. The silk and cotton textile industries are located in the north around Zürich and St. Gallen, and the manufacture of machinery, watches, and textiles is found in Geneva and Bern, the capital. The cities and areas bordering the famous Swiss lakes are tourist centers, as are the Alps.

TRADE AND PROBLEMS

The prosperity of Switzerland depends upon the export of at least 30 per cent of the industrial production. Machinery, watches, chemicals, pharmaceuticals, precision instruments, and high-grade textiles are the chief exports. Watches and watch movements form 19 per cent of the value of exports. Leading imports are iron and steel, chemical products, industrial heavy machinery, coal, wheat, automobiles, petroleum, forage crops, and cotton. Neighboring industrial countries and the United States are the chief trading areas. The adverse balance in trade is offset by transit traffic on Rhine barges and the Swiss railroads, tourism, foreign insurance and investments, strong currency, and the recently begun merchant marine, which numbers 28 ships and 150,000 tons and is largely based in Italian ports.

LIECHTENSTEIN

Liechtenstein, an independent principality of 16,000 inhabitants on the eastern Swiss border, has an economic union with Switzerland. The majority of the people are of German origin and are Roman Catholic. Agriculture is the main occupation. The capital and chief city is Vaduz. The people pay no taxes, the Prince securing his income from fees of foreign corporations that are licensed by Liechtenstein, and from the sale of postage stamps to collectors.

AUSTRIA

Neutral Austria, strategically located in the heart of Europe astride vital modern rail, water, and air routes, forms a link between the West and the East. The 1,648-mile boundary line is shared with seven countries; on two-thirds of the boundary Austria touches Communist territory.

The population numbers 7,100,000; 24 per cent live in Vienna (Wien) and most of the remainder in lowlands such as the Danube Valley. The sparsely populated Alps occupy three-fourths of the area. Though nearly 98 per cent of the people speak German, cultural and other differences from the Germans are apparent. About 94 per cent are Roman Catholic.

Present Austria, created from the Austro-Hungarian empire in 1918, possesses the following percentages of former land and resources: area 12.5, labor 30, steam-power capacity 20, coal 0.5, and food production 20. Banking, industrial, educational, and administrative facilities, organized for 50 million persons, now serve about 7 million. Psychological adjustment to these losses has been a major problem.

After the forced union with Germany in 1938, Austria was dominated by the Nazis until 1945. It was then divided into four zones of occupation. The 1955 peace treaty restored complete sovereignty to Austria but required neutrality and heavy reparation payments to the Soviet Union for a period of ten years.

PHYSICAL SETTING

Austria is dominated by the Alps; only one-fourth consists of plains and low hills. The climate is transitional, with tempera-

Figure 8-25 Mariazell in the province of Styria, Austria. The cleared slopes and valley bottoms support dairying. The eastern Austrian Alps have a valuable forest cover. (Courtesy of Information Department of the Austrian Consulate General.)

ture extremes increasing to the east and at higher altitudes. Soils are varied. The most fertile are found in the Danube Valley and in favored basins. Approximately 21 per cent of the total area is arable; 28 per cent is in meadow and pasture, fostering an important grazing and dairying development, and 37 per cent is in forests, making Austria one of the few European exporters of timber products and paper. It ranks high in the production of hydroelectric power. Important petroleum fields are located in eastern Austria, but until 1965, 1 million tons a year must go to the U.S.S.R. as reparations. The Styrian low-quality iron ore fields are in area among Europe's largest. Other significant minerals are coal and magnesite.

ECONOMIC DEVELOPMENT

Approximately 40 per cent of the labor force are engaged in manufacturing and 32 per cent in agriculture and forestry. Consumer goods, machinery, and metallurgy are the main types of manufacturing. Mining employs many. Vienna, Linz, Graz, and Salzburg are the principal industrial centers. Industrial levels have advanced rapidly since independence in 1955, but Austria's progress still does not rival that of Switzerland.

Agricultural production supplies about 85 per cent of the Austrian food requirements. Wheat, rye, barley, oats, potatoes, and sugar beets are the chief crops. Dairying and pig raising are very important. There are some areas of fertile valley land, but the average farmer wrests a living from small, rugged farms with hard work and a minimum of machinery.

The severely folded Alps reach their maximum width in Austria. The highest peak is Gross Glockner, 12,461 feet. Grazing and forestry are dominant on the rougher slopes, with crops such as rye, oats, potatoes, and hay concentrated in

valleys and small basins. The Arlberg and Brenner gaps contain important arteries of trade and traffic through Austria. Tourism is also of importance. Salzburg and Innsbruck are the major cities. Northern Austria is a forested plateau.

Limited areas in the east and south and the narrow Danube Valley compose the lowlands. The more favorable soil and climate of the lowlands result in the growth of wheat, corn, vineyards, and garden crops along with dairying. Lumbering is important on lower slopes. The eastern lowlands contain the valuable oil deposits producing 2.5 million tons. Linz, Graz, and Vienna are the leading cities. Vienna is a major problem as it is too large a capital city for present Austria; its industry is largely finishing and processing manufactures.

Austria is one of the most important producers of electricity for the international exchange of power, ranking third in Europe after Germany and Switzerland. The physical geography of the country with its rugged mountain system and high Alpine streams in the west, plus the power of the Danube in the east, gives it an outstanding water power potential. The shape of Austria, with its long east-west axis, also makes for ease in exporting electric power to the heavy-industry areas of Germany, Italy, and the other bordering nations plus France. In the late 1950s the countries adjacent to Austria were using over 40 per cent of their potential power production whereas Austria had just touched its potential. It has been estimated that by 1975 Switzerland, Germany, and northern Italy will be almost fully developed, but that Austria will have reached only about 50 per cent of its possible output. With the building of storage dams Austria can be a producer during the entire year. In western Austria, during the summer season, the water from melting glaciers can be used for the generation of power and then stored to be used again at lower elevations during the winter season. Eastern Austria and adjacent countries can be supplied by developments along the Danube.

TRADE AND PROBLEMS

Austria, with its limited resources, must trade or die. Foodstuffs, coal and coke, raw cotton and wool, and heavy machinery are Austria's principal imports. Forest products and paper are the leading exports, along with iron and steel products, textiles, magnesite, and machinery. Trade with Eastern European countries and the U.S.S.R. decreased from over 40 per cent of the total value in 1938 to 18 per cent at present. Western Germany, Italy, Switzerland, Great Britain, and the United States are other major trading partners. Between 50 and 60 per cent of Austria's trade is carried on with Common Market countries and only 14 per cent with EFTA, of which it is a member.

Increased utilization of existing resources and expansion of industry, agriculture, transportation, and trade are necessary to overcome the lack of resources. The 1955 peace treaty posed economic problems, for Austria was required to pay the U.S.S.R. 150 million dollars a year in cash for six years, deliver 1 million tons of oil a year for ten years, and assume the burden of maintaining an army. Austria's painstakingly achieved neutrality also may preclude a much desired membership or association with Common Market Europe.

IN PERSPECTIVE

WESTERN EUROPE, ITS IMPORTANCE

The political expansion and economic growth of Western Europe that followed the discovery of America and the sailing routes to the Far East was the outstanding geographic development after the fifteenth century. Many European governments emerged from feudalism. Discoveries of new lands and peoples led to the establishment of colonies and trade overseas. Inventions and the increased use of minerals and other resources, especially the application of power to manufacturing, resulted in the industrial revolution, which caused great growth in density of population, particularly in the population of cities. The world was largely dominated by the countries of Western Europe; until World War II most of Africa and Oceania, much of Asia, and parts of America were governed from European capitals. Since 1946, however, most former European possessions have become, or soon will become, independent nations.

The culture of Europe spread to distant lands; European languages were used in trade and education; the Christian religion gained adherents abroad; and many backward peoples learned the principles of self-government. The contributions of Western Europe to the advancement of civilization are great. Today most European countries have made a remarkable recovery from World War II both in industrial production and in bettering standards of living for their citizens. Even greater advances can be made by solving political and economic problems that hinder commerce and hamper the exercise of human rights.

Not only is Western Europe the site of huge and varied manufacturing, but the area also has a noteworthy output of agricultural products. Wheat and other breadgrains, potatoes, sugar beets, fruits of many sorts, vineyard products, and vegetables, along with dairy products, pigs, beef cattle, and sheep are among the produce of Western European farms. Soil, rainfall, length of growing season, experienced farmers, and closeness of markets are among factors that favor agriculture. Coal, iron, and other minerals are present in great abundance, and forest and fishery resources are locally in large supply. Most important of all the factors affecting the growth of industries are the skill and experience of the factory workmen, the efficiency of management, and the availability of capital. Although exports of manufactures help to provide income for the countries of Western Europe, the large local populations constitute a big market within themselves. Movements such as the Common Market represent attempts to take advantage of the large markets and the diversity of physical and human resources in member countries. Europe has much of historic and cultural interest to visitors from abroad, and the more than 1 billion dollars which tourists spend annually is available for the purchase of foodstuffs, minerals, and other materials and goods not manufactured in sufficient quantity on the Continent itself. Although Western European countries have lost most of their colonial empires and other nations have developed into commercial and industrial rivals, the region remains, for its size, the most influential in the world.

SELECTED REFERENCES

Dollfus, Jean: *Atlas of Western Europe,* Rand McNally & Company, Chicago, 1963.
A short but excellent atlas dealing with the Benelux, the British Isles, and Scandinavia. Excellent summary physical maps as well as rather detailed maps on land use, population, and economic activities make it a highly useful reference. The brief text-and-photograph section is of much less value than the atlas portion.

Gottmann, Jean: *A Geography of Europe,* 3d ed., Holt, Rinehart and Winston, Inc., New York, 1962.

The third revised edition of a standard reference on the general geography of Europe. The emphasis is upon human geography, and the organization reflects the French school of regional geographers. It is very readable, but the maps are of limited value.

Hoffman, George W. (ed.): *Geography of Europe,* 2d ed., The Ronald Press Company, New York, 1960.
This general treatise on Europe is authored mostly by geographers who have spent a part or all of their lives as natives of the countries about which they write. Equal emphasis is given to the physical, historical, and economic geography of major segments of Europe as well as to each country. The text is well illustrated with photographs and maps, and a useful statistical summary of significant items is included in the appendix.

Monkhouse, F. J.: *A Regional Geography of Western Europe,* Longmans, Green & Co., Inc., New York, 1959.
A detailed regional analysis of Benelux and France based on physical regions. It is well illustrated with aerial photographs and detailed maps concerning the regions discussed.

Pounds, Norman J. G.: *Divided Germany and Berlin,* D. Van Nostrand Company, Inc., Princeton, N.J., 1962.
A concise paperback on the major geographical aspects of the German and Berlin problems. Though intended for the general public, it is a well-written treatise on this world problem.

————, and Sue Simons Ball: "Core Areas and the Development of the European States System," *Annals of the Association of American Geographers,* vol. 54, no. 1, pp. 24–40, March, 1964.
The purpose of this study is to examine the physical nature of and the geographical role performed by the core area in the formation of a particular group of states, namely those of Europe.

Somme, Axel (ed.): *A Geography of Norden,* J. W. Cappelens Forlag, Oslo, 1960.
An analysis of Norway, Sweden, Finland, Denmark, and Iceland, published in conjunction with the International Geographic Congress in Stock-

holm in 1960. Excellent coverage of the physical and economic geography of the countries involved as well as a general analysis of the whole area. Well illustrated with photographs and maps, including a valuable color-map appendix setting forth the major characteristics of the Scandinavian (Norden) area.

Stamp, L. Dudley, and S. H. Beaver: *The British Isles,* 4th ed., Longmans, Green & Co., Inc., New York, 1954.

A standard reference concerning the geography of

the British Isles from a typically British point of view, emphasizing physical regions but also including the total geography of this important island group.*

Stone, Kirk H.: "Swedish Fringes of Settlement," *Annals of the Association of American Geographers,* vol. 52, no. 4, pp. 373–393, December, 1962.

A study of the movement and settlement of people to the fringe areas of previously uninhabited land as exemplified by northern Sweden.

chapter 9
SOUTHERN PENINSULAR EUROPE

Figure 9-1 Mediterranean Europe is a discontinuous and fragmented land. Three great peninsulas reach southward into the sea, each peninsula broken into many separate and distinct regions by hills and mountain ranges, so that regionalism is nurtured and communication made difficult. Few plains exist, and the uplands are steep and eroded.

*T*HE LONG ARM OF THE MEDITERRANEAN Sea, reaching from Gibraltar to Suez and the Dardanelles and penetrating in the form of smaller seas among the land projections of southern Europe, has given a unified character to the countries that border its basin—a unity which is expressed climatically, historically, culturally.

Three large peninsulas that project into the sea make up Southern Peninsular Europe. Spain and Portugal share the blocky bulk of the Iberian Peninsula, a plateau attached to (or separated from) the rest of Europe by the lofty Pyrenees. Italy angles into the sea from an equally solid mountain base, turning southwestward toward Cape Bon in "the toe of the boot" nearly to close off the western basin of the Mediterranean from the eastern. The outlines of these two westward peninsulas are relatively smooth. But to the east lies the third peninsula, an irregular mass of land that splashes and splinters into the sea, fingering outward in innumerable smaller peninsulas that are usually rocky headlands, as well as strewing the waters with hundreds of islands that range from mere rocks to tracts the size of Cyprus and the Peloponnesus (the latter an island now that its slender connective thread has been breached by the Corinth Canal). Greek control extends over most of this peninsula and associated islands; however, the eastern portion, which reaches to the Bosporus and the Dardanelles, includes European Turkey.

The sheltered nature of the sea, and the interspersal of land and water have moderated the climate; they also, very early, encouraged man to venture from shore and explore. He tested himself farther and farther from his home base, up to and even beyond the Pillars of Hercules (Strait of Gibraltar), up into the waters by which the lands of the Golden Fleece were bounded (namely, the Black Sea), thus navigating through the narrows of the Bosporus–Sea of Marmara–Dardanelles waterway. Very early Mediterranean peoples were probing the farthest pockets of the inland sea from end to end, until the Carthaginians, inheritors of the colonizing Phoenicians from the eastern Mediterranean, imposed control over the western basin, and later, Rome from the west reached east and south and conquered a ring of lands encircling the entire inland sea.

The protected basin, intimate in its enclosed setting and homogeneous environment, fostered communication among its inhabitants. Continuous intercourse back and forth across the water bound the peoples of the basin together economically and led to an interchange of ideas. As a result, aided by likeness of landscape and climatic environment, Mediterranean culture took on an essentially similar character, and something that might be called a Mediterranean civilization arose. Particularly did the pattern of land use develop along nearly identical lines. At once challenging man and assisting him to adapt and invent, the Mediterranean region was like an incubator in which culture was bred and nurtured: many of man's earliest advances unfolded here—in agriculture, art, literature, religion, commerce, navigation, and law.

Contacts were along two main thoroughfares, the land bridge of Asia Minor and the sea itself. The land bridge, a peninsula of plateaus, mountains, and westward-trending valleys, viewed three seas and looked toward Europe from across the Dardanelles and the Bosporus. It connected the European world with that of the Orient to the east. The seaway, long and narrow, landlocked, with little tide, and studded with steppingstones—islands that stretched from Cyprus to the Balearics—was easily navigated, while the many promontories and peninsulas provided a

Figure 9-2 The Claudian aqueduct near Rome is one of the many magnificent ruins that remain as monuments to the splendor and eminence of past Mediterranean civilizations. (Courtesy of Trans World Airlines.)

long coastline. Progress began first at the eastern end of the basin and filtered westward as group borrowed from group. And so, from the river valleys of Western Asia and Egypt, and from the coastal lands of the eastern Mediterranean, contacts diffused civilizations toward Gibraltar. Over a period of centuries, a series of culture and power centers arose along the inland sea from east to west. All of Southern Peninsular Europe participated in the spread of ideas and influence. Crete, Phoenicia, Greece, Rome, Spain, and Portugal rose to eminence in succession. As one receded another succeeded to first place. Thus Rome overthrew the power of Greece and, in its prime, reached out to conquer North Africa and the barbarians of Northern Europe. The statement that "all roads lead to Rome" became literally true, for Rome ranged east, north, and south to extend its political and economic influence. But eventually Rome declined. In the Dark Ages that followed, much that had been learned in the past almost disappeared.

During the Middle Ages, Italian Genoa and Venice, her rival, were the great ports of trade. Milan, situated at the foot of the St. Gotthard pass, was a city of wealth and power. Under the Medici, the trading and financial center of Florence became the leader in the Renaissance movement that carried Europe from medievalism into the modern period. It was in the basin of the Mediterranean, and particularly in the cities of Venice and Florence in Italy, that the Renaissance had its first and greatest expression.

For nearly 2,000 years the Mediterranean was dominant. During all that time, European civilization faced south. The ebb of this brilliant period of Mediterranean supremacy came at the beginning of the sixteenth century as control of the spice trade slipped from the hands of the Turks. Hitherto, the products of the East had flowed by caravan through Egypt or by way of Baghdad and Aleppo, the route of the Fertile Crescent, to the Levantine ports. Here they were met by the galleys of the Italian cities and transported westward. By 1503, however, practically no spices were arriving at the ports of the eastern Mediterranean. They were being carried in Portuguese vessels, by way of the ocean route around Africa and thence to Lisbon, to be picked up there and distributed by the ships of the Hanseatic League.

Dominance moved westward to the two countries of the Iberian Peninsula, Medi-

Figure 9-3   Sheep grazing among the olive trees, a typical rural scene on the Greek island of Corfu. The island is covered with olive groves and dark cypress trees. (Courtesy of Ewing Galloway.)

terranean lands that faced also upon the Atlantic. It was the Portuguese and Spanish who opened up the highways of ocean transport: The Portuguese navigators traced the outline of Africa and led the way to the Indies with daring and skill, proved that the world was round by circumnavigating the globe, and opened the routes of trade and treasure by their courage and initiative. They and the Spaniards took possession of lands far and wide, and at one time divided the unclaimed and as yet undiscovered lands of the world between them. The Pope drew the line, in 1494, that should designate the spheres to which each state could lay claim.

In time they, too, declined. With the dying out of the royal line, Portugal came under Philip II of Spain, and Spanish interests were pushed to the elimination of those of the Portuguese. Though it had its illustrious days, Spanish colonial history is notable not only for the spread of its influence but also for its swift ebb after attaining a glorious climax. Spain went into eclipse, through bankruptcy, at the defeat of the Armada by England.

So the Mediterranean faded as a center of power and progress, and the center of

influence moved north. For a time, the bypassed Mediterranean became a backwater in the affairs of the world. Though there was a revival of Mediterranean commerce in the first half of the nineteenth century, only with the opening of the Suez Canal did that sea return to a place of great prominence as a route of trade. The states that bordered the sea, however, remained in relative obscurity. Not until the past half century have there been indications of recovery. Nevertheless, the inventions in economics, politics, navigation, and culture originating here, in this enclosed basin, carried Western man from barbarism into advanced civilization, and form the base for many of his present-day achievements.

THE MEDITERRANEAN ENVIRONMENT

What is the nature of the Mediterranean landscape?

Typically, it is a region of alternating fragmented, littoral plains and projecting headlands, backed by lofty mountain ranges toward the Continent and fronted by the waters of the inland sea. Add to this a prevalence of sunny, cloudless skies, with a pattern of precipitation that shows a winter maximum and comes in short, quick, heavy showers; paint in the vine, the olive, the citrus, the cork oak, wheat, barley, and some goats; sketch in a proud people with a great past, and you have the landscape almost in its entirety. The limits of the Mediterranean zone are quite clearly defined, for both the climate and adjustment change as the coast is left behind and distance from the sea increases.

PHYSICAL SETTING

RELIEF FEATURES   The Mediterranean topography is one of mountains, hills, and constricted valleys; large plains are a rarity. The Po Valley and narrow coastal plains in Italy, portions of coastal Portugal and Spain, and the coastal region of southern France are the most important lowlands. Greece, dissected by mountains and fringed with multitudes of islands, is a jumble of ranges and valleys and promontories thrust into the sea so that the coast is an alternation of forbidding cliffs and deep indentations, Thessaly being the largest of the lowlands. Offshore, the islands are the tops of submerged ranges that are a continuation of the mountains of the mainland.

CLIMATE   Over much of this southern fringe of Europe the Mediterranean climate prevails. Though this climate takes its name from the Mediterranean Sea region, it is found distributed in other areas in the world, along west coasts of continents in latitudes that range between 30° and 40° north and south. The principal areas in the European Mediterranean region where other kinds of climate prevail include northwestern Spain, which has a marine west-coast type, interior Spain, where semiarid steppes occur, and northern Italy, which has considerable summer rainfall and a greater seasonal range of temperature than do Mediterranean lands. North Italy's climate is, therefore, modified continental rather than Mediterranean. In winter, cold winds from Northeastern Europe sometimes blow through the gaps that pierce the mountain barrier north of the Mediterranean. The mistral of the Rhone Valley and the bora of the Adriatic and Aegean Seas are examples.

The Mediterranean climate has two seasons, a cool winter, with rain usually

Figure 9-4   Goats are one of the animals most typical of Mediterranean regions—well adapted to their environment because of their ability to subsist on poor forage. This photograph shows a Spanish herder and his flock, resting in their obviously sparsely vegetated pasture. (Courtesy of Trans World Airlines.)

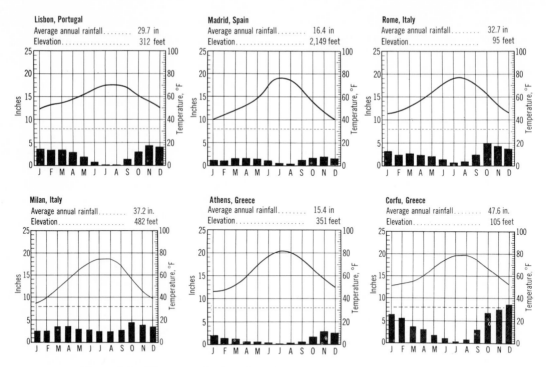

Figure 9-5   Climate graphs for selected Mediterranean stations.

associated with cyclonic storms, and a hot, dry summer. Rarely does the temperature drop to freezing, for mountain barriers shut out most of the cold winds from continental interiors. Even during the winter, the proportion of sunny days is high. Summer is a period of drought broken only occasionally by showers, of brilliant sunshine, hot south winds, and, in some places, of dust storms that blow across the sea from the Sahara. This dry season parches the lands so that grass and other vegetation is brown and scorched-looking. Fields are bare and often plowed in readiness for the planting that takes place with the oncoming of the wet season. Precipitation, averaging between 15 and 35 inches, varies considerably from place to place and from year to year but is dependable for the growing of winter crops. Only by careful water conserva-

tion, however, are the people of the Mediterranean able to maintain a supply that satisfies even the minimum requirements. Irrigation supplements rainfall in many vineyards, orchards, and gardens, and is essential where rice is grown.

VEGETATION   Plant life shows a high degree of adaptation to these climatic conditions, being of the drought-resistant variety, such as maqui. Thorned flora—cacti and thorny shrubs—are found in great number and variety. Deep-rooted plants, like the grape, fig, and olive, penetrate to the level of permanent ground water for moisture sustenance. In fact, the olive is a classic example of the type of vegetation known as Mediterranean, found only within Mediterranean regions. Its long roots help the olive to survive drought during the hot, dry period. Another such typical plant is the cork oak, indigenous only to the Mediterranean region and a part of its landscape. Its thick, pulpy bark acts as an insulator to cut down the evaporation of moisture from its surface.

Because of the extended dry season, pasture is scarce. Hence the goat, sheep, and little donkey are the characteristic animals of the Mediterranean. Only nimble-footed creatures who thrive on poor forage can scramble among the rough scrubby lands and survive.

CULTURAL LANDSCAPE

The two factors of topography and climate have acted to shape Mediterranean life throughout the ages. Here man has more completely exhausted the possibilities offered him than in most regions. Three types of agriculture are carried on side by side: growing winter grains using natural precipitation; terracing and raising tree crops whose deep roots reach down to subsoil water and live through the drought period; and irrigation agriculture.

Wheat and barley are the two Mediterranean grains par excellence. Wheat takes the better-watered and more fertile soil; barley is planted on the marginal lands where wheat will not do so well. The grains are planted in the fall, grow under the moisture of the winter rains, and are harvested in the spring. Even then, in this land of high evaporation, the method of cultivation known as dry farming must be employed to make the most of the uncertain and scanty precipitation that is typical of Mediterranean lands. Under this method, fields are planted in alternate years; during the fallow year they are plowed and frequently reworked to keep the soil loose and free from cracks and weeds, so that the rains can penetrate and

the moisture can be stored. By this technique, two years of precipitation is used to grow one crop of grain.

Since the amount of plains area is definitely limited, even intensive use of the lowlands is insufficient to provide a livelihood for the large population; therefore, hillsides are cultivated. To combat erosion, the slopes are terraced, often from bottom to top. Steps walled with broken stones and filled with soil, frequently carried up from the lowlands, are planted to vines; fig trees and the gray-green olive crown others. These crops are produced without irrigation.

In a land that is characteristically a non-dairy region, the oil of the olive replaces butter and cooking fat in the diet of the people and also provides a skin lotion against the intense summer heat and sunshine. The vine, another typically Mediterranean crop, supplies not only fruit for eating but the major drink as well. Wine is consumed in place of water, and is served with every meal. The grape frequently occupies lowlands as well as hill slopes. On the plains, in order to keep the plants off the grounds, the vines are generally trained on trellises or other supports that extend between trees. Between the widely spaced rows of trees and trellis there are frequently interplantings of other crops. Land is intensively used, and no amount of hand labor is too great to assure a good yield.

The grains, wheat and barley, depend on the winter rains. The orchard crops of olives, figs, grapes, and even citrus fruits, at times, exist through the drought of summer. Other crops, such as rice, vegetables, small fruits, and, in times of great and prolonged drought, the citrus fruits, require irrigation. Wet rice, a somewhat unusual crop in Mediterranean lands, is grown in selected places as, for example, the river valleys of the Po, Ebro, and

Figure 9-6   The largest city in each of the Mediterranean countries in Europe is the national capital. Italy has the greatest number of large cities due largely to the development of heavy industrial centers in the Po Valley.

Tagus (Tejo), the coastal plain near Valencia, and on the reclaimed salt flats of Greece, where rice cultivation is a new project. Vercelli, Italy, is the major rice market of Europe.

Because the environment is meager for the large population that is found everywhere in the Mediterranean Basin, and also because the sea invites, fishing and commerce have become important occupations. Fish ranks high in the diet of Mediterranean peoples. Large quanitities of dried fish are imported to this area from the North Atlantic fishing countries because the amount caught locally is too small to meet the demand.

TABLE 9-1   SOUTHERN PENINSULAR EUROPE

Country	Area, sq. mi.	Total population	Density, sq. mi.
Andorra	190	6,500	37
Gibraltar	2.3	26,000	11,304
Greece	51,169	8,385,000	163
Italy	116,311	50,464,000	433
Monaco	0.6	22,500	37,500
Portugal	35,589	9,108,000	256
San Marino	23.5	15,100	642
Spain	194,345	30,090,000	164
Turkey (in Europe)	9,254	2,300,000	324
Vatican City	0.2	1,050	5,250

In few regions of the world have topography and soil, climate, and even the sea itself had a more direct bearing on human development. It can also be said that there are few areas where man has worked so closely with nature to make a garden of waste places. The development of the techniques of Mediterranean agriculture took centuries. Through trial and error, by the interchange of ideas, there slowly unfolded the "precocious form of intensive tillage" that characterizes Mediterranean lands today.

THE IBERIAN PENINSULA: SPAIN AND PORTUGAL

No explanation of the political partition of the Iberian Peninsula into Spain and Portugal can be found in the ethnographic composition of the two countries. The peoples are closely similar, for all Iberia is of very old Mediterranean stock and, though this unity has been modified by invasion and colonization by Vikings, Moors, and other aliens, the basic character of the people has been little changed.

Because the peninsula lies between Europe and Africa, it was long the battleground of Islam and Christianity, with Europeans and Moors seesawing back and forth across it for many centuries, all a part of the "turbulence of ethnic commingling" with which all Europe seethed for a millennium. The wars subsided earlier in Portugal than in most parts of the continent. Welded together by more than six centuries of struggle against the foreign Moorish civilization inflicted upon them by the Moslem invaders from North Africa, the people of this compact little land were early bound into social and political unity. Two hundred and fifty years before neighboring Spain was liberated and unified, the African Moors had been ejected from Portugal, and the area had emerged as a national state.

While the Portuguese were slowly following the outline of coastal Africa, the Spanish were having experiences like those that their western neighbor had had in creating a nation. The original success of the Moorish invasion lay less in the organization or strength of the invaders than in the social and regional disorganization of the people of Spain. From the middle of the fourteenth century, Spanish history reveals a long and painful process of unification.

The early division of Iberia into two sovereign and distinct nations can be explained, then, only in historical terms. But once the division had been made, geographic factors tended to perpetuate it. Separate action by Portugal and its eventual independence arose, in part, as a result of its physical seclusion on the coastal edge of the tableland, for it is separated from the rest of the peninsula by the rough mountain country that features the plateau margin on the western side. Even within Spain itself, according to Isaiah Bowman, "patriotism is a local thing—reflecting the geographical division of the country; a man says he is a Galician, an Asturian, a Castilian, an Andalusian; he rarely thinks of himself as

Figure 9-7 A typical countryside scene in Portugal, one of many that make the country a paradise for landscape artists. Many of the buildings and all the fences are built of stone— picked from the fields to clear them. Notice the windmills. (Courtesy of Pan American Airlines.)

a Spaniard." [1] Dialects and even languages differ from one localized area to another, for Spaniard is separated from Spaniard by physical barriers, by language, by custom, and by social class. Only the forced collaboration against the Moorish invaders of the half-dozen little Iberian realms, of which Castile and Aragon were the most important, brought about coalescence into a nation, a unity that has precariously endured to the present.

The geologic structure and the physiography of Iberia have much to do with the orientation of the two countries. Portugal faces the Atlantic. The boundary between Spain and Portugal lies along a zone where it is easier to travel downhill to the west coast than to go uphill and across the plateau to the Spanish centers.

Portugal slopes to the sea. The value to the land of its coastal location is enhanced by the fact that the lower reaches of the Douro (Duero) and Tagus (Tejo) Rivers are navigable. Thus the Portuguese are naturally sea-minded; historically, they were among the first great navigators of Europe. Fishing currently holds an important place in the economy of the country although Portugal's present interest in oceanic trade is negligible.

Spain, largely plateau, is oriented landward. Though it had a brilliant career as an exploring and colonizing nation, the period of conquest was but an episode, relatively short-lived because the potential of Spain as a sea power is weak. Although half of the country's population live near the coasts, the fine harbors of northwest Spain are not easily accessible from the interior, and much of the coast offers meager opportunity for modern harbor developments. The Castilians, plateau dwellers, show little aptitude for the sea.

[1] Isaiah Bowman, *The New World,* 4th ed., World Book Company, Tarrytown-on-Hudson, N.Y., 1928, p. 215.

Figure 9-8 Alcazar castle at Segovia, in the southeastern part of Old Castile, Spain. (Courtesy of Pan American Airlines.)

Recently, however, there has been a revival of interest in trade, and at present the Spanish merchant marine amounts to a little over 1 per cent of the world's total.

RELIEF FEATURES

The Iberian Peninsula lies between the Mediterranean Sea and the Atlantic Ocean and, cut off from the rest of Europe by the lofty Pyrenees, it acts as a land bridge between that continent and Africa. It is a bulky block of land, the greater part of which is made up of an ancient massif—an eroded stump of old folded mountains whose margins, formed by faulting, are steep and straight. It is tipped higher in the east than in the west, so that the longest rivers—the Douro, the Tagus, the Guadiana, and the Guadalquivir—rise near the eastern margin of the block, cross the plateau, and empty into the Atlantic Ocean. Faulting also occurred in the interior of the tableland, where huge upthrusts of rock were projected above the surface to form mountain ranges. The greatest of these, the Sierra de Guadarrama, extend through the center of the plateau from Portugal to Aragon. Faulting also explains the Cantabrian Mountains near the northern edge and the Toledo Range to the south of the Sierra de Guadarrama.

To the north and south of the central range are two large basins known respectively as Old and New Castile. Great areas of these basins are extremely flat. They have, however, been dissected in such a way that broad, level tablelands alternate with wide terraced steps and valleys. Though the plateau is over 2,000 feet above sea level, the surface has the character of a plain which, at intervals, is interrupted by steep rises a few hundred feet high ascending to other flat tables.

Young, folded mountains were crushed against the northern, northeastern, and southern edges of the plateau to form highland barriers. In the south, the highest of these, the Sierra Nevada, mount to 11,660 feet, towering abruptly above the plains of the Guadalquivir. In the north, the plateau is partially rimmed by the Cantabrians and the Pyrenees, which rise almost as high as the southern ranges. Though not so lofty as the Alps, the northern mountains form a more formidable barrier to communication than do the mountains that separate Switzerland and Italy.

Between the folded structures and the plateau are wedgelike lowlands. One of these, the valley of the Ebro River, is separated from the Mediterranean Sea by the Catalonian coastal ranges; the other, the plain of Andalusia, drained by the Rio Guadalquivir, opens into the Atlantic through the Gulf of Cadiz. Narrow plains are found along the coast of the peninsula, widest in the west in Portugal and along the Mediterranean shore of eastern Spain. Most of the fertile land of Iberia lies in these lowlands.

CLIMATE AND VEGETATION

Iberia is like a miniature continent, for the massive bulk and mountain barriers make the interior an isolated, continental region, although the sea surrounds it on more than three sides. Latitude, relief, and position with respect to the oceans are responsible for the climatic contrasts found on the peninsula. Because of the direct effects of the westerly winds, especially during the winter months, the climate of Portugal is somewhat moderated. In general, it shows less range of temperature and receives greater amounts of precipitation than does any part of Spain except the north and northwestern coasts and the Spanish Pyrenees.

Three types of climate are found in Iberia—marine, Mediterranean, and continental. Although the peninsula is relatively small and the situation seemingly favorable, maritime influences are singularly lacking in the interior, making climatic conditions unexpectedly severe for the latitude and location. Because of the latitude, the Mediterranean pattern of a dry summer and a winter with precipitation holds true. During the winter months, however, the Meseta (central plateau) is dry as compared with most other parts of Spain and Portugal because of local high pressures that form over the plateau. Madrid, most centrally located, averages less than 17 inches of precipitation annually, and large areas—about one-third of Spain, including portions of the Ebro

Valley in the northeast—receive only 12 to 16 inches. Temperatures are likewise more extreme on the plateau than elsewhere, with Madrid, at 2,000 feet elevation, averaging 40°F in January, the coldest month, and 77°F in July.

The drought that prevails over the interior is reflected in salt flats and treeless steppes, grasslands that are suited to the raising of sheep. In both Old and New Castile, large areas are adapted to the growing of winter wheat, whereas the valleys in the south support Mediterranean vegetation. In the western portion of the plateau, on the borderlands between Spain and Portugal, greater humidity and milder temperatures favor the growth of the cork oak, and the region is an important producer of this forest product.

There are two sets of climatic contrast in Iberia, one between the interior and coastal areas, and the other between the east and west coasts. The most marked distinction is found between the northwest (Galicia) and the southeast. In the former area as well as in the mountainous north, a typically marine climate exists, with year-round precipitation, though showing a winter maximum, and with characteristically mild temperatures throughout the year. Mean temperatures range from a low of 45°F for the coldest month, to not above 70°F for the warmest month. Precipitation varies from 30 to over 60 inches annually. The result is a rich forest vegetation interspersed with grasslands, and a prosperous agriculture, producing fruits as well as grains. Climatically this is the best part of Spain, and though topographically less favorable than the flatter plateaus and lowlands, it is one of the most progressive. Unfortunately, the areal extent of the marine region is small.

Southward along the Atlantic coast from Galicia, the westerly winds continue to moderate temperatures and bring suf-ficient precipitation so that a view of Portugal presents a land with green and lush vegetation. The dry summer season prevails, but the period of drought is short; rainfall reaches nearly the amounts that are typical in the lowlands of northwest Spain. For example, Lisbon has more than 29 inches of rain annually.

In southern and eastern Spain, a true Mediterranean climate obtains. Bare hills, maqui-like vegetation, and dry, brown fields characterize these lowlands in summer. Only the gray green of the drought-resistant olive and the almond, and the green of irrigated crops such as rice, citrus, and sugar cane, break the barren monotony produced by lack of rain.

AGRICULTURE AND LAND USE

Iberia is a domain of cultivators and graziers, its culture a product of the land and climate. Land and climate, however, and social conditions which are in part cause and in part result, are not always kind, so that agrarian conditions in Iberia are backward, the levels of living low. Though 45 per cent of the peninsula is cultivated and another 40 per cent grazed, for several reasons neither Spain nor Portugal is self-sufficient in food. In the first place, methods of cultivation are outmoded. Crude wooden plows prepare the soil for planting. Where irrigation is practiced, the techniques are primitive; water is generally raised from a well by a mule-driven pump to which is hitched a blindfolded animal, plodding round and round in a circle all day long. Seeds are hand-sown, and the grains harvested with hand sickles. The threshing floor, where grains are trodden from the stalks by animals, recalls the methods used in Mediterranean lands during Biblical times.

Most of the farmers till infertile, semi-arid soil, moistened by rainfall that is erratic in amount, varying at times as much as 50 per cent from one year to the next. The inability to depend upon precipitation means that anticipated yields can never be counted upon, and the serious inadequacy of the supplies of nitrogen fertilizer keeps the gross output unnecessarily low. While it is possible for Iberia to be largely self-sufficient, the goal cannot be reached and maintained until at least double the present volume of fertilizer is put on the land annually. Small crops almost invariably mean poverty and little surplus capital for improvements. These conditions lead to social

and often political unrest, as has been evidenced in Spain during the past two decades.

The difficulties are intensified by the system of land tenure. Large estates prevail, especially in the south. Owned generally by absentee landlords, the estates are worked by peasants. They reside in villages and go out each morning from the villages to the fields, traveling on foot or, for those who can afford them, in carts drawn slowly by oxen or mules for distances of as much as five miles. The time consumed in going to and from the fields makes working hours short. This loss of

Figure 9-9   Terracing the rugged slopes for cultivation in Calabria, Southern Italy. (Courtesy of the Italian Information Center.)

Figure 9-10   Oxen-drawn carts, Castile, Spain. Oxen are the most usual beasts of burden used for field work in Southern Peninsular Europe. In Iberia and Greece they are generally black or brown in color, in Italy, white. (Courtesy of Trans World Airlines.)

time, combined with backward techniques of cultivation and climatic handicaps, results in poor crops; an oversupply of laborers keeps wages low and causes unemployment. Even where most of the land is owned by the peasant himself, holdings generally are barely large enough to support a family at even a meager subsistence level.

The pressure of people upon the land is not apparent from statistics, for the density per square mile averages but from 166 in Spain to 275 in Portugal. For the present level of Iberian agricultural technology, however, population pressure is excessive.

Livestock is important in the economies of Iberia. In the humid marine north, dairy cattle and beef cattle feed in the mountain pastures; bulls for the arena are carefully bred; besides those kept in pens, droves of pigs roam about the oak forests of the western plateau, fattening on the acorns; several million goats scramble among the maqui in the rough and scrubby landscape of the Mediterranean sections; oxen, and even cows, as well as horses, donkeys, and mules, draw carts and work in the fields. As in all Mediterranean lands, the little donkey, always seemingly burdened beyond his size and

strength, is one of the most familiar sights. Although cultivation is infringing on their steppe lands, 20 million sheep are found throughout the peninsula, spreading from north to south. Mainly of the Merino type, they are superior for their wool.

Northern and northwestern Iberia is a wheat-corn country. The humid climate makes possible the growing of maize, not found elsewhere on the peninsula. Apple trees are scattered about the pastures, and potatoes and rye are raised. The Meseta is a sheep and wheat country with a scattering of other crops. Wheat is grown in all parts of the plateau but most extensively on the Meseta to the north of the dividing ranges. Although it is the principal agricultural crop of both Spain and Portugal, yields per acre are low, compared with those of most European countries. Barley is produced in the more marginal areas of the upland to the east of the major wheat lands and in the south, where better than average grazing conditions exist but where soil and rainfall are not suited to the growing of the preferred grain, wheat.

The cultivation of the Mediterranean sections approaches horticulture. Rice, grown under irrigation on some of the rich river lands, is a specialized crop.

Figure 9-11 Picking olives, Portugal. (Courtesy of Casa de Portugal.)

Though limited in area, the yields per acre are high, European Spain frequently exceeding in this respect even the famed rice lands of the Asiatic Far East.

The olive tree is almost coextensive with Mediterranean Iberia. Only in the north, northwest, and parts of the Meseta where rainfall and altitude make the climate unsuitable, does the olive tree disappear. Most of the fruit is pressed for its oil, this being the most usual cooking fat for the people of the peninsula. In Spain, however, a considerable quantity of olives are pickled; table olives are the leading Spanish export to the United States. In Portugal a large share of the oil is used by the sardine-canning industry.

Although grapes are grown over much of Spain and Portugal, the cultivation of the vine is especially important along the sheltered sides of the river valleys, where the vineyards are on terraces that cover the slopes. Vine cultivation is the most important of all farming activities in Portugal. Certain localities have become famous for their products of the vine. Among these are the port wine of the Portuguese Douro—named after Oporto, the city located at the mouth of the river —the sherry of Andalusia, and the table grapes of Almeria. Wine is a leading export from both Spain and Portugal.

It was the Moors who brought the orange to the peninsula and introduced it to Iberian culture. Although citrus fruit is grown all around the southern periphery, it attains the greatest importance in the vicinity of Valencia. Spanish oranges find their market in Northern Europe. Almonds, raised in the south, are becoming an increasingly important item in the export trade.

Portugal is the world's foremost producer of cork, normally supplying about 50 per cent of the cork exports moving into international trade. The major producing area in Iberia is located on the

Figure 9-12 Carrying the grapes after picking. Douro Valley, Portugal, one of the prime vine-wine regions of the world. (Courtesy of Casa de Portugal.)

western border of the plateau, in the boundary region between the two countries.

FISHERIES

Fishing nets wreathe the Atlantic coast of the Iberian Peninsula, for the coastal waters off Western Europe are alive with fish. One of the most important sources of national wealth, the fishing industry of Portugal takes in three main fields of activity. The coastal fishery, of which sardines are by far the most important variety taken, also includes catches of tunny, anchovies, mackerel, and chinchards. Trawl fishing on the high seas for such species as whiting, pargo, and sea bream is mainly off the coast of Africa. Cod fishing, by a large modern fleet of Portuguese schooners and trawlers, is carried on in the Newfoundland Grand Banks and off the west coast of Greenland. Of lesser importance is the whaling carried on off the coast south of Lisbon and in the Azores.

Fishing is vital to Portugal both as a source of food and as raw material for a large canning industry. Tinned sardines and tunny are important in the list of exports from the small country; Portuguese sardines are found in markets all over the world. The little fishing villages that send their men out to sea are no less colorful than the hardy fishermen themselves in their traditional wool caps and striped sweaters. The sailing galleys resemble those of the early Phoenicians.

Figure 9-13   Cork trees. This hardy oak tolerates the stripping of its bark every ten years or so. A newly stripped cork forest presents a striking effect, for the red color of the inner bark makes the trees stand in stark contrast to the green grasslands surrounding them. (Courtesy of Ewing Galloway.)

Figure 9-14 Drying fish nets on the beach, Nazare, Portugal. (Courtesy of Trans World Airlines.)

The Basques and Galicians of northern Spain, who are famous for their fishing, are the only real seafarers of that country. A spare, mountainous land with many sheltering harbors and a sea rich in fish encouraged these northerners to take to the water. In fair weather or foul, Basque and Galician fishermen set out in their ketch-rigged boats to take the sardines, tunny, and other fish found in the coastal waters. Vigo, La Coruña, and Bermeo along the northwest and north shores are the leading fishing ports in Spain. Despite the relatively greater importance of fishing to the Portuguese economy than to that of Spain, the Spanish fishing fleet is the larger and the Spanish catch nearly twice as great as that of Portugal (866,500 metric tons as against 475,100).[2] Fish canning is important in both countries.

MINERALS

Iberia has notable mineral resources, most of them concentrated in Spain. The famous Rio Tinto deposits of the southwest have been mined for their copper since 1240 B.C. Huelva is the main outlet for these ores. Deposits of lead and silver exist. In the north between Santander and Bilbao is one of Europe's important iron reserves. Exported in considerable quantity, largely to the United Kingdom and Germany, the ore is also the basis for a small Spanish iron and steel industry. Coal, found in the northwest, is important for Spain. The deposits could support an expansion of iron smelting and fabrication, whereas at present, the Spanish steel mills generally use imported coal. Mercury is secured from the Almaden mines in south central Spain, and smaller de-

posits occur in several other regions. Sulfur, potash, and several of the alloy metals are also produced. Although mining has been carried on for centuries, and though the variety of Spanish minerals is large and the deposits substantial, the industry is still in its infancy.

Mining is a traditional activity in Portugal, yet the exploitation of mineral resources is relatively unimportant, and exploration and mapping of the deposits far from complete. Portugal does produce small quantities of coal, iron, kaolin, wolfram, tin, and manganese.

INDUSTRY

Manufacturing is not well developed in Iberia. There are, however, three areas of industrial concentration in Spain. One is in Barcelona, the center of a textile industry that was originally based on wool from the Meseta; another is an area of heavy industry around Bilbao; and at Madrid, there is a center of diversified manufacturing. Compared with the manufactures of northwest Europe, these industries are still small. Copper refining, food processing, some shipbuilding at Bilbao and at Barcelona, cotton textiles, a little silk manufacturing, some leather work, paper and cement, wine production, and handicrafts almost complete the list of Spanish manufactures. A recent development has been that of the chemical industries, particularly the production of nitrogenous fertilizer and superphosphates. Spain has latent possibilities for manufacturing. These include not only the resources noted but also water power, in which the country is estimated to have a greater potential than either Switzerland or Sweden.

Food processing, including fish canning, sugar refining, flour milling, and the production of olive oil, is an important part of Portuguese manufacture, although textiles dominate, employing 40 per cent of the people engaged in manufacturing. Lisbon is the center of this industry, which produces almost entirely for a home market. Handicrafts, such as embroideries, and the making of wine are widespread, the latter especially notable in the Douro River valley.

TRADE AND TRANSPORTATION

Iberia imports more than it exports. Foodstuffs, raw materials, machinery, and consumer goods are the major imports of both countries. Spain likewise brings in large quantities of nitrogenous fertilizer and phosphate rock for agricultural purposes. Among the exports of Portugal, cork, both in the raw and manufactured form, heads the list, normally accounting for one-sixth of the total export value. Wine and sardines rank next. Portugal is also an important producer of naval stores and ranks second, though far behind the United States, in the export of rosin and turpentine. The economy of Spain relies heavily on foreign trade, and Spain's exports are ten times as great as those of Portugal.

Though the railroad system of Spain and Portugal connect with each other, transportation is inadequate and not up to modern standards in either country. Roads have been improved and extended, and commercial air transport has steadily increased since World War II. Because of their geographical position, Lisbon and the Azores are of great importance in international air commerce, Lisbon serving as a major European air terminal and transit point; fifteen foreign lines, including two American, make regularly scheduled stops in that city. The Azores airport on Santa Maria Island is a stopover on mid-Atlantic crossings.

TOWNS AND CITIES

Iberia is a land of many small agglomerations. Along the coasts of Portugal and the Bay of Biscay these take form of numerous picturesque fishing villages, where nets, stretched for drying and repairing, fish-drying racks, and many small fishing craft dominate the scene. On the Meseta, as well as elsewhere in the interior, the agricultural villages are scattered. Often dull in appearance, and frequently some distance from good highways, the villages reflect the depressed economic condition of their inhabitants.

Madrid and Barcelona are the two largest cities of Spain and of the peninsula, Madrid having a population of about 2 million, Barcelona somewhat over 1½ million. Portugal's two largest cities, Lisbon and Oporto, are considerably smaller, with populations of approximately 800,000 and 285,000. Spain has a number of other large cities, including Valencia, which has well over 500,000 people, and Seville with more than 425,000.

Landlocked Madrid owes its size and importance to the fact that it is the political center of the nation. It is situated centrally on the plateau nearly equidistant from the Mediterranean Sea, the Bay of Biscay, and the Atlantic Ocean. But it occupies a relatively barren area, and the city is handicapped by an inadequate water supply. Madrid is relatively young—younger than such capital cities as Rome, London, and Paris. It is nevertheless a thousand years old, and has links that tie it to the earliest days of settlement in the Western Hemisphere. It was not until Philip II made it his capital, in 1560, that the city began to attain importance. Previous to that it had stood an isolated, lonely village in the midst of the treeless, sun-baked tableland. Today Madrid is a modern city with many industries and the hub of the Spanish transportation system.

Barcelona, however, is Spain's most important economic center. It is Spain's great port—the gateway on the northeast coast for the export of cork, wine, olives, and citrus—cosmopolitan, and exuding an atmosphere of world importance; and it is Spain's most important industrial city. Situated on a good harbor, and in one of the best agricultural areas in Europe, the city has a favorable location for import-export trade. Large textile manufactures —cotton, linen, and wool—have been developed.

Valencia and Seville, the third and fourth largest cities respectively, are old, historic centers, located in irrigated areas and surrounded by citrus orchards and

Figure 9-15 Lisbon, Portugal. The photograph shows the city's main avenue, Praca dos Resturandares, and some of the beautiful mosaics that decorate many of Lisbon's plazas and streets. (Courtesy of Pan American Airlines.)

gardens. Here notable churches, narrow streets, historic walls, and ancient buildings attract the tourist trade. Various industries have also been established.

Bilbao, the principal northern port, lies in a valley surrounded by high and fairly steep hills. Railroads enter the city through tunnels. Iron mines not far from the city supply the chief item of export. Modern steel mills, fueled with imported coal, are among the heavy industries that have developed here and in nearby Santander.

Lisbon and Oporto, the chief urban centers in Portugal, are both ports situated on the Atlantic coast at the mouth of a great river, Lisbon on the Tagus, Oporto on the Duero. Lisbon, the capital, is one of the principal commercial centers of the world, having the best harbor on the Iberian Peninsula and one of the finest in Europe. It ranks as an important center for transshipment and entrepôt activities, and is one of the leading airports on the globe. Industry has developed, but most of the manufactures are consumer goods. It is also an important tourist center. Oporto, the second city and second port, is noted chiefly for its wines, although the city manufactures numerous other items.

OVERSEAS TERRITORIES

Portugal is the last of the European colonial powers to retain most of its large overseas empire. Twenty-three times greater in size than little Portugal, the colonial territories once constituted a domain that was the fourth largest foreign empire in the world. Only Britain, France, and Belgium had greater holdings within the twentieth century. The Azores Archipelago, consisting of nine islands with a total area of 888 square miles, is situated in the Atlantic some 800 miles due west of Portugal. The island of Madeira, approximately 600 miles to the southwest of the Continent, is 308 square miles in area. For political and administrative purposes these islands are treated as integral parts of continental Portugal. The status of the other colonies was changed, after World War II, to Overseas Provinces of Portugal. The most important of these are Mozambique and Angola in Africa. Of her once vast holdings in the Far East, only part of the East Indian island of Timor and Macao in China remain. The population of the colonies exceeds that of Portugal, approximating 13 million as compared with the 9 million for the European nation. Many people besides the Portuguese speak the Portuguese tongue. It is the official language not only throughout the colonial territories but also in Brazil, a former colony, where about 70 million people show this former tie with the little Iberian state.

The colonies of Spain, only one-sixth the size of those of Portugal, are inconsiderable as compared with those of her neighbor. What remains of a worldwide empire is found in small areas scattered along the coast of Africa from the northwest to the Gulf of Guinea. The total population is small, and except for the island of Fernando Po, which exports cacao, the colonies' trade is insignificant. All of Spanish Morocco, except Ceuta and Melilla, became a part of the Kingdom of Morocco upon the independence of the French territory. The Spanish Sahara (Rio de Oro) and Ifni remain Spanish although both are claimed by Morocco as rightfully hers. Ifni, tiny enclave that it is, is a thorn in Morocco's side.

ITALY

Italy has a past of brilliant accomplishment, a history that is perhaps unique in majesty. From Italy came a progression of stirring accomplishments—the reach of Imperial Rome, the might and power of the Roman Catholic Church, the genius of the Renaissance. Three times Italy has ruled the world, once in government, once in religion, once in art.

This was a long time ago, before and up into the Middle Ages. However, as the Mediterranean ceased to be a vital link in the trade between Europe and the Orient, as the Middle Ages passed into the modern era, as the industrial revolution introduced big machines and the factory system with their enormous capacity for processing materials, and as political power became concomitant with great space endowed with large resources, plenty of land, and industrial might, Italy could not hold her place.

During the first fifty years of the twentieth century the economy of Italy merely limped along. Under Mussolini the government attempted to spur production and inject vigor into the country's economic activities, but a philosophy and course of military aggression turned the economy away from trends that might have benefited the people.

The Italians had participated in the scramble for possessions in Africa, but they entered late and were thwarted in part by the stronger European states, so that although territorially the African acquisitions were large—greater in area than the peninsular kingdom itself—they were marginal in the extreme, and costly and difficult to develop. Included were Libya and Italian Somaliland, Eritrea, and for a brief period, Ethiopia.

The colonies were looked upon and used as outlets for surplus population. But the Italian overseas possessions were not rich territories, offering unbounded opportunities and treasure and tropical products, like the empires of the Iberian states and those of the countries of northwest Europe. The Italian colonies had not much more than prestige value (up until the middle of the twentieth century, when oil was discovered in Libya, by which time they were lost to Italy).

For many decades overpopulation and underproduction have been, as in the rest of the Mediterranean countries, the foremost problems of the Italians. The pressure generated by too many people on too little land has been the plague of Italy. The land itself is overworked and rocky and too dry during too much of the year; the areas of greatest water need have the least water, and resources are meager or have long awaited an advanced technology for development. As long as populations were not large, and industry was handicraft and did not make the huge demands for raw materials and fuels that modern industry makes, Italy did not feel this pressure too much; and the pressure has always been partially relieved through emigration.

Migration will continue to offer an outlet for some of Italy's people because large numbers emigrate every year. In fact, more people leave Italy for other lands than go from any other West European nation. Predictions are that between 1955 and 1970 about 2¼ million Italians will leave their homeland, a loss that will aggregate more than that from the next four highest countries. The majority of the emigrants from Mediterranean lands go to Latin America, but a considerable stream, especially from Italy, flows into France, Switzerland, Belgium, and other North European states.[3]

Beginning about 1950, however, Italy entered a period of economic resurgence. So strong has been the recovery that Italy has already been carried into the front ranks of industrial nations. Products bearing the label "Made in Italy" are competing for markets all over the globe. This record-breaking industrial development and economic growth has been assisted by loans to industry from the United States and by membership in the Common Market. Living standards have risen, and in the last ten years Italian labor productivity has increased faster than that of any other West European country and three times as fast as in the United States. The gross national product has risen by nearly 6 per cent annually—one of the highest rates in the world. Since 1952, industrial output has doubled.

Despite this progress, industry has not freed Italy of all of her population problems. The greatest still remain: There are two Italys, a North and a South, the one well endowed and developed, the other (the South) underdeveloped and poverty-plagued. Most of the industry is located in the North, much of it within the small triangle of land that lies between Milan, Turin, and Genoa; in the Po Valley is found the bulk of the fertile farmland of the country. The vast gap in wealth and development between the two areas is sharp and striking. While income levels in the North compare quite favorably with those of Northern Europe, those in the South are among the lowest on the Continent. Only other Mediterranean and near-Mediterranean lands can show a comparable poverty.

The farther south one goes along the peninsula the less industrialized the country becomes; fertile plains are fragmental along the coasts; the interior is rugged and difficult. About midway between Naples and Rome a line could be drawn that would designate the approximate beginning of the underdeveloped south—the Mezzogiorno.[4] Naples lies within it, and Sardinia and Sicily are also included; 40

---

[3] J. F. Dewhurst, John O. Coppock, P. L. Yates, and Associates, *Europe's Needs and Resources,* The Twentieth Century Fund, New York, 1961, pp. 46–48.

[4] Called the Mezzogiorno after the Cassa per Il Mezzogiorno (Southern Italy Development Fund).

per cent of the Italian population live here, and they account for about 20 per cent of the national output; nearly all of the 1⅓ million unemployed are found here. Unemployment and underemployment are critical.

This imbalance between North and South was recognized as serious at least 50 years ago, and it probably has had its origins far back in history. The land problem was due in large part to the prevalence of landed estates on which extensive holdings were not even worked, while all around was a landless peasantry and worse, a tenant peasantry that could not even get land to cultivate. This was the first problem attacked. By the 1950s the demand for economic betterment—and equilibrium between North and South—became so insistent that the government had to act quickly. One of the four major objectives of a 10-year-development program, initiated in 1955, was to decrease the imbalance between the North and South, and to raise living standards in Southern Italy. Land reforms have been a large part of this effort. Land has been distributed and irrigation developed. One of the greatest public works undertaken in Italy's program in the South is the Campano Aqueduct, begun in 1951 and completed in 1959, which brings water out of the Apennines to the large plain of Campania, where lie Naples and Salerno, supplying the entire area with water for drinking, irrigation, and power. Included also are attempts to reduce unemployment by two-thirds, to do away with underemployment, and to open up opportunities for youth as they emerge into the labor market. Labor is one of Italy's greatest attractions to investment; she has a pool of unskilled but trainable manpower. Yet labor is one of her greatest problems because so many are unemployed.

Another project involves the building of a system of modern highways to and in the South, the hope being that good roads will transform the area into a tourist mecca. There is much in the South to attract tourists, including the natural beauty and volcanic wonders of the area and the ancient cities of Magna Graecia, the remnants of Greek colonies that were established in Southern Italy. Some of the ruins of these old cities are now being excavated.

Three *autostradas* will be opened into the South. One will follow the west coast from Salerno to Reggio Calabria. This will be an extension of the Autostrada del Sole that connects Milan and Salerno by way of Bologna, Florence, Rome, and Naples. A second highway runs along the east coast from Bologna to Bari, and the third will cross the peninsula to connect Naples and Bari. The road southward from Salerno follows the way of the road built by the Romans in the second century B.C. from Capua to Reggio Calabria. Milestones of the ancient Roman roads have been uncovered during construction of the new one. Work on this system of highways was begun in January, 1962.

Another immense project that will facilitate movement between Italy and Western Europe and that should make travel by car into Italy most attractive is the joint construction by Italy and France of the Mont Blanc tunnel. Seven and a half miles long, it pierces a hole through one of Europe's highest mountains, and it will shorten the driving distance between Paris and Rome by 125 miles. The Italians began tunneling on May 14, the French on January 8, 1959, and they met at the "hole-through" point on August 14, 1962, 3⅛ miles from either end at a depth of 7,400 feet under the mountain's rugged peak. The tunnel was ready for traffic in the spring of 1964.

The Italian state-owned railroads con-

Figure 9-16 a. Industrial production; b. system of autostradas (highways) for the rejuvenation of the South; c. semiautonomous regions of Italy: Regions 1 through 4 are already autonomous; the possible autonomous status of Friuli-Venezia Giulia (Region 5) is under consideration.

nect all major centers, and ferryboats are employed for the railway crossing of the Strait of Messina between the peninsula and Sicily. Since these boats transport up to 1,500 railroad cars daily, the water barrier between the island and mainland is no longer a bottleneck to traffic. Highways between the largest cities are paved and in good condition. Passenger bus service is excellent, even when compared with that of the United States. Since 1948 both trucking and air transport have shown a marked increase.

According to tonnage, Italy ranks among the first ten maritime nations of the world. Although commercial shipping was almost totally destroyed during World War II, it has made a remarkable recovery in the postwar period. Italians have drawn sunken vessels from the bottom of the sea, reconditioned ships returned by the Allies, and built and bought new tonnage. As a result, the Italian merchant marine has been brought up to about 90 per cent of its prewar level. Income from its shipping partly supplies Italy with funds to help overcome its unfavorable balance of trade. The construction and operation of fine, large ocean liners provides employment and helps to attract tourists to the country.

INDUSTRY

Industry has now replaced agriculture as the dominant sector of the Italian economy. It accounts for one-half of the total income of the country. Agriculture, while remaining important, accounts for only one-fifth of the national income, and employs one-third of the labor force.

Leading the industrial products of Italy are machines, which range from automobiles and locomotives to sewing machines and precision instruments. Among the products that have had a recent large development are chemicals, steel, and machines (cited above). Textiles are one of the traditional manufactures from the past. As Table 9-2 shows, the making of textiles also has expanded but to a lesser degree than other manufactures.

Although most of the Italian factories are small, and often family enterprises, Italy has some of the largest industrial companies in Europe, for example, Fiat (automobiles), Montecatini (chemicals), SNIA Viscosa (synthetic fibers), Pirelli

Figure 9-17 Marble cutting in the famous quarries of Carrara, Italy. (Courtesy of Italian Information Center.)

(tires), Olivetti (office machines). The government is an important stockholder in industry: IRI, the government's giant holding company, controls about 30 per

TABLE 9-2 ITALIAN INDUSTRY

Industry	Total increase, %, 1950–1960	Total increase, %, 1959–1960
Total	133	15
All manufactures	135	16
Chemicals	270	17
Basic metals	221	24
Metal products	140	21
Food and beverages	59	6
Textiles	32	9
Mining	161	5

Source: "Facts on Italy for American Businessmen," published by the Chase Manhattan Bank, p. 2.

cent of Italy's industrial capital, including much of the steel, machinery, shipping, and electrical power; ENI is a huge, government-owned oil and gas complex.

Industry works under handicaps in Italy, however, in that the industrial resources are meager. Most of the raw materials and fuels (aside from electricity generated on water in the North and volcanic power in the South and Central parts) must be imported. Genoa is Italy's great port of the North through which the articles of trade flow to and from the industrial Po Valley across the densest network of roads and railroads in Italy. Italy's long coastline favors shipping, although not all portions of the coast are blessed with protected harbors: The east coast is remarkably straight and practically devoid of harbors. Imports, in order of importance, include food (15 per cent of the total), mineral fuels (14 per cent), textile fibers and waste, base metals, and machinery and chemicals. Machinery (13 per cent), textiles (12 per cent), transport equipment, fruits and vegetables, and shoes and clothing lead as exports. The value of imports generally exceeds that of the exports, but the difference is paid for by invisible earnings—mainly tourism and remittances from abroad.

PHYSICAL SETTING

REGIONS Italy falls with apparent simplicity into four natural regions. To the north is the Alpine border where the boundary in general follows the crest line. Though the Alps Mountains seems to isolate Italy from the rest of the Continent, the Italian ranges actually provide the natural transit zone between Continental Europe and the Mediterranean. In early days, passes like the Simplon, Great and Little St. Bernard, St. Gotthard, and Bren-

ner, situated at the heads of valleys, permitted ranges to be crossed in spite of ice and snow. Today, railroads and tunnels have almost eliminated the Alps as a barrier.

A number of long narrow lakes are interspersed along the frontal zone where the mountains drop to the plains. Occupying valleys deepened by the action of glacial ice and dammed by terminal moraines that impounded the waters, the lakes are of great economic significance to Italy for the development of power and irrigation, especially for the agricultural and industrial Po Valley. The Italian lake district is milder than the plains below, for it lies on the warm, sunny, south-facing slopes. Foehn winds that descend from the higher Alps also have a tempering effect. This region is famous as a winter and tourist resort.

The Po Valley is the northern end of the Adriatic depression that has been filled with alluvium carried down the mountainsides by tributaries of the Po and other streams. An actively building delta is extending the plain still farther toward the east, noticeably encroaching upon the quiet waters of the sea. Fertile soil and level land, combined with a favorable climate and water for irrigation, make this one of the great agricultural plains of the world. Though the political center lies to the south in Rome, the economic core is focalized on these plains in the north.

The Apennine Mountains, running the length of the narrow peninsula, constitute, with Sicily, the third natural region. The surface configuration is one of a central folded mountain backbone bordered by marginal plains. A zone of active and quiescent volcanoes extends along the western coast from Rome southward through Sicily. In the north, the Apennines are considerably lower than the Maritime Alps with which they merge.

Farther south, however, the peninsular ranges become higher and more rugged, with elevations in the central portions reaching over 9,500 feet. As a whole, the Apennine country is difficult of access. Railroads are few and have been costly to construct. Paved highways, built during the Fascist regime, cross the mountains to connect major cities. Though excellent, they are narrow and breathtaking, with many curves.

Slowly and transitionally, geology and geography change the mountain scene from north to south. Where the northern Apennines meet the Mediterranean along the Ligurian coast, steep slopes rise high and shut out the cold winds from the north. Here a narrow strip of land, known as the Italian Riviera, edges the sea. As a resort center, it is a close competitor with the Riviera in France, just across the border.

From the northern mountains, which are relatively green and well covered with trees, with distance southward the hills become barer, the soil grayer, the olive more prominent. Throughout, vines climb hills from base to summit, or run on trellises between trees on the plains. Close-up views in the bordering lowlands reveal hedges of big-lobed cacti growing beside low stone walls, pastel houses—yellow, blue, green, pink—making picturelike compositions in their carefully tended settings, and white oxen, along with other beasts of burden, drawing plows, preparing the land for cropping or fallowing.

The Apennines, with their jutting spurs and foothills, occupy most of the peninsula, leaving few plains. Of importance, however, are the three fertile but isolated lowlands along the western shore, each centered by a commanding city. First, there is Tuscany in the valley of the Arno with Florence, the art center of all Italy, in a strategic position at a major pass through the Apennines. Then there is Lazio in the Tiber Valley focusing on the ancient city of Rome. Third is Campania, to the south, spread around the beautiful Bay of Naples, on which the great port city of the same name is situated. The lowlands of the east are of lesser importance than those of the west, though the largest of the peninsular plains is found here, occupying the heel of the boot of Italy and extending northward along the shore to the Gargano peninsula. Other areas of level land are small and separated from each other by projections of rough country.

As a result of poor drainage, swamps have infested the plains with malaria so that their development has been retarded. Though an extensive drainage and disease-extermination program was begun under Mussolini, it was not until World War II that malaria was appreciably brought under control by the systematic use of DDT by American troops. More was done to eradicate malaria at this time than at any previous period. There is much land still to be reclaimed, however, and malaria is by no means conquered.

AGRICULTURE

Twenty-five per cent of the cultivated land is planted in wheat, a crop of particular importance in Italian agriculture. Grown throughout all of Italy, this typically Mediterranean grain is produced most heavily in the Po Basin, the breadbasket of the country. This region is dominated by cereals, with wheat leading and corn ranking second in importance. The upper valley of the Po, where Alpine streams provide water for irrigation, is the center of rice production. Grapes for wine are prominent as well as the two industrial crops of sugar beets and hemp. The olive, scattered throughout most of Italy, is not

Figure 9-18   The valleys of northern Italy are intensively farmed. The headwaters of the river shown in this picture are in the Alps. The river is a tributary of the Po.

found in the north where cold winters inhibit its growth.

Stock raising and dairying are better developed in the North than elsewhere, and a high proportion of the land is in improved pasture and fodder crops. These extend into the mountains, where agriculture takes on an Alpine character. In favorable parts of the northern foothills wheat is grown, but in general rye replaces the wheat, corn, and rice of the lowlands. Potatoes are also a major crop, and grapes are important in most parts of Italy.

Mediterranean Italy is characterized by two types of agriculture that might be classed as horticultural or nonhorticultural, depending on the intensity of the cultivation and the variety of crops raised. In the former type, intensive methods of land use, including irrigation, terracing, high fertilization, and triple-cropping, produce fruits and vegetables in a garden type of agriculture. Here grapes attain their highest perfection. Olives are especially important in the heel of the boot in Southern Italy. Lemons, oranges, and peaches, along with some vegetables, move from these lands of intensive husbandry into the markets of Northern Europe. Sicily is the center of citrus production, especially lemons, though lemon culture extends along the western side of the peninsula to Naples, and oranges grow almost as far north as Rome. In the Mediterranean regions where the less intensive type of agriculture is practiced, five crops predominate, wheat, oats, grapes, olives, and beans. Few cattle are reared in the Mediterranean lands; because of sparse and poor grasses, sheep and goats typically replace the larger animals.

Sardinia, though a part of Italy, is remote from the rest of Italian life. Rugged, deforested, and eroded, it is a spare land. Although Sardinia produces famous wines and cork and has some areas of intensive cultivation, it is principally a pastoral land. Animals, especially sheep, are grazed on the plateau and mountain country which occupies seven-tenths of the island. The inhabitants are known for their hardy endurance and interest in livestock.

CITIES

The world has no cities more famed than those of Italy. Every year millions of dollars of income flow into the country as tourists and religious pilgrims pour in to enjoy the beauty of the Italian countryside, the delight of her agreeable climate, and perhaps most of all, the splendor of her historic cities.

No city in the world puts on a better spectacle than Rome. From ancient days it has had a reputation for circuses, celebrations, coronations, fêtes and fairs, torchlight parades, and the corteges of emperors and popes. Because the Vatican, the residence of the popes, is here, the millions of the world's Roman Catholics look upon Rome as the "Holy City." It is well known for its historic and religious associations, its art treasures and its ruins, and its educational institutions. It is first of all a cultural city, but as the capital of Italy and of the Catholic Church it is also political.

Although the Eternal City has passed through many changes of fortune, it has never ceased to be important. Even during the fourteenth century, when malaria reduced the population to around 17,000 persons, and when Venice, Florence, Pisa, and Naples were eclipsing it with their international trade and their activity as centers of the Renaissance movement, Rome survived on her "heritage of the Caesars and the Apostles." In this modern day it ranks also as an important manufacturing center for such things as precision instruments, electronics, pharmaceuticals, food processing, printing, and communications equipment. Rome is situated along the Tiber River on its seven hills; and it occupies a central position on the western side of the peninsula, dominating Tuscany.

About 125 miles southward lies Naples, the only large and industrial city in the Mezzogiorno and Italy's second port. It circles around a magnificent bay that gives Naples one of the most beautiful sites in the world, sweeping from the coastal plain up slopes to lofty heights. As a backdrop stands Mt. Vesuvius across the bay from the city—at some periods quiescent, at times sending curls of smoke into the air as reminders of the potential violence of this destructive volcano. The slopes of the mountain are green, and cultivation and houses nestle at the base and even climb some distance upward. Although temporarily driven away by threatened or actual eruption, people soon move back to Vesuvius, seemingly oblivious of the potential danger, as the ruins of Pompeii, bleached and deserted, testify. The whole southern portion of the peninsula is an unstable area: earthquakes, at times strong enough to devastate entire villages, are frequent; volcanism produces Europe's greatest volcanoes; in addition to Vesuvius, there are Mt. Etna in Sicily and Stromboli, north of Sicily about equidistant from the island and the peninsula. Although destructive, this prevalence of volcanic activity has several beneficial effects: volcanic ash and disintegrated lava produce very fertile soils, and modern technology has permitted the volcanic gases to be harnessed for power production; sulfur occurs, and is one of Italy's valuable minerals.

Because of these and other tourist attractions, Naples is an important passenger port. It also handles several million tons of goods annually, and has developed such industries as chemicals and plants for processing food.

Around it spreads the fertile Campania with its intensively farmed soils that produce citrus, vegetables, and some cereals, and that would produce more if the land could be irrigated. But throughout most of the Campania water must be carried to water the plants. The Campania marks the beginning of the Mezzogiorno: it spreads eastward into the mountains, blends southward with Calabria. Population densities are 910 persons per square mile—

greater than Lombardy with its great industrial cities of Milan and Turin, greater than Liguria that holds Genoa. But the Campania does not have the industry of these two regions, and as the people from the surrounding country have flowed into Naples seeking employment, they have contributed more to its misery than to its upbuilding. Naples, like a jewel in its setting, shows greater contrasts than possibly any city in the Western world, contrasts between wealth and beauty on the one hand and poverty, filth, and misery on the other. Jean Gottmann sensitively characterizes this quality of Naples when he writes: "There is something momentous and tragic in the opposition between the great reputation of Naples and the reality of its slums. Every large city has its blighted sections, but the proportion here is frightening."[5]

[5] Jean Gottmann, *A Geography of Europe,* 3d ed., Holt, Rinehart and Winston, New York, 1961, pp. 588–589.

Figure 9-19   Naples, Italy, showing a part of the bay and Mt. Vesuvius, which forms a backdrop of impressive grandeur. Mountain and bay make the situation of Naples one of the most beautiful in the world. (Courtesy of Trans World Airlines.)

Genoa is the great port of the North, Italy's greatest port, and the second port of the Mediterranean ranking after Marseilles. Even as it tried to challenge Venice for leadership in the Middle Ages, so it has attempted to rival Marseilles in the modern era. It is a great port, serving as outlet not only to the industrial triangle of the Italian North—of which it is the "maritime tip"[6]—but also for some of the trade of Switzerland; the entire Po Valley and much of the Alps are its hinterland. There is little space, however, on which industry can develop because Genoa clings to the coast in a narrow strip of plain that actually plays out in places as the Italian Alps approach the shore. Houses and buildings mount the hills and ascend to the top of the mountains that rise within the city and look two ways—out toward the harbor and the Mediterranean, and northward toward straggling sectors of the city that have grown up on the far side of the peaks. The heights are attained by funicular cabs that are pulled by cable up the seemingly perpendicular slopes. It is a colorful city. The stone home of Columbus's boyhood still stands at the foot of the ramp leading to a great and ancient gateway, while in contrast to the small dwelling a modern skyscraper rises many stories in height. The atmosphere of the whole city seems to be of the sea, or of the mountains.

Milan, second city in size, is the financial and economic center of Italy. Its stock exchange exceeds that of Rome in importance, and the head offices of most of the large industrial firms are found here. The products of its factories are varied, ranging from silk and other textiles, machinery that varies from those used in agriculture to airplane engines, electrical equipment and precision instruments, basic steel and copper, pottery, drugs, and the like. Industrial though it is, Milan is a city with great cultural traditions and reputation. The original painting of Leonardo da Vinci's "The Last Supper" is found on the walls of an old Milan abbey; its cathedral is one of the masterpieces of world architecture; La Scala is of world repute for its opera. In its immediate vicinity are many industrial centers satellitic to Milan. It is a "tense" city, and the mood of Milan is reflected sensitively in Italian politics.

Venice dominates the eastern sector of the Po plain. It is a city built on islands, and its channels of traffic are canals. The Grand Canal is the throughway of the city, the only "street" along which "buses" run (which are launches, in Venice, that zigzag from side to side of the canal to pick up and let off passengers); gondolas are the taxis of this remarkable city.

The city had its beginnings on the islands of a lagoon when refugees from barbarian invasions of the mainland chose this site for their village in the fifth century A.D. because it was protected by the surrounding water. The first doge was elected in 697. The settlement grew and spread onto the mainland along the Adige River, and by the beginning of the thirteenth century had become one of the "queens" of the Mediterranean, with an empire that included Crete, islands in the Ionian Sea, Epirus in Greece, and other sectors in the eastern Mediterranean. With the defeat of Genoa in 1381, Venice achieved a monopoly over Mediterranean traffic, and for the next century was the center of commerce for most of Europe. It spread its control over Northern Italy, the trans-Alpine trails, and along the Adriatic coast.

The decline of Venice came with the decline of the Mediterranean Sea as a major route of traffic and trade. As ships began to ply the waters around the Cape of Good Hope, the brilliant period of financial and commercial control faded,

[6] *Ibid.,* p. 579.

Figure 9-20 A narrow side canal feeds toward the Grand Canal, Venice, Italy. Along the base of the buildings, a portion of the foundations affected by the water is exposed at lower tide. The gondolas are the taxicabs of the city. (Courtesy of Pan American Airlines.)

population dropped by half, and Venice became largely a tourist center.

It remains a tourist center today, but it is also an important port, at times rivaling Naples for second place; industry (especially glass manufacture) and handicrafts have grown up in the outskirts to feed the tourist trade. There is much to attract travelers to the city. Foremost are the canals, which so intricately interlace the city that all movement, except foot travel, moves on the water. The buildings drop directly into the water, fronting the canals; gondolas, launches, and other small craft tie up along the edges; bridges arch and cross over the canals. So famed is Italian Venice for its beauty as a canal city that other cities of the European North one after another characterize themselves as the "Venice of the North."

However, the canals of Venice are slowly eating into the heart of this unique city. The salt waterways that divide Venice into about 180 little islands are corroding the foundations of hundreds of priceless palaces and churches. Lapping incessantly against the bases of the buildings that flank the canals, the water wears tiny furrows which gradually widen into fissures and then become dangerous cracks. In some buildings the decay has already advanced too far to save the structures. Strengthening the foundations is a slow, difficult work. But it has been begun, and it is to be hoped that the efforts will proceed fast enough to prevent Venice from falling and sinking into the sea.

Florence on the Arno—practically an art museum—Pisa, and Trieste, the outlet for Central Europe and a port of the Balkans, are among the many other significant and lovely cities of Italy.

THE ITALIAN DOMAIN

Following World War II, the Italian overseas possessions were taken away; the territory of the country is today confined to the peninsula and the offshore islands, including Sicily and Sardinia. Of the large colonies in North Africa—Libya, Eritrea, and Somalia—only Somalia remained for a time under Italian administration. Italy held it as a United Nations trusteeship until it gained independence in 1960, at which time Italian Somaliland united with British Somaliland to form Somalia. The port of Trieste remains with Italy, but adjacent Istria has become a part of Yugoslavia as have also the Dalmatian coastal islands of Cherso, Lussino, and Lagosta, and the city of Zara on the mainland, all formerly Italian territory. Most of the Italians in these places were repatriated to Italy. To Albania went the island of Saseno, small but strategic, in the narrows that control the entrance to the Adriatic Sea; to the Greeks, the Dodecanese Islands in the Aegean; and to China, Italy's former concession in Tientsin.

It is possible that Trieste will be accorded a status of greater autonomy within the Italian political structure. In the summer of 1962 a bill in the Chamber of Deputies proposed that a new region on the border between Italy and Yugoslavia, to be known as the Region of Friuli–Venezia Giulia and composed of the provinces of Trieste, Gorizia, and Udine, should be constituted. It would establish the fifth "region with special statute," with the same type of powers that have been accorded to the already existing semi-autonomous island regions of Sicily and Sardinia, and the Alpine border regions of Trentino–Alto Adige (or the South Tyrol), and Val d'Aosta. These "regions" exercise jurisdiction over such local matters as education, public works, and tourism. The areas that have been set up as regions have ethnically mixed populations, and the regional autonomy is designed to safeguard minority rights.

GREECE

Greece is situated at the tip of the Balkan Peninsula. Washed on three sides by seas and indented by many inlets and bays, it has one of the longest coastlines in Europe. Across the northern frontier lie Albania, Yugoslavia, Bulgaria, and to the east, Turkey.

PHYSICAL SETTING

A rugged mountain country, with four-fifths of the area made up of mountain chains and spurs, Greece is probably the most barren and sterile among the Mediterranean lands. The Pindus, a series of long, continuous ranges, extend southeast through central Greece. East of the Pindus the topography is one of basins separated by southeast- and eastward-trending spurs. The principal plains are in the eastern portions and in central and western Macedonia.

Northern Greece is very mountainous, the central section less so. Here are located Athens and Piraeus, the main seaport. To the south lies the Peloponnesus, separated from the mainland by the Corinth Canal, which was cut through a narrow isthmus to sever the former peninsula from the Continent. The many islands in the bordering seas make up nearly one-sixth of the total area of Greece.

The Mediterranean climate predominates throughout Greece, though prevailing winds, altitude, and continental location cause differences from place to place. The south and east are drier and warmer, generally, than the north and west. The lowlands are warmer and have less rain than the uplands. Corfu, for example, off the extreme northwestern tip of Greece, has 47.6 inches of well-dis-

Figure 9-21 Windmill on the Greek island of Mykinos in the Aegean Sea. (Courtesy of Pan American Airlines.)

tributed annual rainfall, whereas Athens, in the southeast, averages 15.4 inches and shows a marked summer dry period. Salonika, on the other hand, receives 21.5 inches of precipitation, fairly well distributed throughout the year, though the three summer months get somewhat less than the others. Large parts of Greece have averages that correspond to those of Athens.

PROBLEMS OF LAND AND POPULATION

On an area about the size of North Carolina live 8.3 million people trying to eke a living from the land. Although only 15 per cent of Greece is cultivated, about one-half of the population is classed as rural. As in Italy, overpopulation and under-employment have been the foremost domestic problems. The per capita income is one of the lowest in Europe, while at the same time living costs are phenomenally high.

Other difficulties face Greece. Mountain barriers isolate one small plains region from another, particularly in the southern part of the country. Of the cultivated area, more than 60 per cent is over 750 feet above sea level with the result that most of the land is steep, rocky, and cut by gullies. The holdings of the Greek farmer are small and fragmented.[7] On well-drained plains, the land is frequently divided into many small units, each peasant holding several of these plots scattered throughout the cultivated area. Although fertile, the lower lands are generally poorly drained.

American economic aid has done much to help the Greeks with problems of land reclamation, drainage, erosion, flood control, irrigation, and soil conservation. Spectacular results have been attained in the reclamation of alkali lands through rice production. Thousands of acres of such areas, which have been considered useless since before the time of Christ, are being sweetened by the steady flow of fresh river water poured in to irrigate the grain. It is expected that within a few years the soils will be sufficiently cleansed to permit the raising of other crops such as wheat and cotton. Greece is a large importer of rice, but it is presumed that the rice produced on these reclamation projects will meet its needs. Many swamps and lakes have been drained and large areas provided, for the first time, with irrigation through the drilling of new wells and the channeling of rivers which for centuries have drained off, unused, into the seas.

AGRICULTURE

Agriculture remains the backbone of the Greek economy. The main crops, produced in valleys that nestle between or among mountains, are tobacco, wheat, grapes, and olives.

[7] Hectares per farm family in 1900 averaged 10.1; in 1950, 7.3.

Tobacco, making up over 40 per cent of the Greek exports, provides Greece with its leading trade item. In spite of its importance, the growing of tobacco is on a modest scale. Farms are small and the soils in the tobacco area probably the poorest of the cultivated lands in Greece. Greek tobacco is classed as Oriental. Interestingly enough, Macedonia and Thrace, the major areas of tobacco production, are those that were settled by Greeks repatriated, between 1907 and 1928 from Turkey, where they had learned the skill of growing this demanding crop. It is used generally as a blend because of the distinctive aroma. The Oriental tobacco produced in Greece is the highest quality grown in the world. Tobacco represents 13½ per cent of the value of Greek agricultural products.

Cereals, including wheat, corn, barley, oats, and rice, are the most basic and widespread of all crops. Potatoes, pulses, olives, fruits, including citrus fruit and grapes, nuts, and cotton also rank high. As in other Mediterranean lands, the vine is extensively cultivated and provides a money crop, many of the Greek grapes being dried and exported as currants and raisins. Together they make up nearly 15 per cent of the export value.

Greece occupies fourth place in the production of olive oil.[8] Though slow in growth, requiring fifteen to twenty years to mature, the olive is a sturdy plant that lives and produces for centuries. Spreading from Albania southward through the Peloponnesus and north to the Macedonian coast, olive culture extends eastward to within 50 miles of the Dardanelles. Olive and other oils make up 6 per cent of Greek exports and rank third in export value.

[8] *Statistical Yearbook, 1961,* United Nations, New York, 1962.

RESOURCES AND INDUSTRY

MINERALS Beneath the bare and rocky hills of Greece are minerals which, if properly developed, can contribute much toward national solvency and prosperity. Although not rich in natural resources as compared with many countries, Greece can claim minerals as one of her few assets. Fourteen basic minerals, in quantities and qualities worth mining, are known to exist. They include, among others, iron, lead, zinc, lignite, magnesite, chromite, manganese, bauxite, and emery.

One resource, virtually untouched until recent years, is lignite, the single most important development in the mining field. The largest reserve is that of the Ptolemais field in Macedonia, about 26 miles from the Yugoslav border. These lignite mines have been termed the fuel bin of the nation; they feed practically all the powerhouses. Another significant undertaking has been the revival of the extraction of chromite at Domokos in central Greece.

Near Lavrion, at the tip of the peninsula of Attica, important deposits of zinc and lead, yielding by-products of silver and iron pyrites, are being worked. This is the site of the famous silver mines that, over 2,000 years ago, supplied Athens with wealth. North and south of the city are located the two mountains, Pentelicus and Hymettus, from which were quarried the marble for the Greek buildings and statues.

Though Greek rehabilitation has been slow, industry produces electricity, textiles, metals (bauxite and copper manufactures), chemicals, foodstuffs and brewed goods, cigarettes, and leather. The Athens-Piraeus district is the major industrial area. Textiles and food processing are the two principal manufacturing industries, accounting for nearly 50 per cent of the total industrial product. Despite the fact that both a good grade of domestic raw cotton and an abundant labor supply are available to the textile manufacturers in Greece, the industry is poorly equipped with machinery, and the domestically produced textiles seem unable to compete with imported textiles. Most Greek manufactures produce for domestic consumption and are unable to find an international market. Despite a rise in the average gross national product of 8.5 per cent between 1952 and 1957, and an even higher rise since then (to over 11 per cent in 1961), large investments of capital are needed to bring about any major improvement in industry.

TRANSPORTATION

SHIPPING Invisible earnings make up an unusually large part of the balance of payments in Greek trade, exports paying only 60 per cent of the receipts. In recent years the largest part of these invisible items have come from wages to sailors, shipping receipts, remittances from Greeks living abroad, and earnings from tourists. The Greek merchant marine is sixth largest in the world. Although two-thirds of its merchant navy had been destroyed by the end of World War II, it has made a remarkable recovery. Early in 1962 the fleet capacity (over 1,160 ships capable of handling 6,350,000 tons) was nearly five times greater than in 1955 and substantially more than three times greater than the prewar fleet. Repatriation of ships previously flying "flags of convenience"—those of Panama, Canada, Honduras, South Africa, the United Kingdom, the United States, Sweden, Israel—has made up a considerable part of this increase. Most of this repatriation occurred in 1960, when 246 vessels (2,105,895 tons) transferred to the Greek flag. The Greeks are the main carriers of the Mediterranean.

Because the topography is so rugged, coastwise shipping constitutes a major form of transport. Many passenger and cargo vessels are thus engaged in coastwise and interisland shipping. There are no navigable rivers in Greece although, during high water, short stretches of some of the larger rivers, such as the Vardar, may be used by flat-bottomed craft.

Greece has approximately 1,700 miles of railroads. Because of the increasing importance of trucking, the railways now transport about one-fourth less tonnage than previously. Air transport is gaining in importance. Besides two Greek lines, the planes of seventeen international companies make scheduled stops at the Ellenikon airport at Athens.

FISHERIES Another of the major occupations in Greece and probably one of the most ancient is fishing, though the Mediterranean Sea falls short of some of the requirements of a great fishing ground. A specialty in the warm waters of the Aegean and along the African coast of the eastern Mediterranean is sponge gathering. Greeks bring up about 80 per cent of the Mediterranean take and before World War II supplied over 50 per cent of the world's sponges. The boats go out in fleets of ten or twelve vessels, fish for the first few weeks in Greek waters and then move on to the sponge fields along the African shores of Libya and Tunisia, where lush, fine sponges are found on the rocky ledges at depths ranging from 120 to 150 feet.

Several things have begun to cut in on this dangerous but traditional occupation of the Greeks. First, artificial sponges are capturing the markets, displacing the costlier natural product. The United States is still the greatest buyer of Greek sponges, taking about 40 per cent of the total catch. Second, the sponge-fishing grounds are being depleted, and despite greater efforts by the hard-toiling Greek divers, the catch is growing smaller. Previous to World War II about 200 tons of sponges were taken; by 1961 the production was less than 80 tons. Third, the governments of the North African states, along whose shores some of the finest sponges are taken, have imposed severe restrictions. Egypt demands 18 to 20 per cent of each catch for permission to operate in her waters; Libya imposes a high tax on each diving team. Beyond this, African divers now share in what was formerly a Greek monopoly.

Few sponging expeditions are without casualties. Every year several divers lose their lives; many more return to Greece paralyzed by the "bends"—the body crippling affliction of men who dive too deeply, carelessly, or too frequently. Living conditions aboard the caiques (sponge boats) are difficult, also. In about the last ten years the number of sponging vessels that have put out from Greece has halved: in 1950, 224 caiques with some 2,600 spongers went out; in 1960 the number had dropped to about 100 caiques and 1,200 men.

Kalymnos, a bleak mass of rocks among the hundreds of small islands that stud the Aegean Sea, is the main sponging base in Greece. With the decline of the industry, many young Kalymnians are forced to migrate from the Mediterranean to other parts of the world where their diving skills can be used. Some have gone to Australia to try their luck at pearl diving; others have joined the thriving colony of Greek sponge fishermen at Tarpon Springs on the Gulf coast of Florida.

CITIES

Greece is not a country of large cities. Rough topography, poor highways, and adverse economic conditions make for small and sometimes isolated settlements. Athens is the political, economic, and cultural center of the country. One of the oldest cities in the world, established before 1000 B.C., Athens has long been noted for its culture—for architecture, sculpture, philosophy, drama—and the early development of democratic forms of government. Modern Athens and Piraeus, the leading seaport of Greece, form a continuously built-up urban area. Within them are located over 60 per cent of the country's industrial facilities. Piraeus is also ancient, built more than 2,500 years ago. It has suffered many catastrophes, including great destruction during World War II. Reconstruction in the postwar period has made it one of the most modern ports in the Mediterranean. Aside from new port facilities in the old harbor, a new harbor has been built, the Irakleus, close to the old one.

The Athens-Piraeus urban center is growing rapidly. Athens itself has increased in population by one-third in the last decade, to 1,850,000 inhabitants. This is causing concern in Greece, and it has been suggested that the capital be moved from Athens to Pella, in northern Greece, a city that was once the capital of Macedonia in the time of Alexander the Great.

Salonika is the second port of Greece. Situated at the mouth of the Vardar River, whose valley, with that of the Morava, forms the most important north-south gateway through the rugged Balkans, this port is a leading outlet and commercial center and thus plays a role that is centuries old. The city sprawls over a slope, rising from the edge of a large and sheltered harbor.

Salonika was founded in 315 B.C. by Cassander, King of Macedonia, who named the city after his wife, Thessaloniki, sister of Alexander the Great. Its earliest role was that of port for Macedonia. As the Romans came in they built the Egnatia Road, which led from the Adriatic Sea through Thessalonica to the Bosporus. This road made the city a center of east-west as well as north-south traffic. In population it ranks second to Athens, and as an industrial center only Athens surpasses it. High among manufactures are food and tobacco processing, leather products, and machine repair. It still is the "hub of Macedonia," a land that is now divided among Greece, Yugoslavia, and Bulgaria.

EUROPEAN TURKEY

All that remains of the European portion of the empire of the Ottoman Turks is a little sector of land, 9,254 square miles in area, at the eastern extremity of the Balkan Peninsula. It reaches toward Asian Turkey in a double land bridge the points of which are separated from Anatolia by the Bosporus on the north and the Dardanelles on the south, the two straits joined by the Sea of Marmara which lies between. This small bit of land is the only political division of the Balkans that con-

Figure 9-22   The Rumeli Hisar (European citadel) at Istanbul, Turkey, built by Mohammed II to command the narrowest point of the Bosporus. Robert College now occupies the site of the citadel grounds. (Courtesy of Pan American Airlines.)

sists, in the main, of lowlands, the only one in which there are no mountains of any great height. About 2,300,000 people live here, or approximately 9 per cent of the population of Turkey, on a little more than 3 per cent of the land.

Most of European Turkey is fertile and could support a larger population; but agriculture does not give the small region its great importance. The holding of this small bit of Europe places all of the strategic and historic "Straits" within Turkish territory. The Dardanelles-Marmara-Bosporus waterway has had and still has a quite extraordinary importance. It is the gateway to the Black Sea. Control of the Straits by Turkey has been a thorn in the side of the Russians ever since Catherine the Great succeeded in securing a foothold along the Black Sea, and, as that water body has increasingly became a Russian lake, Russian efforts to gain some control or supervision over the water passage, or to secure a bypass that would bring Russian control on to the Mediterranean itself, have increased. In peacetime, ships of most types of all nations pass freely through these waters; in wartime the Straits readily become a bottleneck.

Guardian city of this waterway is Istanbul, situated at the southern end of the Bosporus, overlooking the Straits from the European side. It is the Constantinople of the past, a city that served as the capital of empires from the fourth century up into the twentieth—until Ataturk transferred the Turkish capital to the plateau at Ankara.

The erection of Constantinople began in A.D. 330, when the Roman emperor Constantine selected this site, on the shores of the Bosporus where the ancient settlement of Byzantine stood, for his city and capital of the Eastern Empire. For a thousand years it was one of the leading centers of the Christian world, becoming the traditional capital of Orthodox Ca-

BULGARIA

BLACK SEA

Edirne

EUROPEAN

BOSPORUS

GREECE   TURKEY

Instanbul   Üsküdar

Alexandroupolis

SEA OF
MARMARA

Ankara

Kumkale

Troy

ASIAN   TURKEY

AEGEAN SEA

DARDANELLES

Izmir

"THE STRAITS"

–·–·– Political boundaries in the
　　　Aegean Sea

++++ Railroads

SCALE
0   50   100

MILES

MEDITERRANEAN SEA

Figure 9-23 European Turkey and the historic Straits. Notice how narrow both the Dardanelles and the Bosporus are, and therefore how effective both are as control points along the water passage. The railroad (formerly known as the Berlin-to-Baghdad Railroad) is shown, passing through Istanbul and into Asian Turkey, where it branches in several directions.

tholicism. It was captured by the Turks in 1453, from which time until 1923 it served as the capital of the Turkish empire and a center of the Moslem world. As a political and religious center of great importance it was beautified with palaces, magnificent churches and mosques, and gardens. The site is one of the most magnificent in the whole Mediterranean, and its situation is commensurate with the role it has had for several hundred years, namely, guardian of the Straits. Like Helsingor in Denmark on the Kattegat, its purpose has been to command the waterway, and in the political arrangements that have followed on the two world wars, its dominant role has been to prevent the Straits from falling into the hands of the Soviet Union.

There is perhaps no better example in the world of a crossroads than the area of the Straits. The Dardanelles-Marmara-Bosporus waterway cuts across what looks like an isthmus of land that would otherwise connect Asia and Europe. People and goods therefore have not only moved by water across this little sector of land but also east and west by land, negotiating the narrow straits of the southern Dardanelles and the northern Bosporus. Armies and goods and migrants have swept from continent to continent via the two land bridges. The Fertile Crescent route between Baghdad and Aleppo continued on, westward and northward, across the Turkish peninsula and the land bridge of Asia Minor, and the Berlin-to-Baghdad railroad was built to follow the same course, passing through Istanbul.

The role of Istanbul today is less commercial and more greatly strategic, less commercial because, although the Straits are the outlet for all the Black Sea hinterland, most of the cargo passing in and out simply sails past Istanbul. Strategically and centrally located though it is, Istanbul stands along the side of the flow and, so to speak, merely observes it.

TINY MEDITERRANEAN COUNTRIES

Four very small independent countries— Andorra, Monaco, San Marino, and Vatican City—and the British Crown Colony of Gibraltar are located in the Mediterranean area. The nations of Andorra, Monaco, and San Marino are relic nations, the remains of states established in mountainous areas centuries ago. The Vatican City, as it exists today, was established by the Lateran Treaty of 1929. It has, however, existed for many centuries, for the popes have held temporal authority over certain areas in Italy since the establishment of the Roman Catholic Church. The British colony of Gibraltar is important as a military installation because of the strategic situation of "the Rock."

ANDORRA

A country of narrow mountain valleys and a few high peaks, Andorra is located in the heart of the Pyrenees. It is an area of cold winters and cool to mild summers. For many months of the year most of the mountain passes are snowbound. In the valleys, during the short growing season, subsistence crops are grown. Many people are engaged in sheep raising. Important economic activities include smuggling and tourism. Politically the nation is a semi-feudal state, being governed by an elective council which rules under a joint suzerainty of the President of France and the Bishop of Urgel. Andorra is the largest city and the national capital.

The principal natural resources of Andorra are extensive growths of pine, iron ore, and marble. Although some iron ore is mined and a small amount of marble quarried, the chief industries are related to the nation's agricultural production. The small manufacturing activities include spinning, wool combing, and tobacco processing and are centered primarily around the town of San Julián. Since the most important valleys of the nation open on the south side of the Pyrenees, communication is easier with Spain. However, a good road connects the French and Spanish frontiers by way of Soldeu, near the iron mines, Les Escaldes, where a large hydroelectric plant is located, Andorra, and San Julián.

MONACO

Near the Italian-French border is Monaco, an independent principality which is in a customs union with France. This country, with an area slightly greater than ½ square mile and a population in excess of 20,000, is, after the Vatican City, the smallest sovereign state in the world. On a rocky promontory facing the Mediterranean is the old capital, Monaco. The most noted part of the country today, however, is Monte Carlo, famous for its gambling casino and luxurious hotels, which form a primary attraction for Riviera tourists. The country receives its income from the casino, tourists, and the sale of postage stamps.

Monaco is one of the principal resort areas along the French Riviera. The small but deep sheltered harbor is a favorite port of call for wealthy tourists. Good highways connect with the highway system of France, and the trains that serve the French and Italian Riviera also serve Monaco. In addition to its gambling casino, such places as the fifteenth-century palace, the nineteenth-century cathedral, and a noted oceanographical museum are also of interest.

SAN MARINO

San Marino is said to be the oldest independent nation in Europe and the smallest republic in the world. Located only twelve miles from the Adriatic coast in the Etruscan Apennines, the nation has a total area of some twenty-three square miles enclosed within an irregular frontier completely surrounded by Italian territory. The country is mountainous; Mt. Titano, the highest peak, has an elevation of 2,300 feet. Most of San Marino is in the drainage basin of the Marecchia River.

Agriculture is the chief occupation; grapes, fruits, wheat, and corn are the principal products grown. Cattle and swine are the most common animals. Most industry is for local needs except in the case of souvenirs made for the tourist trade. Transportation is provided by highway and rail connections made with those of Italy.

The city of San Marino, located on the western slope of Mt. Titano, is the national capital. At the eastern edge of the city, the mountain has a sheer drop of almost 1,000 feet. San Marino is a walled city, and it is inside these walls that the government offices are located. Most business is conducted in Borgo Maggiore, 600 feet below San Marino. Government revenues are largely from the tourist trade and the sale of postage stamps which are issued for collectors.

VATICAN CITY

The smallest nation in the world is the Vatican City, its total area being only slightly more than 100 acres. The city-state, located on the west side of the Tiber River, is entirely surrounded by Rome. St. Peter's church, the largest Christian church in the world, the Vatican, and the pontifical palaces are among the important buildings located within the area. As the home of the pope, this small nation is an ecclesiastical state with worldwide influence out of all proportion to its physical size.

GIBRALTAR

Gibraltar occupies a narrow peninsula connected to Spain by a low isthmus. Located at the northeast entrance to the Strait of Gibraltar, it is ideally situated for controlling the western entrance to the Mediterranean Sea. Much of the peninsula is covered by a huge rock which attains an elevation of approximately 1,400 feet. Natural caves within the rock have aided in making it a very strongly fortified naval base. Securing fresh water is one of the principal problems confronting the people, and large areas of the very steep eastern slopes of the Rock have been cemented to prevent water from soaking into the shallow soil and to direct the rapid runoff into underground storage basins. Most of the people living in Gibraltar are military personnel, and almost all civilians are employed by the various military departments. Many shopkeepers and laborers come in daily from Spain.

IN PERSPECTIVE

EUROPEAN MEDITERRANEAN, LAND OF OLD CULTURES

Three peninsulas, Iberia, Italy, and Greece, form much of the northern shores of the Mediterranean Sea, with Iberia also constituting the chief bordering land on the west. These lands and associated islands are called Southern Peninsular Europe. The regional unifying characteristics include mountains that dominate the landscape, the Mediterranean climate, closeness to the ocean except in interior Spain, similarities in crops, the drought-resistant natural vegetation except that growing in the higher mountain areas or along the rainy west coast, the preponderance of the Mediterranean race, and a culture that stems from that of Greece and Rome.

Although manufacturing is important in North Italy and at Barcelona, in general the most common occupation is farming, mostly done on small holdings with simple implements, often by hand methods. The same grains—wheat, barley, and rice—are grown throughout the region, and vineyards, fruit and nut orchards, and olive trees are important. The chief animals are the goat, sheep, and donkey; even cattle and pigs are scarce in some sections. Houses are mostly built of stone and adobe, and the people prefer to live in villages and cities. Standards of living are generally lower than in Western and Northern Europe. The fishing industry is common along many of the coasts. Italy and Greece are important in ocean shipping. The scenery and historic monuments in the region are major attractions to visitors, and especially in Italy is the tourist industry an important source of income. Both Italy and Spain have developed large amounts of hydroelectricity, which is a partial substitute for the small output of coal and petroleum; Italy also generates a little power from steam tapped from underground by wells.

SELECTED REFERENCES

Dewhurst, J. Frederic, John O. Coppock, P. Lamartine Yates, and Associates: *Europe's Needs and Resources,* The Twentieth Century Fund, New York, 1961.

Excellent analysis of major problems of the underdeveloped areas, of the latest developments in agriculture, industry, resources, and trade, of economic integration, of needs. It deals splendidly with almost every aspect of the societies and economies of the countries that it discusses.

Dovring, Folke: *Land and Labor in Europe, 1900–1950,* Martinus Nijhoff, The Hague, 1956.

An analysis of the structural features in European agriculture, with focus upon the relationship between land and labor. Such related factors as settlement types, land fragmentation and land tenure, and agricultural cooperation are also dealt with. The lack of an index is unfortunately a handicap in using the book.

Economic Reports, World Trade Association, U.S. Department of Commerce.

The following are very helpful in bringing material up to date: "Basic Data on the Economy of Spain, 1960." "Economic Developments" in Greece, Italy, Portugal, Spain, Turkey, 1961.

Italian Business and Economic Topics and *Italian Trade Topics,* Office of the Commercial Counselor, Italian Embassy, Washington, D.C.
Italian Trends, monthly letter from the Banca Nazionale del Lavoro.
Italy's Economy, Cassa di Risparmio delle Provincie Lombarde, Milan, 1961.

Among the material put out by agencies of the foreign governments or business enterprises, the above will prove most useful.

Pounds, Norman J. G.: *Europe and the Mediterranean,* McGraw-Hill Book Company, New York, 1953.

Chapters 23 to 26 are devoted to a study of the Mediterranean area of Europe. An introductory chapter is followed by a comprehensive chapter for each of the three peninsulas. These present the richness and variety of the Mediterranean area, its culture, and the roots of its present civilization as well as its geography.

Price, Edward T.: "Viterbo: Landscape of an Italian City," *Annals of the Association of American Geographers,* vol. 54, no. 2, pp. 242–275, June, 1964.

The study "presents a comprehensive temporal cross section which produces an urban landscape different from an urban landscape" that will be found in the younger countries of the world.

chapter 10

EASTERN EUROPE:
THE SHATTER BELT

Figure 10-1 Eastern Europe is a region of rugged topography. Numerous mountain groups—Carpathians, Transylvanian Alps, Balkans, Rhodopes, and others—surround large areas of fertile plains like the Alfold, Walachian, and Maritsa.

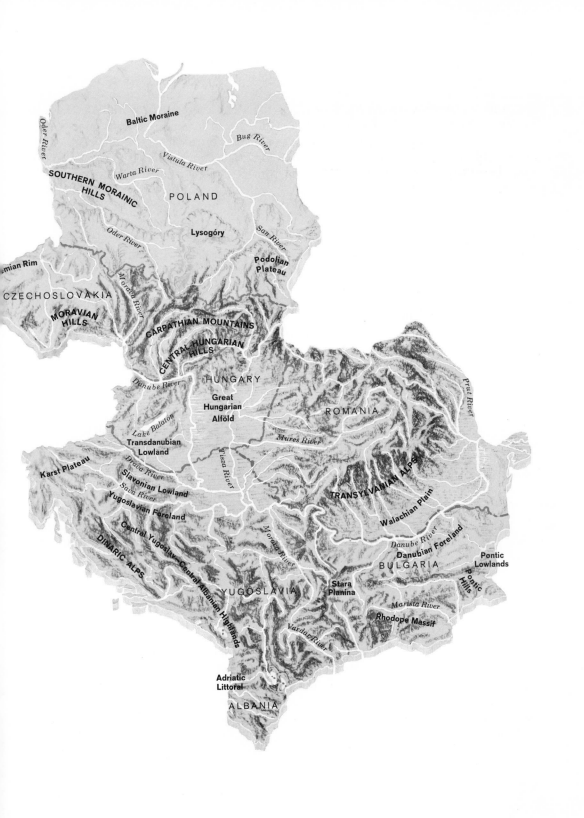

*T*HE SHATTER BELT OF EUROPE EXTENDS from the Baltic a thousand miles southward to the Ionian Sea, and 800 miles eastward from the Adriatic to the Black Sea. The seven countries of Albania, Bulgaria, Czechoslovakia, Hungary, Poland, Romania, and Yugoslavia are within this broad belt. Together, they embrace an area of some ½ million square miles, which in size is equivalent to the combined areas of Minnesota, Wisconsin, Michigan, Illinois, Iowa, Missouri, Kentucky, Ohio, and Arkansas. The appellatives used to designate this area conform more to common usage than to actual conditions. The expression, Shatter Belt, on the one hand, implies political instability; but long history has proved the indigenous cultures more shatter-proof than the political boundaries enclosing them. On the other hand, the locational term, Eastern Europe, signifies relative position; but Budapest, located in the midst of Eastern Europe, is as far west of Moscow as it is east of London. Geographically, then, Eastern Europe is the central core of the European Peninsula where intra-Shatter Belt conflicts have been far fewer than is popularly supposed.

Located between the more populous, unified, and powerful Germanic and Russian realms, Eastern Europe was the chosen war area of the expansion-bent greater neighbors. The times of tranquillity were few and short. The last was at the turn of the century, when Austria-Hungary, Turkey, and Russia dominated the scene. The nearsighted jealousies of the fragmentary Succession States after World War I were a continuing threat and an insurmountable obstacle to enduring peace in Europe. Individually small and weak, the Eastern European states, victor and vanquished alike, looked to powerful allies for security or redress. The great powers, taking selfish advantage of the situation, used these nations as pawns in their game of power politics. The last two great wars were sparked in Eastern Europe. The aftermath of World War II swept all Eastern European nations under Communist control. The ensuing close ideological, economic, and military ties to the Soviet Union resulted from forced Soviet military imposition rather than from free popular preference. Dissatisfaction with the forced arrangement, so explosively expressed by the Hungarian uprising of 1956, may see Eastern Europe spark another war. Although local chauvinism contributed its share to feelings of political impermanence, the repeated boundary adjustments came prefabricated from distant world capitals.

Over 100 million people inhabit the area, most of whom are Slavs. Nevertheless, a strong core of Magyars, Romanians, and Germans lies in their midst, and lesser centers of Albanians, Turks, and Macedonians are found along the area's southern borders. The Poles, Czechs, Slovaks, and Ruthenians make up the northern Slav group; the Slovenes, Croats, Serbs, and Bulgarians represent the southern Slavs. The racial kinship of Slav and Orthodox Eastern Christians tied the Balkans, but more especially the southern Slavs, closer to imperial Russia, but the northern Slavs were oriented westward. Although Christianity—Catholic, Orthodox, and Protestant—as well as Islam and Judaism are traditional religious preferences, in recent years public declarations of atheism have been popular.

Eastern Europe is noted for physical and cultural diversity. Highly developed industrial areas give way, especially as one travels eastward and southward, to some of the poorest farmlands on the Continent. Brilliant cosmopolitan centers of art and refinement are offset by hamlets of backward peasants. Ancient structures

Figure 10-2   The Shatter Belt includes seven nations located in the central part of Europe. Each is a Communist nation, although Yugoslavia and Albania are not directly connected with Moscow.

exist in the shadow of ultramodern edifices. Grandiose post-World War II plans for industrialization and agricultural collectivization have yielded spectacular local results, but the planned opulence has not yet pervaded Eastern Europe. If heterogeneity is a typical characteristic of Europe, then the Shatter Belt is most typically European.

PHYSICAL SETTING

RELIEF FEATURES

The rugged Alpine Mountain System, with its adjacent flat lowlands, dominates the southern half of the Shatter Belt. But the mountains flatten northward to form the Central Uplands. Farther to the north, descent produces the great European Plain which eventually slips beneath the Baltic Sea. Thus the topographical simplicity of the northern sector is offset by complexity prevalent in the central and southern two-thirds of the region (Figure 10-3).

ALPINE SYSTEM AND ASSOCIATED LOWLANDS
The steeply upfolded and downfolded Alpine Mountain System is genetically akin to the Rocky Mountains of North America. Frequently towering above the snow line, deeply incised by rivers, and trenched by former glaciers, the Alpine System everywhere displays a youthful stage of erosional development. Glacial scour produced a large number of passes which provided ready access routes across the high mountains, and diastrophic downsinking produced even lower and broader passageways known as corridors or gateways. These afforded ready avenues for the movement of peoples and the development of trade routes, railroads, and motor roads.

The Alps (1)[1] proper terminate in the Alpine Forelands (11) in Austria. They are separated by the valley of the Upper Danube and the Vienna Basin (20) from the great double horseshoe arc of the Carpathian-Transylvanian-Balkan mountain system. Although the Carpathians themselves are generally low, the High Tatra (2A) ranges within them attain altitudes of over 8,000 feet and are snow-covered.

[1] The figures in parentheses which occur in the following discussion refer to the code which appears on the physiographic map (Figure 10-3).

PHYSIOGRAPHIC REGIONS OF THE SHATTER BELT

I. THE ALPINE SYSTEM

A. MOUNTAINS AND PLATEAUS
  1. Alps
  2. Carpathians: A. High Tatra
  3. Transylvanian Alps
  4. Balkans: Stara Planina
  5. Karst Plateau
  6. Dinaric Alps
  7. Central Yugoslav-Albanian Highlands
  8. Rhodope Massif
  9. Bihar Mountains
  10. Central Hungarian Hills
  11. Alpine Forelands
  12. Yugoslavian Foreland
  13. Danubian (Balkan) Foreland
  14. Deli-Orman
  15. Dobrogea (Dobrudzha) Platform
  16. Pontic Hills

B. ASSOCIATED LOWLANDS
  17. Great Hungarian Alföld
  18. Little Hungarian Alföld
  19. Walachian Plain
  20. Vienna Basin
  21. Transdanubian Lowland
  22. Slavonian Lowland: A. Fruska Gora
  23. Transylvanian Basin
  24. Morava-Vardar Valley
  25. Maritsa Valley
  26. Sofiya Basin
  27. Adriatic Littoral
  28. Aegean Lowlands
  29. Pontic Lowlands

II. THE CENTRAL UPLANDS
  30. Bohemian Rim: A. Bohemian Forest,
      B. Ore Mountains, C. Giant Mountains,
      D. Sudeten Mountains.
  31. Moravian Hills
  32. Bohemian Basin
  33. Sudeten Foreland
  34. Lysogóra
  35. Podolian Plateau
  36. Moravian Corridor

III. THE EUROPEAN PLAIN
  37. Southern Morainic Hills
  38. Glacial Valley
  39. Baltic Moraine

  —·—·—· Political boundaries
  ▬▬▬ Regional boundaries
  — — — Sub regional boundaries
  ▬ Elevations over 3,000 feet

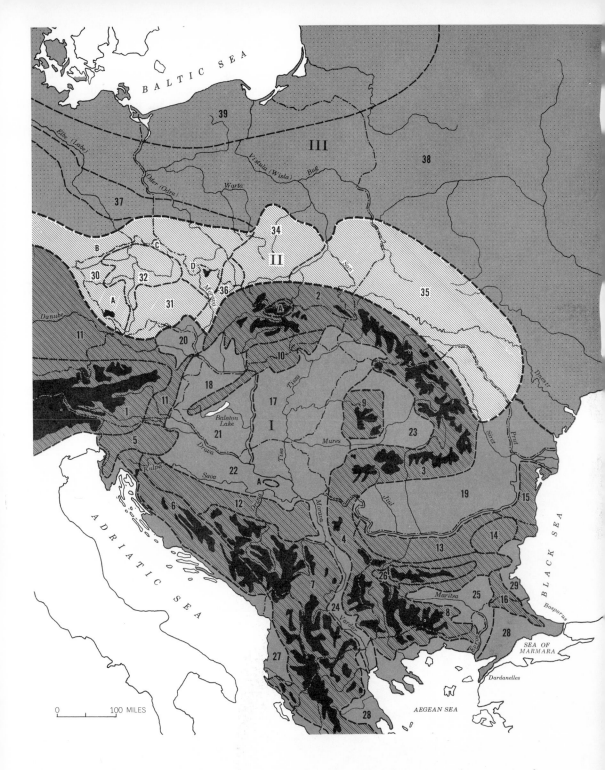

Figure 10-3 The Shatter Belt contains thirty-nine physical regions—a fragmentation that makes for isolation and, in some areas, lack of progress among the peoples.

Three notable Carpathian passes, the Uzok, Veretski, and the Jablonica, provide access from the Ukrainian S.S.R. to the Great Hungarian Alföld. After World War II the Soviet Union gained a highly strategic foothold by incorporating this segment of the Carpathians, and Ruthenia as well, within the Ukraine. While the Transylvanian Alps are generally higher than the Carpathians, the Stara Planina of the Balkan Mountains (4) attains the highest altitude and forms the most effective barrier of the threefold system. The Carpathians and the Transylvanian Alps, despite the easily negotiable passes through them, stood as definite barriers and stable political boundaries for about a thousand years.

The various mountains of Yugoslavia form a corrugated arch with one limb rising from the Adriatic and the other from the Alföld. The folds are neither so steep nor so intense as those in the mountains elsewhere. Aside from the parallel valleys and ranges, the key to topographic development is the thick limestone and dolomite strata present nearly throughout. These calcium carbonate rocks were subjected to solution, especially after deforestation, with the result that inumerable sinkholes, caverns, poljes, and dolines now dot, if they do not dominate, much of the landscape. The features produced by rainwater on soluble strata are termed collectively Karst topography, after their excellent development in the Karst highlands and plateaus (5).

The narrow Adriatic littoral (27), with its many elongated offshore islands, is wedged between the sea and the Dinaric Alps (6). The coastal strip is as accessible from Italy as from the interior. Once forested, the backing Dinaric Alps appear

Figure 10-4   The heavily timbered Carpathians form the watershed and boundary between Poland and Czechoslovakia. (Courtesy of Czechoslovakian Embassy.)

white because of the light-colored lime-stone and the absence of vegetation and soil. The geological complexity of the central Yugoslav-Albanian highlands (7) is augmented by rugged relief, solution, lack of surface water, and lack of any broad flatland with fertile soils. The many poljes, representing inset windows dissolved from limestone, are local steep-sided basins with tillable flat floors. These are oases of good agricultural and spring-watered lands. Unfortunately, the possessors frequently fought over poljes and developed an inbred, isolated, clan social system therein. Empires came and vanished, each leaving some imprints on the people, but no empire was able to bring them completely into its own cultural community.

Alternating crests and valleys form the Rhodope Massif (8). Running water, rather than glaciers, cut deep valleys into the upstanding igneous mass, but broad areas of high meadows remain above the forest-covered slopes. Racial diversity compensates for population sparsity, especially on the western parts of the Rhodopes. Here, side by side yet almost completely separated, live Serbs, Bulgars, Pomaks (Bulgars converted to Islam), Greeks, Turks, Jews, and Macedonians, speaking different languages, using different scripts, having different social organizations and mores, and often ready to fight each other.

Between the mountains and lowlands are several forelands (11 to 16), any of which may be appropriately termed a piedmont. The forelands are generally level to gently rolling plateaus or hill lands. But the broad, downfolded features of the Alpine System are the associated lowlands. These lowlands (17 to 26) contain most of the people, most of the arable land, the densest transportation network, and the most intensive economic activi-ties. If the lowlands are the most lively in terms of human effort, then the Danube is the central nerve of these mountain-segmented basins.

The Danube has some 300 tributaries, nearly all in the Shatter Belt, draining over 300,000 square miles. It is neither blue nor known anywhere along its course by the name Danube. Called the Donau in Germany and Austria, Duna in Hungary, Dunav in Slavic lands, and Dunarea in Romania, its seasonally green and mud-yellowed waters run through all but two of the Shatter Belt nations—Poland and Albania. The Danube enters the Little Alföld only to shift in braided channels across deposits of its own making. The constricting Central Hungarian Hills or Bakony Forest (10) stand as the final obstacle to its southward flow. Here the Hungarians plan large hydroelectric installations. From the Bakony Forest the Danube flows across the flat and low alluviated floor of the Great Hungarian Alföld (17). The Alföld itself is a large diastrophic basin partly filled with alluvium. Two lesser topographic units adjoining the Alföld are the Transdanubian lowlands (21), with a rolling plain surface and the large freshwater Lake Balaton, and the Slavonian lowlands (22) between the Sava and Drava Rivers. The domal, igneous, but subdued Bihar Mountains (9) separate the enclosed Tertiary Transylvanian Basin (23) from the Alföld. While on the Alföld, the Danube is joined by its important Drava and Sava affluents as well as by the flood-prone Tisza. It leaves the Alföld through a spectacular canyon, the Kazan pass, whose left wall marks the Transylvanian Alps and the right wall the Balkan Mountains. The rapids, called the Iron Gate, just below the canyon, were cleared for navigation by blasting the channel during the 1860s. The Danube is navigable throughout its entire Shatter Belt course, and it is, indeed, an international stream.

The Walachian Plain (19), genetically and topographically similar to the Alföld, consists of irregular amphitheater-shaped lowlands open to the Black Sea. The Balkan foreland (13) and the Dobrugea Platform (15) are higher bench levels looking onto the marshy Walachian Plain. The right bank of the Danube swings near the escarpment-marked edges of these upper levels. The topographic break causing these two distinct levels has long served as a stable political boundary between Romania and Bulgaria. The yellow, accreting muds of the Danube delta caused the Walachian Plain to protrude into the Black Sea. The boundary of the Soviet Union is now contiguous with the lowest segment of the Danube.

The Moravian Corridor (36), a low gap between the Sudeten Mountains (30D) and the Carpathians, connects the European Plain (III) with the Vienna Basin and thus provides a northern outlet from the Danubian lowlands. The Morava-Vardar Valley (24) affords a southern outlet to the Aegean lowlands (28). Both gateways have been witnesses to historic peaceful and wartime uses. In addition to these gateways, the emergent flat Pontic lowlands (29) and the broad Maritsa Valley (25) of Bulgaria represent the two other relatively flat and densely inhabited areas of the south.

CENTRAL UPLANDS Having a central location with reference to the European Plain and the Alpine System, and attaining elevations of over a thousand feet, the name Central Uplands (II) appropriately conveys the significance of relative position and elevations. The hilly and well-watered Bohemian Basin (32) is rimmed by the quadrilateral diamond-shaped higher

mountains, whose igneous summits and sediment-overlapped flanks were subdued by erosion. The Bohemian Forest (30A), Ore Mountains (30B), Giant Mountains (or Riesengebirge in German) (30C), and Sudeten Mountains (30D), although not nearly so high and serrated as those of the younger Alpine System, are densely forested and therefore form barriers between the Germanic and Slavic peoples. Although the Czech people occupied the basin, the Germans inhabited both flanks of the mountains. The Elbe and its tributaries, including the Moldau River, drain the Bohemian Basin through the wide gap, the Elbe Gate, between the Ore and the Giant Mountains. The eastward-lying Moravian Hills (31) are a lesser structural flexure, lower in altitude than the four mountain ranges. The Moravian Corridor (36) is a broad structural and topographic depression between the Sudeten and Carpathian Mountains. Drained northward by the Oder and southward by the Danube tributaries, the Moravian Corridor is a historic avenue of communication between the Danubian basins and the European Plain.

The northward flattening and inclination of strata produce a gently inclined plateau surface adjacent to the Sudeten and Carpathian Mountains. Interrupted by the through-flowing Oder and Vistula Rivers, and elsewhere incised by their tributaries, these upland surfaces are not continuous; rather, they are known separately as the Sudeten foreland (33), Lysogora (34), and the Podolian or Volbynian plateau (35). Their partly glaciated and loess-covered surfaces are generally hilly and very productive agriculturally. Underlying Paleozoic strata contain high-grade coal that is extensively mined, especially in Silesia. The Sudeten foreland, lying between the Oder-Neisse Rivers and the Sudeten Mountains, as well as the Lysogora are now entirely within Poland. But only the westernmost portion of the Podolian plateau, which is known as the Volbynian plateau in the U.S.S.R., is in Poland.

EUROPEAN PLAIN   Extending from the Urals as an ever-westward-narrowing wedge whose apex in Belgium points to the Atlantic, the European Plain is by far the largest flatland on the Continent. The portion of this vast plain from the Oder-Neisse Rivers to the Pripyat' Marshes and a 300-mile breadth from the Baltic Sea to the Lysogora together compose the northern one-third of the Shatter Belt. Besides the low surface sloping toward the Baltic, an essential key to the European Plain is glaciation. While the continental ice sheet extended to the foothills of the Carpathians, Sudeten, and other mountains farther west, it did not advance or retreat at a uniform pace. Nor was the glacier clean; great quantities of ground-up rock were incorporated within the ice body. Where the rate of melting exceeded forward motion, the stranded rock debris was spread as a flat, low, and waterlogged till or drift plain. But where the rate of melting and the forward motion were in balance, long and higher ridges, known as moraines, accumulated in front of the ice sheet. The Southern Morainic Hills (37) and the Baltic Moraine (39) are parallel belts of morainal hills sandwiching the broad glacial valley (38) between them. The accumulating moraines, especially the Baltic Morainic Hills, dammed the northward-flowing rivers into proglacial lakes. Addition of glacial meltwaters raised the lake levels until the waters coalesced and began draining westward in great, shallow glacial spillways. After glacial recession the spillways were drained, and the present drainage pattern was established. The east-west spillways were easily canalized

to provide interconnecting waterways between the present rivers. The excellent network of inland waterways facilitates the vigorous barge traffic in bulky products.

The Oder and the Vistula Rivers break through the Baltic Moraine to flow sluggishly across the low marshy Baltic Sea coast. The coastline is made irregular by the deep indentations of the Pomeranian and the Danzig bays which, in turn, are separated from the inner lagoons by off-shore islands consisting of sand dunes. Backed inland by the higher lake-dotted and poorly drained Baltic Moraine, and fronted by the Baltic Sea, this coastal strip has seen the eastward march ("Drang nach Osten") of Germanic colonists since medieval times. Although the coast became German, the hinterlands beyond the moraine remained Slavic. The Germans established large port cities at the mouths of rivers and through them—and often in confederation with the Hanseatic League —controlled the commerce of the hinterlands and the Baltic. The expanding German and Slavic populations together with the attendant growth of agriculture and trade caused these ports to become centers of international intrigue and strife; and the Slavic fortunes of the past two wars finally bereft the Germans of their centuries-old coastal settlements. Indeed, even farther inland, the Oder-Neisse Rivers now form the *de facto* boundary of the westward-marching Slavs.

CLIMATE

Because of latitudinal position and extent, central position, and exposure, the Shatter Belt falls under the influence of four distinct climatic realms. The Mediterranean and the humid subtropical climates are restricted to narrow southern and southeastern sectors. One-third of the

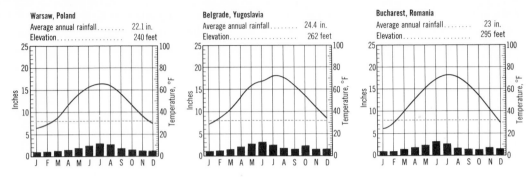

Figure 10-5   Climate graphs of selected stations.

Shatter Belt, especially the basins of the Danube, lie under the warm or long-summer-phase influence of the humid continental climate; but the area's larger northern portion is dominated by the short, cool summer phase of the humid continental climate. Other than the main climatic controls of latitude, the Atlantic Ocean, the Eurasiatic Continent, and the Mediterranean Sea (Figure 10-5), the mountains provide secondary controls, causing intricate local diversity within the highlands. Although winter cyclonic storms are prevalent throughout, they are rare occurrences along the southern periphery during summer. The hurricane and tornado are unknown.

The mean annual temperatures are expectedly higher in the south and the lowlands than in the north and the uplands. However, the generally higher elevations of the south partly offset the expected warming effect of lower latitudes. Thus the January temperature of Warsaw (24°F) is only 10° lower than that of the Albanian lowlands. The average July temperature of 65°F along the Baltic increases to nearly 80°F in interior valleys of the south, but is between 73 and 75°F along the Adriatic. Despite the vast size of the Shatter Belt, the summer and winter temperatures in any two given localities do not vary more than 20°F.

Precipitation generally decreases with distance inland from the main Atlantic moisture source. Thus, the 24-inch maxima of the west taper to less than 15 inches on the Dobrogea Platform in the east. The eastward-decreasing precipitation is associated with a tendency for summer concentration and with lessening reliability. Moisture decrease and variability are controlled by the intensified continentality of the eastward-widening land mass. With the notable exception of the southern coastal strips, the Eastern European summers are everywhere wet and warm to hot. Only along the Balkan littorals are summers dry. Winter snows occur throughout Eastern Europe, but the snowfalls are heavier, more frequent, and longer-lasting in the north and the uplands. Precipitation is largely convectional and cyclonic in origin; nevertheless, the mountains, especially along the Adriatic, induce orographic rainfall. Occasional summer hailstorms pelt the lowlands of the southeast but are more frequent in the mountains.

HUMID CONTINENTAL   The short and the long summer phases of the humid continental climate dominate nearly the entire area of the Shatter Belt. The long summer phase, sometimes referred to as the Central European climate, extends over the Alföld of Hungary, interior Yugoslavia, most of Romania, and northern Bulgaria. Akin to the climate of Iowa, it is often called the Corn Belt climate or that of the oak-hickory deciduous forest. Although the four seasons are well developed, the longer summer and milder spring and fall produce a decidedly longer growing season than in climates of adjacent northern lands. The winters (25°F for January) are about 50°F colder than the summers (74°F for July). While less than one-fifth of the precipitation, mostly in the form of snow, falls during the winter, nearly three-fifths of the total annual precipitation of 20 to 25 inches comes in the summer half of the year. The summers are wet and humid, but the winters tend to be relatively dry and crisp. A large number of thundershowers account for the May-June rainfall maxima especially on the Alföld.

The short summer phase of the humid continental climate, much like the climate of Minnesota and Wisconsin, is distinguished by longer winters, cooler summers, shorter growing season, and by somewhat less precipitation, particularly along the eastward margins of the Shatter Belt. Poland, Czechoslovakia, and north central Romania underlie the short-summer phase climate. Winters are not only long, but decidedly cold and relatively dry despite frequent snowfalls. Summers are short, cool, and wet. The average July temperature of 65°F is some 40° higher than the January average of 25°F. The short growing season and the less reliable rainfall limit agricultural productivity to levels below those of the adjacent climate of the southlands.

HUMID SUBTROPICAL   The sheltered Maritsa Valley of Bulgaria and the Yugoslavian highlands facing the Adriatic experience mild winters (January average, 35°F) and year-round precipitation in excess of 26 inches. Even though the Maritsa Valley

is densely inhabited and intensively tilled, the calcareous uplands of Yugoslavia are severely leached and sparsely populated. Rice and cotton fields of the Maritsa Valley attest the subtropical character of the climate. These restricted portions of the Shatter Belt find Tennessee a climatic, if not a topographic, kin.

MEDITERRANEAN   The California-type climate of the Shatter Belt is narrowly confined to the Adriatic islands and the coastal strip of Yugoslavia and Albania, and to the lesser southward-facing valleys of the Rhodopes of Bulgaria. While winter temperatures are above freezing, occa-

Figure 10-6 About 100 miles west of Zagreb, Yugoslavia, is a forested, hilly region of lakes and waterfalls that are, in part, a result of the climate of the area. (Courtesy of Consulate of Yugoslavia.)

sional frosts and snowfalls do occur. Also, the disagreeably strong and cold north winter wind, the bora, at times drains into valleys with devastating results to plant life. Nearly all precipitation falls during late autumn and winter, leaving the summer months hot (July, 73 to 80°F) and dry. Depending upon local altitude and exposure conditions, the average yearly rainfall varies in amount from 20 to 60 inches. The comparatively high winter temperatures, together with scenic location along marginal seas backed by mountains, make the Mediterranean one of the most popular "playground climates" of Europe.

MOUNTAIN   An endless variety of climates prevail in mountains. Although elevation and slope facings produce myriad local departures, in the main the regimes of the four principal climatic realms are discernible in the Eastern European mountains. Generally mountains have the coldest temperatures and receive the heaviest summer rains and deepest winter snows. While many are high enough to extend above the timberline into the tundra-type climate, only a few peaks attain the zone of eternal snow.

VEGETATION AND SOILS

Eastern European occupation has been so long and continuous that only isolated marshes and mountains have escaped radical alteration. Man seems to be always in competition with natural vegetation for the use of the land. However, after long association and a continuing need for wood and pasture, man has learned conditional competition. In most areas he now practices tree farming rather than forestry; he regulates tree cutting and meadowland grazing, and elsewhere he reforests cutover lands.

Originally at least two-thirds of the Shatter Belt was forest-covered. Today, after two millenniums, less than one-third remains in forest. Over one-fourth of the total areas of Romania, Bulgaria, Yugoslavia, Albania, and Czechoslovakia is classed as forest land. Generally, the densely forested lands are coextensive with the mountain slopes otherwise unattractive for agriculture. The principal zone of the forest lies between the upper limit of tree growth at 6,500 to 7,000 feet down to the less steep foothills. Valuable stands of softwood conifers, mainly the spruce and pines, yield to the beech and the oak hardwoods in the lower lands or along the stream courses. The countries least and most forested are Hungary (13 per cent) and Albania (46 per cent). Lumbering is a leading activity in the Eastern European highlands.

Distinctive low, Mediterranean-type xerophytic brush dominates the vegetational landscape along the Adriatic strip and atop the physiologically dry calcareous rocks of Yugoslavia. This dense thorny vegetation bursts into green leaf and brilliant flower after winter rains, only to be withered dusty gray by summer drought. Herds of goats browse in the midst of the maqui for lack of more palatable vegetation.

Originally, coniferous forests covered much of the Polish sector of the European Plain; but only isolated wood plots remain today. The ever-encroaching hygrophitic vegetation of the glacial marshes has filled many lakes to a stage of extinction, only to provide a source of peat for the present-day inhabitants. By contrast, the landward-drifting dunes along the Baltic fringe are barren or precariously anchored by low, drought-resistant plants.

The eastern part of the Walachian Plain and lesser open parks upon the Dobrugea Platform were originally grass-covered.

But the most extensive natural grasslands of Eastern Europe have always been the *puszta* of the Alföld. This treeless steppe was the choice grassland and subsequently the choice plowland of the Shatter Belt. The early home-seeking Magyars, guided by their grassland economy, deliberately chose it as their permanent homeland.

Through extensive drainage in the northlands and local irrigation in the south, and through long use over the entire area, the soils of Eastern Europe have been greatly altered and generally improved. Although the gray, podzolic, glacial soils of Poland tend to be water-logged and leached of soluble plant nutrients, they respond readily to drainage and fertilization. But the reddish terra rossa soils prevalent within the Mediterranean strip and upon limestone surfaces represent the accumulated insoluble residues of chert and clay that are seldom fertile or easy to alter. Large-scale transfer and mixing of the limestone-derived pedocals of the south with the glacially derived pedalfers of the north would greatly benefit both soil groups. But possibilities for radical change in soil characteristics are far less than those for altering the vegetation cover.

The most naturally fertile soils of East Europe are the chernozems developed under grass cover in the Alfölds and the Walachian Plain. Slightly less fertile, but nevertheless highly productive, are the loessal soils along the northern forelands of the Carpathian and Sudeten Mountains of southern Poland. Generally, the glacial soils of Poland are naturally the least fertile and productive. Although wide variations in soil type and fertility are present along alluvial or diluvial strips and within poljes, the swifter rivers, steeper slopes, and calcareous rocks permit only rubble-strewn skeletal soil development.

HUMAN RELATIONSHIPS

POPULATION

The hypothetical spreading of 100 million Eastern Europeans over a ½ million square miles would result in an average of some 200 persons to each square mile. Such even distribution is not found; rather, limited areas of intense concentration alternate with larger areas inhabited by few people. Hungary's population density of 275 to the square mile stands in contrast to Albania's density of 135 per square mile. The population densities of the other five nations are between these extremes. Although density figures are indicative of areal carrying power, they are not altogether reliable either with reference to present land capabilities or to potential future capacity. While most of the land of Hungary is arable and productive, most of Albania is high, rugged, dry, malarial, or otherwise limited. Selected portions of Eastern Europe have been inhabited since prehistoric times, and population increase has been numerically steady since then; nevertheless, not every part of the region has been occupied with equal thoroughness. Disadvantageous topographic conditions, soil fertility, emplacement of minerals, and stages of economic development have contributed their share to the unequal dispersal of people.

In the main, Eastern Europe has been agricultural in regions where the best farmlands and the densest population stood in direct correlation. This is still largely true. The densest population of over 250 persons per square mile along the best soils of southern Poland are matched by similar high densities within the Danubian basins. By contrast, the high and rugged Carpathians, Balkans, Rhodopes, and Dinaric Alps, as well as the Baltic Moraine zones, exhibit the low average densities of 61 to 125 persons to the square mile. Densities in the central Yugoslav-Albanian highlands fall to record lows of less than 60 per square mile.

But the continuously improving transportation facilities and new discoveries of minerals in the mountains have provided the bases for urban concentrations in the midst of agricultural lands as well as for huge industrial clusters in mountainous lands. As an example, the minerals of the Sudeten Mountains have magnetically attracted people until today they are perhaps the world's most densely populated mountains. Many major contemporary economic developments are predicated upon the minerals emplaced in mountains, particularly in Bulgaria, Yugoslavia, and to a lesser extent in Romania. What minerals did for population density in the Sudeten Mountains may well be repeated in other mountains of the Shatter Belt.

Good roadways enable the farmer to transport his agricultural products to central focal points where they are prepared for the table or used as industrial raw materials for other products. As transportation facilities improved, large cities grew in the midst of agricultural lands. Budapest, with nearly 2 million people, is the largest metropolitan city in Eastern Europe. It is approached in size by Bucharest, its sister city on the edge of the Danubian plain. Warsaw is the only other city with a population in excess of 1 million. Poland, with twenty-one cities over 50,000, has the greatest number of big cities; Albania has only one in this class, Tirana, the capital.

Generally, urbanism in Eastern Europe does not attain the high levels common in Western Europe. Indeed, the Shatter Belt is historically a land of villages and smaller rural settlements, where even towns of more than 25,000 people retain aspects of overgrown villages. Recent agricultural

collectivization, however, and more especially, planned industrialization, are causing rapid urban growth.

Again generally, while the birth rate is highest in Poland and lowest in Hungary, the death rate is highest in Hungary and lowest in Bulgaria. Infant mortality rate is highest in Yugoslavia (also the highest in Europe) and lowest in Czechoslovakia. But statistics are less accurate in the revelation of losses from wars or from racial and political persecutions. Changing boundaries have often meant the wholesale expulsion of unwanted minorities. Neither higher education nor higher living standards seem to have lessened man's inhumanity to man. This proclivity, however, is not confined to Eastern Europe alone. Large-scale repatriation of minority groups was a deliberate policy of Poland and Czechoslovakia. Forced recruitments for work in the Communist bloc nations, political deportations, and surreptitious escapes to other lands are less carefully documented aspects of shifting Shatter Belt populations.

CULTURAL DIVERSITY

Although all Shatter Belt countries are superficially united under the aegis of a Communistic social utopian system, deep-seated cultural forces preclude both uniform standardization and everlasting unity. In lands where traditional cultures were badges of identity, mutual respect for the other man's cultural heritage was readily obtained, simply because it was so fiercely retained. Cultural identity is the one thing Shatter Belt peoples are prepared to fight for. The Western individualistic, free, and democratic attitude and the contrasting Eastern collectivistic, fatalistic, and autocratic viewpoint represent two differing ideological streams flowing through Eastern European life.

Shatter Belt developments may be understood in the light of this conflict between Occidental and Oriental ideologies.

LANGUAGES   If language is a basic tool for human communication, then there is neither scarcity nor sparsity in the Shatter Belt, where no less than seventeen languages are spoken. The Slavic languages, all closely related, are spoken by the largest number of people. The Poles, Czechs, Slovaks, and Ruthenians belong to the north Slav group and prefer the Latin alphabet for written communication. The Serbs, Croats, Slovenes, Montenegrins, and Bulgars belong to the south Slav category. While the Croats and Slovenes use the Latin script, the other south Slavs learn the Cyrillic alphabet.

Major non-Slavic languages used in the area are Hungarian, Romanian, and Albanian. German, Yiddish, Italian, Turkish, and Gypsy are minor languages spoken by numerically decreasing communicants. The Hungarian language is unrelated to any in the area. Although by

Figure 10-7   Major language and religious groups of Eastern Europe.

virtue of prolonged contact, modern Hungarian employs some Turkish, Latin, and German expressions, the main language body is Finno-Ugric with strong Sumeric affinities. The Albanian language is an amalgam of ancient Illyric with modern Slavic and Turkish. Romanian is Latinized Dacian with a strong admixture of Slavic, Hungarian, and Turkish words. These major non-Slavic ethnic groups employ the Latin script, but the older Turkish (Arabic) script has not yet faded from use by some small Moslem groups.

RELIGIONS Roman Catholicism, Greek Orthodoxy, and Protestantism are the dominating religions. Poland is almost entirely Catholic; Czechoslovakia is about three-fourths so. More than 2 million Hungarians represent the largest Protestant group in Eastern Europe, but two-thirds of Hungary is Catholic. The Slovenes and Croats are largely Roman Catholic, but elsewhere Catholicism finds fewer adherents. The main body of Greek Orthodox adherents are found among the Bulgars, Serbs, and Romanians; but again, fewer numbers are present in Poland, Albania, and Czechoslovakia.

With two-thirds of the population adhering to the teachings of the Koran, Albania is the only Moslem country in Europe, although large Moslem groups live along the Yugoslav-Bulgarian border.

Perhaps the world's largest concentration of Jews was in southeastern Poland; to this area many Americans of the Jewish faith are able to retrace their national origins. Although all Shatter Belt countries have Jewish minorities, the number of Jews was small in the Balkans. The unfortunate events of World War II saw many of these Jews killed or expelled; yet about ½ million Jews still remain in the Shatter Belt.

ECONOMIC DEVELOPMENT

Eastern Europe is richly endowed agriculturally and mineralogically. Southwestern Poland, Bohemia, Moravia, and western Hungary boast a high order of economic development, but the eastern sectors of the area are just now planting the seeds of an industrial revolution. Through recent plans, each country ambitiously projects a "great leap forward" hoping to reap thereby the fruits of planned industrialization.

AGRICULTURE Agricultural output is sensitive to peace and war. During normal conditions Eastern Europe produces a significant food surplus. Wheat, concentrated in the Danubian lands, is the principal crop; it is trailed by maize in the southeast and by rye and potatoes in the northern glaciated sectors. Oat fields are common in central Poland and in the highlands of the south. Rice, a cereal recently introduced, is restricted to eastern Hungary and to several Balkan valleys. Barley is grown nearly throughout. The sugar beet is intensively cultivated in Poland, Czechoslovakia, and Hungary for domestic use and for export. Hemp, flax, and hops are raised in the north; corn and tobacco are important crops in the south. Fruit orchards and vineyards, although common throughout the area, become specialties on sandy soils and slope facings in the foothills of Hungary, Poland, Czechoslovakia, and Yugoslavia. Soybeans, cotton, sunflowers for seed, roses for oil, and opium poppies are of local agricultural significance.

Animals have always been important in the agricultural economy of Eastern Europe. Beef cattle, especially in Hungary, are most numerous in the northern areas, but large dairy herds have replaced the horned cattle in western Poland and Bohemia. Sheep and goats are the dominant animals in the Balkans. Poultry, including millions of ducks and geese, are ubiquitous but most numerous in the western sectors. Horses and oxen are the traditionally employed draft animals on better farmlands; mules and donkeys are still used on poorer southern farmlands. Collectivization has provided for central tractor stations where agricultural mechanization displaced a large number of draft animals.

At present most of the Eastern European employable labor force is used in agriculture. In Romania and Bulgaria over 80 per cent of this force are farmers; only in Czechoslovakia and Poland is less than one-half of the labor force engaged in agriculture. Agricultural development was retarded throughout the area by centuries of Russian rule and wars over Poland, and by long Turkish occupation of the Danube basins and the Balkans. Wars not only drained off needed farm workers, but ensuing boundary changes reoriented, if they did not disrupt, agricultural practices and markets. The problem of landless peasants and absentee aristocratic landowners became a sociopolitical storm center for which everybody, within and outside the Shatter Belt, offered fail-proof panaceas. The large landed estates—incidentally, often smaller than an average 250-acre farm in Iowa and never as large as a Western ranch in America—were broken up and parceled out among the peasants. These small parcels were promptly collectivized into really large kolkhozes or sovkhozes administered by absentee agropolitical officials. The question of who and how many own the land and the livestock, and whether or not new owners and new social systems can en-

Figure 10-8   Bountiful crops of wheat and corn from the fertile chernozem soils of the Great Hungarian Lowland account for the agricultural well-being of Hungary. (Courtesy of Legation of the Hungarian People's Republic.)

courage cows to give more milk, sheep to have more lambs, and hectares to yield more corn, remains to be answered.

Agricultural output seems to have remained on a plateau during the past decades. In the case of Hungary, a traditional wheat exporter, the nation now finds itself unable to meet domestic wheat requirements. Aside from man-induced difficulties, the soils of the northern glacial lands and the southern rugged lands are weak or outright infertile. Fertilization and other practices would greatly increase the farm output, but heretofore the individual farmer has had little capital for soil improvement. Over much of the area climate, too, if not actually marginal, is capricious enough to limit agricultural production. The yields are therefore lower than in northwestern Europe, and farm-labor productivity is below that of the American farmer. Farm mechanization is not likely to increase productivity; agricultural machinery produces more efficiently, not more abundantly.

MINING AND MANUFACTURING The mountain-and-basin–warped rocky crust of Eastern Europe affected not only the topography, climate, hydrography, soils, and vegetation of the area, but it also brought many different minerals within minable depths. Coal and lignite, petroleum and natural gas, bauxite, copper, zinc, lead, iron ore, potash, salt, and many other earth resources are mined on large scales, and increased production quotas are strongly promoted by the governments of all seven nations. Under the Soviet system, all earth resources, like other aspects of the economy, are nationalized. The Romanian petroleum fields are the largest in Europe, with the exception of those in the U.S.S.R. The production of petroleum in Hungary and Yugoslavia is also significant; Bulgaria, Poland, Albania, and

Figure 10-9 Romania is the principal petroleum producer in Eastern Europe. This refinery is located at Brazi. (Courtesy of Legation of Romanian People's Republic.)

Czechoslovakia are lesser producers. Poland and Czechoslovakia possess premier coalfields, but the other four nations (Albania excepted) operate important fields as well. Czechoslovakia, Hungary, Yugoslavia, and Poland work the leading lignite deposits of the area. Altogether, the Shatter Belt produces over 140 million tons of coal, 130 million tons of lignite, and 15 million tons of petroleum annually. In addition to the power fuels, all the nations except flat Hungary have great hydroelectric potentials, which are only slightly developed even by those countries most industrially advanced. Nevertheless, hydroelectric installations are being constructed at rapid rates throughout the region.

Eastern Europe produces some 10 million tons of iron ore annually, mainly from mines in Czechoslovakia, Poland, Yugoslavia, and Romania. Bauxite from Hungary and Yugoslavia; lead and zinc from Yugoslavia, Bulgaria, and Poland; and copper from Bulgaria, Yugoslavia, and Poland are nonferrous metals produced in larger amounts. Although some minerals have been mined since prehistoric times, frequent changes in management, wars, and markets have retarded large-scale and long-continued development. Many nations worry over the industrial demand exceeding the supply of mineral resources. In Eastern Europe this concern is reversed; development lags behind known mineral resources.

The lifeblood of industry flows from the mines. Czechoslovakia and Poland are the leading miners and, correlatively, are the most industrialized nations of the Shatter Belt. Czechoslovakia perhaps has as many industrial establishments as the other six countries together. Poland, however, is now in possession of Silesia, one of the principal industrial workshops of Europe. Other nations, hoping that an industrial economy will find firm support around the newly formed iron-steel backbone, built steel plants at Zanica, Yugoslavia; Sztalin-város, Hungary; Dimitrovo, Bulgaria; and Hunedoara, Romania. Without exception, industrial production of the past decade has risen at an accelerated pace in all Shatter Belt countries.

TRANSPORTATION Over one-half of the more than 42,000 miles of railroads serving Eastern Europe are concentrated in the western sectors of Poland and Czechoslovakia. Railway mileage elsewhere reflects the relative size as well as the geographic disadvantages of the other countries; small and mountainous Albania, for example, has only 26 miles of railway. The excellent prewar railway system of Hungary radiated from Budapest, but the changed World War I boundaries disrupted the system by placing international boundaries between the radial and the peripheral connecting trackage. Indeed, in one instance the town was left in Hungary, but the tracks and the railroad station were adjudged to Czechoslovakia. Such matters not only impaired transportation efficiency, but also embittered the participants and increased the neighbors' willingness to go to war. Ignoring regional cultural differences, the all-Communist leadership of the Shatter Belt has encouraged an all-region "internationalization" of railway traffic oriented toward Soviet Union needs. Ideological comradeship travels more freely across international lines.

Nearly ¼ million miles of public roads traverse Eastern Europe. Again, the denser and better highway pattern of the west gives way to sparse and poor roads—often dirt country roads—farther east and south. Nearly all 6,000 miles of navigable inland waterways are in Poland, Yugoslavia, and Hungary. The Baltic and Adriatic Seas afford the large Polish and Yugoslav merchant marine access to deep international waters; the Black Sea gives the small Romanian and Bulgarian fleet only local coastwise contacts. Even though all major Shatter Belt cities are served by airlines, Prague, being the westernmost exponent of the "Prague to Moscow axis," sees the densest international air traffic.

COUNTRIES OF EASTERN EUROPE

Despite the scheme of treatment in this book, it would be unrealistic to consider the seven countries of the Shatter Belt as forming a homogeneous geographic or an indissoluble socioeconomic unit. Although all are united by captive foreign-trained governments whose common passion is to make international communism succeed, the light of long history and traditions illuminates the broad cultural and physical differences.

In a cultural and religious sense Poland, Czechoslovakia, and Hungary for centuries have been oriented to the West. On the other hand, the Balkan states of Yugoslavia, Romania, Bulgaria, and Albania have looked to Greek Orthodoxy and the Byzantine autocratic political systems of the East. Moreover, Poland, Hungary, and Bulgaria have maintained historic friendships, while the Slovaks, Croats, and the Transylvanian peoples were for centuries an integral part of the Magyar domain. The southern Slavs, united by the common misfortune of long Turkish rule, found themselves in transitory entente with Romania and Czechoslovakia. It is unfortunate that the unconstructed political conditions after World War I and again after World War II were not appreciated by the decision-making greater powers. It is unfortunate also that the spirit of "The enemy of my enemy is my friend" prevailed over the democratic process of "Let the people most intimately affected decide for themselves." Prolonged happiness and mutual satisfaction with political compartmentalization have not been the outstanding experiences of Shatter Belt peoples. They await the use and mutual commitment to democratic machinery.

POLAND

SHIFTING BOUNDARIES   Poland is the largest and the most populous Shatter Belt state. The nation's area is larger than that of

Michigan and Wisconsin combined; its population of 30 million exceeds that of the four southwestern states from California to Texas. Poland slopes from the Carpathian-Sudeten crests of neighboring Czechoslovakia across the glaciated European Plain to the Baltic Sea. While its western Oder-Neisse riverine boundary is contiguous with restive East Germany, the nation's longer eastern boundary, unmarked by natural features, is shared with the Soviet Union. The eastern and the western boundaries of Poland are as vulnerable as they are new. Indeed, the resilient Poles have lived within historically

LARGER TERRITORIAL CHANGES SINCE W.W. II

A   Poland to U.S.S.R.
B   Germany to Poland
C   Romania to U.S.S.R.
D   Romania to Bulgaria
E   Italy to Yugoslavia
GC   Alternately German and Czech
F   Hungary & Czechoslovakia to U.S.S.R.

Hungarian boundaries changed alternately with
neighboring countries during war.

Figure 10-10   Larger territorial changes since World War II.

more transitory than stable boundaries, and have always known the fate of a buffer state where many new starts were made in organizing political independence.

The cultural heart of Poland lies around the ancient capital of Krakow in the upper Vistula Valley. From here Poland once ruled the lands between the Baltic and the Black Seas and from the Oder to the Dnepr Rivers. Her powerful legions not only checked the eastward-marching Teutonic Knights, but also entered Moscow and defeated the westward-marching Turks at Vienna (1683). After three partitions between Russia, Prussia, and Austria, Poland disappeared from the scene (1795), only to be resuscitated by Napoleon in 1812. A short-lived three-year period of independence was ended by repeated Russian occupation that lasted to the end of World War I. Following the peace treaties of Versailles and Riga, expanded Poland included German, Russian, and Lithuanian minorities, which at once embroiled newly independent Poland with her neighbors. Nazi Germany and Communist Russia jointly invaded Poland in 1939 to free German and Russian minorities, precipitating thereby World War II and the fourth partition of Poland. Post-World War II arrangements provided for a revived Poland. The eastern Polish territories were transferred to the Soviet Union, while Pomerania, Silesia, and the southern part of East Prussia were transferred from Germany to Poland. Thus, the Polish nation was shifted westward.

The Polish state came out of the war richer and with better boundaries than it had before. While the ceded eastern strip, as large as Missouri, was poor and undeveloped, the occupied western part, as large as Kentucky, was geographically rich and highly developed. Poland fell heir

Figure 10-11 The marketplace in Krakow. This city, once the capital, is located just north of the Carpathian Mountains. (Courtesy of Embassy of Polish People's Republic.)

to (1) Europe's largest and second-best coalfield in exchange for most of its oil fields and potash deposits; (2) the industrial capacity of Silesia; (3) the navigable Oder River; and (4) the Baltic seaports of Stettin and Danzig. Pending a final peace treaty, the United Kingdom and the United States consented to this arrangement as a *de facto* solution at the Potsdam Conference.

Contemporary Poland is almost free of ethnic minorities. But the price for cultural homogeneity was paid in millions of human lives lost or displaced. Some 3 million Galician Jews were killed or dispersed during temporary Nazi occupation; the Soviet Union claimed the Ukrainian, Belorussian, and Lithuanian minorities; and the Poles and Russians expelled or annihilated some 8 to 9 million Germans. Several million Polish workers and peasants from Poland proper joined the stream of Polish expatriates from the east to take up new homes on former German farms and cities of the west. Here, the expression *Shatter Belt* is not without an implication of vengeance.

GLACIATION AND CLIMATE   The northern two-thirds of Poland is a low plain ribboned by parallel east-west morainal ridges and intervening valleys. Although the sluggish Vistula and Oder Rivers drain the nation's waters to the Baltic, innumerable shallow relict mud-basin lakes and marshes remain atop the surface. The podzolic soils are frequently stony, acidic, infertile, and heather-covered when not in cultivation or under wood plots. The soils, moraines, spillways, lakes, and rivers are all of glacial origin.

The southern one-third of the nation consists of a discontinuous plateau surface blanketed by loessal soils of unusually high fertility. This marginally dissected plateau merges southward with the rapidly ascending and densely forested slopes of the Carpathian and the Sudeten Mountains.

The Polish climate, like that of Minnesota, is characteristically continental. Since higher altitude cancels out the advantage of southern latitude, the Polish temperatures are remarkably uniform nationwide. The 24-inch yearly precipitation is fairly evenly distributed throughout the year; the west, nevertheless, is slightly wetter and warmer than the east.

AGRICULTURE AND INDUSTRY   The observation that the best farmer gravitates toward the best lands and that the inefficient farmer ruins the best farms may be proved in western Poland. Many poorer Polish farmers from agriculturally backward eastern sectors replaced the traditionally careful and productive German farmers along the western lands. Although the western and the southern sections of Poland are agriculturally most productive,

over one-half the nation's area is tillable; however, slightly less than one-half of the Poles are agriculturists. The main cereals grown are rye, wheat, oats, and barley. In addition to potatoes, of which Poland is the next-ranking world producer after Germany, large quantities of sugar beets and lesser amounts of hemp, flax, and hops are grown. Approximately 10 million cattle and larger numbers of hogs, together with fewer sheep and horses, are kept on Polish farms. Fish from inland and coastal waters and poultry augment the nation's food supply.

The Silesian coalfield is the cornerstone of the Polish industrial economy. This highly developed industrial area, acquired virtually unimpaired from Germany, is the "Polish Ruhr." Katowice, Zabrze, Chorzow, and Bytom are the larger industrial and mining cities clustered around the Silesian coal deposits. More than 100 million tons of bituminous coal and 10 million tons of lignite are mined yearly and used in the coking plants, blast furnaces, and steel mills of the area itself. Some coal, however, is exported in exchange for foreign iron ores, which when added to the domestic ores from Silesian, Radom, and Kielce mines yield about 10 million tons of crude steel annually. The manufacturing of heavy machinery, coke, and chemicals makes Silesia the center of Polish heavy industry.

Zinc, lead, low-grade copper, arsenite, pitchblende, and smaller quantities of petroleum and natural gas are produced from areas along the southern foothills.

Warsaw, the political and commercial center of the country, is located on the Vistula River, which is spanned by many bridges linking the industrial area east and northeast of the river with the rest of the city. Much of Warsaw, destroyed during the war, has been rebuilt. Outstanding manufacturing activities include metal-

Figure 10-12   A grocery shop in Warsaw. (Courtesy of Embassy of Polish People's Republic.)

working industries, electrical appliances, and the making of tractors and automobiles.

Lodz, sometimes termed the "Polish Manchester," is a textile-processing center; but metallurgical, chemical, and food-processing plants raise the city's industrial rank. Wroclaw and Poznan are the third and fourth largest Polish cities; they are regional trade and manufacturing centers. Gdansk and Szczecin are the nation's two chief ports. Gdansk is a transshipment point for places on the Vistula; Szczecin serves the Oder and the canals connected with it. Each has numerous industrial establishments including shipbuilding yards. Krakow, the capital of the country until 1595, is also an important trading and commercial center of southern Poland; Walbrzych and Lublin serve similar functions; Czestochowa is the nation's foremost religious shrine and the objective of Polish Catholic pilgrimages.

TRADE AND OUTLOOK   In addition to agricultural and industrial improvements, the westward-shifted Polish boundaries improved transportation and communication facilities as well. In terms of value,

Polish exports generally exceed imports. Coal and its products, meat, sugar, semimanufactures, and textiles are leading exports. Iron ore, petroleum and chemicals, cotton and wool, and machinery are principal imports. The bulk of Polish foreign trade is consummated with the Soviet bloc.

For the future, as in the past, Poland faces great problems. Aside from the tyranny of an alien ideology, the status of the western occupied lands is not clear. Recrudescent Germany, dissatisfied with heavy territorial losses, will no doubt press for a more favorable settlement at an opportune time. However, if left in its present form without another partition, Poland may yet promote an opulent civilization. It has the geographic resources to do so.

CZECHOSLOVAKIA

NEW STATE WITH OLD PROBLEMS   Entirely landlocked Czechoslovakia is slightly larger (49,366 square miles) and more populous than Pennsylvania. The Czechs (Böhmer in German, Bohemians in English) themselves represent the old Slavic peoples within the basin of the Vltava, where they experienced earlier independence and prolonged political and cultural associations with the neighboring Germanic peoples, especially the Austrian Hapsburgs. The modern Czechoslovakian state was carved out of the old Austro-Hungarian empire in 1918. Prominent Czech emigrés, armed with a strong passion for independence and an astute appreciation of profitable political connections, were successful in convincing the victorious Allied Powers of the righteousness of their cause. Pan-Slavism was a correlative of Czech independence; the new state synthesized the Moravians, Slovaks, and Ruthenians with the Czechs themselves. Czech national aspirations were supported by France's desire for a weakened Austria, Germany, and Hungary. Thus abetted, Czech ambitions were permitted to extend beyond Slavic-inhabited lands, and the new state included about 4 million non-Slavic peoples of German and Hungarian ancestry. Launched with the blessings of some diplomats as a "shining example of self-determination and democracy," a reputation appreciated more in distant lands than among its neighbors, Czechoslovakia was drawn into immediate difficulty with Germany, Austria, Hungary, and Poland. The relentless pressures applied by neighboring states having claims on Czechoslovakia were significant factors leading to World War II.

While the predominantly German fringes were joined to Germany, the Bohemian and Moravian coreland became a subdivision of the Reich. Slovakia, shorn of her Magyar areas which were returned to Hungary, became an independent, pro-German republic. At the war's end the Allies reestablished the *status quo,* with the exception of Carpatho-Ruthenia which was incorporated into the Soviet Union. As partial compensation for this loss, Czechoslovakia received about 26 square miles of additional Hungarian territory near Bratislava and, like Poland, gained the right to expel the German and Hungarian minorities. Today about 90 per cent of the state is Czech and Slovak.

PHYSICAL SETTING The Bohemian Forest and the Ore and Sudeten Mountains rim the Bohemian Basin on three sides with the low Moravian Hills forming the less prominent fourth side. Chief egress from this fortresslike topographic basin is through the Elbe Gate and eastward through the Moravian Corridor. The Carpathian arc effectively separates Slovakia from the Bohemian Basin and its Moravian foreland. All natural passageways through Slovakia follow the river valleys and lead to the Alföld and Budapest, not to Prague. The forest-covered and mineralized mountains of food-deficient Slovakia are naturally complementary to the treeless food basket of Hungary. But the international boundary between the two has made economic integration impossible; instead, a senseless rivalry has prevailed to the detriment of both countries.

Generally, the climate of Czechoslovakia is the humid continental cool summer type and much like that of Pennsylvania. The mountainous character of the country, however, produces a variety of local conditions dependent on altitude and exposure.

AGRICULTURE AND INDUSTRY While the Czech portion of the country is mainly industrial, the Slovakian sector is primarily agricultural. Nevertheless, agriculture in the Bohemian Basin is intensive and highly productive. In Slovakia agriculture is extensive with lower yields. Rye, barley, potatoes, and sugar beets are dominant crops, but wheat, oats, tobacco,

Figure 10-13   The dense industrial pattern of western Czechoslovakia gives way to lesser centers in the east like the one here in the Slovakian foothills. (Courtesy of Czechoslovakian Embassy.)

hay, hops, and deciduous fruits are grown on smaller acreages restricted by soil and climate. The cold climate precludes corn growing away from the lowlands adjacent to the Hungarian border.

Dairy cattle, pigs, and poultry are numerous, but fodder crops must be intensively cultivated to feed the large animal population. The production of both cereals and meat falls short of home demands.

As a member of the Austro-Hungarian empire, the Bohemian Basin was deliberately assigned an industrial function. Hungary was to be agricultural and Austria the administrative center of the realm. The assignment was in keeping with the characteristic resources of the empire; development along these lines was rapid, and prosperity was high. The Czechs fell heir to one of Europe's most highly developed industrial regions. Czechoslovakia today is the most thoroughly industrialized member of the Soviet bloc. Perhaps in deference to its large contribution to overall Soviet economic aims, Czechoslovakia seems to enjoy preferential treatment by the Soviet Union.

Besides owing much to the skill of its workers, Czechoslovakian industrial might is based on mineral resources, especially coal and iron ore. Some 65 million tons of high-grade coal is mined annually from the southern extension of the Silesian fields at Ostrava; another 30 million tons of lignite is produced from scattered fields elsewhere. Although Czechoslovakia is the second-ranking coal producer in the Shatter Belt, the small amount of petroleum from the southern Moravian fields is insufficient to meet domestic needs. Czechoslovakia is the leading iron ore producer in Eastern Europe. The iron ore, as well as some wolframite, pitchblende, and manganese, is produced mainly from the Ore Mountains. The mines of Slovakia also yield iron ore, but the production of magnesite, antimony, copper, lead, zinc, and mercury is more notable. The manufacture of china and several chemical industries depend on kaolin and rock salt mined within the nation's borders.

Czechoslovakian industry is centered around Ostrava, secondarily in a belt from Prague to Pilsen, and thirdly within the Ore Mountains. Brno and Bratislava are smaller detached centers of industry. The Prague-Pilsen belt produces armaments, locomotives, electric motors, airplanes, automobiles, machinery and machine tools, textiles, and many other types of products. Brno, the second largest city of the country, is the chief textile center of the nation; but armaments factories, chemical plants, machine shops, and breweries augment the city's industrial economy.

Bratislava, besides being a bridge city, rail and road center, a provincial capital with many food-processing and light industrial establishments, is also the principal Danubian port of Czechoslovakia. The largest historic and crossroads city is Prague, the political, cultural, and commercial capital of Czechoslovakia.

COMMERCE   Czechoslovakia is Eastern Europe's principal trader. Although it has no direct outlet to the sea or a merchant marine, access is available to the Danubian, Elbe, and Oder inland waterways. In addition to an excellent network of transportation lines, it is also served by international rail, road, and air lines. Exports normally include munitions and armaments, iron and steel products, machinery, textiles, glass and chinaware, shoes, and sugar. Principal imports are foodstuffs, cotton, and iron ore. In previous times trade was oriented westward, but at present Czechoslovakia's trade alignments are largely with the Soviet Union and its satellites.

Figure 10-14   A view of Prague, the historic capital of the Czechs. (Courtesy of Czechoslovakian Embassy.)

HUNGARY

THE MAGYARS AND THE WORLD WARS Equivalent in area to the state of Indiana but twice as populous, Hungary is one of the small and densely inhabited European states, and at the same time it is one of the oldest. Preceded by earlier kindred peoples, the Magyars—the only name by which the Hungarians ever call themselves—entered and settled the Alföld more than a thousand years ago. Their chronically inflammable relations with the Germanic peoples to the west, the Tataric invaders from the east, Turks from the south, and more recently the Slavs from north and south have repeatedly consumed their energy and outweighed domestic difficulties. With the loss of the main industrial areas to Czechoslovakia, the richest farms to Yugoslavia, and the best mines and timberlands to Romania, World War I bereft them of much of their domain, wealth, and population. Their uncontrollable passion to regain these lost lands and the Hungarians living therein led them into World War II—and a repetition of the previous disaster, with the appended tragedy of Russian occupation and sovietization. Late in 1956 their desperation resulted in a popular uprising which was crushed within a fortnight by Soviet arms. Beaten in their wrecked cities and demoralized on their farms by foreign "forces of liberation" supplied by the Nazi Germans and the Communist Slavs during World War II, the Magyars remain in dumbfounded stoicism; they are unable to regain their nostalgic past or to see hope in a Communist future.

The two world wars left truncated Hungary almost entirely homogeneous in language and culture; such a condition is unduplicated in any other country of Eastern Europe. The Magyars, speaking a language unrelated to any other in Europe, are characteristically proud, meditative, and industrious. Their traditional nationalism and individualism make the acceptance of international communism incompatible and unpopular.

PHYSICAL SETTING Hungary is landlocked within the downwarped Carpathian Basin where only the Central Hungarian Hills stand interposed between the generally low, flat, and deeply alluviated floor of the great structural and topographic basin. The Danube River, entirely navigable in its 255-mile length in Hungary, further divides the basin into Transdanubia, or the lands west of the Danube, and the Alföld, or the lands east of the Danube. Although most Hungarian soils are chernozems developed under steppe-grass cover, lesser areas of alluvial, loessal, and volcanic soils produce local variations. The climate, again like that of Iowa, is typically humid continental.

AGRICULTURE AND INDUSTRY Nearly two-thirds of Hungary is arable land, and nearly one-half of the population are engaged in agriculture. Hungary has been among the world's leading wheat and corn producers, and these grains are still the dominating crops. Barley, oats, rye, and the recently introduced rice are cereals grown on a smaller scale. Sugar beets, potatoes, and tobacco are cultivated intensively, but flax, hemp, and cotton occupy smaller acreages. Two Hungarian specialties are the Tokay grapes produced from extensive vineyards along the volcanic slopes of the Central Hills, and the paprika grown around Szeged. Truck crops, some under irrigation, as well as deciduous fruits, are produced for domestic markets and for limited exports.

Cattle, pigs, and poultry are the principal meat animals; smaller herds of horses and sheep are kept in the eastern part of the country.

The nation's ambitions for increased industrial economy are frustrated by insufficient power fuels and metalliferous ores. Hungary's water power potential is correlatively low with topographic relief. The 25 million tons of lignite mined annually rank Hungary second to Czechoslovakia, but even with the 3 million added tonnage of bituminous coal produced around Pécs, the nation's industry depends on coal imports. Although the better bituminous coal is used by blast furnaces, the lignite is consumed by thermoelectric installations, chemical industries, and by individuals for heating homes. Hungarian petroleum production, amounting to some 1.4 million tons annually, falls short of meeting domestic needs.

About 15 per cent of the world's bauxite reserves lie along Lake Balaton, where the annual production of this ore amounts to some 1 million tons. Although most of the ore is exported, domestic concentrators account for 50,000 tons of alumina. Hungary's only iron ore mine, near Miskolc, yields less than ½ million tons of ore annually. Lesser quantities of uranium, manganese, lead, and copper are produced from the nearby Matra hills.

Hungary's industrial capacity has far greater local than international significance. With the exception of the three main centers, Miskolc, Györ, and Budapest, industrial establishments elsewhere are insignificant. The rapidly expanded steel center around Miskolc produces heavy machinery and armament. It depends on imported ores and coal from the Soviet bloc neighbors. Györ, the second center in the northwest, has notable glass and chinaware factories in the midst of

Figure 10-15   Budapest is the capital of Hungary and the largest city in the Shatter Belt. The Danube which separates the two parts of the city is crossed by many bridges. (Courtesy of Legation of the Hungarian People's Republic.)

larger cement, chemical, and metallurgical plants. The size and dominance of Budapest overshadows all other Hungarian cities. Located on both banks of the Danube, it is an important bridge city, river port, and the cultural, political, commercial, and industrial center of Hungary. A cluster of light industrial establishments process the domestic agricultural products. Textile mills, shipbuilding, refineries, tractor plants, and factories manufacturing electrical goods further augment the city's industrial economy. Szeged and Debrecen are regional commercial centers.

Cut off from many of its resources, from its integrated transportation systems, and ready access to earlier industrial centers, residual Hungary found itself underdeveloped. World War II interrupted and retarded planned industrial and social adjustments. Less from internal choice than from outside coercion, Hungary today is in total alignment with the Soviet Union and its Shatter Belt satellites. Foreign trade is consummated largely within this bloc. The nation's main exports are bauxite, electrical goods and machinery, textiles, pharmaceuticals, and small quantities of agricultural products. Wood products, cotton, coke, ores, and petroleum are the principal imports.

ROMANIA

Territorially, Romania is slightly smaller than Oregon, but it is ten times as populous. Historically, the nucleus of modern Romania began in 1861 with the unification of Walachia and Moldavia. With the acquisition of Transylvania, part of the Alföld of Hungary, and smaller segments of adjacent Russia and Bulgaria, Romania doubled in size after World War I. Boundaries, however, are changed more easily than human personalities. The heteroge-

neous character of the added peoples created wide cultural discrepancies, if not outright resentments, that led to mutual liabilities and a checkered political development. Indeed, Romania grew more rapidly territorially than any other European country; but growth was attributable more to the grace of the victors of World War I than to her own military or administrative prowess. Although the indigenous trained technological and political talent of the newly acquired peoples was unacceptable to the new Romanian rulers, the low-level educational, technological, and administrative training of the Romanian himself proved unequal replacement. Romania thus became a prime example of an underdeveloped country—large in area, diversified geographically, rich in resources, but low in trained manpower.

Economic stagnation, the restive minorities, and the claims of neighboring nations involved Romania in World War II. On the basis of the dominant Hungarian population, part of Transylvania (Székelyland, 16,650 square miles) was returned to Hungary (Second Vienna Award, 1940). Today, however, it is again part of Romania with the status of an "Autonomous Hungarian Territory," where most Magyars are Protestants. The Soviet Union reoccupied Bessarabia and incorporated it into the Moldavian S.S.R., and Bulgaria regained southern Dobrugea.

Romania forms the easternmost wedge separating the northern from the southern Slavs. Some two-thirds of the 18 million people speak Romanian, a language derived from Latin, Slav, Magyar, and Turkic. About 1.8 million speak the Magyar tongue. A lesser number of Germans and Bulgarians and smaller groups of Serbs, Jews, Turks, Greeks, and Gypsies are also present within the confines of the present boundaries. Pointed toward the West by language and toward the

East by Greek Orthodoxy and other cultural characteristics, Romania is a transitional link between the two cultures.

There are striking similarities between Romania and Czechoslovakia. Both are recently created countries; both are rent by the Carpathian Mountains; both harbor large minorities; both have rich mineral and forest resources and the best water power potentials in the Shatter Belt. But where resemblances end, contrasts begin. The Czechs were the most highly developed peoples in their country, while the Romanians of the Old Kingdom were generally on a low level of industrial and cultural development. Transylvania showed a higher order of progress in all fields of human endeavor than did Old Romania. From prolonged underdevelopment Romania had a long way to go; and if for no other reason, evidence now seemingly points to remarkable progress.

PHYSICAL SETTING   Romania is dominated by the densely wooded, well-watered, and snow-silvered Carpathian Mountains. The great Walachian Plain, lying between the Carpathians and the Danube River, merges northward into the somewhat higher dissected Moldavian lands again lying between the Carpathians and the Pruth River. The eastern third of the state is thus bounded by the two rivers and the mountains. To the west the domal Bihar Mountains are cradled within the great westward-arcing Carpathians. Between the subdued and forested Bihar and the higher Carpathians themselves, the Transylvanian Basin, another flatland surface, opens westward onto the Alföld. All physiographic regions are structurally and topographically related to the Carpathians; only the small Dobrogea Platform lying between the Bulgarian border and the Danubian deltas stands unrelated.

The Walachian Plain, like the Alföld, has fertile chernozem-like soils which form the basic asset for an agricultural economy. Elsewhere farming is limited to alluvial soils along the many riverine strips. The Bihar and Carpathian Mountains contain dense stands of coniferous evergreen forests; the Transylvanian Basin and lowlands support large oak and beech groves. The climate, similar to that of New York, is generally the humid continental type.

AGRICULTURE AND INDUSTRY   Two-fifths of Romania is arable land on which four-fifths of the total working population are employed. Corn and wheat, the principal crops, occupy three-fourths of the arable lands. Despite the low yields associated with the extensive type of farming, the cultivation of large acreages enables Romania to rank as the leading corn and wheat grower of the Shatter Belt. Since corn is the main staple of the Romanian peasantry, the bulk of the wheat remains for export. Barley, oats, rye, and potatoes are cultivated largely on farms operated by Magyar and German peoples in Transylvania. Although the sugar beet is restricted to the Banat, and soybean, linseed, tobacco, rice, and cotton are grown on limited acreages elsewhere, peas and beans and sunflowers are widely distributed. Fruit orchards and vineyards are most common in Transylvania. The principal handicaps of Romanian agriculture have been the traditionally poor farming methods used by the peasantry. And collectivization does not seem to have increased farm output.

The Romanian is traditionally a sheepherder, keeping some 13 million multipurpose sheep in the mountains, where a strong transhumance movement has developed on the drier eastern lands. Cattle and horses as well as pigs are most numerous on the Danubian plains, but the water buffalo is popular only in Transylvania. Although many fish abound in the inland streams and the Black Sea, fishing is underdeveloped.

Romania's mineral wealth equals its surface riches. With the exception of petroleum and natural gas, the mineral resources are as underdeveloped as its surface potentialities. The Ploesti fields contain some 1,000 million barrels of reserves and yield about 10 million tons of petroleum annually. In addition to its foremost position as a petroleum producer, the gas fields of Ploesti and the Banat districts enable Romania to rank second only to the U.S.S.R. as a gas producer. Most of the petroleum is exported through Danubian and Black Sea ports to the Soviet Union and other members of the Communist bloc.

The nation's 4.5 million tons of coal, and somewhat smaller production of lignite, are utilized largely by the rapidly expanding blast furnace capacities in the Banat district. Some 1.8 million tons of iron ore, when augmented by imported iron ore, enable Romania to produce nearly 2 million tons of crude steel annually. Mountainous Transylvania has numerous mines producing salt, phosphate, gold, silver, copper, lead, zinc, manganese, and bauxite. The highlands and heavy precipitation provide great hydroelectric potential which remains almost undeveloped.

Urban and industrial life are confined to the capital city of Bucharest, the cities of the former Hungarian territories, and to Ploesti, Galati, and Braila. Villages and smaller towns, however, are very numerous. The modernity of Bucharest's central section gives way to sprawling tracts of small houses and unpaved streets. Many of its 1.5 million inhabitants are engaged in services, general trading, or work in heavy industrial establishments, machine shops, flour mills, textile facto-

ries, and distilling and chemical plants. Cluj and Timisoara with their large Hungarian minorities are the regional capitals of Transylvania and the Banat respectively; they are the only other towns with populations in excess of 100,000. The population decline of Brasov, Galati, Ploesti, and Iasi is attributable perhaps to the large-scale deportation, if not outright extermination, of many former inhabitants. While Braila and Galati are principal Danubian ports, Constanta is Romania's chief port on the Black Sea. Apart from the rapidly developing Banat mining and metallurgical complex, the diversified industries of Bucharest, and the petroleum refining of Ploesti, the only other manufacturing centers of Romania are the smaller wood-working establishments and wool-processing plants of Transylvanian towns.

Romania's principal exports are petroleum, timber, wheat and flour, and animals. Machinery, iron ore and coke, and chemicals are leading import items. Most of Romania's foreign trade is consummated within the Soviet bloc nations.

YUGOSLAVIA

Yugoslavia, with an area of 98,766 square miles and a population of 18.5 million, is as large and populous as the states of Pennsylvania, Virginia, and Maryland combined. A recently founded country, Yugoslavia was created in 1918 out of a patchwork of Balkan and peripheral peoples living in one of Europe's politically most sensitive sectors. Today, Yugoslavia lies between the Adriatic Sea and seven inland neighbors.

Largely through the aid of the victorious Entente, Serbia, liberated after four centuries of Turkish occupation and serving as the nucleus for the ensuing condominium, succeeded in uniting the various Slavs formerly under the disintegrating

Austro-Hungarian and Turkish empires. The Croatians, formerly united with the Hungarian kingdom for eight centuries, and the Slovenes formed with the Serbs a post-World War I union known as the "Kingdom of the Serbs, Croats, and Slovenes," which subsequently became Yugoslavia. The Serbs, however, considered the new state an enlarged Serbia, which assumption immediately created difficulties with the related Slavs, especially the Croats. Again, as in Poland, Czechoslovakia, and Romania, the large minorities from peripheral nations were included within the newly formed state. Beset by domestic Slavic troubles and by outside irredentist pressures, Yugoslavia in 1941 became the object of Italian and German invasion. Italy, Hungary, Bulgaria, and Germany temporarily annexed those parts of Yugoslavia inhabited by kindred peoples. Guerrilla warfare raged for four years among the Slavs themselves over the unsolved ethnic, political, and religious issues. Backed by the United Kingdom and the Soviet Union, the political-military movement headed by Marshal Tito succeeded in reestablishing former boundaries and later acquiring former Italian islands in the Adriatic and part of the Trieste zone. Since Soviet "armies of liberation" at no time entered Yugoslavia, the domestic Communist regime chose to follow an independent course based on conditional cooperation and a practice of utmost opportunism in its relations with the Western democracies and the Communist bloc. The intent of Yugoslavian leadership, together with its geographically sensitive location, seem to have qualified the troubled state for heavy United States aid. American aid, in turn, appears to have contributed to Yugoslavian economic development and abetted the Yugoslav one-party-one-leader domestic arrangement. International power politics still take precedence over unsolved ethnic and political problems, even over principles of self-determination.

The members of the Federal People's Republic of Yugoslavia consist of the Serbs, Croats, Slovenes, Montenegrins, and Macedonians who, on the basis of close ethnic relationship, formed a separate federal republic. Ethnically mixed Bosnia and Hercegovina were together added as the sixth member. Voyvodian (Bacska and Banat), with a large Hungarian minority, was made a semiautonomous oblast.

PHYSICAL SETTING The Adriatic laps against the narrow littoral at the base of the Dinaric Alps, whose parallel ranges and intervening valleys descend, one by one, toward the Alföld. The topographic dominance of the Dinaric Alps is reflected in the hydrographic pattern: three-fifths of Yugoslavian rivers empty into the Danube. With the exception of the Vardar, the other rivers flowing to the Adriatic and the Aegean Seas are few, short, and swift. Two-thirds of the country is mountainous or otherwise rugged. Moreover, the solution-honeycombed calcareous strata are filled with sinkholes, caverns, dolines, and poljes. Karsting thus intensified the natural inhospitality of mountains and, at the same time, encouraged isolation and the development of provincialism.

Aside from the alluvial soils of the narrow valley bottoms, the residual soils of the dolines and poljes represent the only tillable lands in the mountains. Yugoslavia's most extensive flatlands containing the most fertile alluvial soils lie north of the Sava River toward the Hungarian and Romanian borders, more especially in the Banat-Bacska district sometimes known as the Voyvodina. About one-third of the country is forested. Although the limestone and dolomitic mountain surfaces and the low Danubian lands are only sparsely wooded, the mountains of the south, especially near the Albanian border, are densely forested. Yugoslavia is mainly under the humid continental climatic influences. Nevertheless, the southward-opening Vardar Valley and the Adriatic littoral exhibit Mediterranean tendencies. Exposure and altitude produce wide local temperature and precipitation variations. The windward Adriatic side of the mountains receives over 180 inches of annual precipitation, but this amount decreases rapidly on the leeward side until not more than 20 inches falls on the lowlands of the Voyvodina. The Adriatic Sea itself, although it abounds in valuable marine life, scenery, and historic tradition, remains largely unexploited.

AGRICULTURE AND INDUSTRY Agricultural and industrial development vary widely, if not spectacularly, from one to another section of the country. While only one-third of Yugoslavia is arable, two-thirds of the working population are farmers. The best plowlands by far are in the northeastern parts of the country where, paradoxically, the Slavic population is sparse in the midst of the traditionally small Magyar landowners and dense farm communities. Without these former Magyar lands the country's agricultural production would be almost insignificant. Agriculture in the mountains, particularly in Bosnia and Hercegovina, is reduced to subsistence levels.

Corn, wheat, barley, and oats are the leading cereals. In normal years the corn yield in the Voyvodina is, if not the highest, at least one of the highest in Europe and is often better than that of the United States. Sugar beets and hemp are also widely grown. A quick-maturing variety of cotton, although locally significant, is still a new agricultural venture. Yugoslavia is the main tobacco grower of the Shatter Belt, but rice, like cotton, is produced for local consumption. Within sheltered valleys and on favorably exposed slopes, the orchards and vineyards produce a variety of fruits and grapes. Plums are especially abundant in Slavonia and Bosnia. When not exported as fresh fruit, the plums are desiccated by dry weather and exported as prunes, or more frequently they are distilled as fruit brandies.

Sheep are the country's dominant animals, partly because of rugged topography but more particularly because of tradition and the Moslem populations' penchant for mutton. Both hogs and cattle are most numerous on the best agricultural lands of the northeast.

Isolation breeds conservatism and an attitude of "What was good for grandfather is good enough for me." Thus, after forced agricultural collectivization, the Yugoslav peasantry reacted with traditional hostility, if not open sabotage, and agricultural output declined. But in the wake of relenting government decrees and increased farm mechanization, production again attained prewar levels. Agriculturally, Yugoslavia is the least collectivized country in the Shatter Belt.

The unfavorable agricultural environment of the mountains is offset by the abundant mineral resources in them. The high value set on a planned program of industrial expansion encouraged extensive mining operations. Some 2.2 million tons of iron ore are produced from mines in Ljubljana and elsewhere in Bosnia. Moreover, Yugoslavia is one of the ten leading world producers of copper, lead, antimony, chromite, and bauxite. Mercury, zinc, manganese, asbestos, salt, and gypsum are also mined on increasingly larger scales. While most of the ores are exported as raw ores or concentrates, several notable ore-dressing and refining centers have appeared on the new industrial skyline.

Yugoslavian lignite production, amounting to 22.8 million tons when augmented by the 1.4 million tons of coal, is next to that of Hungary, which country it is likely to displace as the third producer of the Shatter Belt. Petroleum production from the northern foothills increased rapidly to 1.4 million tons annually. Nevertheless, neither coal nor petroleum is sufficient to meet the fast-growing industrial demands.

The northern foothills from Ljubljana to Belgrade is the incipient "Ruhr of Yugoslavia." Nearness to raw materials, dense railway network, the navigable Sava, and the proximity of the Adriatic contribute their share to industrialization along this axis. The new Zenica steel complex, along with the metalliferous industries of the foothills belt, are surrounded by plants for the production of building materials, timber, paper, leather, and chemicals.

Yugoslavia, like Romania and Hungary, is a land of small cities and numerous villages. Located near the confluence of the Sava, Danube, Tisza, Temes, and Morava Rivers, Belgrade has been historically a nodal and gateway city. Despite its strategic site, ancient origin, and function as the capital, it is still small. The other large cities were developed and are located in the former Austro-Hungarian territories. Zagreb, Ljubljana, Subotica, and Rijeka are regional capitals with added functions of trade and recent industrialization. Sarajevo and Skoplje are the largest communities in "Old Serbia" carrying the undeniable imprint of the earlier Moslem occupants.

Rijeka, developed as the chief port of the Austro-Hungarian monarchy, was inherited by Italy and more recently by Yugoslavia. Although the outlet from the Danubian lands is difficult, nevertheless Rijeka is Yugoslavia's best port, handling annually some 6 million tons of inbound and outgoing sea trade. Dubrovnik, Sibenik, Split, Zada, and Pola are small

Figure 10-16 The Zanica Metal Works, largest in Yugoslavia, are located about 100 miles northwest of Sarajevo. The plant includes a steel rolling mill with a capacity of about 440,000 tons a year. (Courtesy of Consulate of Yugoslavia.)

Figure 10-17   Public building in Belgrade, capital of Yugoslavia. (Courtesy of Consulate of Yugoslavia.)

but important ports, naval bases, and resort centers along the rocky but climatically pleasant Adriatic coast.

Yugoslavia's principal exports of nonferrous ores and metals, chemicals, fruits and vegetables, tobacco, hides, timber, and pulpwood are exchanged for the main imports of machinery, coal, petroleum, cotton, and various foodstuffs. West Germany, Italy, the United States, and the United Kingdom, followed by the U.S.S.R., are Yugoslavia's principal trade partners.

BULGARIA

Bulgaria (42,796 square miles) is as large as Tennessee but twice as populous (7.8 million). Although the land now Bulgaria was occupied in Paleolithic times, the vestiges of the historic Thracians, Greeks, Romans, and Byzantines remain mute evidences of early civilizations. Indeed, the land was well known to Alexander the Great and to his renowned teacher, Aristotle. The early Bulgars themselves

were Fino-Ugric peoples, related to the Magyars. They appeared, horse-mounted, on the Balkan scene in the seventh century, turned to the Greek Orthodox form of Christianity in 865, and quickly expanded their sway over the entire Balkan Peninsula. The Bulgars were eventually absorbed by the probably indigenous if not the southward-migrating Slav population, until today only their name remains as a memento of their non-Slav past. Modern Bulgarian alphabet, language, and religion, together with present political commitment, are closely akin to those of Russia.

The national independence gained in 1878 did not efface five centuries of Turkish occupation; today some 10 per cent of the population still speak Turkish. However, nearly 90 per cent of the population speak Bulgarian, with only a few enclaves of Greeks, Romanians, and scattered Gypsies. As an ally of Germany in both World Wars, Bulgaria had as her objective the winning of territory inhabited by kindred peoples. With the exception of southern Dobrugea, all acquisitions were temporary.

PHYSICAL SETTING Bulgaria is dominated topographically by the rounded ranges of the Balkan Mountains and the nearly parallel serrated ranges of the Rhodope Mountains. Between the two the wedge-like Maritza Valley opens to the Black Sea, and laterally to the Aegean and the Sea of Marmara. It is the nation's principal lowland. The Balkan Mountains descend northward to form a discontinuous and dissected plateau surface (Danubian Foreland) which terminates as an escarpment overlooking the Danube River. The country is predominantly mountainous.

Forest, confined largely to the mountains, covers nearly one-third of Bulgaria's surface and represents a great source of national wealth. The mountains and the northern plateaus are under humid continental climatic influences, but the sheltered Maritza Valley has the milder humid subtropical climate similar to that of the Carolinas. Mediterranean climate penetrates the southward-oriented small valleys of the Rhodopes. The broad interfluves of the northern forelands contain fertile residual limestone and transported loessal soils, but the soils of the Maritza Valley owe their fertility to alluvial and diluvial origins. Despite the broad frontage on the Black Sea, the Bulgarians have not turned to seafaring.

AGRICULTURE AND INDUSTRY Although only about two-fifths of the country's surface is arable, nearly four-fifths of the country's working population are engaged in agricultural pursuits. Agricultural lands are confined largely to the forelands north of the Balkan Mountains and to the valleys of the Maritza. Wheat and corn are the main crops cultivated, but rye, barley, oats, and rice are also produced. Sugar beets, potatoes, flax, alfalfa, sunflowers, and cotton together with lesser acreages of soybeans and opium poppies are significant local crops. Bulgarian tobaccos and wine grapes are famous internationally; but more renowned is the attar of roses

Figure 10-18   Herds of sheep graze on the meadows and steep slopes of the forested mountains of southwestern Bulgaria. (Courtesy of Legation of People's Republic of Bulgaria.)

obtained from roses grown in the Tundzha Valley.

Numerous pigs, cattle, and horses are raised on lowlands, but Bulgaria, like neighboring Yugoslavia, is best known for its larger number of sheep and goats. Bulgarian cheese and yoghurt made from ewe's and goat's milk are nearly as famous as its rose gardens.

Bulgarian agriculture is the most highly collectivized in the Shatter Belt. The government's eagerness, if not unrealistic program, to increase agricultural production twofold in the next decade remains to be accomplished.

Bulgaria has made a successful leap forward in developing her mineral resources. Lignite production, now amounting to 2 million tons, quadrupled in the past five years as new coal mines yield over ½ million tons annually. Some 200,000 tons of petroleum are pumped yearly from recently discovered fields, and new hydroelectric installations utilize part of the country's great water power potential. Some 400,000 tons of domestic iron ore are smelted in the new steel plant at Dimitrovograd, where more than 250,000 tons of crude steel are produced annually. Lead, zinc, copper, manganese, chromite, rock salt, and gypsum are mined in increasing quantities.

Previously the modest Bulgarian industries processed food products and tobacco leaf and made fertilizers and textiles. The recent emphasis on heavy industry enables Bulgaria to produce its own metals and machinery. Nevertheless, machinery, iron ore, and petroleum are still the most significant import items. The principal new industries center on the lignite fields of the Maritza Valley and near Sofiya.

Sofiya, aside from its important nodal position on the Balkan Peninsula, is the nation's capital and largest city, with outstanding trading and manufacturing func-

Figure 10-19 The large-scale cultivation of roses, from which rose attar is distilled, has earned Bulgaria the name "Land of Roses." This view is in the Tundzha Valley. (Courtesy of Legation of People's Republic of Bulgaria.)

tions. Plovdiv, the second largest city, is the main commercial center of the Maritza Valley. While Rushchuk is the leading Danubian port city, Varna and Burgas are Bulgaria's main Black Sea ports. Dimitrovograd, Kolarovgrad, and Pleven are regional trade centers, but more recently they are assuming mining and manufacturing functions as well. Tobacco leaf is an export item of leading value, but attar of roses, fruits and vegetables, cereals, timber, and hides are also exported. Nearly all Bulgarian foreign trade is correlated with the Soviet bloc economy.

ALBANIA

Albania (10,629 square miles), slightly larger than Maryland, is only half as populous (1.4 million). But size is not the only criterion for importance among nations. Albania lies strategically a mere 50 miles from the Italian heel, across the narrowed southern Adriatic strait. The Albanians have the unenviable tradition of being Europe's most foreign-ruled people. After two thousand years of rule by Romans, Byzantines, Goths, Serbs, and Turks, the country obtained independence in 1912, mostly to forestall the claims of rivaling neighbors. During World War I the country was prey to Italian, Greek, Serbian, Austrian, and Bulgarian forces; during the interwar years it became a political dependency of Italy. Following the Axis Powers' occupation in World War II and the establishment of a Communist regime at the end of 1944, Albania nearly became a political and economic satellite of Yugoslavia, her larger neighbor.

The ancient Illyrian tongue, antedating all other languages used on the Balkan Peninsula, is preserved in the Gheg dialect in the northern, and by the Tosk in the southern, parts of Albania. Five centuries of Turkish occupation bequeathed Islam, a religion professed by three-fourths of the population. Roman Catholicism and Greek Orthodoxy are minority religions; Turkish and Greek are lesser languages.

Albania looms from the Adriatic to elevations of 7,000 feet within a 50-mile distance inland to the Yugoslavian border. The short swift streams emanating, if not jumping, from the mountains unloaded their rocky burden and thereby provided a flat coastal plain. Despite its marshy and malarial-mosquito-infested character, the littoral is the population, agricultural, and economic center of the country.

The country's agriculture, if not its entire economy, is based upon subsistence farming and sheep raising. Although the California-like climate permits the cultivation of citrus and olive orchards, the predominant crops are corn and wheat; tobacco, cotton, and rice are also cultivated.

The magnificent stands of timber in the mountainous interior, as well as the known copper, chromite, bauxite, bitumen, asphalt, and lignite resources, remain practically unworked. Petroleum production of some 400,000 tons annually is by far the nation's leading resource. While most of it is exported, a smaller amount is refined at Cerrik. Like agriculture, manufacturing, too, is done on a modest scale in establishments devoted to processing agricultural products. Albania has no towns with populations of over 50,000. Tirane, the capital, Shkoder, Durres, and Vlone are the largest communities. With the exception of a short railway, modern means of transportation are not developed. Modest exports of petroleum, chrome, and copper ore are traded for imports of manufactured goods and machinery.

IN PERSPECTIVE

THE SHATTER BELT, AN UNSOLVED PROBLEM

Diastrophism, glaciation, and the workings of a blast furnace are easier by far to understand than nationalism, tradition, and the workings of political ideologies. Moreover, the human geographic problems posed by a 1,300-year uninterrupted record in Bulgaria are on a different level from the same problems involved in 100-year-old Kansas. While many similarities are present in the physical geography of the two areas, the historical geography of the Shatter Belt is quite unlike that of the United States. The history of the United States is short; the history of the Shatter Belt is long. Since the present, and more emphatically the future, is understood in terms of the past, a brief evaluative account of the Shatter Belt past has been deliberately presented. But history without land is meaningless; the two are transmuted into the human geography of the Shatter Belt, which at times may seem superficially tortile if not negative.

The world's largest land power, the Soviet Union, and secondarily the great powers lying to the west of the Shatter Belt appear driven insatiably and relentlessly toward territorial expansion. When not passionately defending their heritage, the small intermediate nations, not altogether innocent of dreams of aggrandizement, have become willing allies of the greater powers. The resulting wars have left a human aftermath of minorities, expellees, and pent-up resentment that wait for powerful allies to set right that which went wrong. But who or what is to set things right? Not a desire to "cast the first stone," but a concerted effort to cast ballots; not a warlike frenzy to count the dead for fatherland, but a peaceful counting of votes for every man's freedom. These are the sorely needed adjustments in the Shatter Belt. Unlike forced expulsions and exterminations of minorities, self-determination has never been tried on a grand scale in the Shatter Belt. The outcome of free elections, if ever allowed, would bring about a popular settlement of long-standing disputes more acceptable than the resentful, if not vengeful, present adjustments.

Large and diverse in area, rich agriculturally and mineralogically, populous and rich in human ingenuity, the Shatter Belt is well endowed geographically. Indeed, the geographic environment is far kinder than the domestic or foreign human neighbors. The Shatter Belt problems are evidently less the results of geography than of human psychology.

SELECTED REFERENCES

Byrnes, Robert F.: *Yugoslavia,* Frederick A. Praeger, Inc., New York, 1957.

Part II, Geography and Demography, *is divided into two chapters, "The Land" and "The People." The chapter entitled "The Land" discusses the regional and physical geography of the country and also points up certain geological features. The chapter entitled "The People" discusses the distribution of population, the labor force, and social and economic factors.*

Fischer-Galati, Stephen (ed.): *Romania,* Frederick A. Praeger, Inc., New York, 1957.

Chapter 2, "The Land," is a discussion of the physical geography of Romania—location, regions, climate, hydrography, and soils. Chapter 3, "The People," discusses population distribution, migration, and socioeconomic factors.

Hoffman, George W.: *A Geography of Europe,* 2d ed., The Ronald Press Company, New York, 1961.

Chapter 8 deals with the cultural and historical background and the physical landscape of the Shatter Belt as well as with the countries individually.

Kerner, Robert J. (ed.): *Yugoslavia,* University of California Press, Berkeley, Calif., 1949.

Chapter 1, "The Geographical Scene," was written by Griffith Taylor. It is a brief but concise geographical review of the physical and economic geography of the country, which serves as the basis for the development of such topics as economic conditions, cultural development, and Yugoslavia among the nations.

U.S. Bureau of the Census, *International Population Statistics Reports,* ser. P-90, *The Population of Czechoslovakia,* no. 3, 1953; *The Population of Poland,* no. 4, 1954; *The Population of Hungary,* no. 9, 1958; *The Labor Force of Czechoslovakia,* no. 13, 1960; and *The Labor Force of Rumania,* no. 14, 1961.

These volumes go beyond their intent of presenting a detailed and technical account of the population problems, for they also include valuable observations on the historical and geographical backgrounds for population growth and distribution. Numerous source materials are listed in these publications.

Vagacs, Andras: *A Short Geography of Hungary,* University Printing House, Budapest, 1961.

A study of Hungary's physical, regional, and economic geography, profusely illustrated by photographs, maps, and comparative statistical information.

chapter 11

UNION OF SOVIET
SOCIALIST REPUBLICS

Figure 11-1   The Soviet Union is the world's largest nation, having an area comparable to that of North America. The nation extends across 170° of longitude and 45° of latitude. Plains dominate the landscape west of the Yenisey River, but mountains and hills are the common landforms east of the river. Much of the drainage of the U.S.S.R is through rivers flowing into the landlocked Caspian Sea or the Arctic Ocean.

ARCTIC OCEAN

NOVAYA ZEMLYA

Kola Peninsula

TIMAN RANGE

Byranga Plateau

Indigirka River

ANADYR RANGE

KORYAK RANGE

Indigirka Plain

Kolyma River

KOLYMA RANGE

CHERSKI RANGE

Kamchatka Peninsula

VERKHOYANSK RANGE

Lena River

Lena Basin

SEA OF OKHOTSK

KURIL ISLANDS

URAL MOUNTAINS

Vasyugan Swamp

Ob River

Central Siberian Plateau

Yenisey River

STANOVOY MOUNTAINS

SAKHALIN

SIKHOTE ALIN

West Siberian Lowland

BAYKAL RANGE

Vitim Plateau

Amur River

n Plain

ger

Irtysh River

SAYAN MOUNTAINS

Lake Baykal

YABLONOV MOUNTAINS

ALTAI MOUNTAINS

Turgay Gate

Kazakh Uplands

pian Sea land

-Urt teau

ARAL SEA

Lake Balkhash

Kyzyl-Kum

TIEN-SHAN

Kara Kum

Fergana Valley

PET-DAG

PAMIRS

*W*ITHIN A RELATIVELY SHORT PERIOD OF thirty years, the Union of Soviet Socialist Republics has risen to a position of industrial importance second only to that of the United States. Its industrial strength, too, is matched by its military might and its astounding prowess in space exploration.

Because the U.S.S.R. is also the principal citadel of the worldwide Communist movement, which seeks to promote economic, political, and social revolution everywhere, it compels our close attention and study. We must seek greater understanding of the country and what it stands for, if we are to be in a better position to defend and strengthen our own freedoms and way of life.

The Union of Soviet Socialist Republics,[1] ranking first in size among the sovereign states of the world, covers an area of 8½ million square miles or roughly one-sixth of the earth's land surface. Essentially continental in dimensions, it is somewhat larger than South America and nearly as large as North America. Moreover, its size exceeds by about 2½ times that of some of the large countries of the world, notably the United States, China, and Brazil.

Extending from 19°30′ east longitude, just west of Kaliningrad on the Baltic Sea, to 169°30′ west longitude in the Bering Strait, off Alaska, the Soviet Union spans a distance, from west to east, of nearly 7,000 miles. This vast longitudinal extent marks a difference in time of eleven hours, or four times the difference in hours between New York and California. The latitudinal spread, while much shorter, is nevertheless impressive. From Cape Chelyushkin at 77°35′ north latitude to Kushka at 35°15′ north latitude, on the southern border with Afghanistan, the

distance is nearly 3,000 miles. Relative to North America, the southern border of the U.S.S.R. lies at approximately the same latitude as Memphis or Chattanooga, Tennessee; the latitude of the northernmost mainland point is that of the Queen Elizabeth Islands of the Canadian Arctic (Figure 11-2).

Although it extends to subtropical latitudes, the Soviet Union is essentially a northern land. It has physical characteristics which are similar in many respects to those of Canada. Three-fourths of its territory lies to the north of the 49th parallel, which in turn forms the southern boundary of Canada. Moreover, one-fourth of Soviet territory lies north of the Arctic Circle.

The vast size of the Soviet Union is reflected in its extensive boundaries. The combined length of its coastline and land borders reaches more than 37,000 miles. Of this distance, coastlines account for two-thirds or 27,000 miles. Yet in spite of its extensive coastline, the Soviet Union exhibits climatic characteristics which are on the whole continental rather than marine. The country appears locked up in its enormous size and territorial spread. One-half of the Union, in fact, is situated more than 400 miles from the sea. For the most part the coastline is regular, and there are few good harbors. The coastal waters of the Arctic and Pacific Oceans are cold, and except for a stretch of the Barents Sea coast near Murmansk, they are icebound in winter. The northern part of the Caspian Sea is also frozen in winter, as is much of the Baltic coast. Ice may also form along the north shore of the Black Sea.

Many Soviet ports are located on seas whose entrances are controlled by other countries. The approaches from the Atlantic Ocean to the Soviet Baltic Sea ports are flanked by territories of Western European

[1] The spelling of the English transliteration of the Russian place names is based on *Goode's World Atlas.*

Figure 11-2   About one-half of the United States is south of the latitude of the Soviet Union. In area the U.S.S.R. is almost three times as large.

countries. The Black Sea exit to the Mediterranean and Aegean Seas is controlled by Turkey. Even the southern and central exits from the Sea of Japan, off Vladivostok, are bordered by Japan and South Korea.

The Soviet Union has a land boundary in common with twelve other countries, both in Europe and Asia. From the Black Sea to the Pacific Ocean, the Soviet Union borders Turkey, Iran, Afghanistan, the Chinese People's Republic, the Mongolian People's Republic, and the Korean People's Republic. Over most of its 8,000-mile extent, the boundary passes through sparsely populated desert and mountainous areas. In fact, throughout its length, the boundary is crossed by only four railroad trunk lines.

The 900-mile boundary, extending from the Black to the Baltic Seas, borders the People's Republics of Romania, Hungary, Czechoslovakia, and Poland. The European boundary, unlike the Asian, passes through lowlands which, for the most part, are well populated. No less than fifteen railroads link the Soviet Union to the countries of Eastern Europe.

Whereas the Asian boundary has been altered little in recent times, the western boundary has fluctuated greatly. Since 1939 it has been pushed farther to the west. The Soviet Union regained in 1940 the provinces of Northern Bukhovina and Bessarabia held by Romania since 1918. Bessarabia was subsequently added to the Moldavian Autonomous Soviet Socialist Republic to form a new constituent republic, the Moldavian Soviet Socialist Republic. From Czechoslovakia, after the war, the Soviet Union gained Ruthenia, which, including a portion of the Carpathian Mountains and the upper Tisza River Valley, was added to the Ukrainian Soviet Socialist Republic. This cession not only gave the Soviet Union access to the middle Danube, but it also afforded a common boundary with Hungary. The present boundary with Poland lies as much as 200 miles west of its position prior to World War II. The Soviet incorporation of the eastern territories of Poland was accompanied by an expansion of Poland westward at the expense of Germany to the Oder-Neisse Rivers. Though unrecognized as a final settlement by the Western powers, the Oder-Neisse line remains the *de facto* western boundary of Poland. Similarly, the German exclave of East Prussia was divided between Poland and the Soviet Union, the latter gaining the city of Königsberg and its surrounding territory, now Kaliningrad Oblast. Finally, in 1940 the Soviet Union seized the independent Baltic republics of Lithuania, Latvia, and Estonia; the annexation of this territory resulted in an expanded Soviet frontage on the Baltic Sea.

The remainder of the western boundary, extending from the Gulf of Finland to the Barents Sea, was altered also as a result of the Russo-Finnish War of 1939 and World War II. Consequently, the Karelian Isthmus, formerly one of the richest districts of Finland, was ceded to the Soviet Union, along with other borderlands to the north including the Pechenga district (Petsamo), containing rich nickel mines. The loss of Pechenga deprived Finland of its Arctic coast and established a common boundary between Norway and the Soviet Union.

THE SOVIET CORE AREA

While the territorial extent of the Soviet Union is very large, only a relatively small part of it, frequently called the fertile triangle, is suitable for intensive economic development. In that triangle live approximately 80 per cent of the Union's 220 million people. Yet the area in which the bulk of economic activity is presently concentrated, the core area, is an even smaller region within the fertile triangle. The Soviet core area lies within the west central part of the country, extending from Leningrad eastward to and including the middle Urals, thence through Volgograd (formerly Stalingrad) and Rostov to the southwestern boundary of the country (Figure 11-3).

Enclosed within the delimited area are many of the large cities of the Union including, besides the above mentioned, Moscow, Kiev, Gor'kiy, Kharkov, Kuybyshev, Sverdlovsk, Stalino, Dnepropetrovsk, and Odessa. These and other cities of the core area account for 75 per cent of the country's manufacturing. In the core, too, the transportation net, especially rail, is most dense. Finally, much of the richest agricultural land of the Union lies within the core, mainly in the black-earth steppe of the southwest.

This area of concentration of economic activity has its roots in development beginning in the tsarist period. On the eve of the Bolshevik Revolution of 1917, the main centers of manufacturing were St. Petersburg (now Leningrad), Moscow, and nearby cities, and the southern Ukraine, where extensive deposits of coal and iron ore favored a metallurgical industry. In the early eighteenth century an iron industry had grown up in the Urals,

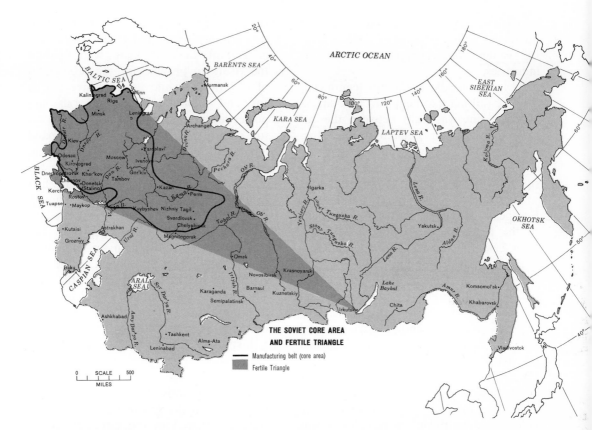

Figure 11-3   The core area and the fertile triangle are both best developed in the European part of the Soviet Union.

but by the end of the nineteenth century it had lost its preeminent place in Russian production to the Ukrainian cities in the Donets Basin, or the Donbass.

The bulk of the population of tsarist Russia, too, was located in the European part of the country. Especially dense was the rural population settled in the southwest. Beyond the core, however, the land was only sparsely inhabited. Settlement had been undertaken in the steppe region of Western Siberia, stimulated by the emancipation of the peasantry in 1861 and the construction of the Trans-Siberian

Railway in 1894, but much of eastern and indeed all of Northern Siberia remained virtually uninhabited, save for small bands of native tribesmen. In the Trans-Caucasus and in Central Asia, which the Russians had annexed in the nineteenth century, the native peoples followed a way of life centuries old, which modern economic development had scarcely touched.

Though industrialization did not begin in the Russian empire until late in the nineteenth century, large towns and cities had appeared much earlier. Linked mainly by an intricate system of rivers, these population centers functioned as seats of provincial administration as well as trading centers and centers of handicraft industries.

From the middle of the nineteenth century the rail net had begun to take shape. The first line was built between the imperial capital of St. Petersburg and Moscow in 1851. This was followed by lines linking the grain-producing regions of the steppe with the cities to the north. Later, to facilitate grain exports to Western European countries, railways were built to the ports on the Baltic, Black, and Azov Seas. The growth of heavy industry in the Ukraine resulted in additional lines between the mines and mills and between the southern centers of production and the northern markets. Finally, the need for raw materials and a governmental policy of territorial expansion compelled the construction of long rail lines into the Caucasus and Central Asia, as well as across Siberia to the Pacific Ocean.

The economic development of the core area before the Bolshevik Revolution was enhanced, too, by accessibility to Western Europe. Here, at the time of Russian industrial expansion, lay the major sources of capital, machinery, equipment, and technology, as well as markets for lumber, furs, and grain, important earners of *valuta,* or foreign currency.

Under Soviet rule, a program of rapid industrial development begun in 1928–1929, accompanied by an enforced collectivization of agriculture which released a large surplus population for industry, contributed substantially to the further growth of the core area. Old centers of manufacturing were rebuilt and expanded. New industries appeared in ancient towns, and new manufacturing centers were built elsewhere. Additional rail lines were laid to support the new

industry, and waterways were improved by building canals and by increasing the navigability of rivers. Dams were built on the rivers to provide for the production of electricity, while an extensive search for and exploitation of minerals and power resources began throughout the entire country. The Soviet drive to expand its industrial base, and particularly that of heavy industry, led above all to the emergence of new industrial regions, first in the Urals and then beyond. Though rich in iron ore, the Ural Mountains lack adequate supplies of coking coal; but this deficiency resulted in an immediate expansion of coal production in the rich Kuznetsk Basin, 1,000 miles to the east. The marriage of Kuznetsk coal to Urals iron ore not only led to the establishment of large new metallurgical and machine industries in the Urals, which included such centers of production as Magnitogorsk, Sverdlovsk, and Chelyabinsk, but also to the founding of a smaller producing center in the Kuznetsk. Finally, new centers of manufacturing have emerged in more peripheral areas of the country such as in the Trans-Caucasus, Central Asia, Eastern Siberia, and the Soviet Far East. Yet, in spite of these developments and a shift of industry eastward both during and after World War II, the traditional core area remains the economic heart of the country.

THE GOALS OF SOVIET GEOGRAPHIC DEVELOPMENT

The main objective of Soviet geographic development has been the erection of a citadel of socialism in the U.S.S.R. from which the revolution, preserved and strengthened, might be exported to other parts of the world.

At the time of the Bolshevik, or Communist, revolution, Russia was still essentially a backward agricultural country. Lenin and his fellow revolutionaries originally believed that the revolution in Russia could not succeed unless it had the support of an international revolutionary movement, originating particularly in the industrial countries of Western Europe where Marx had predicted the Communist revolution would occur first anyway. However, in the years immediately following the Communist seizure of power in Russia, a Communist revolution did not sweep over the Western countries. Before his death in 1924, Lenin came to realize that the rebuilding of Russia along Marxist socialist or Communist lines would, therefore, not have support from abroad, while his successor, Stalin, proclaimed the unorthodox idea that socialism could be built in one country. But, if socialism were to survive in Russia, that country must be strengthened, said Stalin, to guard against attack from its enemies, the capitalist countries.

In order to build a strong socialist state, the Soviet regime launched in 1928 a series of Five-Year Plans designed to speed the development of industry under tight governmental control. Initiated also was a complete reorganization of the countryside, which involved the merger of small private peasant holdings into numerous collective farms or kolkhozes and the creation of large specialized state farms, or sovkhozes.

Up until the Nazi invasion of the Soviet Union in June, 1941, two Five-Year Plans had been completed and a third introduced. Industrial output had risen substantially over that of 1928, but at great cost and suffering to the Soviet peasant or farm worker and the city dweller. As a result of peasant hostility to collectivization, even by the outbreak of the war agricultural production had not regained its precollectivization level. After the war a fourth Five-Year Plan begun in 1946 aimed at rebuilding the economy damaged severely by the war. A fifth plan, introduced in 1950, was followed by a sixth in 1956, only to be discarded two years later in favor of a longer-range plan, the current Seven-Year Plan, which will be concluded in the mid 1960s.

Soviet plans operate, according to Soviet political economists, under the socialist law of planned proportional development. This means that under socialist planning, all parts of the country (as well as all branches of the economy) undergo even development, as opposed to the situation under capitalism, where development, said to be uneven, results in the core area developing and exploiting at the expense of the peripheral areas. Under socialism, it is claimed, development would occur everywhere; differences between advanced regions and backward regions and between town and countryside would thereby be eliminated.

An even development of all parts of the Soviet Union would necessitate an even distribution of resources. Yet because the Soviet Union has such a huge extent, resources are not evenly spread, and distances between consuming areas and producing areas may be very great. It should be remembered, moreover, that the Soviet Union is a northern land with an intemperate climate. Both climate and soils impose severe limitations on crop production in many parts of the country. The vast size of the country and its varied and unequal natural conditions create major difficulties for Soviet planners attempting to work under the framework of an ideology which refuses to recognize the limitations imposed by nature.

PHYSICAL SETTING

RELIEF FEATURES

To a considerable degree, the U.S.S.R. consists of extensive lowlands lying to the north of a complex belt of mountains and plateaus which form much of the southern border zone of the country. The plain, which predominates in the European part of the country, is continued east of the Urals in the vast Western Siberian lowland and to the south in the desert basin of the Aral Sea. The eastern limit of the lowland is set by the Yenisey River, but the plainlike character of the land continues, for the most part, throughout the Central Siberian Plateau. Only in the northeastern and eastern portions of Siberia east of the Lena River do mountains break the lowland expanse.

EUROPEAN RUSSIA   The Russian Plain, which occupies the greater part of European Russia, is a broad structural basin, composed mainly of horizontal layers of sedimentary rocks. Its average elevation is 300 feet above sea level, but in places uplands appear, rising to 1,000 feet, which give the land a gently rolling character. Some upland areas, notably the Central Russian Upland, between the Dnepr and Don Rivers and the Pre-Volga Heights between the Don and Volga Rivers, result from a warping of the earth's crust. Other uplands, such as the Azov-Podolian Shield west of the Dnepr River, are formed where older and more resistant crystalline rocks appear near the surface. The lowland plain has been affected, too, by glaciation. Of three glacial advances from northern Scandinavia, the third, or Würm, having covered the northwestern and northern parts of Russia, left the most evident traces, especially in extensive morainic ridges. One of these is the Smolensk-Moscow Ridge; others, making up the Valdai Hills, form the divide for rivers flowing to the Baltic and those flowing to the Black and Caspian Seas. Lakes, bogs, and marshes are found in many places. The most extensive area of poorly drained land is the Polesye in Belorussia. The southern part of the plain, which remained unglaciated, is covered by accumulations of loess, a fine silt transported by wind and derived from clay and sandy glacial outwash material deposited near the edge of the glaciers. Erosion of the loess has caused the formation of numerous ravines and gulleys.

The Russian Plain is bordered on the northwest by the Karelian Shield, a region of ancient hard rock scoured by glaciation, which, in the Kola Peninsula, rises to heights of over 4,000 feet. On the east the Urals form the boundary, stretching for 1,600 miles in a north-south direction. The mountains are not a formidable divide, however, since the elevation of the middle section is low and easily traversed. Between the industrial cities of Chelyabinsk and Nizhniy Tagil, it does not exceed 2,500 feet, and at Sverdlovsk it is less than 1,000 feet. The northern and southern Urals, on the other hand, are higher, with elevations rising from 5,000 to 6,000 feet. In the north a spur of the Urals, the Timan Ridge, extends in a northwesterly direction, interrupting the northern portion of the Plain.

In southern European Russia, apart from the Black and Caspian Seas, the Plain ends at the high Caucasus Mountains (18,000 feet) and at the Yaila Mountains (5,000 feet) in the Crimean Peninsula. In the southwest, the Carpathian Mountains form the border. On the west, the Plain remains unbroken, except for the Polesye, and it sweeps into Poland and beyond as part of the North European Plain.

ASIATIC RUSSIA   The Asiatic part of the Soviet Union may be divided, for convenience of description, into Western Siberia, Central Siberia, Eastern Siberia, the Soviet Far East, and Soviet Central Asia.

Western Siberia, extending between the Ural Mountains and the Yenisey River, is composed of a vast and extremely flat lowland. Across the lowland flows the Ob' River and its major tributary, the Irtysh. The flatness of the lowland is apparent in the fact that the Ob' River is less than 300 feet above sea level some 1,800 miles from its mouth. The lowland has been affected, in its northern part, by glaciation, but evidences of it have been largely removed by stream erosion. Vast flood plains have been formed as streams meander across the lowland; indeed, the distinction between flood plain and interfluve is almost imperceptible. The interfluve between the Ob' and Irtysh Rivers is, in fact, an extensive waterlogged area called the Vasyugan Swamp. The southern part of the lowland, though for the most part flat, is better drained.

On the south, the lowland terminates in the Kazakh Uplands and in the broadened base of the southern Urals. Between the two, a lowland route, the Turgay Gate, leads into the Aral Sea basin in Soviet Central Asia. To the southeast, the West Siberian lowland is bordered by the Altai and Sayan Mountain systems. Within these uplands, but open on the north to the West Siberian lowland, is the Kuznetsk Basin, and to the east along the upper Yenisey is the Minusinsk Basin.

Central Siberia comprises the territory lying between the Yenisey and Lena Rivers. An upland region, dissected by the major tributaries of the Yenisey and Lena Rivers, it has the appearance, over much of its area, of a broad horizontal tableland. Elevations ordinarily do not exceed 3,000 feet. On the north, the plateau descends to lowlands which stretch along the Arctic coast. On the south, it is terminated by the Sayan and Baykal Mountains, with deeply set Lake Baykal.

Eastern Siberia is situated between the Lena River and the Pacific coast ranges. The region is composed of an array of mountain systems, enclosing rolling plateaus and swampy lowlands. The major

Figure 11-4   The taiga in Central Siberia is an upland area dissected by major rivers. In this area the Lena River has cut a broad valley through the dense forest. (Courtesy of Tass.)

ranges are the Verkhoyansk, the Cherski, and, in the extreme northeast, the Kolyma. To the east of Lake Baykal stretch the relatively low, rounded Yablonovy and Stanovoy Mountains.

The region known as the Soviet Far East comprises the Pacific coastal portions of Siberia, the Kamchatka Peninsula, the Kurile Islands, the basin of the lower Amur River, and Sakhalin Island. The region is predominantly mountainous, with only narrow coastal lowlands. However, behind the Sikhote Alin (Range), a broad and poorly drained valley has been formed by the Amur River and its major tributary, the Ussuri. Mountains prevail in southern Sakhalin, but the northern part is relatively low and flat. The Kurile Islands form a chain of volcanic islands extending from Kamchatka Peninsula to Hokkaido, the northernmost island of Japan.

The last of the Asiatic regions, Soviet Central Asia, consists mainly of the interior drainage basin centering on the Aral Sea. Sandy deserts, such as the Kara Kum and Kyzyl Kum south of Aral, are extensive. The lowlands are bordered almost entirely by plateaus and mountains. Between the Caspian and Aral Seas lies the Ust Urt Plateau, which is virtually lacking in surface water. On the Soviet border, to the south, are a series of mountain systems including the Kopet Dag, the high Pamirs, the Tien Shan, the Dzungarian Ala-Tau and, to the east, the Tarbagatay Range and the Altai Mountains. The permanent snows of the mountainous borderlands, particularly in the Pamirs and Tien Shan, form the sources of rivers such as the Amu Dar'ya and Syr Dar'ya which flow across the sandy desert to the Aral Sea. Smaller streams, such as the Zeravshan, descend into the lowlands, but disappear eventually in the sands. At the base of the mountains, irregular zones of loess foothills occur, and mountain spurs enclose fertile valleys, of which the most important, the Fergana Valley, is drained by the Syr Dar'ya.

CLIMATE

The Soviet Union lies, for the most part, in the higher middle latitudes of the Northern Hemisphere, where the land mass reaches its greatest extent and much of the country is far removed from the moderating influences of the oceans. A northerly location on the largest of the continents thus gives to the Soviet Union an extremely continental climate. Its winters are long and cold and its summers short and hot. Precipitation is moderate to low. These characteristics of its climate intensify from west to east.

The moist, mild air from the Atlantic and Pacific Oceans does not penetrate deeply into the country. Such air, entering from the Atlantic, affects, fairly strongly, only the western and northwestern parts of European Russia. The moderating effect of the Pacific Ocean is limited only to Pacific coastal areas. The latitudinal position of the Soviet Union, on the other hand, exposes it to strongly developed cold air masses of Arctic and polar origin that, in the absence of any east-west trending mountains, often move far into the southern reaches of the country. Tropical air from the southern oceans is prevented from entering because of high mountains and plateaus along the southern border of the country.

The effect of maritime air is limited further by the development in winter of a zone of high pressure, centering over Eastern Siberia, with a narrow ridge of high pressure extending into European Russia approximately along the 50th parallel. Outward from the high-pressure areas flows cold, dry air. Thus all of Siberia as well as Central Asia, the south-eastern parts of European Russia, and even the Pacific coast receive the impact of this outblowing air in winter. Northwestern European Russia, with some marine influences, is not as dry or as steadily cold in winter as the country as a whole. The average January temperature in Leningrad is 18°F, whereas farther into the interior at Omsk in Western Siberia it is −3°F, and at Verkhoyansk in Eastern Siberia, −58°F.

A very limited area on the south Crimean coast, which is bordered by mountains on the north, as well as parts of Transcaucasia and the valleys of extreme

southern portions of Central Asia, because of their low latitudes and protected positions, have relatively mild winter temperatures. Sochi, on the Black Sea coast, has a January average temperature of 43°F, and Fergana, in southern Central Asia, 28°F.

In summer, westerly and northwesterly Atlantic air predominates over much of the country, because of a much weakened or virtually absent high-pressure system. During this season air moves inward also from the cooler Pacific Ocean. Summer is the period of maximum precipitation for the country except on the Black Sea coast. From northwestern Russia, precipitation

Figure 11-5   In general, the climatic and agricultural zones extend from west to east across the nation. Note the relationship of these belts to latitude.

AGRO-CLIMATIC MAP

—————— 20-inch annual Isohyet
•••••••• 10-inch annual Isohyet
– – – – – 110 days frost free
∴∴∴∴∴∴ Northern boundary of Chernozem

0   SCALE   500
MILES

totals decrease toward the interior, except in upland and mountain areas where the orographic influence is pronounced. Summer temperatures are high, except along the Pacific and Arctic coasts. The hottest parts are in Soviet Central Asia, where the July averages range from 80 to 90°F.

For purposes of agriculture, the length of the winter season, relieved by short, though generally warm summers and only brief spring and autumn periods, is a definite handicap. A short frost-free period, in fact, places the northern part of European Russia and most of Siberia beyond the limits of crop production. The short growing season, too, narrows the variety of crops which may be grown, and helps to account for the large acreages of barley and spring wheat, crops which mature relatively rapidly.

Deficiency of moisture exerts an even greater limitation on agriculture than the length of the frost-free season. Only the western parts of the country, together with the eastern Black Sea and Pacific coast areas, have precipitation exceeding 20 inches a year. Only in these regions is there adequate, though not in all cases abundant, precipitation for crop production. Indeed, where poorly drained land prevails, the problem is often one of too much rather than too little moisture. The black-earth country to the south and east of Moscow, the most important agricultural region of the country, receives between 15 and 20 inches yearly. To the southeast, precipitation drops off sharply. With 12 inches at Volgograd on the middle Volga, the total at Astrakhan at the mouth of the Volga is only 6 inches. Less than 6 inches per year is found extensively in the Aral Sea Basin. Almost all lowland areas of Siberia have less than 16 inches of precipitation annually. Much of Central and Eastern Siberia, in fact, has less than 12 inches per year, but the lower temperatures reduce evaporation.

It is important to note, then, that the larger part of the Soviet cropland has less than 20 inches of precipitation per year. Moreover, in these subhumid and semiarid regions precipitation is unreliable, and the land is, therefore, subject to frequent droughts. Years of adequate amounts are followed by years of very little moisture. Indeed, because of moisture deficiency, extensive areas in the Soviet Union are unsuited to agriculture without irrigation.

NATURAL REGIONS

Even though the Soviet Union is of large size, the number of distinctly different natural features is limited. There are relatively few contrasting climatic regions, for example. Climate tends to be broadly similar over wide areas, and changes in climate appear only gradually. These gradual changes are explained, in considerable measure, by the broad expanses of lowland and the lack of any appreciable interruption of them by mountains. As with climate, there are broad zones of vegetation and soils, and these zones reflect to a large extent the dominance of climate. The Soviet geographer, L. S. Berg, has grouped the complex of climate, vegetation, and soils, as well as native animal life, into wide latitudinal zones called natural regions, the natural features being more or less similar throughout the extent of each region. Within the lowlands from north to south, these regions are the tundra, taiga or coniferous forest, mixed forest, wooded steppe, steppe, desert, and subtropical forest. In the mountains, vertical zones of many of the latitudinally arranged lowland features also appear (Figure 11-6).

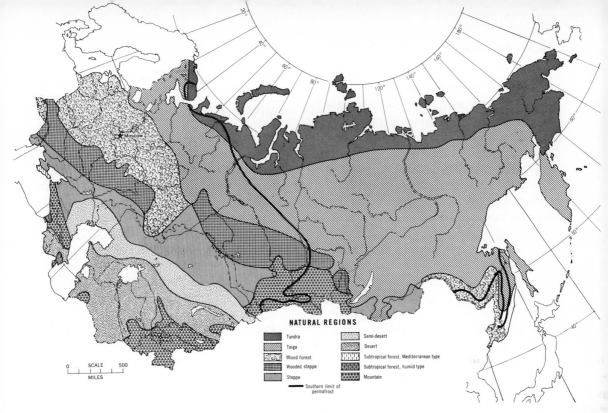

Figure 11-6   The regions follow closely the climatic zones across the Soviet Union. The taiga is one of the great forest regions of the world.

TUNDRA

The zone of Arctic tundra is an unforested region with moss and lichen vegetation predominating. Where valleys offer protection, and particularly toward the south, low, dwarfed birches, spruces, and larches appear. Bogs and marshes are widespread.

The long and severe winters, with strong winds, make it impossible for trees to grow. Summers, too, are cool and short. Their short duration is offset by long hours of daylight, which does permit small flowers to bloom. Annual precipitation is light, averaging 8 to 12 inches, but sufficient, because of low evaporation, for the vegetation mentioned above to grow.

Tundra soils are thin and, because of the coolness of summer temperatures, contain little decaying organic matter. Moreover, the poorly developed soils rest upon permanently frozen subsoil. Wet ground is common in summer, as the soil above the permafrost undergoes a brief period of thaw.

TAIGA

South of the tundra lies a broad zone of coniferous forest, or taiga, extending from the western borders of the country to the Pacific coast. In European Russia the taiga lies, for the most part, to the north of the core area. The cities of Leningrad, Ivanovo, Yaroslavl', and Gor'kiy lie on or close to the southern boundary of the taiga.

The taiga is composed principally of coniferous species, notably spruce, larch, fir, and pine, with some aspen. The transition from the tundra is gradual. At first trees are dwarfed, but with increasing moisture, higher temperatures, and more gentle winds, trees become taller and the stands denser. Bogs are widespread in the Northern European and Western Siberian parts of the taiga. In parts of Western Siberia, waterlogged areas, in fact, occupy entire interstream areas. Bogs are few, however, in Central and Eastern Siberia.

The climate of this vast forested region may be classed as subpolar continental. The features of the climate vary considerably within the region, but, in general, the winters are cold and long and the summers warm. January average temperatures range from 20°F in the west, where Atlantic influences are felt, to below −50°F in Eastern Siberia. July temperatures average between 50 and 68°F, but daily temperatures during the short summer in Siberia may exceed 85°F. Precipitation is moderate to light. More than 24 inches a year occur at Leningrad. In winter, in the west, many of the days are cloudy, while the snowfall forms a thick cover over the earth. Toward the east, snowfall is lighter, but prolonged low temperatures cause the snow to remain on the ground throughout the winter.

The soils of the coniferous forest are known as podsols. With a highly leached, ashy-gray upper horizon, the podsol is infertile. Large amounts of lime must be applied to the soil to counteract its acidity before the podsol can be productive. Moreover, the short growing season prevents the cultivation of anything but a few vegetables and hardy grains.

Permafrost, or permanently frozen subsoil, underlies much of the Siberian taiga. Its thickness varies from 3 feet to many hundreds of feet. During the short summer, thawing occurs only on the surface, usually to a depth of from 6 to 10 feet.

MIXED FOREST

South of the taiga, in European Russia, deciduous broad-leaved species become mixed with conifers. The mixed forest region forms a wedgelike zone, which on the western border of the country extends from Leningrad to the western Ukraine, at approximately the latitude of Kiev. Thence, the zone gradually narrows eastward to the middle Urals. In the valley of the Amur River, in the Soviet Far East, there is another, less extensive region of mixed forest, with species differing from those of European Russia. The mixed forest zone of European Russia, first settled centuries ago, was the heart of the old principality of Muscovy and today forms the northern half of the Soviet core area. Among the deciduous species are oak, elm, maple, and ash. Oak is especially prevalent, an indication of more favorable soil and climatic conditions.

In general, there are fewer bogs here than in the north, despite the existence of the Polesye, a poorly drained forested lowland in the basin of the Pripyat River.

The climate of much of the region may be considered humid continental. Winters remain long and cold, but summers are warmer and wetter than in the taiga. At Moscow, the average January and July temperatures range from 12 to 66°F respectively. Precipitation varies from over 30 inches in parts of the Baltic republics to less than 20 inches in the east. Summer rain predominates and is an aid to agriculture. Snowfall is heavy and lies on the ground from October to March. Upon thawing in spring, it provides a valuable reserve of moisture for agriculture.

The gray-brown forest soils of the region, developed under broad-leaved deciduous or mixed forest, are more fertile than the podsol soils of the taiga. Less acidic, they contain more humus than the podsol. Glaciation, however, has produced in many places sandy and gravelly soils of low fertlity.

WOODED STEPPE

The wooded steppe forms a zone of transition between the mixed forests on the north and the grasslands to the south. Both forests and grass vegetation prevail, with grasses becoming increasingly predominant southward toward the true steppe or grassland zone. Beginning at the western borders of the country, the forest steppe extends to the Urals, and beyond the Urals across Western Siberia as far as the foothills of the Altai Mountains. In the west, the wooded areas consist almost entirely of oak, which in Siberia is replaced by birch and aspen. Small isolated areas of wooded steppe may be found in the southern valleys of Central Siberia.

Being transitional, the zone has in the north a climate similar to that of the mixed forest and in the south, a climate more nearly like that of the steppe. The southern border, in fact, coincides with the axis of high pressure that extends across the Ukraine in winter. As a result, the northern part is affected by moisture-bearing winds from the Atlantic. In the south, on the other hand, the winds coming from the north and east are dry. The mildest and wettest conditions are found in the extreme western part, in the southwestern Ukraine and in the Moldavian Republic.

January temperatures decrease to the east, from an average of 12°F in the western Ukraine to −3°F near the Urals. July temperatures are more nearly uni-

form, ranging from 69 to 72°F. In Siberia, conditions are more extreme. While the July temperatures are comparable to those in the European part, January temperatures are lower. Throughout the wooded steppe, precipitation is moderate. Totals range from 18 inches in the north to 14 inches in the south.

The soils of the wooded steppe are described generally as degraded chernozems, that is, leached black-earths. Leaching of the surface horizon occurs, but it is not excessive. On the other hand, because of the decay of the grasses, the soils are rich in humus. In fact, humus composes up to 10 per cent of the content of the soil. Beneath the horizon of humus accumulation is a horizon of lime accumulation. The lime, derived from the bedrock or parent material, gives to the soil a columnar structure and improves its physical qualities. In the western part of the wooded steppe are extensive loess deposits which enhance further the fertility of the soils.

On the whole, the wooded steppe zone, with its more favorable climatic conditions and fertile soils, forms one of the best agricultural regions of the Soviet Union.

STEPPE

The steppe or grassland zone covers a vast area extending from the southwestern borders of the country as far east as the foothills of the Altai Mountains in Western Siberia. It is entirely unforested except for the river valleys. Its soils are predominantly chernozem or black and chestnut-brown.

The steppe climate is warmer and drier than the climate of the forest zone to the north. Moderate precipitation prevails everywhere, ranging from 16 inches to about 10 inches annually, decreasing toward the lower Volga and into Northern Kazakhstan. Most of the rainfall occurs in early summer; its effectiveness for agricultural purposes is reduced by the fact that high summer temperatures induce a high degree of evaporation. Moreover, precipitation fluctuates in amount from year to year. Adding further to agricultural difficulties are the frequent dry and usually hot winds, the sukhovey, from the Aral Sea basin.

In the northern half of the steppe, the soils are black and rich in humus, having developed under a tall grass cover. In the Ukraine, where a heavy loess mantle prevails, the soils are especially productive. Southeastward, however, as precipitation decreases, the humus content falls, and the soils become lighter and browner in color. On the whole, Siberian chernozems are neither as extensive nor as rich as those in the European part. Moreover, east of the Volga, the increasing incidence of alkalinity makes the soils unsuitable for wheat, the predominant crop. Such soils are referred to as solonetz-chernozems.

In the southern steppe, where precipitation is both light and highly irregular, the grasses are shorter and sparser. Here the soils are decidedly chestnut-brown in color. Low in humus, they are easily eroded by the strong winds that sweep unobstructed across the steppe. Alkalinity and salinity are more extensive and pronounced than in the chernozem region. However, in years when the warm-season precipitation is sufficient, the chestnut-brown soils may yield good harvests of grain.

DESERT

The desert region lies to the south of the steppe. It extends through the lower Volga and Aral Sea basins as far as the foothills of the southern mountain region. It comprises extensive flats of stony, clayey, and sandy desert, in many places virtually devoid of vegetation.

The desert has meager precipitation, the annual total everywhere being less than 10 inches. Most of the precipitation appears in summer in the form of short and heavy showers. Summer downpours, coupled with sparse vegetation, result in excessive runoff. Winters are cold, especially so in the northern parts, which are strongly affected by winds from Central Siberia. At Kazalinsk, the average temperature is 11°F; at Tashkent, to the south, it is 32°F. Summers are very hot

Figure 11-7   A camel caravan in the desert south of the Aral Sea. (Courtesy of Tass.)

throughout the region, with absolute maximum temperatures reaching as high as 122°F.

Gray desert soils predominate. They contain little humus and are highly alkaline and saline. On the loessal piedmont plains along the base of the mountains forming the southern border of the country, the soils, while low in humus, are high in lime and are little salinized. These soils, together with the alluvium along the rivers, are extremely fertile, and crops grown on them give substantial yields when irrigated.

SUBTROPICAL FOREST

Along the southern coast of the Crimea and the southern slopes of the Caucasus Mountains, from Novorossiysk to Tuapse, a Mediterranean-type climate prevails. Winters are mild and rainy and summers hot and dry. January average temperatures are about 38°F, and July temperatures average 76°F.

These mild regions have a rich and varied vegetation. Open groves of oak and juniper, characteristic of the shores of the Mediterranean Sea, are prominent. They appear on the coastal lowlands and up to 1,000 feet on the mountain slopes. There is also a variety of evergreen woody plants. Less evident, however, are the shrub thickets (maquis) so typical of true Mediterranean lands. Many exotic plants from the regions of mild climate of other countries have been introduced. Among them are the Italian cypress, palm, magnolia, and wistaria.

Farther south, in the western part of Transcaucasia, the climate is humid subtropical. Precipitation which occurs throughout the year totals between 90 to 100 inches, and the high rainfall is combined with high relative humidity. Under these conditions, there is a luxuriant and rapidly growing vegetation, both in the Colchis lowland and on the lower mountain slopes. Mixed broad-leaved and coniferous types appear together with many vines and ferns. Much of the Colchis is swampy and remains unreclaimed.

On the eastern coast of Transcaucasia, the Talysh or Lenkoran lowland is also subtropical in character, but continental influences are somewhat stronger than in western Transcaucasia. Summers are hotter, and winters are occasionally severe. Rainfall, though abundant, is somewhat less, and a definite dry season prevails in summer. The vegetation, though less luxuriant than that of the Black Sea coast, is of similar type. Much of the original forest cover in the lowland is gone and has been replaced by crops. Alluvial soils are widespread on the lowland, but they give way to lateritic types with increasing elevation.

MOUNTAIN REGIONS

The mountain regions often display on their slopes the same vegetation zones that the Russian lowlands possess latitudinally. Sometimes the vegetation may change from desert types at the base of the mountains into grasslands, thence to forests, Alpine meadows, and tundra. On the loftier peaks of the Caucasus and the mountains of Central Asia, there are permanent snowcaps. In summer the Alpine meadows, with abundant grasses and cool temperatures, provide a favorable base for livestock grazing; they are lacking, however, in the mountains of Eastern Siberia and in the Soviet Far East.

POPULATION

On the basis of population, the U.S.S.R. ranks third in the world after China and India. In January, 1959, according to the first official postwar Soviet census, the population totaled 208.8 million. This estimate represented an increase of nearly 70 million since 1913, or nearly 40 million since 1939 (prewar boundaries) (Table 11-1). Not all of the increase was due to natural causes, however. As a result of the extension of the Soviet boundary during and after World War II, principally westward into Europe, more than 20 million persons were brought within the Soviet fold. On the other hand, had the war not taken so many lives, the Soviet population today would have reached probably 240 million or more, assuming, of course, that prewar demographic trends had prevailed. As it is, the most recent Soviet estimate gives a total population of approximately 220 million.

From the 1959 census, it is clear that, since the war, the Soviet population has been increasing at a rate close to 1.75 per cent, representing about 3.5 million persons per year. Such a growth rate is high compared with that of western industrial countries. It is high, too, when one recalls the severe losses that were sustained by the people of the U.S.S.R. during the war, particularly by men of marriageable age. Indeed it is often said that the U.S.S.R. has the highest proportion of

TABLE 11-2   POPULATION BY REGION

	1959
U.S.S.R.	208.8
European Russia (including Urals)	152.8
Ukraine	41.9
Belorussia	8.1
Moldavia	2.9
Baltic republics	6.0
Siberia and Northern Kazakhstan	29.3
Soviet Central Asia and	
Southern Kazakhstan	17.2
Trans-Caucasus republics	9.5

Source: *National Economy of the U.S.S.R. in 1960*, Moscow, 1961, pp. 44–49.

widows of any country in the world, a fact that helps to explain the large numbers of older women in the labor force. Any visitor to the U.S.S.R. will find women not only driving taxis and sweeping streets, but also involved in heavy construction work.

The high natural rate of increase prevalent in the U.S.S.R. since the war is due primarily to a sharp drop in the death rate from 18.3 per 1,000 in 1940 to 7.6 per 1,000 at present. While the figures represent a sharp decline in infant mortality, they indicate, if true, that the Soviet death rate is lower than that of the United States. The Soviet birth rate, which stands at 25.3 per 1,000 compared with 24.1 in the United States, has been declining also, but much more slowly—from 31.3 per 1,000 in 1940. Urban migration and other factors associated with modern industrial societies probably account for the lowering Soviet birth rate, but a decline in urban fertility is somewhat offset by increases in births in the more backward, non-Russian areas of the U.S.S.R., notably in Soviet Central Asia.

Of the total population, over 153 million, or 72 per cent, live in the European part, including the Urals (Table 11-2).

TABLE 11-1   POPULATION GROWTH OF THE U.S.S.R. (1913–1962)

	Total	Urban	Rural	Urban, %
1913*	139.3	24.7	114.6	17.7
1926*	147.0	26.3	120.7	17.9
1939*	170.6	56.1	114.5	32.9
1939†	190.7	60.4	130.3	31.6
1959†	208.8	99.8	109.0	48.0
1962†	219.7	111.8	107.9	50.8

* Within boundaries as of Sept. 17, 1939.
† Within present boundaries.
Source: *U.S.S.R. in Figures in 1961*, Moscow, 1962, pp. 28–29.

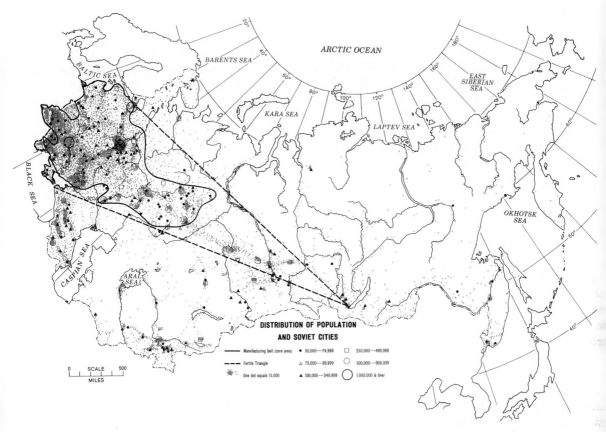

Figure 11-8   Most of the population and most of the large cities of the Soviet Union are located in the European part of the country.

Most of these people, roughly 143 million, are found in the core area (Figure 11-8). Between the Urals and the Pacific Ocean, in Siberia, and the adjacent steppe region of Northern Kazakhstan live 30 million, while in Soviet Central Asia, together with the southern oblasts of Kazakhstan, live 17.2 million. An additional 9.5 million live in the republics of Transcaucasia. In short, most of the Soviet people live in the western central part of the Union, with smaller but important concentrations in Soviet Central Asia, the Trans-Caucasus, and the Soviet Far East.

While the average density for the Union as a whole is about 24 persons per square mile, in the core area, outside the cities and industrial areas, it rises to 130 persons or more. The greatest rural densities in the Union are found in the rich chernozem zone in the southwestern Ukraine. Here, they reach over 260 persons per square mile.

In the steppe region of Western Siberia and Northern Kazakhstan, the population forms a narrow wedge about 300 miles wide astride the Trans-Siberian Railway. Densities range from 25 to 65 persons per square mile. To the north, because of the presence of the Vasyugan Swamp, and to the south, because of the arid wastes of the Aral Sea basin, the population dwindles rapidly. To the east, beyond the Yenisey River, a lower density also prevails, and most of the inhabitants are found within a short distance of the railway. The only sizable concentration is north of Vladivostok in the Lake Khanka plain in the Soviet Far East. Throughout the whole of northeastern Siberia, the scattered population forms a density averaging from 2 to 4 persons per square mile. On the other hand, in the oases and irrigated valleys of Central Asia as well as in much of Transcaucasia, densities reach European Russian proportions.

Unlike the population of the United States, which until recent times was augmented by large numbers of immigrants from the countries of Western Europe, the population of tsarist Russia, in addition to natural increase, grew mainly through the conquest or annexation of lands and peoples in the path of imperial ambitions. As the empire pushed out from European Russia to the shores of the Pacific and to the lofty mountains of Central Asia, there was an accompanying movement of Russian and, to a lesser extent, of Ukrainian settlers. During the latter decades of the nineteenth century, apart from organized military settlements along portions of the Asian frontier, much of the population movement into the new territories was attracted by opportunities for agricultural development. This was especially true of the migration into the steppe lands of Siberia.

The Bolshevik Revolution, if anything, initiated an even greater movement of people out into the peripheral areas of the Union. Since much of the good land had already been occupied, these Soviet migrants were sent into new mining and lumbering areas and to the cities expanding under the industrialization drive. From 1913 to 1939, well over 3 million persons moved eastward to the Urals and Siberia. During World War II and especially in the years following, additional millions went east. According to the 1959 Soviet census, it is evident that a number of older regions in the western part of the Union have suffered net losses, while eastern regions have grown significantly. Since 1939 the population of the Urals has increased by over 25 per cent, of Western Siberia by over 19 per cent, of Eastern Siberia by over 24 per cent, and of the Soviet Far East by 69 per cent. Since 1953–1954, the expansion of crop cultivation in Northern Kazakhstan, under the so-called virgin and idle land program, has resulted in an influx of several hundred thousand persons and has contributed to the increase of over 39 per cent in that republic's population. Important gains are also reported in the Central Asian Republics and in Armenia in the Trans-Caucasus.

Along with the general migration eastward or into peripheral areas, since the beginning of the First Five-Year Plan a pronounced movement to the cities has taken place. Whereas in 1928 about 18 per cent of the population were listed as urban, this ratio had increased to over 50 per cent by 1964. Indeed, apart from the migrants to the virgin lands, much of the eastward movement of population under the Soviets has been into the cities. Collectivization of agriculture released millions of workers for industry, not only because they were no longer needed on the farms, but also because living conditions in the countryside became so unsatisfactory that life in the cities seemed preferable. Consequently, from 1926 to 1959 the number of cities with a population of 100,000 or more grew from 31 to 148. At present, 25 Soviet cities have reached 500,000, of which 6 are near 1 million. Three cities, Moscow, Leningrad, and Kiev, each total over a million.

On the other hand, it should be noted

Figure 11-9   Moscow is the largest city and the political center of the U.S.S.R. This photo is a view of Moscow looking southeastward from the Kremlin across the Moskva River. (Courtesy of Tass.)

that nearly one-half of the Soviet population still lives in the countryside or is associated with rural life. Increasing mechanization of agriculture, if accompanied by greater efficiency per worker on the farm, could release many additional workers for industry, as has happened in the United States where presently less than 10 per cent of the total population are able to produce more food than the nation can ordinarily consume. On the other hand, the U.S.S.R. is still unable to provide food in adequate quantities for its population because of farm mismanagement and inefficiency.

MINORITY GROUPS AND SOVIET NATIONAL POLICY

The expansion of Muscovy from the fifteenth century on created a multinational empire. Presided over by the Great Russians, the empire included, besides related Slavs, peoples of widely differing race and culture, such as the fair-haired Finnic peoples of the northern forests, the dark-haired Turco-Tatars and Mongols of the grasslands and desert, the mixed peoples of the Caucasus, and the primitive tribes of northeastern Siberia.

The early expansion had been into lands sparsely inhabited by peoples less culturally advanced than the Russians. In those areas assimilation had come easily, largely through Russian settlement. However, the conquests and annexations of the late eighteenth and nineteenth centuries had led to the imposition of Russian control on peoples who had an older history than the Russians and who were, in many instances, more culturally advanced. The tsarist government was faced, therefore, with a difficult problem of control.

An uprising among the subject Poles in 1863 aimed at establishing an independent Polish state led the tsar, Alexander II, to adopt a policy of Russification. This policy took the form of tighter central control and the imposition of Russian as the universal language of the empire; the measures were accompanied, too, wherever possible, by the conversion of the people to the Russian Orthodox faith. In time, Russification was directed at the Finns, Ukrainians, and other non-Russian peoples. Those who resisted were persecuted and exiled. Finally, at the turn of the century, pogroms broke out against the Jews, mainly in the western part of the empire; all who were able migrated to Western Europe and North America.

The collapse of tsarism in 1917 provided an opportunity for some of the subject peoples to break away and establish independent republics. Prior to the revolution, the Bolsheviks, hoping thereby to hasten the break up of the old order, had promised self-determination to all the minority groups. In reality, however, what the Bolsheviks had in mind was not the formation of a number of independent states on the ruins of the Russian empire, but something quite different. They hoped that the minorities would throw off the autocratic yoke of the tsars, establish working-class states, and then reunite with the Great

Russians to form a new socialist republic. Later, after having seized power, the new Bolshevik or Communist regime did its utmost to ensure that the minorities remained part of the larger Soviet state. Though the Finns, Latvians, Estonians, Lithuanians, and Poles did manage to break away, independence movements in the Ukraine, the Caucasus, Central Asia, and the Far East collapsed with the advance of the troops of the Red Army or the conspiracies of the Communist party. But in 1940 the Soviets were able to regain control of the Baltic peoples; the Poles were reduced to satellite status in 1945; and the Finns were left to enjoy, thereafter, an uneasy independence. Nevertheless, in the early years of Soviet power, nationalism remained a powerful force among the minorities of Russia. The new regime was compelled to make concessions to national feeling—on paper at least.

The diversity in ethnic structure led the Soviet regime to proclaim, in the early days of its power, a "Declaration of the Rights of the People of Russia." Embodied later in the constitutions of 1924 and 1936, this principle theoretically guaranteed the sovereignty and equality of all the peoples associated in the Soviet Union. In an effort to maintain the semblance of local national autonomy, a hierarchy of political-territorial units was established corresponding to the size of the respective minority groups and the degree of their cultural development.

At the highest level, constituent national republics were established. These are the soviet socialist republics, of which there are 15 at present (Figure 11-10). Only peoples who represent a distinct, stable nationality totaling 1 million or more and who live on the borders of the country may enjoy socialist republic status. According to the constitution, loca-

Figure 11-10   The U.S.S.R. is divided into fifteen unions of varying size. Each union in turn is also subdivided. The largest of the unions is Russia. Of the ethnic groups within the nation, the Great Russians are by far the most numerous.

tion on the border is a prime necessity, so that the national group may exercise its right of secession—a right not yet implemented by any of the republics.

The largest of the Union republics is the Russian Soviet Federated Socialist Republic, which, in addition to its Great Russian majority, includes numerous smaller national groups. On the west the Russian republic is bounded by the Soviet republics of Estonia, Latvia, and Lithuania, established in 1940; the sister Slavic republics, Belorussia and Ukrainia, both of which obtained representation as

"sovereign states" in the United Nations in 1945; and Moldavia, created in 1940 when Bessarabia was annexed from Romania. Along the southern border are the three Transcaucasian republics, Georgia, Armenia, and Azerbaidzhan, and the five Central Asian republics, the Turkmen, Tadzhik, Uzbek, Kirghiz, and Kazakh. All these republics had been established by 1936.

The autonomous soviet socialist republics represent a lower order in the political-administrative structure and comprise national minorities which do not meet the

Figure 11-11   The Park of Culture and Rest in Tashkent. Note the different characteristics—features, expressions, clothing—of the persons shown. (Courtesy of Embassy of the U.S.S.R.)

prerequisites of the soviet socialist republics. Moreover, they are directly subordinate to the Union republic in which they are located. Altogether there are 20 A.S.S.R.s, of which 16 are in the Russian Republic. The autonomous oblasts and the lowest of all, the national okrugs, have even less of the trappings of autonomy.

Stalin described the national-administrative system as one which was "national in form, socialist in content." In reality, this credo allowed the minority groups to preserve their folk songs, costumes, dances, and literature so long as these did not conflict with the interests of the Soviet state. At the same time it meant that in every important aspect of life, direction would come from the Communist party of the Soviet Union. All power would emanate from Moscow, and administration would remain in the hands of Great Russians or of individuals like Stalin, the Georgian, who had assumed the outlook of the Russian or the new Soviet man. Finally, in the planning of the country's economy, the national units were in no way given preference over the nonnational units, the oblasts and krais into which the rest of the country is subdivided (Table 11-3).

According to the 1959 census, the U.S.S.R. is composed of more than 100 separate nationalities, of which the largest is the Russian (Table 11-4). Closely related in language and culture are the Ukrainians and Belorussians. Altogether,

TABLE 11-3   THE SOVIET POLITICAL-ADMINISTRATIVE STRUCTURE

U.S.S.R. (15 union republics)					
	R.S.F.S.R.*			S.S.R.*	
A.S.S.R.*	Krai† (territory)	Oblast† (province)	A.S.S.R.*	A.O.*	Oblast† (province)
	A.O.*				
		N.O.* N.O.*			

* National units.
† Nonnational units.

the East Slavs account for three-fourths of the total population.

Most of the national variety is found among the non-Slavic groups. The largest of these embraces peoples who speak languages of the Altaic family: the Turco-

Tatars, the Mongols, and the Tungus-Manchurians. Distantly related to the Altaic family is the Uralian family, which includes the Finns and Karelians, the Estonians, the Mari, Udmurts, and Samoyeds. The Japhetic peoples, located

TABLE 11-4   GENERALIZED LIST OF MAJOR NATIONAL (ETHNIC) GROUPS IN THE U.S.S.R. (1959)

East Slavic (Indo-European):			B. Volga Finnic	
1. Russian	114,114,000		26. Mordvinian	1,285,000
2. Ukrainian	37,253,000		27. Mari	504,000
3. Belorussian	7,913,000		C. Permian	
Other Indo-European minorities:			28. Udmurt	625,000
4. Lithuanian	2,268,000		29. Komi-Permiak	431,000
5. Latvian	1,400,000		D. Northern Urals, Ugrian	
6. Moldavian	2,214,000		30. Khanty-Mansi	26,000
7. Armenian	2,787,000		E. Magyar	
8. German	1,619,000		31. Hungarian	155,000
9. Polish	1,380,000		F. Samoyedic	
10. Tadzhik	1,397,000		32. Nenets	25,000
Altaic:			Japhetic:	
A. Turkic			A. South Caucasian	
Southwest group			33. Georgian	2,692,000
11. Azerbaidzhani	2,940,000		34. Abkhaz	65,000
12. Turkmen	1,002,000		B. Dagestanian	
Southeast group			35. Avar	270,000
13. Uzbek	6,015,000		36. Lezgin	223,000
Northwest group			37. Dargin	158,000
14. Tatar	4,968,000		38. Kumyk	135,000
15. Kazakh	3,622,000		C. Chechen-Ingush	
16. Kirghiz	969,000		39. Chechen	419,000
Northeast group			40. Ingush	106,000
17. Yakut	236,000		D. North Caucasian	
18. Tuvinian	100,000		41. Kabardinian	204,000
B. Mongolian			42. Adige	80,000
19. Buriat	253,000		Semitic:	
20. Kalmyk	106,000		43. Jews	2,268,000
C. Tungus-Manchurian			Palaeo-Asiatic:	
21. Evenki-Eveni	34,000		44. Chukchi	12,000
22. Korean	314,000		45. Koryak	6,000
Uralian:			46. Nivkhi	4,000
A. Baltic Finnic			Miscellaneous:	
23. Estonian	989,000		47. Chuvash	1,470,000
24. Karelian	167,000		48. Gypsy	127,000
25. Finn	93,000			

Source: *National Economy of U.S.S.R. in 1960*, Moscow, 1961, pp. 14–16.

entirely within the Caucasus, include, among others, the Georgians and Dagestanis. Finally, there are significant minorities of Jews, other European peoples, and Tadzhiks (Iranians), as well as small bands of primitive Palaeo-Asiatics.

AGRICULTURE

Although the U.S.S.R. has made great strides in its program of forced industrialization, it remains to an unusual degree an agricultural country. Nearly half of its population is engaged in farming. Yet though the Union has considerably more land in crops and more people in agriculture than does the United States, Soviet output on the whole remains below that of the latter. In fact, in the United States the problem is one of surplus production in most commodities, whereas in the Soviet Union it is one of deficiency. Indeed, Soviet agriculture has lagged far behind Soviet industrial growth, and for that reason is often called the Achilles' heel of Soviet economic development.

The reasons for the lag in Soviet agriculture are varied. It is true that the Union is a northern land where climate and soil impose serious limitations on crop production. But the Soviet regime has never invested heavily in agriculture, and at the same time, since the beginning of collectivization in 1928, shocking deficiencies have persisted in agricultural planning and farm management. Moreover, the hostility and resentment created in the peasantry by collectivization remain factors in peasant or farmer attitudes even today. Finally, World War II inflicted heavy damage on the farm structure, especially in the western and southern regions of the European part of the country. Since then, and more particularly after the death of Stalin in 1953, the Soviet regime has attempted through a number of institutional and economic changes to boost Soviet output. Though some degree of success has been achieved, the results have not been adequate to meet the needs of the Soviet state with its growing urban population.

In spite of its huge size, the Union does not possess enormous agricultural resources. Only 27 per cent of the country is suitable for crop production and livestock raising. Only 10.6 per cent of the country, or approximately 600 million acres, is considered tillable. This figure is somewhat inflated, however, because it includes farmland that, by American standards, would be considered marginal. At any rate, since 1913 the area sown to crops has been increased by over 200 million acres. It would seem now that no further expansion of sowings is possible, since much of this increase has been at the expense of fallow land. In future times additional increases in output will have to be achieved through higher yields per acre.

Much of the land currently in crops, about 500 million acres, lies within the so-called fertile triangle (Table 11-5). The northern boundary of the triangle coincides with a frost-free period of 105 to 110 days, the thermal limit of wheat culture. On the southern margin where the annual precipitation falls to less than 12 inches, crop cultivation without irrigation becomes hazardous. Yet even within the triangle, farming may suffer from drought or frost or may involve soils that are low in natural fertility.

Throughout the nonchernozem zone, apart from the acid soils, the major handicap is the short growing season. In the steppe, generally, where the soils are rich, precipitation is unreliable. East of the Urals, in Western Siberia and Northern Kazakhstan, frost and drought may singly or together seriously lessen the harvest.

Clearly, then, only a relatively small portion of Soviet farmland enjoys a growing season and precipitation sufficient for most temperate crops. Such favorable conditions may be found in the western Ukraine, in parts of the western North Caucasus, and along the Black Sea coast. In the valleys of Soviet Central Asia, a long growing season permits cotton to be cultivated if irrigation is available.

Soviet farming involves, essentially, two types of farm organization: the collective farm or kolkhoz and the state farm or sovkhoz. The bulk of the peasantry belong to kolkhozes. As a result of mergers and amalgamations, however, the number of collective farms has rapidly declined from 123,000 in the early 1950s to 41,300 at present.

Theoretically, the collective is a voluntary association of peasants, working (in common) the land, which in effect is leased from the state in perpetuity. In return, the collective delivers to the state a large portion of its annual harvest. Until 1956, the collectives were not allowed to own and operate heavy farm machinery; such equipment belonged to Machine Tractor Stations, which contracted to do the plowing, harvesting, and other heavy work required by the farm. For these services the collectives paid another portion of their harvest, after deliveries had been made to the state. What was left over, after seed had been set aside for the following year and other obligations had been met, was divided among the kolkhoz workers according to their work on the farm. Frequently the return to the workers was very low. Since 1956, however, collectives have been permitted to purchase and keep their own farm machinery, while the MTSs have been converted into Repair Tractor Stations, whose task is simply to service machines. Moreover, in 1958, the Soviet regime established a system of purchase prices which were higher than the earlier obligatory delivery prices, and the result has been higher farm income. Even so, the lack of incentive continues to affect seriously the efficiency and productivity of the farm worker.

Collective farms vary in size and in number of member households. About one-half contain less than 300 homesteads and may comprise from 1,000 to 4,500 acres. Individually owned peasant farms are not important in the U.S.S.R., but

Figure 11-12   A collective farm market near Tbilisi in Georgia. Note the aridity of the slopes. (Courtesy of Douglas Jackson.)

TABLE 11-5   MAJOR SOIL GROUPS AND CULTIVABLE AREA*

Zone	Area, million acres	Total area of U.S.S.R., %	Estimated area suitable for cultivation (crops and fallow), million acres
1. Tundra	420.0	7.6	—
2. Podsolic and swampy	1,730.0	31.4	116.0
3. Gray podsolic and degraded chernozem	296.0	5.3	123.0
4. Typical chernozem inc. saliferous and carbonaceous soils	353.0	6.5	240.0
5. Chestnut brown	300.0	5.4	62.0
6. Sierozem and desert soils	521.0	9.4	23.0
7. Red soils	0.7	—	0.7 (up to)
8. High ground (vertical zonation)	1,883.0	34.4	23.0
Total	5,503.0	100.0	587.0

* Zones 3 and 4 occupy the heart of the fertile triangle, but on the north the triangle includes the southern part of zone 2, and on the south, the northern part of zone 5. The acreage cultivated in zone 6 involves mainly irrigated land in southern Soviet Central Asia and to some extent in the arid Caucasian regions on the west coast of the Caspian Sea. Zone 7 pertains largely to the small humid subtropical region on the east side of the Black Sea in Georgia.

Sources: *The Great Soviet Encyclopedia, Union of Soviet Socialist Republics*, "Soils," Moscow, 1948, pp. 168–182. S. Udachin, "The Land Fund of the U.S.S.R. and its Utilization," *Socialist Agriculture*, no. 1, pp. 63–72, 1956.

collective farmers are permitted to work for their own use small kitchen gardens or private plots. These are usually under an acre in size, but are adequate to provide for the peasant's needs and permit a significant surplus for sale in the free collective farm market. Indeed, the private plots are said to provide up to 30 per cent of the foodstuffs available to city dwellers. Because of serious deficiencies in Soviet transportation and food handling, the government-owned state stores, unlike the farm markets, have only a few fresh vegetables. Farm-market prices, however, because they are unregulated, are higher, and consequently bring the collective farmer additional income.

The Soviet regime considers the state farm to be the highest form of socialism in the countryside. While there are only 8,300 state farms, their number is growing rapidly. More specialized than the collective, the state farm is operated like a factory, where the workers are paid a cash wage. The state, accordingly, is able to take virtually all the farm's produce. In recent years, many collective farms have been converted into state farms, and new state grain farms have been established, especially in the virgin lands. State farms average nearly 60,000 acres in size.

Because yields per acre have ordinarily remained low over the years of Soviet power, the regime has sought to increase farm output through expansion of the sown area. Much of this expansion has occurred in the eastern steppe region where there were extensive reserves of long-term fallow or idle land. The most ambitious program of expansion began in

1953, when Khrushchev directed that over 70 million acres of these reserves be plowed for wheat and other grains by 1956. By 1957, the Soviets revealed that instead of 70 million, almost 90 million acres of new land had been plowed. Since then, additional acres have been plowed, and the Soviet regime has indicated that reserves still remain.

Evidence to date, however, indicates that the program has not been an unqualified success. The harvests that Khrushchev anticipated have not been achieved. Fallowing has been drastically cut in an area where, barring other means to conserve soil moisture, it is essential. More-

over, because delivery quotas to the nation are high, state and collective farms are compelled to sow wheat year after year in the same field, a practice that rapidly causes soil deterioration. Soil erosion in parts of Northern Kazakhstan has already become a serious problem.

In addition to enlarging the area of dry farming, the Soviets have also reclaimed land from the deserts and swamps. Since 1913, the irrigated area has been expanded by 7 million acres to reach 18 million. More than two-thirds of the irrigated area is in Soviet Central Asia, in the valleys of the Syr Dar'ya and Amu Dar'ya. Other irrigated areas are in the Trans-Caucasus

Figure 11-13   Zones of specialized agriculture.

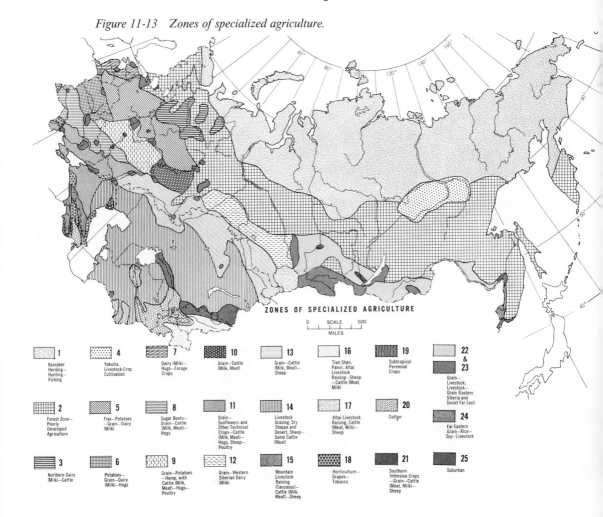

ZONES OF SPECIALIZED AGRICULTURE

1 — Reindeer Herding—Hunting—Fishing

2 — Forest Zone—Poorly Developed Agriculture

3 — Northern Dairy (Milk)—Cattle

4 — Yakutia, Livestock-Crop Cultivation

5 — Flax—Potatoes—Grain—Dairy (Milk)

6 — Potatoes—Grain—Dairy (Milk)—Hogs

7 — Dairy (Milk)—Hogs—Forage Crops

8 — Sugar Beets—Grain—Cattle (Milk, Meat)—Hogs

9 — Grain—Potatoes—Hemp, with Cattle (Milk, Meat)—Hogs—Poultry

10 — Grain—Cattle (Milk, Meat)

11 — Grain—Sunflowers and Other Technical Crops—Cattle (Milk, Meat)—Hogs, Sheep—Poultry

12 — Grain—Western Siberian Dairy (Milk)

13 — Grain—Cattle (Milk, Meat)—Sheep

14 — Livestock Grazing, Dry Steppe and Desert, Some Cattle (Meat)

15 — Mountain Livestock Raising (Caucasus)—Cattle (Milk, Meat)—Sheep

16 — Tian Shan, Pamir, Altai Livestock Raising—Sheep—Cattle (Meat, Milk)

17 — Altai Livestock Raising, Cattle (Meat, Milk)—Sheep

18 — Horticulture—Grapes—Tobacco

19 — Subtropical Perennial Crops

20 — Cotton

21 — Southern Intensive Crops—Grain—Cattle (Meat, Milk)—Sheep

22 & 23 — Grain—Livestock; Livestock—Grain (Eastern Siberia and Soviet Far East)

24 — Far Eastern Grain—Rice—Soy—Livestock

25 — Suburban

and the North Caucasus. Because of the long growing season, these irrigated areas produce mainly cotton. In the future it is to be expected that irrigation agriculture will be more widely practiced in the Soviet Union, particularly in the lower Volga basin and the southern Ukraine. Irrigation here should do much to raise the yields of corn and other grains sown. The Soviet regime has also reclaimed wet land, especially in the Polesye and in the Colchis lowland, but in neither case has the effort increased crop acreage significantly. The Colchis lowland, if properly drained, is important to the Soviet Union because its humid subtropical climate permits a wider choice of crops than elsewhere.

Prior to Stalin's death in 1953, a grandiose scheme "to change nature" was proclaimed. In practice this involved the extensive planting of shelter belts in the lower Volga basin to break the hot winds from Central Asia. Shelter belts may serve a useful purpose, but the Stalin afforestation project was a failure because the trees died from aridity and lack of care.

A major feature of Soviet agriculture is the predominance of grains in the crop patterns. That this is so is due mainly to the fact that Soviet cropland is suitable, to a large extent, only for grains. Consequently, Soviet diet consists essentially of

Figure 11-14   South Siberian grain field in early September. (Courtesy of Douglas Jackson.)

bread, potatoes, and a few vegetables. Meat and dairy products have, until recent years, been extremely scarce. Under the Soviet regime, however, there has been a relative decline in the position of grains. Whereas in 1913 grains accounted for 90 per cent of the total sown area, at present the ratio is only 68 per cent. On the other hand, under the Soviet policy of self-sufficiency in basic agricultural products, acreages devoted to sugar beets, cotton, and forage crops have increased substantially.

Of the grains, wheat, a crop of the steppe zone, is the most important, occupying about 50 per cent of the acreage. The virgin-lands program has caused an eastward shift in acreage, so that almost two-thirds of the wheat is grown in the territory between the Volga and the Altai Mountains. Practically all of this wheat is spring-sown. Winter wheat is found mainly in the Ukraine and North Caucasus, where the winters are milder.

Although the Soviet regime attempted in the 1930s with little success to establish a "secondary wheat base" in the mixed-forest zone of European Russia, the soils of that area are more suitable for winter rye. Rye is a hardy, adaptable crop, but in recent decades acreage has been declining. Clearly, consumer preference in the Soviet Union has shifted from the traditional black bread of the peasant to white wheat bread.

Of the feed grains, oats and barley are the oldest crops, and corn has, since 1953, undergone a remarkable increase in acreage. Oats, a crop of the humid central part of Russia, has been declining in importance, especially as the number of horses has decreased. Barley, on the other hand, is a versatile crop and is grown for human consumption as well as for livestock. In the north, it produces *kasha,* a traditional Russian porridge; in the west, it is used in

TABLE 11-6   MAJOR CROPS IN THE U.S.S.R.

	1913		1953		1961	
	Million acres	%	Million acres	%	Million acres	%
Total sown area	292.1	100	388.4	100	505.6	100
Total grain	258.5	88	263.7	68	317.0	60
Spring wheat	61.0	23	75.4	28	112.4	35
Winter wheat	20.5	7	44.0	16	42.7	13
Rye	69.7	26	50.2	19	41.3	13
Barley	32.9	12	23.7	8	33.1	10
Oats	47.2	18	37.8	14	28.4	8
Corn	5.4	1	8.6	3	32.6	10
Total industrial	12.1	4	28.4	7	33.6	6
Cotton	1.7	14	4.6	15	5.8	17
Sugar beets	1.7	14	3.9	13	7.7	22
Sunflowers	2.4	19	9.6	33	10.4	30
Flax	3.1	25	3.1	10	4.0	11
Potatoes and vegetables	11.9	4	23.7	6	25.5	5
Feed and forage crops	8.1	2	70.9	18	128.2	25

Source: *U.S.S.R. in Figures in 1961*, Moscow, 1962, pp. 172–175.

the manufacture of beer; in the south, in the Ukraine, it serves as high-protein feed. Prior to 1953, grain corn was limited to the humid western Caucasus and the southern Ukraine. In an effort to improve the feed situation, Khrushchev directed that corn be sown widely throughout the southern regions as well as elsewhere in the country, where, though it may not ripen, it can be cut green for silage.

The basic industrial crops include cotton, flax, sugar beets, and sunflowers. Cotton, the principal fiber crop, is grown entirely on irrigated land in Central Asia and the Caucasus. Moreover, as a result of improved seed, the use of fertilizers, and higher incentives to cotton farmers, Soviet cotton yields have, in recent decades, increased threefold. Flax, for linen, is grown primarily in the forest zone of European Russia. The flax plant requires heavy fertilization, and consequently flax cultivation is found in association with dairying and livestock raising. Sugar beets are the only domestic source of Soviet

sugar. The main region of cultivation is in the northern Ukraine and in the neighboring Russian Republic. Acreage has been expanded into other areas, notably in the North Caucasus as well as in southern Kazakhstan where the crop is irrigated. Sunflowers, a drought-resistant crop, are grown for oil for domestic use in the eastern Ukraine and lower Volga basin.

Potatoes and vegetables occupy only a small part of the total sown area. Irrational shipments of potatoes from one region to another have been reported in the Soviet press, but none of this movement involves the transport of early potatoes from southern regions to northern industrial cities. In addition to grapes and other fruits, the U.S.S.R. also grows tea in western Georgia and tobacco along the east coast of the Black Sea.

Collectivization between 1928 and 1930 resulted in widespread slaughter of livestock by the peasantry who opposed joining the kolkhozes. Since then, the situation has remained serious. Some improvement took place during the latter 1930s, but the war inflicted extensive losses. Only in recent years have the numbers of livestock reached prerevolutionary levels; but the growth in population means that there are no more livestock units per capita than in 1913.

The reasons for the slow growth in livestock numbers are to be found primarily in the poor care given to collective herds—inadequate housing, and above all insufficient forage and feed—as contrasted with the attention given to the cow or goat fed on the private plot. The expansion in corn acreage, however, is an attempt to provide better nutrition, in the hope of rapidly overtaking the United States in the output of meat and dairy products. Greater output has, indeed, been achieved, but lack of an adequate distribution system and refrigeration means that the urban dweller has not yet been able to realize fully the improvement.

Most of the dairy cows are concentrated in the central, northern part of European Russia. In past years, almost one-half of the cows have been kept on private plots, although the regime has forced some transfer of herds to the collectives. Dairying, which has been traditional in the northern European part of the country, has lately been shifting to the Ukraine. The reasons for the shift are not clear, but it may be due to the fact that in the north in winter the cows get insufficient exercise, being confined to barns for months. Moreover, the collective farmer in the Ukraine may be finding it more profitable to put his feed supply into milk rather than into meat. Pigs are found principally in the central western parts of the country, especially where farming is mixed. In the warmer, drier regions, sheep and goats are more numerous than cattle or pigs. Severe losses in sheep and goats were suffered in the 1930s, but some relaxation of control over the formerly nomadic livestock raisers in these areas has contributed to the rapid upswing in numbers. As for horses, the general trend toward mechanization of farm operations has been largely responsible for the continuing decline in their numbers.

MINING AND MANUFACTURING

Beginning with the First Five-Year Plan in 1928, the Soviet Union launched a program of rapid industrialization designed to transform, in the shortest possible time, the economy of the entire country. The objective was the establishment of a base of heavy industry upon which further industrialization could proceed. The plans placed considerable emphasis, therefore, on metallurgical engineering and related industries. Consumers'-goods industries

TABLE 11-7 LIVESTOCK IN THE U.S.S.R.* (million head)

	1916	1928	1933	1947	1953	1956	1962
Cattle	58.4	66.8	33.5	47.0	56.6	58.8	82.1
Milk cows	28.8	33.2	19.0	23.0	24.3	27.7	36.3
Pigs	23.0	27.7	11.5	8.7	28.5	34.0	66.6
Sheep and goats	96.3	114.6	36.5	69.3	109.9	116.2	137.4
Horses	38.2	36.1	17.3	10.9	15.3	13.0	7.0

* As of the beginning of each year.

Sources: *Current Digest of the Soviet Press*, vol. 5, no. 39, November, 1953, p. 25; *U.S.S.R. in Figures in 1961*, Moscow, 1962, p. 191.

have, on the other hand, received scant attention and little investment.

While the cost of the program has placed a heavy burden on the collectivized peasantry and the urban factory workers, nevertheless, the U.S.S.R. today ranks second after the United States in its output of heavy industrial goods. Moreover, in recent years the U.S.S.R. has challenged the United States, not only to an economic competition but also to a race into space with all its attendant military implications. Soviet pronouncements make it clear that the U.S.S.R. intends, through its industrial might, its science and technology, and its military machine, to dominate the earth. Consequently it is important that we understand and appreciate the quality and extent of Soviet industrial resources and the nature and patterns of the Soviet industrial base.

In order to build a heavy industrial base, extensive search has been made in the U.S.S.R. for new metals and new sources of fuel and power. In a country of such vast size and varied geological features, extensive investigation has uncovered large reserves of coal, oil, and natural gas, as well as a variety of metals. The hydroelectric-power potential, too, has grown to enormous proportions, as surveys of Siberian rivers have revealed the feasibility of this or that major project.

FUEL AND POWER RESOURCE

COAL The geological reserves of coal total 8.6 billion tons, sufficient to last for centuries at the present rate of exploitation. Coal is used not only for coke in the metallurgical industry, but also in the generation of thermal power. Total coal production now reaches 510 million metric tons, nearly double that of 1950.

The geographical distribution of the coal deposits, however, is generally unfa-

vorable. About 90 per cent of the reserves lie in Asiatic parts of the country. In European Russia the reserves are not all of high grade, and some deposits are located in the extreme north. Since the core area is by far the chief consumer, local coal supplies must be supplemented by large volumes hauled from distant sources. Coal movements tend to be costly because they are largely by rail. To prevent transportation congestion and to minimize the length of coal hauls, local deposits of soft coal and lignite, though of poor quality, are also worked.

Most of the coal for metallurgical purposes is produced at four centers, namely the Donets Basin (Donbass) in the southern Ukraine, the Kuznetsk Basin (Kuzbass) of Western Siberia, the Karaganda Basin of north central Kazakhstan, and the Pechora Basin in the European North (Figure 11-15). Several scattered coalfields in the Urals have a relatively high total output, only a small part of which, however, is suitable for coking purposes. There are, in addition, numerous small fields in Eastern Siberia, the Soviet Far East, Central Asia, and Transcaucasia.

The Donets Basin, the leading field in the Union, accounts for 37 per cent of all coal produced and, moreover, contributes 60 per cent of Soviet metallurgical coking coal. Having been worked very intensively since the latter nineteenth century, the more easily worked deposits of the Donbass are nearly depleted. Mining difficulties have increased, so that production costs have risen to levels higher than those associated with the Kuznetsk Basin and Karaganda. Nevertheless, because of the high concentration of industry nearby as well as in the Central Industrial Region to the north, the output of coal in the Donbass continues to expand.

The Kuznetsk Basin ranks second to the Donbass in output, but its importance

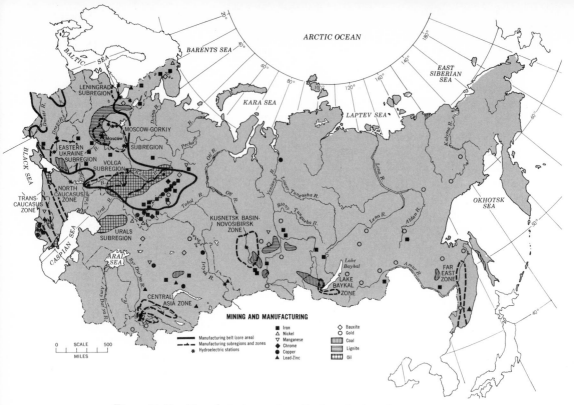

Figure 11-15 Manufacturing regions. Fuels and mineral resources.

is increasing steadily both absolutely and relatively. Much of the coal is shipped to blast furnaces in the Urals. The coal seams are thick and of high quality, and, by open-cast methods, the coal may be easily mined. Production costs, therefore, are among the lowest in the Union. Cost advantages are offset, however, by distance from consuming centers to the west.

The Karaganda Basin is the Union's third major producer. Though total reserves are considerably less than in the Donets and Kuznetsk Basins, more than half is suitable for metallurgical purposes. Development began in the 1930s with more than one-half of its output going to Ural industrial centers. Its use locally will increase with the completion of a metallurgical plant near the coalfields.

The exploitation of the Pechora Basin was started just prior to World War II. In the early years of the war, the construction of a railroad provided a link with northwestern European Russia; shipments of

coal have in fact been confined to the northwest.

Although some coking coal is obtained from the Kizel field in the Urals, the need for metallurgical coal in that region far surpasses local supplies and accounts for heavy shipments from the Kuzbass and Karaganda.

Heavy emphasis is placed on the use of coal in the production of thermal electricity, especially in the Central Industrial Region and in the Urals. The lignite fields near Moscow assume importance in this regard because of their proximity to the populated and industrialized core. Peat also serves as a source of thermal power, although it is of low heat value. The abundance of peat supplies in European Russia, favorably situated relative to demand, accounts for their use.

PETROLEUM AND NATURAL GAS   In order to lessen dependence on the use of coal for fuel and power in the core, increasingly more attention is being given to oil and natural gas as substitutes. In fact, the production of petroleum has increased from 71 million metric tons in 1955 to 166 million in 1961. A similar upsurge in natural gas production has raised output from 9 billion cubic meters in 1955 to 61 billion in 1961.

About three-quarters of the oil produced comes from the Volga-Ural fields. The recent expansion of Soviet output is largely a result of exploitation of this source. Lesser and relatively ever-decreasing amounts come from the Baku district in the Azerbaidzhan Republic and from Groznyy and Maikop in the North Caucasus. These districts were formerly the chief source of Soviet oil. Some production occurs at Ukhta in the European North, on Sakhalin Island in the Soviet Far East, and in Soviet Central Asia.

There are widespread deposits of oil shale, the largest of which are found near the middle Volga region and in the Estonian S.S.R. About 85 per cent of production comes from the latter region, in all, equivalent in energy value to about 4½ million tons of coal.

The Volga-Ural fields are ideally situated relative to consuming centers. Although shipments of oil to the Central Industrial Region have been largely by rail, an extensive system of pipelines is under construction, not only to cities in the core but also to the western borders of the country. Moreover, crude oil pipelines have been constructed to Omsk in Western Siberia. In a few years they will be extended to Irkutsk and ultimately will reach the Pacific coast.

The major natural gas–producing centers are located near the Volga-Ural oil fields, as well as in the Ukraine, North Caucasus, and Central Asia. The first pipeline was constructed in 1945, connecting Saratov on the Volga with Moscow. Other pipelines have been constructed, and an extensive network is planned in order to serve Moscow, Leningrad, the Urals, and other fuel-deficient regions. The higher heat value of natural gas is expected to result in a decline in the use of poorer fuels such as peat and lignite.

WATER POWER   The Soviet Union has an enormous water power potential, but, in spite of much publicity given to the construction of hydropower installations, only a small part of the electric power produced at present comes from the rivers. Indeed, of the 327,000 million kilowatt hours produced in 1961, hydropower accounted for only 57,000 million. The bulk of the potential lies in the Siberian rivers, but up to the present, much of the development has taken place to the west of the Urals.

As early as 1920, well before the beginning of the industrialization drive, a scheme of state electrification, known as GOELRO, was formulated as the basis for industrial and agricultural development. Sizable power facilities were constructed on the Volkhov and Svir Rivers in northwest Russia near Leningrad, and a giant hydroelectric station was completed on the Dnepr River near Zaporozh'ye in 1933. Swift-flowing streams in the Caucasus Mountains have also been harnessed. In recent years, large dams and power installations have been built on the Volga River, for example, at Kuybyshev and Volgograd; others are planned or are under construction. When they are completed, the Volga will resemble a long narrow sea, its waters held in check by a "cascade" of dams. Work has been proceeding on the development of the Ob', Irtysh, and Angara Rivers in Siberia, where dams have been built or are under construction. However, since 1958, because of the enormous investments required and the length of time involved in developing the Siberian rivers, Soviet planners have shifted emphasis to less costly and more speedily constructed thermal plants.

FERROUS METALS AND FERROUS METALLURGY

Iron and steel are the sinews of modern industry, and the volume of their output is a key to the strength of a country's economic base. Heavy machinery, transportation, and construction equipment need steel, and steel is essential in an ambitious military and space program. Consequently, extensive reserves of quality iron ore are an asset. Soviet reserves are large, but not of especially high quality.

From 1928 to 1961, the production of iron ore in the U.S.S.R. increased greatly, from 6.1 to 117.6 million tons. The production of pig iron rose during the same period from 3.3 to 50.9 million tons, and the production of raw steel rose from 4.3 to 70.7 million tons.

The bulk of the output of iron ore, pig iron, and steel has come from the southern Ukraine. Iron and steel had been produced there since the late nineteenth century. The proximity of Krivoi Rog iron ore and Donbass coal continued to favor the expansion of the industry in that region during the Soviet period. While the relative share of the Ukraine to total output has declined as new centers have been opened, the region still supplied, in 1961, 51 per cent of the pig iron, 56 per cent of the iron ore, and 40 per cent of the steel. The heavy use of Krivoi Rog ores has depleted the higher-grade reserves, but enormous quantities of low-grade ores suitable for concentration assure a continuing high potential. Metallurgical plants in the southern Ukraine are situated near the source of coking coal in the Donbass, and to a lesser degree in the vicinity of the Krivoi Rog iron ores. A third center at Zhdanov on the Sea of Azov uses low-grade iron ore from Kerch in the Crimea mixed with ore from Krivoi Rog.

With the creation of the Ural-Kuznetsk Combine in the 1930s, there developed a large iron and steel complex in the Urals. Integrated metallurgical plants were constructed at Magnitogorsk, Chelyabinsk, and Nizhniy Tagil. These centers together form the second most important metallurgical center of the Union. In 1940, the Urals supplied 18 per cent of the nation's pig iron and 21 per cent of its steel, but in 1958, 33 per cent and 35 per cent respectively. The high-grade iron ore reserves of Magnitogorsk, having been heavily drawn upon, are being depleted, so that new sources are being sought. The iron mines of the Kustanai area of northwestern Kazakhstan are expected to contribute to the ore requirements of the Urals.

A smaller metallurgical center is situated in the Kuznetsk Basin. Linked to the Urals, the integrated plant there was supplied originally with Urals ore, but depends now upon locally available or Eastern Siberian ores.

In addition to the iron and steel centers in the Ukraine, Urals, and Western Siberia, the Soviet Union has constructed smaller integrated mills as well as separate steel mills using local coals, local ores, or scrap. One integrated mill at Cherepovets in northwest Russia draws its coking coal from as far away as the Pechora Basin and iron ore from the Kola Peninsula.

During the Seven-Year Plan, several new plants are to be constructed in Siberia as part of a developing "third metallurgical base" extending from Kazakhstan to

Eastern Siberia. New sources of iron ore are being exploited in Kazakhstan, in the Altai Mountains of Western Siberia, and in Eastern Siberia to serve these plants. Coking coal from the Kuznetsk Basin will be used for a new plant to be situated there, as well as for plants at Barnaul in Western Siberia and at Taishet in Eastern Siberia. The new plant at Temir Tau in Kazakhstan is based on nearby Karaganda coal.

The Soviet Union is well supplied with ferro alloys. Manganese, especially important in the production of steel, is found at Nikopol in the Ukraine and at Chiatura in Transcaucasia. These two deposits account, in fact, for two-thirds of the world's manganese supply. Nickel is mined in the Urals, at Nikel near Murmansk, and at Norilsk in Northern Siberia.

NONFERROUS METALS

The U.S.S.R. has uncovered, through intensive geological exploration, adequate supplies of nearly all important nonferrous metals needed in its industries. Yet since it has sought to be self-sufficient in this regard, the Soviet Union has undoubtedly placed in production mines and processing facilities at costs considered high by Western standards.

The most important centers of the nonferrous-metals industry are in Kazakhstan, the Urals, and Eastern Siberia. Kazakhstan has the largest reserves and is the largest producer of copper, lead, and zinc. The Urals region has widespread deposits of bauxite. Not only have the Urals become the major center in the Soviet Union of the aluminum industry, but the region also processes a variety of metals shipped from other parts of the Union. Eastern Siberia is the leading producer of gold, and its newly discovered

reserves of industrial diamonds are the largest in the world.

Areas of secondary importance supplying metals are the Kola Peninsula (apatite or aluminum ores) and the Caucasus (lead, zinc, and aluminum). Western Siberia, Central Asia, and the Soviet Far East provide only modest additions at present to the total output of metals.

THE ENGINEERING INDUSTRIES

The engineering industries, which include the production of machine tools, agricultural and textile machinery, mining and metallurgical machinery, transportation equipment, and power generators, consti-

Figure 11-16 Karl Marx Street is one of the main highways through Moscow. Note the modern electric buses and the automobiles. (Courtesy of Soviet Information Bureau.)

tute the largest single group of Soviet manufactures. Together they account for one-third of the Union's industrial employees. In the past, the core area accounted for the bulk of machine production, particularly in Leningrad, Moscow, Gor'kiy, Kharkov, Rostov, Sverdlovsk, and Chelyabinsk. Since World War II, however, many new plants have been located in other parts of the country.

The production of heavy mining and metallurgical equipment, oriented toward the steel-producing centers, is important at Kramatorsk in the Donbass, Sverdlovsk in the Urals, and Novosibirsk near the Kuznetsk Basin. Kharkov in the northern Ukraine and Nizhniy Tagil in the Urals are leading producers of railroad rolling stock and locomotives. Moscow and Gor'kiy were the original producers of automobiles and lorries, but new works have been built in the Urals, at Ulyanovsk on the Volga, and at Kutaisi in Transcaucasia. Machine tools and textile machinery are produced in the central industrial district, and the heavier farm equipment is manufactured nearer the extensive agricultural areas at Kharkov, Rostov, Volgograd, and Chelyabinsk.

THE CHEMICAL INDUSTRY

The Soviet chemical industry has been geared mainly to the production of fertilizers, synthetic rubber, and basic chemicals, such as sulfuric acid, caustic soda, and soda ash from inorganic minerals. But through expansion of the petroleum industry, a wider assortment of products including plastics, synthetic fibers, and detergents is becoming available.

Chemicals based on salts and sulfur ores are manufactured in the Berezniki-Solikamsk area of the Urals. Potash fertilizers are obtained there from enormous potassium deposits, and nitrogen ferti-

lizers are obtained as a by-product of the coking of coal at nearby Kizel. Nitrogen fertilizers are produced also at Gorlovka in the Donbass, at Kemerovo in the Kuzbass, and from lignite at Stalinogorsk near Moscow. The production of synthetic rubber is concentrated in central European Russia, notably at Voronezh, Tambov, Yaroslavl', and Kazan, where potatoes and grain, the chief raw materials in synthetic rubber manufacture, are obtained. New rubber factories, using petroleum, are being constructed in the middle Volga region and near Baku.

THE TEXTILE INDUSTRY

The production of textiles developed in the old industrial areas during the tsarist period and formed the most important branch of Russian industry. During the Soviet period, the industry has received only a small share of the investment in manufacturing, and while production has risen, gains have not kept up with consumer needs.

Cotton milling remains concentrated in the Moscow-Ivanovo area and in Leningrad. In recent years, however, processing centers have been built nearer the cotton fields in Central Asia and Transcaucasia and at consuming centers in the Ukraine, middle Volga region, the Urals, and Western Siberia.

Linen manufacturing has traditionally been located in the Central Industrial Region, and new factories continue to be established in or near the flax-growing areas of western European Russia. The woolen industry is centered in the Moscow-Leningrad areas for the production of finer cloths and in the Ukraine and middle Volga for coarser goods. New mills have been built also in the sheep-raising areas of Central Asia and the Caucasus.

THE FOOD-PROCESSING INDUSTRY

The processing of crop and livestock products is found both in the large consuming centers and in agricultural areas. The major wheat flour–milling and sugar beet–processing plants are located in the black-earth regions of the Ukraine and adjoining areas in the Russian Republic, in the Volga region, and in the North Caucasus. Large meat-packing plants are found mainly in Moscow, Leningrad, Gor'kiy, and Sverdlovsk; some dispersal of these major processing industries has occurred into Kazakhstan, Central Asia, and Western Siberia. Butter and cheese production is associated with the remote areas of dairy farming, notably in the Vologda region of northern European Russia and in the Omsk-Novosibirsk region of Western Siberia. The canning of fruits and vegetables is important in the Ukraine, Moldavia, and the North Caucasus.

FORESTRY AND FISHING

Timber is one of the Soviet Union's most abundant resources. Forests cover 32 per cent of the Union's territory, but about 80 per cent lies in Asiatic Russia. Because of the inaccessibility of most of the Siberian resource, the bulk of timber cutting remains in the European U.S.S.R. Since most of the timber is floated down rivers, saw milling is found at the mouths of logging streams, for example, at Arkhangel'sk, and at important river-rail crossing sites such as Leningrad and Volgograd. East of the Urals, the major logging areas are found in Central Siberia. Igarka, on the Yenisey River north of the Arctic Circle, is the chief lumbering center.

The manufacture of pulp and paper, employing coniferous species chiefly, is centered in the European North. Plywood production, using material from the mixed-forest zone, is located in central and western European Russia. The largest centers of the furniture industry are Moscow, Leningrad, and Kiev.

The major Soviet fisheries are located in the Barents Sea, the Baltic and Caspian Seas, and on the Pacific coast. The Caspian Sea, because of its shallowness and the huge amounts of organic matter carried to it by the Volga and other rivers, has long been a major source of fish. However, with growing Soviet interest in ocean fisheries, the share of the Caspian fisheries to total catch has declined from 66 per cent in 1913 to 15 per cent in 1956. The Pacific fisheries, particularly around the Sea of Okhotsk, and the Barents Sea fisheries are assuming leading roles in total production.

TRANSPORTATION

While tsarist Russian expansion was facilitated by the rivers of the empire, modern economic development in the U.S.S.R. has been based mainly on the railroads. The importance of rail transportation is due to the enormous size of the country and to the fact that in many places and for at least half of the year the rivers offer no alternative. Although river and coastal shipping together account for 13 per cent of the Union's freight, the railroads carry 78 per cent of the freight and more than 80 per cent of the passenger traffic. Only 5.4 per cent of the country's goods are handled by truck and 3 per cent by pipeline.

The densest rail net prevails in the core and looks, indeed, like a spider web centered on Moscow (Figure 11-17). Not all lines are of equal importance. Some of the heaviest traffic is found on the trunk line between the Donets Basin and Moscow,

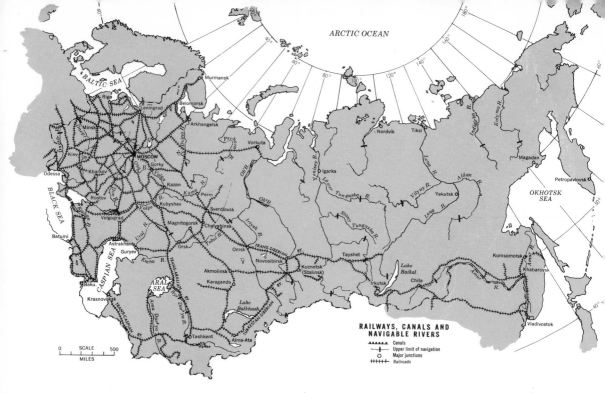

Figure 11-17 The most highly developed system of land transportation is by rail, with Moscow as the principal center. Frequently rivers are used as means of transportation. Many of the longer rivers flow into the Arctic Ocean or into inland seas.

between the Donets Basin and the cities of the Dnepr bend, between Moscow and the Volga cities, and between the major industrial sites in the Urals. Within the core, however, waterborne freight reaches considerable proportions, especially on the Volga system. The Moscow-Volga Canal, linking Moscow with the Volga River, and the later (1952) Volga-Don Canal, between the lower Volga and the Don, afford water transportation between many of the major industrial cities of the north and south, but the bulk of the traffic still occurs on the Volga between the mouth of the Kama and Volgograd.

Beyond the core, the heaviest rail-freight movement occurs on the Trans-Siberian Railway between the Kuznetsk Basin and the Urals, in Kazakhstan between Karaganda and the Urals, and in the Caucasus between Baku and Rostov on the Don. All these movements involve large quantities of raw materials for industry in the core, such as coal and oil.

Since World War II, the Soviet regime has attempted to relieve the heavy burden borne by these long lines feeding into the core. In the transport of oil, increasing use of pipelines is being made, and additional rail lines have been built or are under construction, as, for example, in Western and Central Siberia. Moreover, the rail lines are being modernized and electrified, especially the Trans-Siberian, those in Central Asia, and in the Caucasus.

The Soviet Union has the longest navigable waterway system of any country in the world. Its length is estimated at 248,000 miles, although only about 65,800 miles are used. The usefulness of most of the rivers is lessened by the fact that they are frozen over during three to nine months of the year, and flow either in the wrong direction or through unpopulated regions of small economic importance. Consequently, except for the Volga proper and to a lesser extent the Dnepr, freight movements are, in total, not great.

The Volga River is the most important waterway because it has ample depth, drains a large and populous region, and passes through diversified economic areas. Products carried upstream include oil from Baku, coal from the Donets Basin, salt and fish from the Caspian, and grain; wood is sent downstream. The Volga had the disadvantage of draining into the land-locked Caspian Sea. A 62-mile canal now connects Volgograd on the Volga with Kalich at the elbow on the Don River. This addition extends the Volga's economic influence into the industrial Ukraine, and links Moscow with ports on five seas. Canals also link the White and Baltic Seas with the Caspian and Black Seas, and Lake Ladoga with the Volga.

Such rivers as the Kama, the Northern Dvina, and the Yenisey are important in the movement of logs to mills downstream. The Ob', Irtysh, and Lena Rivers in Siberia, although long, carry very little freight, and transportation is confined to the brief summer months. The Amur has the greatest transport possibilities and is the leading river in Siberia for carrying cargo, since it is navigable by oceangoing vessels as far upstream as Khabarovsk. In recent years, the volume on the rivers of Siberia has undergone a relatively significant increase, because of substantially heavier movements of lumber and oil.

The northern sea route between Murmansk and Vladivostok is shorter (6,800 miles) than navigating via Suez (over 13,800 miles). It transports a million tons of cargo annually and would be used more were it not frozen over much of the year.

Although the output of trucks and automobiles in the U.S.S.R. has risen to over 555,000 annually, there are still only about 2½ million motor vehicles there compared with over 50 million in the United States. Because of the lack of an extensive network of good paved highways, the use of motor vehicles in the U.S.S.R. tends to be local, primarily for hauling from farm to city or from farm to railhead.

Dirt roads predominate over paved, spring thaws and summer downpours often making them impassable. The length of roads totals a little over 1 million miles; about 200,000 miles are called year-round roads, but only about a third of these are hard-surfaced. Three-fourths of the roads are so little improved that seasonally they are lost in mud. Winter is an advantage because sleighs pulled by horses can travel easily over the frozen ground.

The volume of freight carried by the Soviet airlines is less than 1 per cent of all freight carried. Nevertheless, the Soviet regime has built and operates an extensive air service to all parts of the Union. Jet service, too, is available, especially on flights between Moscow and distant centers outside the core, in the Caucasus, Soviet Central Asia, Siberia, and the Pacific coast. The Soviet airline, Aeroflot, operates on international flights to Western Europe, the Middle East, India, and China.

IN PERSPECTIVE

THE U.S.S.R., PROBLEMS OF A WORLD LEADER

The Union of Soviet Socialist Republics holds a vast land area larger than the continent of South America. The country is preeminently a land power and occupies what has been called the heartland, from which it has been probing for weak spots and acquiring contiguous territories for several centuries. Although large parts of the Soviet Union are so cold, arid, or mountainous that they can support only a sparse population, there are also extensive fertile plains, large forests, and a great variety of fuels, metals, and other minerals. Under the tsars, Russia exported grains, lumber, pulpwood, animal products, and a few metals; there was little industrial development, and manufactures were the principal imports. After the Revolution in 1917, the Communists obtained control of the government and began a series of Five-Year Plans intended to increase production of foodstuffs, wood products, coal, petroleum, iron, and other minerals, and especially to industrialize the nation. Peasants were forced onto collective farms; workmen were shifted wherever they were needed; dozens of new manufacturing cities were founded; and thousands of industrial plants were established. Many of the planned goals were not reached, but one should not underrate the accomplishments. Many people perished from famines and purges, but production grew, even if not as quickly as planned. The net result is that the U.S.S.R. has become a powerful state, and whether or not its methods can be approved, its power must be recognized. Furthermore, the Soviet Union has large undeveloped resources, and these constitute the base for additional industrial and population growth.

The Soviet Union and its satellites have for some time been engaged in a cold war with the Western nations. The intensity of this war increases or decreases in relationship to political and economic conditions within the Communist world. During the past decade the U.S.S.R. has spent billions of dollars in the development of space activities, space research, and related industries. In some respects the citizens of the nation have gained more freedom and have increased their personal income. In spite of these gains there is still a great need for improved housing conditions, greater agricultural production, and the manufacturing of more consumer goods.

SELECTED REFERENCES

Berg, L. S.: *Natural Regions of the U.S.S.R.,* The Macmillan Company, New York, 1950.
An excellent synthesis of the climate, relief, soils, native vegetation, and animal life appearing within broad landscape zones of the Soviet Union.

Cole, J. P., and F. C. German: *A Geography of the U.S.S.R.,* Butterworth & Co. (Publishers), Ltd., 1961.
A detailed survey, both topical and regional, of the Soviet Union. Emphasis is placed on population and major economic activities, and an attempt is made to analyze achievements both in absolute terms and in the light of Soviet economic planning.

Jackson, W. A. Douglas: "The Virgin and Idle Lands of Western Siberia and Northern Kazakhstan: A Geographical Appraisal," *Geographical Review,* vol. 46, no. 1, pp. 1–19, January, 1956.
A study of a Soviet scheme to transform the agricultural base of the U.S.S.R., including a survey of the land potentially useful for this purpose and a discussion of the possibilities of success.

Jackson, W. A. Douglas: "The Virgin and Idle Lands Program Reappraised," *Annals of the Association of American Geographers,* vol. 52, no. 1, pp. 69–79, March, 1962.
An examination of the nature and extent of success to date of this ambitious program for increasing crop output.

Jorré, Georges: *The Soviet Union: The Land and Its People,* Longmans, Green & Co., Inc., New York, 1961.
A standard text about the U.S.S.R. that will aid the student desiring more detailed study.

Lonsdale, R. E., and John Thompson: "A Map of the USSR's Manufacturing," *Economic Geography,* vol. 46, no. 1, pp. 36–52, January, 1960.
A detailed map of Soviet manufacturing showing

the relative importance of individual centers, accompanied by a description of major manufacturing regions.

Oxford Regional Economic Atlas: *The U.S.S.R.*

and Eastern Europe, Oxford University Press, Fair Lawn, N.J., 1956.

A fairly comprehensive atlas of the Soviet Union and the Communist world of Europe.

chapter 12

NORTH AFRICA AND THE NEAR EAST

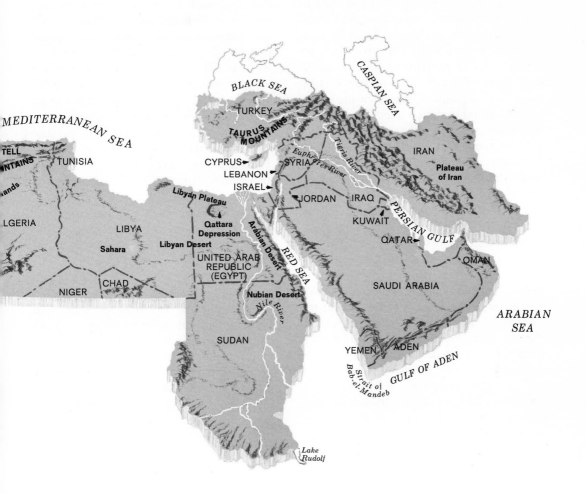

Figure 12-1 North Africa and the Near East are a part of the world's largest dry area. Topographic features range from mountains to plains, but the most noticeable physical characteristics are the great deserts and, with the exceptions of the Nile and Tigris-Euphrates, the absence of large rivers.

*T*HROUGHOUT THE LONG SPAN OF human history, North Africa and the Near East have together been a region of problems—economic, social, and political. Some of the world's earliest recorded history deals with the struggles of early Egyptians, Babylonians, Israelites, and Persians. Part of the economic difficulty is in securing enough water for agriculture in desert oases or Mediterranean regions of light winter rainfall. The populations of oases have sometimes outgrown the water supply; at other times a new culture or administrative system has failed to maintain the dams and canals which supplied farmlands and cities. Nomads from the steppe margins of the deserts have frequently raided farmlands in order to obtain food for themselves and feed for their livestock. Their political and economic condition was one of conflict, strife with one another, and struggle with the meager resources. From this hot, dry desert and semidesert area have come numerous religions. Three—Judaism, Christianity, and Islam—have influenced the thoughts and beliefs of millions of people as well as the actions of numerous nations.

Most of the region was included in the Ottoman (Turkish) empire during the last century. But some parts of the empire gradually drifted from under Turkish control and fell under the influence of European powers; other areas were conquered directly from Turkey by other countries. By the time of World War I, Turkey had lost more than one-half of her empire. In North Africa, France had taken a large part of Morocco, and Spain had most of the rest. France controlled Algeria and Tunisia; Italy possessed Libya; and Great Britain controlled Egypt and the Sudan. In the Arabian Peninsula, Arabs in parts of the interior had thrown off Turkish control, and Great Britain had protectorates around the coasts.

After World War I, the Turkish empire was divided to revive old nations or to form new ones. Syria, Lebanon, Iraq, Palestine, and Transjordan (now Jordan) came into existence and were placed under the supervision of France and Great Britain as mandates of the League of Nations. These areas have now become independent, with Israel occupying most of what was Palestine. Many of the small countries of the Arabian Peninsula have been united to form Saudi Arabia. The former colonial areas of Morocco, Algeria, Tunisia, Libya, Egypt, and the Sudan have also gained independence. The only parts of the region which are not now independent are the Spanish Sahara and Ifni in the far west and some British possessions and protectorates along the eastern and southern edges of the Arabian Peninsula.

The many struggles between Turks and conquered peoples, between colonies and colonial powers, and between Israel and the Arab nations make a long and complicated story. One recent war, the Algerian revolt against France for independence, lasted from 1954 to 1962. Rivalries among nations, competition over the many rich oil fields, and intrigues to unseat unpopular governments further complicate the politics of the region. North Africa and the Near East are indeed a troubled area, where political changes frequently occur.

REGIONAL CHARACTERISTICS

CLIMATE

North Africa and the Near East have many similarities in physical features and in the culture of the inhabitants. Sunny skies and light rainfall are typical. Coastal areas like the Barbary states of northwest

TABLE 12-1   POLITICAL DIVISIONS OF NORTH AFRICA AND THE NEAR EAST

Country	Area, sq. mi.	Approximate population, 1963
Morocco	174,000	11,600,000
Algeria	920,000	10,265,000
Tunisia	48,300	3,900,000
Ifni (Spanish)	740	52,000
Spanish Sahara (Rio de Oro and others)	103,000	19,000
Libya	680,000	1,200,000
United Arab Republic (Egypt)	386,000	28,000,000
Sudan	967,500	11,800,000
Turkey	296,000	28,000,000
Cyprus	3,572	563,000
Iraq	172,000	7,000,000
Iran (Persia)	630,000	21,000,000
Syria	72,000	4,500,000
Lebanon	4,000	1,600,000
Israel	8,000	2,100,000
Jordan	37,000	1,700,000
Saudi Arabia	870,000	6,500,000
Kuwait	5,800	322,000
Oman, Qatar, Trucial Oman, and Bahrein (Br. protectorates)	122,500	800,000
Yemen	75,000	5,000,000
Aden and protectorate (Br.)	112,000	820,000

Africa, the shores of the Black Sea, and the eastern Mediterranean have enough rainfall to support agriculture without irrigation. In such places the natural vegetation is the Mediterranean scrub forest, a scattered open woodland of cork oaks, cedars, or bushes, with a sparse covering of grass between. These lands of light to moderate winter rainfall and the great irrigated valleys of the Nile and the Tigris-Euphrates are the most favorable for agriculture and human settlement, and in them live the vast majority of the inhabitants of the region.

Between the coastal Mediterranean lands and the true deserts of the interior are the steppes. The steppes have a semi-arid climate with occasional rainstorms, usually in winter. These grass-covered plains and plateaus are much better grazing lands than the deserts, and support herds of sheep and goats. Certain favored areas produce wheat, barley, or alfa grass. Some of the nomads of the deserts migrate to the steppes to avoid the terrific heat and prolonged drought of the desert summers.

The great deserts of inland North Africa and Arabia have only rare and scattered rains. In some places, where rivers run from the mountains or from moist tropical areas into the desert, there are strings of oases that produce dates, barley, cotton, and vegetables. For the most part, however, the oases are small, dense settlements

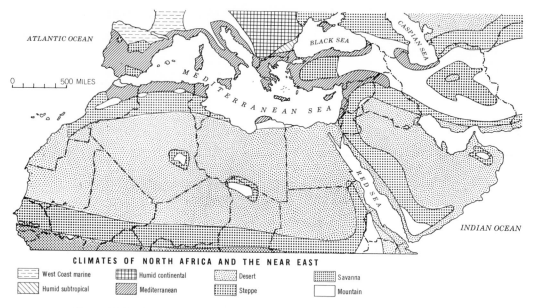

CLIMATES OF NORTH AFRICA AND THE NEAR EAST

West Coast marine   Humid continental   Desert   Savanna

Humid subtropical   Mediterranean   Steppe   Mountain

Figure 12-2   Deserts dominate the climatic regions of North Africa and the Near East. Note that in most places steppes surround the desert.

clustered about wells or springs. Between the oases the desert usually supports a very sparse population of nomads, who travel almost constantly in search of pasturage for their flocks.

THE PEOPLE

The major cultural links among the countries of North Africa and the Near East are language, religion, social customs, and economic life. Arabic is the predominant language from Morocco to Iraq; Turkish, Persian, and Hebrew are related tongues (Figure 12-4). Literary Arabic as used in the Koran, the Mohammedan holy book, is the same throughout the Moslem lands; spoken Arabic, however, varies from place to place. An educated Arab of Algeria or Tunisia, through his study of Arabic literature and the Koran, learns the same written language as the literate people of

Figure 12-3   Climate graphs for selected stations.

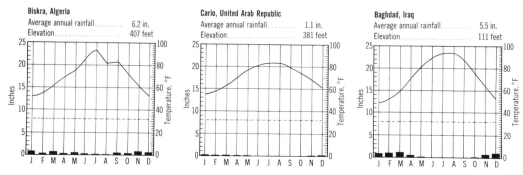

Biskra, Algeria
Average annual rainfall........ 6.2 in.
Elevation...................... 407 feet

Cario, United Arab Republic
Average annual rainfall........ 1.1 in.
Elevation...................... 381 feet

Baghdad, Iraq
Average annual rainfall........ 5.5 in.
Elevation...................... 111 feet

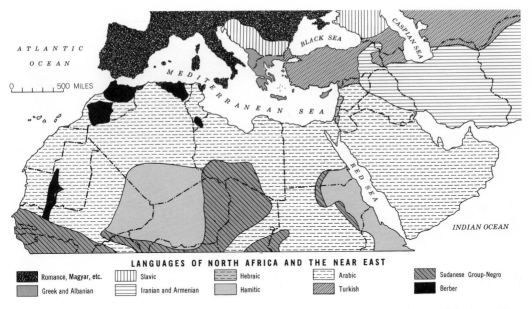

Figure 12-4 Arabic is the common language over much of North Africa and the Near East. The location of the Berbers in the Atlas Mountains is indicated. In Asia the Turkish and Iranian languages are spoken over wide areas.

Egypt or Syria. The Bedouins (nomads) are often illiterate, however, and the spoken Arabic dialects of Morocco and Algeria are as different from the colloquial speech of Arabia as Portuguese is from Spanish. Literary works published in Cairo can be read by Arab scholars everywhere, but the talking motion pictures for the masses of Arabs are produced in one dialect for the people of Morocco and in another for the Iraqi Arabs. Despite the colloquial differences in Arabic and the presence of other languages like the Berber tongues in northwest Africa and the Hamitic dialects in the Sudan, the Arabic language, history, and literature are such a powerful unifying force that North Africa and a portion of the Near East are often called the Arab world.

Islam, the faith of the Moslems, reinforces the unifying power of the Arabic language. Mecca and Medina, the chief holy cities of Islam, are in Arabia. The religion requires five prayers daily while facing toward Mecca and constrains those who are able to make a pilgrimage to Mecca, for which the title of Hadj is awarded. The Koran and other religious writings were originally in Arabic. Moslem countries like Turkey and Iran (Persia) are populated by people who are Arabic neither in origin nor language, but Mecca is the center of their religion, and they adhere to the main tenets of the faith. Islam has united peoples to such a degree that North Africa, the Near East, and additional Moslem areas in Asia are sometimes described as the Moslem world (Figure 12-5).

Islam provides not only a religion but also a system of social customs, economic attitudes, and government rule. If they are strict Moslems, men use no intoxicating beverages, eat no pork, wear the turban or fez as a head covering, and perform their prayers daily, regardless of locality

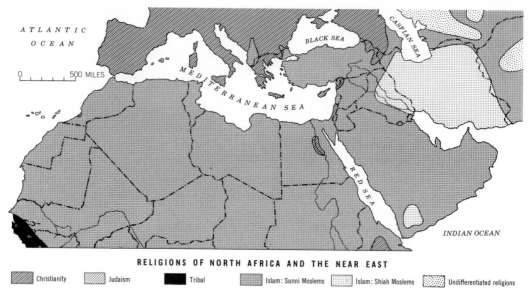

RELIGIONS OF NORTH AFRICA AND THE NEAR EAST

Christianity	Judaism	Tribal	Islam: Sunni Moslems	Islam: Shiah Moslems	Undifferentiated religions

Figure 12-5   Islam is the dominant religion of North Africa and the Near East. It should be noted, however, that like most other religions, Islam is divided.

or occupation. Moslem women live a secluded life in a separate portion of the house or tent (the harem) and are ordinarily not introduced or even mentioned to guests. On the rare occasions when they leave the women's quarters, they are, in many areas, wrapped in a combined hood and robe that covers them from head to foot with only a narrow opening for the eyes. In Turkey and in metropolitan areas elsewhere, this attire for women has been replaced by Western clothing. Although Islam permits a man to have four wives and under certain conditions, additional concubines, economic necessity usually limits a man to one wife. The custom of having several wives is becoming less and less common.

Giving alms to the poor is prescribed by Islam. Among the desert Moslems hospitality is traditional, and the well-to-do provide for the less fortunate. Tribal chiefs have religious as well as governmental

responsibility and leadership. They are legal authorities and official advisers to their people on economic and social matters. Thus Islam provides for all phases of life, and religion is closely associated with government, business, and daily routine. In Turkey, however, government decree has modified the situation, and church and state are separated as in Western countries.

Since early times, herding of sheep, growing of olives, wheat, and dates, and exchanging pastoral products for oasis goods have been typical economic activities. Local travel by donkey and camel has been supplemented by the train, automobile, and airplane; but customs, clothing, foods, and buildings are often strikingly like those described in the history of ancient Egypt and Mesopotamia, in the Bible, and in the Koran. The geographic setting of deserts, oases, and Mediterranean climate partially explains the life of these peoples; for fuller understanding one must also consider history, politics, and religion.

The major themes of the cultural geography of North Africa and the Near East are Mediterranean and oasis agriculture, nomadic herding and caravan trade across the steppes and deserts, Arabs and the Arabic language, and the Moslem religion. Variations upon these themes, or the complete absence of one of them, are factors that often distinguish one place from another. The separation of the Moslem faith from civil law and government in Turkey has been mentioned as one example. Lebanon is an Arab country where Christianity is the dominant religion. The new nation of Israel is almost an island of Jewish people and religion in a Moslem ocean. Egypt is a desert country dominated by the people and agriculture of the gigantic Nile oasis; and Libya is a Saharan country with only minor oases.

Modernization of agriculture, the construction of Westernized cities, and the development of mining are activities that have changed localized areas so that they contrast with the rest of the region. The modern European sections of cities like Casablanca, Algiers, Cairo, and Baghdad are impressive, but they are only exotic settlements in lands that are predominantly Arab and Moslem.

CONTRASTS WITH ADJOINING REALMS

North Africa and the Near East differ greatly from Europe, tropical Africa, and the Far East. Europe is primarily a Westernized Christian region whose people speak Germanic, Romance, and Slavic languages. Mediterranean Southern Europe is closely linked with the culture, language, trade, and politics of the humid and industrialized lands farther north. Nomads, camel caravans, the Arabic language, and oasis agriculture are outside the cultural experience of most Europeans, and Islam is common only in transitional Southeastern Europe.

Although the Arabic language and Islam extend into parts of the grasslands and forests of tropical Africa, there are such important changes in climate, peoples, agriculture, and customs that a traveler soon realizes that he has entered a new geographic realm. The savanna and rain forest replace the Mediterranean and desert lands of the north. Colored peoples predominate instead of white Semites or Hamites. New features appear, like circular villages of mud and brush huts, Sudanese cattle, savanna grasslands, tropical forests, and hoe agriculture. Africa south of the Sahara has no roving Bedouins or historical association with the coasts of the Mediterranean Sea. The barren southern Sahara is an effective barrier between two culture worlds.

Dry lands and the Moslem faith continue eastward across Turkey, Iraq, Iran, Afghanistan, and Pakistan, but Arab people and the Arabic language predominate only as far as Iraq. Iran is a transitional country with a separate culture but with historical, religious, and cultural similarities to the Arab world. Afghanistan and Pakistan are Moslem countries, but they lack the Mediterranean climate, Arabic influence, and historical association with the Mediterranean Sea. They have been more involved with the history of India and are beyond the recent culture or conquest of Turkey or Arabia. China, Japan, and other areas of the Far East are, of course, far different in human geography from North Africa and the Near East.

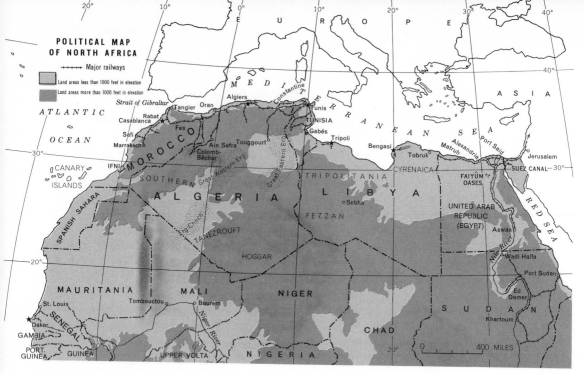

Figure 12-6   North Africa is a land of new independent nations. Morocco, Algeria, Tunisia, Libya, and Sudan have all become independent since World War II. Each nation has serious transportation problems.

THE BARBARY STATES

The moderate winter rainfall of the Atlas Mountains of northwestern Africa provides a much more favorable setting for agriculture and human settlement than do the adjoining regions of the Sahara. This populated western island of Morocco, Algeria, and Tunisia (Figure 12-6) is surrounded by the sea and the desert. Historically, it has often been linked to Europe or other Mediterranean lands. The Phoenicians founded the city of Carthage near the present site of Tunis, and it controlled most of Barbary until destroyed by the Romans. Under the Romans, Barbary became the "granary of Rome." After the decline of Rome, a number of peoples alternated in controlling parts of Barbary —the Vandals, Byzantines, Arabs, Portu-

guese, Spanish, and Turks—before the modern French conquest.

The original inhabitants were the Berbers, white people of ancient and obscure origin, who resemble Italians and Spaniards rather than the peoples of Africa and Asia. The Berbers, from whom the word Barbary was derived, have mixed with their captives and conquerors for many centuries, but comparatively pure groups of Berbers are still found in humid, hilly, and mountainous areas.

The Arab conquest of the seventh century had great and lasting effects upon Barbary. The Arabs converted the region to the Moslem religion, and also introduced the camel, which made possible caravan trade across the Sahara. Although united under one religion, the Berbers and Arabs can often be distinguished by appearance, dress, or language. The Berbers still preserve their spoken dialects without having a written language or literature. They are most numerous in Morocco but also inhabit the high mountains and some other parts of Algeria. Sometimes, without regard to Arab or Berber origin, the peoples of the cities and farmlands of northwestern Africa are called Moors and the nomads of the deserts Bedouins.

RELIEF FEATURES

The Atlas Mountains and associated ranges extend east-west across northern Barbary. The coastal hills, plateaus, and mountains are called "the Tell." This is the main agricultural region of northwestern Africa, although the plains areas are small and many of the fields of wheat and grapes are on hilly land. Morocco has the highest mountains, one peak attaining 13,665 feet. There are three east-west ranges, the Rif Atlas (part of the Tell), the Great Atlas, and the Anti-Atlas. The mountains of Algeria consist of two major east-west chains, the Tell Atlas along the coast and the Saharan Atlas farther south. Between these two ranges lie the high plains and plateaus, semiarid lands that are used for grazing and for producing grain and alfa grass. The two Atlas Ranges come together in eastern Algeria and extend across Tunisia as a single range.

TRANSPORTATION

When Barbary was a part of the Roman Empire, the production of grain was increased. New areas were opened to agriculture, and the Romans built hard-surfaced roads to haul grain to seaports in what is now eastern Algeria and northern Tunisia for shipment to Italy and other parts of the empire. Towns of moderate

Figure 12-7   The greatest railway mileage in North Africa is in the Atlas Mountain area of Algeria. These railroads serve the productive coastal plain and the mountain valleys. Deserts limit rail extension in most parts of the area.

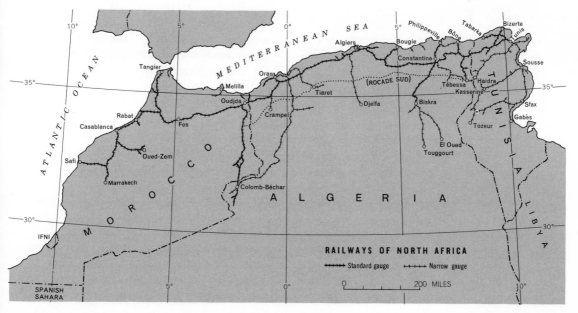

size developed along the coast, with smaller ones at interior crossroads and in the more fertile grain areas. Many of the present cities of North Africa can trace their origin to the Roman era.

The Romans stopped construction at the margins of the Sahara. Their roads were wide and numerous in the more populated areas, but farther south there was only a sparse network of narrow roads, and the routes to the forts at the edge of the desert were little more than trails. Thus agriculture, settlement, and roads declined from north to south in rough correspondence with the zones of Mediterranean, steppe, and desert climates.

When the Roman Empire declined, North Africa passed into the hands of less competent rulers. Cities, aqueducts, wells, and roads fell into a state of disrepair. The Vandals, Arabs, and Turks largely ignored the Roman roads, constructed for wheeled vehicles and legions of foot soldiers. Pack animals, pastoral nomads, and foot travelers used paths instead.

When France conquered Algeria during the 1830s no improved roads were left. The army constructed short wagon roads from the coast toward the interior, and civilian agencies expanded them into a network. Railroad construction was begun later, and after France acquired Tunisia during the 1880s and Morocco in 1912, all three countries were joined together by highways and railways. The present transportation system covers more area and has much more traffic than the old Roman system of roads, but there is the same general correspondence between resources, density of settlement, and trade routes.

The railway network has standard-gauge lines for the main strategic east-west route and for the important farming areas of the Tell (Figure 12-7). Interior agricultural areas of secondary impor-

tance and the mining regions of Algeria and Tunisia are usually served by narrow-gauge lines. The railways of Morocco were constructed more recently than the others. Standard-gauge lines connect the more important regions, and highways serve the secondary areas. Since the main routes run across the mountains and hills of the productive coastal areas, the railways have many sharp curves and steep grades, especially in Algeria.

CITIES

All the larger cities of Barbary are on or near the coast. In Morocco, the city of Casablanca has grown so rapidly in recent years that it is now the largest settlement of northwestern Africa. It is a port and trading center for the grain-producing plateaus of western Morocco. Marrakech, farther south, is a religious capital of the Moslems and a market town for the agricultural and pastoral products of the region. It was the northern terminus for the old caravan trail that ran to Timbuktu (Tombouctou) in the Sudan. Rabat, near Casablanca, is the capital of Morocco. After Morocco became independent it assumed control over Tangier, which for many years was in an international zone on the southern shore of the Strait of Gibraltar. Its strategic location and the rivalry among Great Britain, France, and Spain largely explain this political status.

The settled Tell of Algeria is a long, narrow, hilly coastal zone. Each part ships agricultural or mineral products to Europe through its ports and receives manufactured goods in return. There is little trade in an east-west direction; thus Algeria falls into three parts, each of which forms a separate economic area. These areas center about the cities of Oran in the west, Algiers in the center, and Constantine in the east. Oran and Algiers are ports, but the inland town of Constantine is served by the harbors at Phillipeville and Bône. Algiers, the largest town of Algeria, is second in size only to Casablanca in northwestern Africa, and is the leading cultural, economic, and political center of Algeria.

Tunisia has only one large city, Tunis, the major seaport, capital, and cultural center. The towns of Sousse and Sfax, on the east coast, are local markets and outlets for the interior phosphate mines.

The cities of Barbary have much in common. The large seaports have European sections with hotels and stores similar to those in France. The typical native section, or Medina, however, has narrow streets with tiny shops where Moslem clothing, slippers, jewelry, brassware, and similar articles are sold. The souks, or native markets, also have stands for fruits, vegetables, and pastries as well as shops where goods are made by hand. These shops and their trading customs are similar to those of Damascus, Baghdad, and other cities of the Near East.

A North African city often has a Mellah, or Jewish quarter, and a Casbah (Kasba), or native fort. In Algiers the name Casbah has been extended to include both the fort and the native quarter. It is world-famous for its dark, narrow streets and mixture of peoples—Arabs, Berbers, Maltese, Jews, and others. With the establishment of Israel, many North African Jews left for that country.

ECONOMIC DEVELOPMENT

The areas favorable for agriculture are largely restricted to the Mediterranean and steppe climates, but even there agriculture is not continuous. Many places are too mountainous, and a few, especially in coastal Algeria, are poorly drained. Algeria is world-famous for its wine and typical Mediterranean products like barley, wheat, olives, grapes, and oranges. A variety of vegetables and fruits are grown in scattered spots throughout the Tell. Some of these are small coastal plains and hill lands; others are sheltered and well-watered inland valleys. Corn and oats are among the minor products of Morocco and Algeria, and tobacco has become important in eastern Algeria.

Much of the original Mediterranean forest has been cut for firewood, but the less accessible mountains are still forested and are now being carefully conserved. The cork oak forests of Algeria and Morocco, among other uses, supply stoppers for wine bottles.

The interior semiarid steppes, with their natural growth of short grass or scattered bushes, are most suitable for sheep and goats, which far outnumber the cattle. Mules, donkeys, horses, and camels are

Figure 12-8 Picking oranges in Morocco. The citrus industry of the Barbary states has increased greatly in importance in recent years. (Courtesy of French Embassy Press and Information Division.)

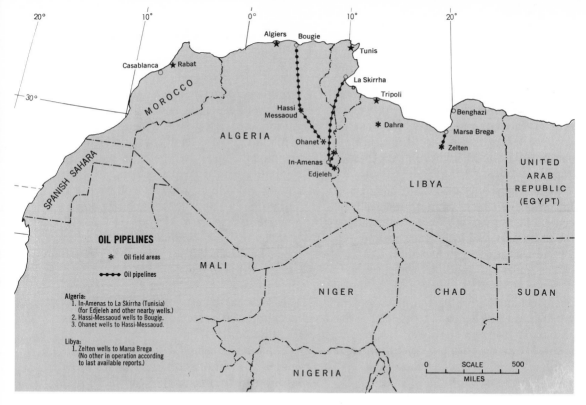

Figure 12-9   One of the most recently discovered petroleum fields is in the Sahara Desert of Algeria.

also raised and are used by the natives for riding and pack animals. The high plateaus of Algeria produce alfa or esparto grass, which is used for making paper.

The fishing industry yields sardines, anchovy, and tuna along the west coast of Morocco, and the canning of sardines is an important industry of the ports of Casablanca, Safi, and Mazagan. In Tunisia, Sfax is the main fishing port. Mullet and whiting come from deep-sea fishing, tuna and sponges from inshore fishing.

Barbary has considerable mineral wealth, especially phosphate rock and iron ore. The phosphate is mined in southern Tunisia, in Morocco, and to a lesser extent, in eastern Algeria. Rich deposits of iron ore occur in a band extending from the Rif of Morocco across Algeria and into western Tunisia. Lead and zinc are mined in Morocco as well as in eastern

Algeria and Tunisia. Small amounts of antimony, cobalt, and copper have also been produced. The only coal mines of importance are in western Algeria, near Colomb-Bechar; they provide only a portion of the fuel needed by the Barbary states. In recent years the manganese mines of eastern Morocco have greatly increased their production.

The discovery of petroleum in the Algerian Sahara in 1957 led to a new phase in the economic and political development of Algeria. It made the French less willing to give freedom to Algeria, and the independence agreements of 1962 provided for joint Franco-Algerian exploitation of the wells. Although the estimated petroleum reserves are well below those of oil-rich countries like Saudi Arabia and Iraq, Algeria now has a new resource which makes its economic future appear brighter.

DIFFERENCES AMONG THE COUNTRIES OF BARBARY

Morocco, Algeria, and Tunisia are similar in that each is a strip of Mediterranean, steppe, and desert country that exports raw materials and imports processed goods. All have been controlled by France. But there are important variations in landforms, peoples, trade, and government, so that each division has its distinct personality.

In Morocco, there are a few French settlers in the former French portion and Spaniards in the area formerly controlled by Spain. The Berber elements in the mountains form a large cultural and political group. Morocco is ruled by a king. The United States is interested in the manganese mines of eastern Morocco and has spent considerable sums for the construction of air bases in the Casablanca area. France is the most important source of Moroccan imports, but American sales of motor vehicles, machinery, and petroleum products have also been important.

The major export of Morocco is phosphate rock, followed by fish, fruits, vegetables, wheat, barley, and manganese ore. Moslems do not ordinarily produce or consume wine, which accounts for its absence from the list of major exports. But like other peoples of the region, the Moroccans demand sugar and tea, and since neither is raised in the country, they rank high among the imports.

Algeria has many more French settlers than Morocco, although thousands fled the country during and after the war of independence. There are also moderate numbers of Spaniards in western Algeria, and Italians in the east. Cities like Algiers, Oran, Bône, and Philippeville have well-developed European sections. Before independence the European population amounted to about 1 million of the total of 9 million.

The French farmers and Mediterranean climate have accounted for the large production and export of wine, in which Algeria ranks high among the countries of the world. Following wine, the other major exports are fruits and vegetables, cereals, and iron ore. These products, of course, are sent mainly to France. Machinery, textiles, petroleum products, and sugar are the major imports. Politically, French control was longer and more intense in Algeria than in Morocco or Tunisia. Tunisia, located just across the Mediterranean Sea from Sicily and Italy and next to the former Italian colony of Libya, has almost as many Italian settlers as French. The Tunisians, although Moslems of Arabic language and culture, differ from the Algerians and Moroccans in that the Berber element is almost entirely missing. Increasing Tunisian nationalism has led to self-government. Adjoining Libya, although less advanced culturally and economically, achieved independence at an earlier date.

Tunisia exports olive oil, phosphate rock, wheat, barley, lead, and wine, mainly to France, England, and Italy. The manufactured imports—textiles, machinery and automobiles, petroleum products, refined sugar, and many other products—come chiefly from France and the United States.

THE SAHARA

The Sahara, or Great Desert, extends from the Atlantic Ocean across the widest part of Africa to the Red Sea. It is larger than the United States. All parts of the Sahara have dry climates, and most of its peoples use the Arabic language and follow the Moslem faith. The tremendous size and the great variations in landforms and water supply, economic development, and settlement give rise to the saying, "The Sahara is a land of a hundred landscapes." Population is, on the average, very sparse, but varies from the absolute emptiness of the barren and level Tanezrouft of southern Algeria through the oases of moderate size in the sand dunes of northern Algeria and southern Tunisia to the gigantic oasis of the Nile in Egypt with its 25 million people. All are parts of the Sahara, but Egypt is so important and so different from the other oases that it will be described as a separate region. Politically, parts of the northern Sahara lie in Morocco, Algeria, Tunisia, Spanish Sahara, Libya, Egypt, and the Sudan. The southern parts extend into the countries of Tropical Africa.

At first the Sahara was believed to be an endless expanse of sand dunes without vegetation. Although some dune regions, or ergs, are larger than Pennsylvania or Illinois, the total sandy surface is only about 15 per cent of the total area. Most of the desert is a low plateau with a gravel or stony surface. A very sparse and withered vegetation of small bushes with weeds and grass is most common. Some areas, like the Tanezrouft, are level and without vegetation, whereas the rocky hills and mountains of the Ahaggar (Hoggar), Aïr, and Tibesti have scrubby bushes and stunted trees.

Although rainstorms are rare, they may occur suddenly and fill the shallow valleys (wadis) to overflowing in a few minutes. After the storm, the dried-up shrubs and the dormant seeds and roots of grass spring to life as if by magic, and the locality turns brown, gray, or green, depending upon the season and the variety of plants. The interior nomads move almost constantly in search of such pasturage for their goats, sheep, and camels. In the north the herds are often moved to the Atlas Mountains for the summer and onto the nearby desert during the period of winter rains.

EVOLUTION OF TRANSPORTATION

Before the Arab conquest in the seventh century the oases and mountains of central and western Sahara were occupied by Negro farmers. Water was then, as at present, obtained from streams that ran into the desert from the more humid mountains, from springs at the edges of plateaus and rocky hills, or from shallow wells that tapped underground sources. Travel between oases was rare and generally on foot or by donkey.

The Arabs spread the Moslem faith and the use of the camel to all parts of the Great Desert. The Negroes were driven from some of the northern oases; in other places they were allowed to remain as slaves or workers for the conquerors. Some of the Berbers, especially the proud and warlike Tuaregs, turned nomad and gained control of parts of the Sahara. They rarely became farmers but often controlled oases, which they used as bases for their raids upon camel caravans and hostile settlements.

Despite the danger of raids and the necessity for camels to halt for long periods of rest at intermediate oases, a number of trans-Saharan caravan routes developed. In the west, one ran from Marrakech to Timbuktu on the southern edge of the desert. Other routes connected Timbuktu with Algeria, and led from Kano, Nigeria, to Tunis and Tripoli on the Mediterranean Sea. Such long trips required many months. Silk, weapons, tea, sugar, and manufactured goods were hauled southward, and the return trips carried ivory, leather goods, ostrich feathers, and cotton cloth. Salt was also a commodity of great importance. It was mined in several places in the Sahara and distributed to the more humid lands on the north and south. Numbers of Negro slaves were also taken across the desert for sale in the cities of Barbary.

Suppression of the slave trade by European nations, the exhaustion of gold mines, and the falling demand for wild ostrich feathers caused a decline in trade across the Sahara. Recent construction of railways and roads from the west coast of Africa into the interior made it accessible from that direction, and most of the remaining long trans-Saharan caravan routes were abandoned.

The camel, however, is still used by wandering nomads for transport in areas of sand dunes and for the declining salt trade. Donkeys serve local needs in oases and farming areas, and horses are used on the margins of the desert. Since about 1930, both airlines and trucklines have furnished commercial transportation across the Sahara. The discovery of petroleum in Algeria and Libya in the late 1950s led to the construction of additional roads and airports to serve the oil fields.

ECONOMIC DEVELOPMENT

The peoples of the desert may be divided into nomads and oasis dwellers. Nomads are most numerous on the steppes and more habitable northern and southern margins of the Sahara. Their herds provide milk, wool, mutton, and hides, which are often traded to the subservient oasis

Figure 12-10   A group of nomads near the Atlas Mountains. (Courtesy of Morocco Tourist Office.)

people for dates, grain, fruits, and vegetables. Nomads may also carry on trade between oases or serve as professional soldiers.

Oases vary considerably in appearance. Huts may be constructed of brown mud, of red or yellow clay, or rarely of blocks of salt. Sometimes the buildings are whitewashed a brilliant white. The site may be a stream valley lined with palms, a flat-topped hill, a vale between gigantic red sand dunes, or a flat dusty plain—wherever springs or wells can provide water. The larger oases are urban in character, with cafés, shops, and marketplaces to serve the desert travelers. The town may be walled for protection against raids. Irrigated gardens usually provide barley and dates, and less commonly, wheat, millet, tobacco, onions, apricots, and other fruits and vegetables. Some oases, like those visited by tourists in the northern Sahara, have modern hotels, curio shops, and cafés, but others are hot, dusty, miserable collections of mud huts. High-quality dates are an export of importance in Algeria and have justified the extension of several rail lines to the more productive oases.

Since the discovery of petroleum, a number of oasis dwellers have found employment at oil wells or on the construction of pipelines, and new oil towns have developed.

THE NATION OF LIBYA

Libya, almost entirely Saharan in character, has recently joined the world family of independent nations for reasons stemming from geography, history, and politics. France was established in Barbary, and England had special interests in Egypt and Suez before Italy became a world power. The desert between, being less valuable, was left under the control of weak Turkey and fell to Italy when that country sought colonial possessions.

In Libya the desert restricts agriculture and animal husbandry to the three habitable islands of Tripolitania, Cyrenaica, and the Fezzan. The main agricultural products are barley, dates, and olives; sheep and goats provide wool, meat, and skins. There are very small exports of animals, wool, and skins, also sponges and tuna from coastal fisheries. With the defeat of Italy in World War II, the administration of Libya was first taken over by the United Kingdom and France. Then, in 1952, Libya became an independent nation in accordance with decisions of the United Nations, although the population is small and the three habitable areas are separated from each other by hundreds of miles of barren desert. American and British financial support, in return for the right to maintain military bases in Libya, is an important element in the economy of the country, but since 1960 petroleum exports have become the major source of income.

UNITED ARAB REPUBLIC (EGYPT) AND THE SUDAN

Civilization in the Nile Valley began several thousand years before the time of Christ. The desert climate provided dazzling sunlight, and the Nile River brought both fertile silt and water for irrigation during the regular floods of the late summer and autumn. The productive delta and narrow plain along the river were served by the navigable stream and had protection from invasion. On the north, the Nile Delta (downstream or Lower Egypt) has numerous distributaries and marshy land and is a difficult area to cross. Along both sides of the fertile Nile Valley are barren zones, the Arabian and Nubian Deserts on the east and the Libyan Desert on the west. The Nile Valley narrows in Upper (southern) Egypt until the river has only a gorge through the desert plateau, and there is a series of rapids which prevent navigation. Thus nature provided a suitable habitat for this early cradle of civilization, and man has occupied the land through a succession of dynasties and other governments, cultures, and religions. Worship, as one might expect, has often been associated with the sun or with the Nile.

NILE RIVER

For centuries the farmers of the Nile Valley regulated their lives according to the floods of the river, without knowing its source or the reasons for its fluctuations. The Nile, one of the longest rivers in the world, has its sources on the equator, 2,000 miles south of the Delta (Figure 12-11). The longest tributary is the White Nile, which drains from Lake Victoria. This large body of water has a constant supply from the heavy rains of the wet equatorial climate. The flow of the White Nile is also stabilized farther north in passing through Lake Albert and the Sudd region of floating vegetation. There the channel of the river was completely covered with masses of papyrus, bulrushes, tall grass, and weeds until British engineers opened a path for navigation in 1904. The gentle gradient and widespread swamps result in a very slow flow of water. Evaporation is high and only about half of the water finally escapes from the swamps. The flow is steady, and if it were not for the other tributaries, there would be no great floods on the Nile.

The Blue Nile and the Atbara Rivers start in the Ethiopian plateau, where the climate is an upland savanna type. Rainfall is heavy in summer and light in winter. In summer the flooded streams flow swiftly from the highlands into the Sudan, bringing large quantities of silt. The Blue Nile joins the White Nile at Khartoum, and from that point northward the river has its seasonal floods. The Atbara adds to the height of the floods, and makes them last longer into the fall. By January the Ethiopian tributaries are at the low level of the dry season. The White Nile continues to supply water from the lakes of the equatorial region during the critical low-water period from January to June. The British constructed the great dam at Aswan in 1903, and others, to store water during the flood season and release it during the low stage of the river, making possible a great expansion of cotton growing in Egypt.

In the Sudan, a dam at Sennar on the Blue Nile, completed in 1925, regulates the flow so that large-scale cotton production has become possible in the Gezira area near the junction of the White and the Blue Nile. Despite the great success of these and other dams, many problems remain. The silt is trapped by the dams so that it no longer adds new fertility to the irrigated fields; commercial fertilizers must now be used. Complete regulation of the Nile should include Lake Tana at the source of the Blue Nile in Ethiopia as well as tributaries of the Nile in countries like Tanganyika and Uganda, but comprehensive agreements among the countries have not yet been made. The population of Egypt is growing rapidly, but the Nile remains the same size. During the four low-water months, dams close the mouths of the river, and all the water is used for irrigation; none reaches the sea. By international agreements originally sponsored by Great Britain when she had full control of Egypt, the priority rights on Nile water belong to Egypt. Irrigation water for the Sudan is taken with Egyptian permission and only at the flood

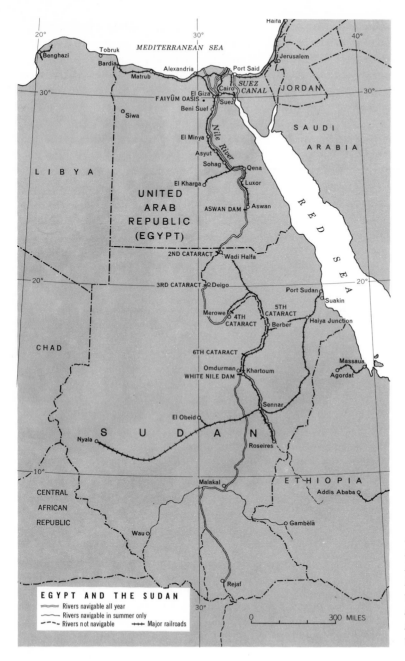

Figure 12-11   The Nile River is the lifeline of Egypt and the Sudan. Note the vast amount of vacant land away from the river and the use of railroads in conjunction with the waterway.

season when Egypt can spare the water. These agreements, however, are now being disputed. The Sudan and Ethiopia claim that since Great Britain no longer controls the territory the agreements are void. Nile water is a strict limiting factor on agriculture in both countries. The present dams hold water during the wet months and release it during the dry ones, but the storage is only annual. The recently completed Owen Falls dam in Uganda has raised the level of Lake Victoria by three feet and added to the amount of stored water. A second dam near Aswan is under construction and will make possible some extension of agriculture in Egypt. Disputes over American, British, and Soviet financial aid for the dam led to the Suez crisis of 1956.

PEOPLE

In the Sudd region of the southern Sudan the primitive peoples are mostly of Negro origin with small interminglings of white, Hamitic blood. The Dinka, Shilluk, and Nuer groups are known as Nilotes. They wear little or no clothing and gain a living mainly by herding cattle, hunting, or fishing. To the northwest, in the hill lands of Darfur and Kordofan, Negroid peoples like the Nuba live by raising millet or gathering gum arabic from acacia trees.

The central part of the Sudan and the northwestern deserts are inhabited by nomadic Arabs who raise camels and sheep, and in the more humid lands farther south, cattle and horses. There are also Hamitic tribes between the Nile and the Red Sea. Because of their bushy hair these people are commonly known as "Fuzzie-Wuzzies." They are remembered for their fight against Britain and Egypt when the two countries combined to conquer the Sudan, in the years from 1881 to 1898. In the northern Sudan most of the farmers of the Nile Valley are Nubians of mixed blood. Some of them engage in native crafts like pottery making and basket weaving.

ECONOMIC DEVELOPMENT

The major export of the Sudan is cotton, followed by gum arabic, which is used for glue, and hides and skins. Most of the people live by raising livestock, but millet, peanuts, corn, and oilseeds are food products or minor exports.

In Egypt the mass of the people comprise the fellahin or sedentary peasant class. In Upper Egypt some are descended from the ancient Hamitic peoples and belong to the Christian Coptic Church. Several centuries of Arab influence, however, have resulted in a racial mixture, and Moslems now outnumber Christians about 10 to 1 for the country as a whole. The nomadic population of Bedouin Arabs is very small.

Cotton is the main product and export of the densely settled valley and delta of the Nile. Wheat, corn, and rice are major foods, but overpopulation and specialization in cotton result in a shortage of cereals. Wheat, tea, and coffee, manufactured goods, and fertilizers are major imports. Concentration on the cash crop of cotton gives the largest monetary return and makes imports possible. Farming methods are primitive. The use of large amounts of labor without mechanization results in high yields per acre but low yields per individual. The fellahin live in mud huts and on very meager diets. Egypt hopes to provide a better living for her dense and increasing population through the expansion of industries such as cotton weaving and food processing and through additional irrigation from the high Aswan dam. Meanwhile, the growing of berseem, or Egyptian clover, in rotation with cotton and cereals, increases the nitrogen content of the soil and helps to maintain its fertility.

Oxen, buffaloes, and donkeys are used as draft animals, and sheep and goats provide milk and wool for the farming population. The Fayûm Oasis, irrigated by canals from the Nile, is the most important farming area outside the Nile Valley and Delta. Western Egypt has a few scattered oases, some of them served only by camel caravans.

TRADE PROBLEMS

The Nile is the main artery of trade in Egypt. There are hundreds of small sailing vessels and dozens of shallow draft steamers plying the river between Cairo and Aswan, at the first cataract. Above Aswan, the Nile is again navigable to Wadi Halfa at the Sudan border. Railways, as well as roads and airlines, parallel this route. From Cairo northward, the delta has radiating distributaries and rail lines to the mouths of the river.

Cairo benefits as the converging point at the head of the delta. East-west commercial and pilgrim traffic along the southern shore of the Mediterranean swings southward through Cairo to avoid crossing the many streams and swamps of the delta—an important factor in the city's early growth. With a population of more than 2 million, Cairo is the largest and most important commercial center of North Africa and the Near East. Although Mecca is the holy city for Moslems as Rome is for Roman Catholics, Cairo is the cultural hub of the Arab world, as Paris is for much of Western Europe. In recent years Cairo has become a great focus of air traffic, and the political center for rising nationalism among the Arab peoples. The modern portion of Cairo is in European style, reminding one of French cities, while the older sections— Arab, Jewish, and Coptic—have the narrow streets, bazaars, shops, and crowded living quarters of other Near Eastern centers. The ancient mosques and palaces, like the pyramids near the city, attract thousands of tourists yearly. Cairo has several suburbs in European style.

Alexandria is the second largest city and chief port of Egypt. Through it pass about nine-tenths of the exports, consisting of cotton and small quantities of rice and onions.

THE SUEZ CANAL

The Suez Canal was built by the French under the direction of Ferdinand de Lesseps, and was opened to traffic in 1869. At that time Egypt was technically a province of the Ottoman (Turkish) empire, but actually a semi-independent area under strong British influence. Great Britain at first opposed the canal, but both Egypt and Turkey supported the Suez Canal Company, and became shareholders in it. In 1875 Great Britain made an opportune purchase of the shares of the Khedive of Egypt, and became an important shareholder. The administration, however, remained predominantly French, even after World War I, when Egypt was detached from the Ottoman empire and placed under British protection.

The Suez Canal is a 100-mile-long sea-level route. Port Said and Suez are the northern and southern terminals. The canal forms a link in the ocean route between Europe and the Far East. In recent years it has become even more important to the countries of Western Europe and the Middle East as a passageway for oil tankers on their way from the Persian Gulf around the Arabian Peninsula to the Mediterranean Sea.

After World War II, rising nationalism in Egypt led to riots against the British and demands for the evacuation of British troops from all of Egypt, including the canal zone. Britain finally agreed to remove its troops from the canal bases in 1954, but the British- and French-dominated company continued operating the canal. Two years later, in 1956, Egypt seized the canal facilities in retaliation for British and American refusals to continue support for the high Aswan dam. France and Britain withdrew their personnel from the canal zone but insisted on continued international control of the waterway. A few weeks later Israel attacked Egypt. Britain and France occupied portions of the canal zone and demanded that both Israel and Egypt cease hostilities, justifying their action on the ground that the canal required protection and should remain in operation under international control regardless of Middle Eastern disputes. The United Nations then sent an international police force to the area to maintain order. In 1957 the canal, which had been blocked, was cleared and reopened to traffic under the control of Egypt.

THE SUDAN

The Sudan has been independent since 1956. The country has much less trade than Egypt. A rail line starts at Wadi Halfa, the second cataract, and extends southeastward to Abu Hamed instead of following the great bend of the Nile. From Abu Hamed through Khartoum to Sennar, however, the railway parallels the Nile and the Blue Nile tributary. A branch line extends westward from the main trunk to tap the oil-seed, cotton, cattle, and gum arabic regions near El Obeid and Nyala. Other lines connect Sennar and Berber with Port Sudan on the Red Sea. Additional lines are under construction or planned for the future.

The largest settlement of the Sudan is ancient Omdurman near the junction of the White Nile and the Blue Nile. It was the capital of the dervishes, a fanatical sect of Moslems who followed the Mahdi, a supposed descendant and successor of Mohammed. Omdurman is still a center for trade in camels, cattle, and gum arabic. The British built the nearby town of Khartoum, which soon became the center for railways, modern hotels, administration, and the cotton trade. In early

days the Arabs shipped slaves from Suakin on the Red Sea, but the harbor has silted and declined to a minor port for small sailing vessels. The newer center of Port Sudan, built by the British, is now the major outlet for the country.

THE STRATEGIC NEAR EAST

The lands of the Near East, extending from Turkey to Iran and southward to include Egypt and Arabia, play a prominent part in the strategy of the modern world. The area forms a land bridge that connects Europe, Asia, and Africa. Since ancient times it has been a crossroads for traders going from Eastern Europe to India, and from Asia to North Africa.

The shape of this land bridge gives it control over the connections between important bodies of water (Figure 12-12). The Dardanelles, the Sea of Marmara, and the Bosporus link the Mediterranean Sea with the Black Sea, thus providing a possible outlet for the southern part of the Soviet Union and the Balkan countries. For thousands of years traders and invading armies have used the land route from India and Persia to Europe by way of the narrow straits. The physical geography, however, makes it possible for Turkey to close the Dardanelles and defend it against superior forces, giving the nation added weight in power politics.

Another traditional east-west route is that from the Persian Gulf across Iraq and Syria to the eastern end of the Mediterranean Sea. It was first used by pedestrians and caravans, and later was associated with railways, airlines, and oil pipelines. When Great Britain obtained a sea route to the East by way of the Mediterranean, the Suez Canal, and the Red Sea, Germany countered with plans for a railway from Berlin to Baghdad.

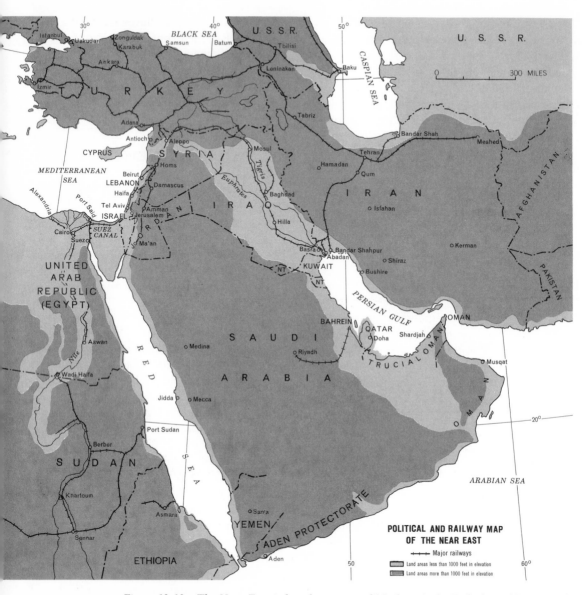

Figure 12-12   The Near East is largely an area of Moslem Arab, Turkish, and Persian culture. Israel, Cyprus, and Lebanon are the only non-Moslem nations. The mountains and northern coastlands have moderate rainfall; the remainder is desert and steppe country.

Construction was started in 1888, but the railway was not completed until 1940. By this time airplanes had come into commercial use, and Baghdad was also a center for airlines. British, French, German, and Dutch planes connected the city with Europe, and certain lines continued toward the Far East.

Since World War II both land and air traffic across the U.S.S.R. has been blocked. The Near East, therefore, controls the shortest land and air routes between Europe and Asia, as well as the Suez sea route. Baghdad, Cairo, and Suez are strategic points in transport and politics.

NATIONALISM, OIL, AND PIPELINES

In recent decades, oil has played a large part in the politics of the Near East. Two factors, world petroleum supply and Arab nationalism, are basic causes of tension. The United States produces about 33 per cent of the world's petroleum and the Near East about 25 per cent. Until after World War II, the United States was a large exporter of petroleum products. Increased consumption caused this country to import from Caribbean America and the Near East. Western Europe has almost no petroleum, and therefore must import from the Near East or elsewhere. The Soviet Union produces about 14 per cent

of the world's oil but needs more, for which the closest source is Iran, Iraq, or Arabia. Thus Western Europe, the United States, and the Soviet Union are all vitally interested in petroleum. The steadily increasing demand for petroleum in Europe and America draws attention to the vast reserves and potential production of the Near East.

The United States, Venezuela, and the U.S.S.R. are the leading oil-producing countries of the world. But the four Near Eastern countries of Kuwait, Saudi Arabia, Iraq, and Iran rank next, and are gaining in importance. Together, of course, they form a region which is second only to the United States in production. And of great importance for the future is the location of oil reserves: the Near East has greater known reserves of petroleum than any other region.

Some of the oil from Iran and Saudi

Figure 12-13   Saudi Arabs and their camels stop for rest alongside a portion of the trans-Arabian pipeline system near Badanah, Saudi Arabia. (Courtesy of Arabian American Oil Company.)

Arabia is piped to terminals on the Persian Gulf (Figure 12-14). Because the oil is destined for Western Europe and the United States, it is more economical to transport the oil by pipelines to the Mediterranean Sea. The lines from Iran and Saudi Arabia, as well as from Iraq, therefore, cross the countries which lie between the oil fields and the eastern Mediterranean—Syria, Lebanon, Israel, and Jordan. Since the Arab-Israeli War of 1948–1949, however, the branch of the pipeline to Israel has not been used.

Securing and keeping concessions for drilling wells, building refineries, and operating pipelines are often difficult tasks.

The Near East countries all desire independence and higher standards of living, but politics and economy vary from place to place. In several Near East countries the strong desire for complete freedom from foreign influence conflicts with the pressing need for income from oil fields which local capital and technical skill cannot effectively develop.

CULTURAL FEATURES

The Near East is not only a strategic crossroads; it is the seat of several early civilizations and the birthplace of three of the world's great religions, Christianity, Juda-

Figure 12-14   The Near East has the greatest reserves of petroleum in the world. The importance of this area is in its mineral wealth. Great pipelines have been built to transport petroleum across the desert to the Mediterranean ports.

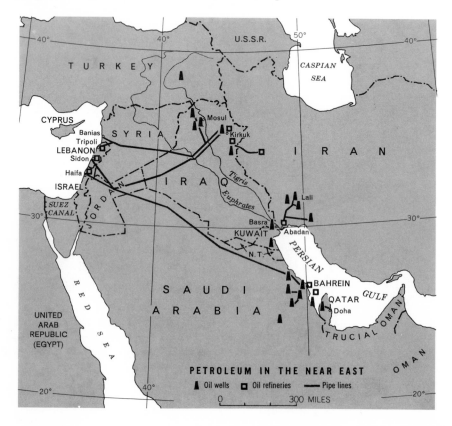

ism, and Islam. Jerusalem is still a holy city for Moslem, Christian, and Jew; and each year large numbers of Moslems make the pilgrimage to Mecca in Saudi Arabia.

The Moslem religion and the Arabic language and culture have spread from Arabia to distant lands like Morocco, with consequences that have been mentioned earlier in connection with the Barbary states. The Jewish faith and Christianity also have spread from the eastern Mediterranean to all the inhabited continents, together with cultural traits like Christian ethics and the Hebrew language. Modern civilization has been built of many elements that had their origins in the ancient civilizations of Egypt, Mesopotamia (now Iraq), Persia (Iran), Syria, and Palestine (now Israel and a part of Jordan).

The Fertile Crescent is a discontinuous belt of cultivated land which starts at the head of the Persian Gulf and extends in a great arc up the Tigris and Euphrates Valleys and across Lebanon and Syria to Israel. Since early times the Fertile Crescent has been famous for its green pastures and its trade centers. The cities of Basra, Baghdad, and Mosul in Iraq, Aleppo and Damascus in Syria, Antioch in Turkey, Beirut in Lebanon, and Jerusalem, divided between Israel and Jordan, are well-known exchange places for the products of fertile fields, nomadic herding, and local handicraft. Damascus claims to be the oldest continuously inhabited city in the world. The Fertile Crescent was the seat of many ancient empires. Among the earliest were those of the Assyrians, Babylonians, Phoenicians, Hebrews, and Hittites. Persians and Kurds came later, and these were followed in turn by Greeks, Romans, Mongols, Arabs, and Turks.

Aridity or light winter rainfall characterizes much of the Near East as well as North Africa. Population is concentrated in the few areas where water is available. In modern times, petroleum has come to

Figure 12-15 Huge underinflated sand tires enable exploration trucks in the Rub' al-Khali desert to travel through the softest sand. (Courtesy of Arabian American Oil Company.)

dominate the economies of several countries, but aside from this, the main products are from farming and grazing. As in North Africa, cultivation is restricted to the areas of Mediterranean climate, and the oases. There is a great contrast between these spots of green fields and the dry steppes and deserts.

Since the spread of Islam by the Arabs, most of the Near East has been linked by the way of life which that religion imposes, as well as by common pursuits followed by people of similar racial and cultural origin in lands of Mediterranean or arid climates. Resemblances among the countries are many, but variations in landforms, location, economic products, and local culture are sufficient to give each unit a personality of its own.

THE PLATEAU COUNTRIES OF TURKEY AND IRAN

Turkey and Iran are somewhat alike in general structure; both are large plateaus with bordering mountains as well as interior highlands that divide the land into a number of basins. Small streams flow from the high rugged mountains onto the dry plateaus, but there are no large fertile river plains like those of the Nile in Egypt or the Tigris and Euphrates in Iraq. Settlements are widely scattered in favorable valleys, but the total populations place these countries in the same class as Egypt. Turkey has about 28 million people, Egypt 28 million, and Iran 21 million. The other countries of the region have much smaller populations.

Like Iran, Turkey has its own language; Arabic is not used. Although the Arab conquest included much of both countries, the Arabs did not settle on the highlands. After converting the people to Islam, they chose to settle mainly in lowland areas like Iraq (Mesopotamia). This is a parallel to the Arab settlement in lowland Barbary, with the original Berbers, converted to Islam, still using their own language in mountainous regions. Persian remained as one language; in Turkey several groups of Turkish peoples later invaded the region from the northeast and further modified the language.

Turkey and Iran are not only somewhat similar in general structure, but both possess large interior dry areas with nomadic populations. Iran depends upon petroleum exports instead of agricultural products and has a strategic frontage on the Persian Gulf instead of control of the Dardanelles. Both countries are intensely nationalistic; both block possible southern outlets for the Soviet Union; and both have been anxious to avoid falling within the Soviet orbit.

TURKEY   During the fifteenth century the Ottoman Turkish nation rose to a place among the Great Powers and conquered most of the territory which had previously been dominated by the Arabs. The empire then declined. In the nineteenth century, France and Great Britain took the provinces of Algeria and Egypt, and the remaining parts of North Africa soon fell to France, Spain, and Italy. The Balkan Wars deprived Turkey of most of her European territory, and World War I resulted in the loss of Iraq, Syria, and Turkish influence on the Arabian Peninsula.

The freeing of the Near East from Turkish and then from European control was accompanied by a great upsurge in nationalism, an Arab awakening which has spread to North Africa. Most of these areas, so long dominated by foreign powers, now have a strong desire to be rid of all foreign interference.

In Turkey, however, the new nationalism has taken a surprising and distinct form. The Turkish awakening had its origins in earlier movements, but the effects came to the attention of the world soon after World War I. Shorn of former Arab possessions and reduced to a core of Turkish peoples with Greek, Armenian, and Kurdish minorities, the reborn nation made a strenuous effort to reform and modernize its political, economic, and social life. The capital was moved from the metropolis of Istanbul (Constantinople) to the interior town of Ankara. The Moslem faith was modified by government decree and separated from the government. Religious leaders no longer have economic, legal, social, and political control of their followers as in the more traditional of the Moslem Arab countries. Against great opposition, women were given legal, economic, and political rights, and the custom of wearing the veil was abolished. Men were forbidden to wear the traditional Moslem cap, the fez.

To replace customary Moslem law and the inefficient Turkish legal structure, the rejuvenated nation borrowed a complete new system from Western Europe. In place of law based upon the Koran and upon sayings attributed to Mohammed, the new nation adopted its commercial code from Germany and its criminal code from Italy. Still more important was acceptance of the Swiss civil code, because that replaced the many complex and ancient rules of the old Turkish law. Thus it is now illegal for a man to have slaves, or more than one wife. Personal liberty is guaranteed regardless of religious belief. National patriotism replaces the Moslem faith as the central principle of the state. The Moslem religion has not been abolished, but merely separated from economy, government, and law, like the churches in Switzerland and the United States. Nevertheless, the customs of centuries cannot be changed overnight, and the struggle to bring practice into accord with written law is still in progress.

The Turkish language has been reformed and simplified. Latin letters are now used instead of the Arabic script, so that the printing resembles that of the Romance languages. In agriculture, industry, education, construction, and most other phases of economic life, Turkish policy is to modernize and Westernize. This imitation of Western Europe, however, is sponsored by a small group of leaders, and the country is in transition. Progress is made each year, but many old beliefs and practices still exist, especially in remote areas. The reaction of other Near Eastern peoples to modern Turkey varies, but perhaps to most of them, Turkey is a mystery. The Moslem religion is still a strong link, but the close political cooperation of Turkey with the West and the adoption of European customs have aroused suspicion and irritation among conservative Moslem elements.

After World War I, Turkey exchanged much of its Greek population of the west for Turkish people in Greece. In old Turkey the Armenian and Kurdish populations of the east were often persecuted. Relations with minorities are now much better, although the Kurds would still like to have autonomy for the parts of Turkey, Iran, and Iraq that they occupy.

Agriculture has been aided by the use of tractors and machinery. The coastal margins on the west and south have a Mediterranean climate with mild winters and 20 to 30 inches of rainfall. Olives, wheat, tobacco, nuts, grapes, figs, and barley are raised in the narrow coastal zone, but the mountain-rimmed interior plateau, with an average elevation of 3,000 feet, is dry, with cold winters. Large areas are grazed by sheep, goats, and camels, and much of the population is nomadic. Most of the interior is semiarid, rather than desert.

The major exports of the coastal areas are tobacco, figs, raisins, olives, and olive oil. Animals, hides and skins, and mohair wool from the renowned Angora goats are typical products from the interior plateau. Besides the traditional manufacture of tobacco products, rugs, and carpets, a newly established iron and steel works is in operation at Karabuk, and small industries have arisen in Istanbul, Izmir (Smyrna), and in many smaller centers. Turkey has important deposits of chromium and coal, and lesser resources of iron, copper, and petroleum.

Many roads and railways have been constructed by the new Turkey, but the network is still loose. The mechanization of agriculture and the establishment of industry are impressive only when compared with former conditions or with undeveloped areas of the Near East. By the standards of Western Europe, Turkey has just begun to modernize and industrialize. Many people have low standards of living, and the country still depends largely on imports of petroleum products, machinery, vehicles, and other processed goods. Modern irrigation projects are rare; pastoral industries still support a considerable part of the population.

Istanbul serves the rolling farmlands and forests of European Turkey and other nearby areas, but is best known as a cosmopolitan and picturesque city of world importance. It is the financial, cultural, and commercial center for a large area. In North Africa and the Near East, only Cairo is larger. Istanbul has many famous mosques and important Greek, Armenian, and Jewish sections. Ankara in the rugged interior uplands is the capital and trade center for Angora wool and grain. It has grown very rapidly and now has wide streets with many modern and impressive buildings. Izmir is presently the major exporting center for Turkey.

IRAN Petroleum is by far the most important product of Iran. The export of oil is, by value, normally several times that of all other exports combined, and the Iranian government largely depends upon the income from oil for its expenses and for foreign exchange. The industry employs almost as many industrial workers as all other industries together. The

Figure 12-16 An aerial view of a tank farm and refinery at Ras Tanura on the Persian Gulf. (Courtesy of Arabian American Oil Company.)

refinery at Abadan, in the southwest, is one of the largest in the world. Most of the oil fields lie near the head of the Persian Gulf.

The great majority of Iranians are farmers. The main crops of wheat, barley, rice, dates, cotton, and tobacco are mostly consumed locally. Only moderate quantities of dried fruits, cotton, and a few other agricultural items are exported. Except for refined sugar and tea, the country is self-sufficient in food. The more productive farmlands of the north make up for the deficit in the drier sections of the interior and the south.

The deserts and mountains of Iran occupy most of the surface. Only about 10 per cent of the land is cultivated. Methods of farming are often ancient and primitive, irrigation facilities are inadequate, and productivity is low. Approximately 90 per cent of the people are illiterate. As in Egypt, there are large numbers of tenants or sharecroppers who work on the estates of wealthy landlords. The main industrial products, aside from petroleum, are handwoven rugs and textiles. Persian rugs have been well known since ancient times and rank next to petroleum as an export.

The major centers of Iran lie in the interior. Tehran is the capital and largest city. It is in an important irrigated district and is the focus for several roads and rail lines. Growth has been rapid since World War I, and the modern buildings contrast sharply with the older sections. Tabriz is the main commercial center for the farmlands of the northwest, and manufactures carpets, textiles, and leather goods. Isfahan is noted for its textiles, cotton, silk, and wool, and is also a center for animal products and dried fruits. In northeastern Iran the oasis town of Meshed lies on the caravan route to India and is connected with Tehran by railway. Products of the region include fruits, cotton, grain, sheep, and goats. All the large centers of Iran have colorful bazaars and ancient and famous mosques. Many of these cities were the capitals of past empires.

Bandar Shahpur, at the head of the Persian Gulf, is the most important seaport of Iran. In 1938 a railroad was built to connect it via Tehran with Bandar Shah on the Caspian Sea. Over this route the Allies, especially the United States, shipped supplies to aid the Soviet Union against Germany in World War II. The central and eastern part of Iran has large areas of desert, salt marsh, and mountains, and is much less productive than interior Turkey.

SYRIA, LEBANON, AND IRAQ

Unlike Turkey and Iran, the countries of Syria, Lebanon, and Iraq are dominated by the Arabic language and culture. Furthermore, the religion of Syria and Iraq, but not of Christian Lebanon, is controlled from the Arabian holy cities of Mecca and Medina. The Turks in former times often carried the brunt of Moslem opposition to Christianity in Southeastern Europe, with Constantinople as their religious capital; but a number of Arab groups refused to recognize the authority of Constantinople. Modern Turkey, of course, has its own modified Moslem religion. In Iran most of the Moslems are of the Shiah sect, which differs from the Sunni Moslem group of Arabia and Africa. Thus, in language and religion as well as in politics, the southern margins of Turkey and Iran form a significant border zone.

SYRIA Syria consists of a Mediterranean coastal belt with interior bordering highlands, the valley of the Euphrates in the northeast, and the central and southern deserts. It is primarily an agricultural country. The seminomadic tribes of the steppes and deserts are tending more and more to settle upon farmlands. Agricultural population is densest in the fertile western valleys. The largest cities, Aleppo and Damascus, are also located in the west.

Most of the people are Moslems who use the Arabic language. A minority, about 10 per cent, are Christians, but they offer no challenge to the dominance of Arabic culture. Agriculture is largely of the Mediterranean type, with about nine-tenths of the farmlands dependent upon rainfall rather than irrigation. Wheat, barley, melons, olives, and grapes are typical products, although cotton production for local industries is increasing. Sheep and goats are raised both in the farming areas and in the dry sections; cattle are of moderate importance in the more humid regions. The pastoral industries are restricted by inadequate pasturage during drier years and by lack of places for watering animals in the grazing areas.

Although modern methods have been introduced in canneries and in some textile plants, the total output is low. Small factories and hand workers make such articles as slippers, rugs, brassware, baskets, and pottery. Cereals and textiles are the leading exports. Syria has no important deposits of petroleum, but oil lines from Iraq and Saudi Arabia extend across Syria to the Mediterranean terminals.

Throughout history the Syrians have been known as farmers, traders, and artisans rather than as nomads. Sometimes it is said, "A Syrian is an Arab who lives in a village or city." The Levant, or eastern coast of the Mediterranean, has been an important trading area since the time of the Phoenicians. A traditional route extends from the Mediterranean Sea through Antioch, now in Turkey but a former center of ancient Syria, past Aleppo to the Euphrates Valley and along it to Baghdad and the Persian Gulf. There are also several alternate routes leading eastward from Aleppo. Damascus is another great caravan and trade center. Cafés, shops, entertainers, and local handicrafts add variety to the urban scene. The city of white buildings, on an irrigated fruitful plain at the edge of the desert, is an impressive sight. Textiles and Damascus ware of brass and copper are sold throughout the Mediterranean and Near East regions.

LEBANON   Formerly a part of Syria, Lebanon has several characteristics that make it a distinct region. The Lebanese are mostly Christians, and the mountainous country has a Mediterranean climate without deserts, steppes, or nomads. Besides its religion, Lebanon has many other cultural ties with Europe and America. Beirut is the center of American and French educational activity in the Near East. The literacy rate is higher in Lebanon than in any other Arab country. In spite of the fact that large numbers of Lebanese have emigrated to the cities of Europe and the United States, the population is fairly dense and is distributed more evenly over the state than in other nearby countries. There are many skilled workers in the cities, and the farmers usually work on their own land instead of sharecropping on large estates. Although standards of living are high for the region, they are low by Western standards, and improvement is sought through increased irrigation and expanded industries.

Lebanon was a part of the ancient Phoenician, Assyrian, Persian, Roman, and Byzantine empires. While Syria was becoming a Moslem area, however, the Maronites, a Christian sect, became established in Lebanon. The Arabs conquered both Syria and Lebanon, but the Lebanese Christians maintained their religion, and later, the Lebanese aided Crusaders who reached the area. The Ottoman Turks conquered the region. After several massacres of Christians, the European powers forced the sultans to grant some autonomy to Lebanon. Under the French mandate following World War I, Lebanon was officially separated from Syria and became completely independent on January 1, 1944. The Lebanese are racially similar to the Syrians, both being segments of the Arab world. Since the partition of Palestine many Arab refugees have entered Lebanon from Israel, so that the population is now about one-half Moslem and one-half Christian. The liberal tradition of the Lebanese Christians, however, is still dominant.

The Lebanon Mountains lie close to the Mediterranean and extend north and south for the length of the country. The Anti-Lebanon Range forms the eastern border with Syria. The coastal plain, the western slopes of the Lebanon Mountains, and the valley between the two mountain ranges provide the best agricultural land of the country. The crops include grapes, vegetables, and grains. Mulberry trees furnish leaves for silkworms. The mountains formerly supplied cedar, but the forests have been reduced to small areas. There are many resorts in the Lebanon Mountains where visitors can escape the hot summers of lowland regions. The major industries are cotton and silk weaving and shoe manufacturing

The largest city and capital is Beirut, a busy port on the Mediterranean. Its functions are largely administrative and commercial. The famous old coastal towns of Tripoli, Sidon, and Tyre have recently regained some importance. Tripoli and Sidon are the terminals for pipelines from Iraq and Saudi Arabia.

IRAQ   Iraq, ancient Mesopotamia, rivals Egypt as a seat of early culture, and it is difficult to determine which first reached a high level of civilization. Egypt was protected from invasion, but Mesopotamia has been one of the busiest of routes for both trade and invading armies. Egypt usually dominated the nearby nomads, but Mesopotamia experienced many raids and was often subordinate to nomadic conquerors. Between the two regions are barrier areas, the Syrian and Arabian deserts.

The heart of Iraq is formed by the Tigris and Euphrates Rivers, which join above Basra to form a single stream, the Shatt-al-Arab, which empties into the Persian Gulf. Only the northeastern part of the country is humid and mountainous, the rest being low-lying and dry. Like Egypt, Iraq is largely a desert dominated by a great oasis belt that is irrigated by river water. The sources of the Tigris and Euphrates lie in the mountains of Turkey.

In recent years, the oil fields of Iraq have provided the major export and a considerable share of the nation's income. The wells are operated by British, American, French, and Dutch concerns, which divide the profits with Iraq. Since the Arab-Israeli war (1948), all the oil has been piped to Syria and Lebanon rather than to Haifa in Israel. Israel and the Arab countries have not been able to come to an agreement, and trade relations remain severed.

Outside of petroleum, agriculture is the major resource of Iraq. Some authorities believe the country is underpopulated for its resources. With income obtained from oil, new irrigation and flood-control projects are under way. Iraq has many miles of date palms on the lower Tigris and Euphrates, and leads the world in date production. Only petroleum exceeds the value of date exports. Cereals are the main food of the people both in the rain-fed zone in the north and in the irrigated region. The oasis lands also produce fruits, vegetables, and cotton; herds of sheep and goats in the arid regions provide milk, hides, skins, and wool. Clothing, sugar, tea, and machinery are the chief imports.

Nomadism is steadily decreasing in Iraq, and farming, sedentary pastoralism, and urban occupations are increasing. About 20 per cent of the population form a Kurdish minority in the north, but the southern economic problems of low standards of living, sharecropping, and shortage of technical skill are generally considered to be more pressing. The Kurdish tribes are not unified as a political pressure group; thus raids and revolts are no longer common.

Baghdad, a railway town, tourist center, and major airport, is the capital of Iraq and a focus of trade and communications. In earlier periods it was a great caravan center and one of the cultural capitals of the Arab world. The period of its greatest wealth and fame is immortalized in the tales of *The Arabian Nights.* Since then the city has been destroyed and rebuilt several times, and few of the ancient structures remain. Mosul is the chief market for the cereals, fruits, and livestock of the upper valley and is also the center of the oil industry. Basra, the principal port of Iraq, is the commercial hub of the lower valley; like Baghdad and Mosul, it has a long and colorful history.

ISRAEL AND JORDAN

Israel is now a Jewish island in the Moslem world. In Biblical times the area was predominantly Jewish, but the people were partially scattered by early invasions and economic problems. The Arab conquests continued the process, and by the thirteenth century the land was almost entirely held by Moslems. For centuries the Jews were exiles without a country, wandering from place to place. Many were traders, shopkeepers, and money-lenders who settled in cities throughout the world. The religion spread to peoples of many races. United by a common faith, many supported Zionism, the plan for a permanent Jewish nation in Palestine.

At the time of World War I, most of the Near East was under the control of Turkey, which was then allied with Germany. At the close of hostilities, temporary mandates under the League of Nations were established for the parts of the Turkish empire that were occupied by subject (non-Turkish) peoples, with the understanding that they were to be prepared for self-government. The area west of the Jordan River became the mandate of Palestine and the region immediately to the east of the river, Transjordan. Britain was designated as the country to supervise both mandates. Arab and Jewish interests clashed sharply over the Palestine question. From the standpoint of the Jews, Palestine was the former homeland and should be returned to Jewish control; this was in accord with certain British promises and with the hopes of the Jewish people. But Arabs had predominated in Palestine since the thirteenth century. The country was not capable of supporting both the Arabs and large numbers of Jewish immigrants, and British officials had promised that the Arabs would be

Figure 12-17 Farming methods harness the sparse rainwaters with terraces and dams to irrigate the cultivable land. Crops grown include grapes, pomegranates, and others. (Courtesy of State of Israel.)

left in control of the lands they had occupied for centuries. It was impossible to find a solution that would satisfy both Jews and Arabs. Palestine continued as a troublesome mandate until after World War II.

The Palestine problem then became more acute. Large numbers of displaced Jews from Nazi Germany, Poland, and other areas made necessary the establishment of a Jewish state. Meanwhile Arab nationalism was growing. In 1945 Egypt, Iraq, Lebanon, Syria, Transjordan, and Saudi Arabia formed the Arab League to deal with common economic and social problems and to oppose the settlement of Jews in Palestine. Both Arabs and Jews, however, moved into Palestine.

The United Nations, which has taken over the work of the former League of Nations, ended the British mandate in 1948, established the Jewish nation of Israel from part of Palestine, and designated the rest as Arab territory. The Arab nations opposed the division by force. After some fighting, a series of truces was imposed by the United Nations, but Arab nations refused to recognize the state of Israel. The reestablishment of economic relations between Israel and the Arab states and agreement on boundaries and a permanent status for the city of Jerusalem are problems that have not yet been settled. The kingdom of Jordan—the name was changed from Transjordan in 1946—is now independent and has taken over the part of Palestine which was not included in Israel.

When Palestine was divided, ½ million Arabs fled from Israel into the adjoining Arab states. Most of them went to Jordan; others migrated to Egypt, Lebanon, and Syria. The great population shift into countries which had difficulty in maintaining adequate living standards even before the influx has created a major problem of the Near East. It is a stumbling block to peaceful relations between Israel and the Arab states.

Israel also had a settlement problem. Thousands of Jewish immigrants entered the country each month. The majority came from Eastern Europe, especially from Poland. Considerable numbers also arrived from North Africa, Iraq, and Yemen. The population of Israel increased from 782,000 in 1948 to more than 2 million in 1960.

Israel, like Palestine before it, is an agricultural country, but European immigrants have patterned its economic and social life after Western standards rather than those of the Near East. Mechanization of farming is already at a high level, and extensive irrigation projects are under way. The major product for export is citrus fruit, which is raised on the Mediterranean coastal plain. The economy of the country has been planned to accommodate the immigrants who arrive each month. The total production of cereals, vegetables, meat, and fruits is only about half the requirement for the population. Thus food must be imported, along with many types of consumer goods, machinery, and feed for poultry and livestock. Plans have been made to use the Jordan River for additional power and irrigation for both Israel and Jordan, but the continued hostility between the two countries has prevented their fulfillment.

To increase exports and decrease imports, light industries were developed and food was rationed. Israel now has a diamond-cutting industry that ranks next to citrus production in value of goods exported. Other industries, all of them small but increasing in importance, include food processing, textile weaving, chemical manufacture, and metalworking. These industries, like agriculture, are as yet unable to supply both the need for exports and the demands of the increasing population. The country is dependent upon loans and gifts from abroad, especially from the United States.

Culturally, Israel may be regarded as an outlying area of Europe rather than a typical part of the Levant. Physically, it is composed of a strip of fertile lowlands along the Mediterranean Sea, the interior rift (depressed block) valley of the Jordan River and the Dead Sea, and the Negev (desert) in the south. In the last few years urban population and urban occupations have greatly increased. Tel Aviv-Jaffa, with a population of approximately 400,000, is the chief port and trade center. Haifa is the second port. Jerusalem is mostly controlled by Israel, but the Arab, or "old," section contains many mosques and religious sites and is occupied by Jordan.

The kingdom of Jordan lies on the plateau which continues eastward from Israel. The capital, Amman, and the best agricultural land are in the west. There sedentary farmers produce cereals, vegetables, and fruits. The eastern part of the country has a nomadic population, under tribal organization, which supports itself with herds of sheep and goats. Jordan formerly had a surplus of wheat and barley. Since the annexation of eastern Palestine and the influx of refugees from Israel, the country has difficulty in sup-

Figure 12-18   Tel-Aviv, Israel, is one of the most rapidly growing cities in the Near East. (Courtesy of State of Israel.)

porting its population. It receives considerable help from outside sources to aid its refugees.

ARABIAN PENINSULA

The peninsula of Arabia consists of a large, almost rectangular block of desert area. It is tilted so that the southwestern edge, along the Red Sea, lies at an elevation of several thousand feet, but the surface slopes downward to sea level along the northeast coast at the shores of the Persian Gulf. The population and cities are largely concentrated in the highlands near the Red Sea, where rainfall is greater and temperatures are somewhat lower than in the central and eastern deserts. Even in the Arabian highlands, however, rainfall is light. Despite the great size of the peninsula the population is about one-half that of Egypt or Turkey.

The Moslem religion had its origins in the cities of Mecca and Medina during the early seventh century. The Arabs spread their faith, as well as their language and culture, to adjoining regions. Islam spread even farther: eastward to parts of India, the East Indies, and the Philippines; westward to Morocco; and northwestward to Turkey and Albania. The Ottoman Turks later took over the initiative in spreading Islam through the extension of the Turkish empire over other nations. At the time of World War I, Turkey even controlled most of Arabia.

Following World War I, with Turkey defeated, the new nation of Saudi Arabia gradually conquered most of the peninsula. The areas of Yemen, Aden, Oman, Trucial Oman, Qatar, and Kuwait, however, lie beyond its control.

Saudi Arabia has its agricultural heart in the highlands near the Red Sea, where the major products are wheat, barley, millet, and coffee. The holy city of Mecca

Figure 12-19 An aerial view of a residential section of Dhahran, Saudi Arabia. The plant in the circular area is central air-cooling equipment which serves this section of town. (Courtesy of Arabian American Oil Company.)

attracts Moslem pilgrims from many countries and gives Saudi Arabia added prestige in the Arab world. Medina, which contains the tomb of Mohammed, is also an important religious center. Jidda is the main port.

The interior of Saudi Arabia is desert country similar to the Sahara. Riyadh, in a centrally located oasis, is a caravan center and capital of the country. In 1951 a railroad was completed from Dhahran on the Persian Gulf to Riyadh, a distance of 366 miles. The nomadic desert tribes move their camels, sheep, and goats in accord with the seasonal rains and resulting temporary pasturage. In the remote section, tribal life and customs have changed little for centuries. Southeastern Arabia contains a large "empty quarter" of stony and sandy desert that rivals the barrenness of the southern Sahara.

An American oil company operates the oil fields near the Persian Gulf and divides profits with the Saudi Arabian government. Oil production rose after World War II until Saudi Arabia rivaled Iran as the leading producer in the Near East. Petroleum is the major source of government income and accounts for 90 per cent of the value of exports. Minor exports of the country are gold, silver, and copper; its chief imports are machinery and other manufactured goods. Saudi Arabia also benefits from American expenditures on the United States air base at Dhahran. The newly constructed areas near Dhahran resemble American towns.

Great Britain controls, in more or less degree, a series of areas along the Persian Gulf. Bahrein Island is an important source of petroleum and like Qatar, Trucial Oman, and Oman is under the nominal rule of local sheikhs and sultans. The port of Aden, at the southwestern corner of the Arabian Peninsula, is a British possession that commands the entrance to the Red Sea.

Kuwait, formerly a British protectorate, was recognized as an independent nation in 1961. Its large petroleum production ranks it with Iraq and Saudi Arabia, and oil royalties have made possible a rapid development of the town of Kuwait, as well as of schools and social services.

Yemen is an independent country with landscapes and products similar to the hill and coastal lands of southwestern Saudi Arabia. The country is noted for coffee, which is one of its major exports. The capital and largest city is San'a.

CYPRUS

During the latter part of the nineteenth century Cyprus came under British influence, and control by Turkey (the Ottoman empire) weakened. At the outbreak of World War I, Great Britain obtained full control, ending Ottoman suzerainty.

Cyprus has been known for centuries as an exporter of copper and a producer of wheat, barley, and wine. It has fertile soils and a Mediterranean climate, and is the most highly cultivated territory of the Near East. Political factors, however, have brought it the greatest amount of attention. About three-fourths of the inhabitants are of Greek language and culture, and the movement for union with Greece was marked by riots against the British. The island is only 40 miles from the Turkish coast but hundreds of miles from Greece, and Cyprus was long a part of Turkey. Consequently, the Turkish minority on the island and the Turkish government argued that any change in the island's status should put it not under Greek but Turkish control. Meanwhile, Cyprus replaced Suez as the United Kingdom's major military base in the Middle East. After prolonged struggle, Cyprus gained independence from the United Kingdom in 1960, with a compromise government including both Greek and Turkish people.

IN PERSPECTIVE

NORTH AFRICA AND THE NEAR EAST, WORLD'S LARGEST DRY AREA

North Africa and the Near East lie south and east of the Mediterranean Sea and north from the Sahara and the Arabian Sea, with the peninsula of Arabia being bounded by the Red Sea on the west and the Persian Gulf on the east. To the north of Turkey and Iran are the Black and Caspian Seas respectively. The region includes about a score of political entities. Of these, almost all are now independent; the rest are colonies, protectorates, and other varieties of dependency.

The unity of North Africa and the Near East is cultural; its people are predominantly Moslem in religion; farmers, herders, and traders by occupation; and Near Eastern in language—which includes Arabic, Persian, and Turkish. Minority groups include Jews, Christians, Kurds, and others. Climatically the region has a water problem, with its vast deserts and semiarid steppes. Only small areas have enough rainfall for crops, and the sections with such a humid climate are often highlands where little tillable land is available. Fortunately, nearly all of the region has a long growing season, so that where water and good soil are available, large yields of crops are possible. Irrigation is widely practiced especially in the floodplains and deltas of the major rivers like the Nile, Tigris, and Euphrates, which support large populations.

Strategically located in regard to Europe, the Far East, and Central Africa, the region has been the site for European penetration. The Western powers established major colonies, and their system of economic exploitation often irked the local populations. From this region Europe draws important quantities of petroleum, metals, cotton, and foodstuffs, and free access to such supplies is essential to the industries of the West. Petroleum is the outstanding mineral resource; the countries that border the Persian Gulf—Saudi Arabia, Kuwait, Iran, and Iraq—produce nearly one-third of the world's output. Exports of petroleum and its products to Western and Southern Europe are large, and the maintenance of a continuous flow via the Suez Canal and overland by pipelines to Mediterranean ports is of great concern to industrialized Western Europe.

Much of North Africa and the Near East has been and still is politically unstable. By 1962 the Barbary states of Morocco, Algeria, Tunisia, and Libya were independent countries with varied political problems.

Farther east, Egypt, which stands astride the Suez Canal, and the other Arab countries of Saudi Arabia, Jordan, Syria, Lebanon, and Iraq have been involved in boundary quarrels with Israel since the end of World War II. Turkey and Iran face the Soviet Union, which apparently hopes that turmoil in the Near East will work to its advantage. The general poverty of the people in North Africa, Egypt, and Southwest Asia, and the hereditary hatreds they hold toward some of their neighbors increase the difficulties of maintaining peace and order. The United States is involved in trying to maintain friendly relations with both Israel and the Arab nations, and with supporting Turkey and Iran against possible Soviet threats.

SELECTED REFERENCES

Cressey, George: *Crossroads: Land and Life in Southwest Asia,* J. B. Lippincott Company, Philadelphia, 1960.

A very readable general geography of Southwestern Asia. There is minor consideration of Egypt, but nothing on the rest of North Africa. Has many illustrations, maps, and tables.

Fisher, W. B.: *The Middle East: A Physical, Social, and Regional Geography,* 4th ed., E. P. Dutton & Co., Inc., New York, 1961.

Includes Southwestern Asia, Egypt, and Libya. This work is more detailed and more advanced than Cressey's Crossroads, *but has fewer maps and no pictures. Includes much historical and physical geography, as well as modern human geography.*

Fitzgerald, Walter: *Africa,* 9th ed., E. P. Dutton & Co., Inc., New York, 1961.

The best and most recent geography in English for Africa as a whole, as well as for northern Africa, which is covered in several chapters. Similar in style to Fisher's book above; detailed and accurate, with a number of small black-and-white maps and no pictures.

SENEGA
GAMBIA
PORTUGUESE
GUINEA
GUI
SIER
LEO

chapter 13

AFRICA SOUTH OF
THE SAHARA

Figure 13-1   Africa is often referred to as the plateau continent. Narrow coastal plains and rapids or waterfalls near the mouths of many rivers probably delayed exploration of the continent. The mountain areas are largely in the eastern interior.

*F*OR CENTURIES THE PHYSICAL BARRIER of the Sahara separated North Africa from tropical and southern Africa; in recent years, however, the barrier of the Sahara has been breaking down. Lands to the north and south are being drawn together by the airplane, by exploration for mineral resources, and by the development of such resources in the desert itself. Even more significant are the new political and economic ties being created by Africa's independent countries. The southern edge of the Sahara, though still a useful boundary, is increasingly arbitrary.

Africa, with an area of 11,635,000 square miles, is the second largest continent. The region south of the Sahara totals approximately 8,300,000 square miles or roughly the combined size of Canada, the United States of America, and Mexico. Africa, extending from the northern tip of Tunis, 37°27′ north latitude, to Cape Agulhas, 34°47′ south latitude, is almost bisected by the equator and has more land between the Tropics of Cancer and Capricorn than any other continent. Many speak of the continent as if it were a country, but the signpost at the Nairobi airport, a few miles from the equator, helps to emphasize size. Some distances are: Cape Town, 2,548 miles; Accra, 2,602 miles; Timbuktu (Tombouctou), 2,973 miles. Karachi, Pakistan, is nearer Nairobi than is Timbuktu.

North Africa developed as part of the Mediterranean world and has a recorded history dating back thousands of years. Africa south of the Sahara formed the "Dark Continent"—unknown Africa. This was a region of great geographic, economic, and cultural diversity. It was inhabited by hundreds of tribal groups, who spoke hundreds of languages and dialects. There was no written language, and historical development was largely unrecorded. Although strong governments did flourish and then fall in west and central Africa, the rest of the world had little interest in Africa south of the Sahara until 1850.

Exploration of this vast portion of the continent was slow; occupation and development by outsiders was even slower. Nevertheless, some settlers from Asia as well as Arab slave and ivory traders were well established on the east coast, especially Zanzibar, when Portuguese explorers rounded the Cape of Good Hope in the late fifteenth century. Slave traders on both coasts greatly changed African societies and economies, but along with more legitimate traders, they introduced such now-staple crops as Asian rice and, from the New World, corn and cassava. Trade routes from Europe around Africa to Asia flourished until the opening of the Suez Canal in 1869 diverted traffic, but settlements established for trading or for repairing ships and supplying food to crews were not concerned with penetration into the interior.

By the nineteenth century explorers were gradually filling in the map of Africa south of the Sahara. Livingstone discovered Victoria Falls in 1855, and Speke, searching for the source of the Nile, which he found in 1862, first saw Lake Victoria in 1858. Of more immediate economic significance was the finding of Kimberley diamonds in 1871 and of Rand gold in 1884. Cecil Rhodes made a fortune in gold and diamonds and added vast territories to the British Empire.

Modern political patterns of sub-Saharan Africa reflect four centuries of colonial expansion by European nations. The Portuguese were followed by other European powers. First came the establishment of coastal forts. Some seven European nations, for example, built forts along the Gold Coast between the fifteenth and eighteenth centuries. These

Figure 13-2   The 1652 Dutch settlement between Table Mountain and Table Bay has grown into Cape Town (foreground). Cape Peninsula with Cape of Good Hope extends southward on the distant left of the picture. (Courtesy of South African Information Service.)

forts and the lands around them changed hands as the balance of power shifted in Europe. The Dutch located on the shores of Table Bay in 1652, but in 1814 ceded Cape Colony to the British. France and Germany occupied large regions south of the Sahara during the nineteenth century. In 1885 Leopold II of Belgium established the Congo Free State, later the Belgian Congo. By the close of the nineteenth century all of Africa south of the Sahara, except Ethiopia and Liberia, had become colonies or protectorates of England, France, Germany, Portugal, Belgium, or Spain. This division was done with small regard for indigenous peoples.

The first half of the twentieth century brought more changes. The Union of South Africa acquired dominion status in 1910. Under the League of Nations, former German colonies were mandated to England, Belgium, and the Union of South Africa. Ethiopia, which through most of its history had maintained itself as an independent monarchy, became part of Italian East Africa from 1936 to 1941. Only Liberia, originating in 1822 as a home for freed slaves from the United States and established in 1847 as a "Free and Independent Republic," has never come under the rule of a European nation.

At the end of World War II there were

Figure 13-3 Africa is a continent of new independent nations. From 1945 to 1964 the number increased from 4 to 35 with more in prospect.

only four independent countries in all Africa: Egypt, Ethiopia, Liberia, and the Union of South Africa. By the start of 1964 there were 35, with more in prospect (Figure 13-3); the number could exceed 50. In the formation of new countries, patterns of colonial occupancy have with few exceptions been maintained; in al-

most every country the official language is that of the most recent governing European nation, and the new country almost invariably still receives financial assistance from its former European mentor.

Much of Africa south of the Sahara is today a product of European occupation superimposed on traditions of living which have experienced little change for hundreds of years. Railroads, highways, airfields, and port improvements provide better transportation for freight and passengers. Plantations have been established and mines developed. Economic crops such as cacao, rubber, sisal, coffee, groundnuts (peanuts), and tea have been introduced. Africa's gold, industrial and gem diamonds, copper, manganese, tin, chrome, iron, uranium, and other minerals are in demand. Dams, such as the Kariba on the Zambezi, are beginning to harness Africa's water power potential, the largest of any continent. Modern cities with multistory buildings, parking meters, and traffic and housing problems have been built. Yet vast rural areas are still cut off from twentieth-century economy. By 1960 only 16 per cent of the children of primary and secondary school age were in school. Malnutrition from lack of protein in the diet remains a widespread problem. There are more than 100 million cases of malaria in Africa. The desire for improved living conditions, a greater share in the development of their resources, and for the social and political equality of individuals has accounted for many of the conflicts between indigenous populations and the immigrant ruling classes in such places as Angola, Kenya, the Rhodesias, the Republic of South Africa, and others. Elsewhere new countries are discovering that political independence does not automatically solve economic and social problems.

PHYSICAL SETTING

RELIEF FEATURES

Relief features were partly responsible for the slow penetration of Africa south of the Sahara by traders, explorers, and settlers. This vast area might be described as a plateau made up of a series of plateaus. In

Figure 13-4 A diamond sorter examining a week's output—about 15,000 diamonds weighing about 13,000 carats—taken from diamond-bearing gravels near the mouth of the Orange River. (Courtesy of South African Information Service.)

many places the plateau rises abruptly from the shoreline or from a narrow coastal plain backed by an escarpment marking the edge of the plateau. The Drakensberg Mountains of Natal in South Africa are the dissected edge of the southeastern escarpment. Elsewhere the ascent is more gentle, often in the form of successive terraces. Rivers from the plateau flow over rapids and waterfalls or through unnavigable gorges in their passage through the escarpment to reach sea level. These conditions are excellent for the development of water power but not for easy access to the interior. The Congo rapids below Leopoldville are said to have the potential for the greatest hydroelectric project in the world, but navigation of the Congo River into the interior starts above the rapids at Leopoldville and Brazzaville, 250 miles inland. North of Lourenço Marques on the Indian Ocean and in West Africa the coastal plain is wide. Offshore waters, however, may be shallow and access to shore blocked by sand bars or reefs. Along great stretches of the coast, Africa lacks deep, natural harbors. The

TABLE 13-1 AFRICA SOUTH OF THE SAHARA

Country	Area, sq. mi.	Approximate population	Political status, Jan. 1, 1964
Angola	481,226	4,870,000	Portuguese overseas province
Basutoland	11,716	708,000	British colony; High Commission Territory under Commonwealth Relations Office
Bechuanaland	274,928	332,000	British protectorate; High Commission Territory under Commonwealth Relations Office
Burundi	10,747	2,500,000	Independent constitutional monarchy
Cameroun	183,381	4,326,000	Independent federal republic
Cabinda	2,800	59,000	Administered as part of Angola
Cape Verde Islands	1,557	205,000	Portuguese overseas province
Central African Republic	227,118	1,227,000	Independent republic; member of French Community
Chad	446,640	2,680,000	Independent republic; member of French Community
Comoro Islands	832	185,000	Overseas territory of France
Congo (Brazzaville)	125,890	900,000	Independent republic; member of French Community
Congo (Leopoldville)	905,329	14,797,000	Independent republic
Dahomey	44,713	12,050,000	Independent republic; member of Conseil de l'Entente
Ethiopia	457,147	21,000,000	Independent monarchy
Gabon	98,283	450,000	Independent republic; member of French Community
Gambia	3,978	267,000	British colony and inland protectorate
Ghana	91,819	7,100,000	Independent republic; member of British Commonwealth
Guinea	94,945	3,000,000	Independent republic
Ivory Coast	124,550	3,410,000	Independent republic; member of Conseil de l'Entente
Kenya	224,960	8,676,000	Independent republic in British Commonwealth
Liberia	42,989	1,290,000	Independent republic
Madeira Islands	308	280,000	Part of Portugal
Malagasy	228,510	5,577,000	Independent republic; member of French Community
Mali	465,050	4,100,000	Independent republic
Mauritania	419,390	791,000	Independent Islamic republic; member of French Community
Mauritius	720	667,000	British colony
Mozambique	297,654	6,650,000	Portuguese overseas province
Niger	459,180	3,112,000	Independent republic; member of Conseil de l'Entente

TABLE 13-1   AFRICA SOUTH OF THE SAHARA   (continued)

Country	Area, sq. mi.	Approximate population	Political status, Jan. 1, 1964
Nigeria	350,291	36,473,000	Independent federal republic; member of British Commonwealth
Northern Rhodesia*	288,129	2,555,000	British protectorate, self-governing
Nyasaland*	49,177	2,950,000	British protectorate, self-governing
Portuguese Guinea	13,944	550,000	Portuguese overseas province
Reunion	970	352,000	French overseas department
Rwanda	10,169	2,685,000	Independent republic
St. Helena Island and dependencies	119	5,000	British colony
São Tomé and Principe	372	64,000	Portuguese overseas province
Senegal	76,153	2,980,000	Independent republic; member of French community
Seychelles	156	43,000	British colony
Sierra Leone	27,925	2,450,000	Independent dominion in the British Commonwealth
Somalia	246,137	2,030,000	Independent republic
Somaliland, French	8,492	68,000	French overseas territory
South Africa	472,550	16,236,000	Independent republic
Southern Rhodesia*	150,333	3,880,000	British colony, self-governing
South-West Africa	317,725	534,000	Mandated to Union of South Africa; South Africa has refused to convert to UN trusteeship
Spanish Guinea	10,828	249,000	Two Spanish provinces, Rio Muni and Fernando Poo, jointly administered
Swaziland	6,705	275,000	British protectorate; High Commission Territory under Commonwealth Relations Office
Tanganyika†	362,688	9,560,000	Independent republic; member of British Commonwealth
Togo	22,002	1,439,000	Independent republic
Uganda	93,981	6,845,000	Independent sovereign state; member of British Commonwealth
Upper Volta	105,879	4,404,000	Independent republic; member of Conseil de l'Entente
Walvis Bay	374	12,568	Integral part of Republic of South Africa; administered by South-West Africa
Zanzibar†	1,026	315,000	Independent

* In 1964 Nyasaland became independent Malawi; Northern Rhodesia became independent Zambia; Southern Rhodesia became Rhodesia.
† In 1964 Zanzibar joined Tanganyika to form the Republic of Tanzania.
Source: "Population and Vital Statistics Report, Data Available As of 1 April 1963," United Nations, *Statistical Papers*, Ser. A, 15(1–2).

Figure 13-5   Looking across the upper portion of the Congo Rapids from just below Brazzaville. (Courtesy of Elizabeth Eiselen.)

coastal plain, when reached, may be difficult to cross because of deserts or malarial swamps. Here rivers are typically shallow and meandering, and some, like the Niger, Zambezi, and Limpopo, have deposited silt to form large deltas.

Once the traveler reaches the interior plateaus, he finds much of the surface level or gently rolling; but here travel is handicapped primarily by vast distances. Characteristic of the plateaus are broad, shallow depressions such as the Niger, Chad, Congo, and Kalahari basins. Many contain extensive swamps, potential agricultural land if properly drained. Reclamation of the Niger swamps above Timbuktu and of those near Lake Chad has been started. Unfortunately even in the interior many rivers are navigable only for short stretches or not at all. They may be intermittent in flow, meandering, or blocked by waterfalls, such as spectacular Victoria Falls on the Zambezi. Railroads are few in number and some of the new countries have none. (Flying over Africa confirms the fact that much of the continent still can be reached only by trails or by roads that are impassable during rainy weather.) Some areas can be reached only by air during rainy seasons. The airplane is having a major influence on shrinking the size of Africa and opening remote regions.

Plateau surfaces are lowest and least continuous in West Africa where most are between 1,000 and 2,000 feet above sea

Figure 13-6   A vast, flat plateau surface near Kimberley, South Africa. This is improved grazing land. The mounds scattered through the field are ant hills. (Courtesy of Elizabeth Eiselen.)

level. Average elevations of the plateaus increase to between 3,000 and 6,000 feet eastward and southward and to between 6,000 and 9,000 feet in Ethiopia, where some elevations exceed 15,000 feet. Variations in landforms are most numerous in the northeastern and eastern highlands. Here are most of Africa's lakes, with Victoria (26,828 square miles), Tanganyika (12,355 square miles), and Nyasa (10,900 square miles) ranking among the world's largest. Here also are Africa's highest mountains, Kilimanjaro (19,565 feet) and Kenya (17,040 feet). In Ethiopia heavy rainfall on the high plateaus has caused erosion and resulted in rugged topography. Lake Tana, the source of the Blue Nile, is located in the northwestern part of the Ethiopian Highlands.

Among the most famous geological features of Africa are the rift valleys of Ethiopia and East Africa. These are long, narrow depressions called grabens, marking a series of parallel faults. The creation of these grabens or rifts was associated with great volcanic activity: lava outpourings in Kenya, Tanzania, and Ethiopia, and the formation of now extinct volcanoes which rise above the plateau surface. The rift system can be traced from the Sea of Galilee and the Dead Sea through the Gulf of Aqaba and the Red Sea to Ethiopia, where it forms a major transportation barrier bisecting the Ethiopean plateau. From there the eastern and principal branch of the rift system is marked by Lake Rudolph and the broad Great Rift Valley of Kenya between Lake Victoria and Mts. Kenya and Kilimanjaro. Parts of the Great Rift Valley are 30 to 50 miles across and in some places 4,000 feet deep. Then comes Lake Nyasa and the valley of the Shire River. The western branch is occupied by Lakes Albert, Edward, Kivu, and Tanganyika, the second-deepest freshwater lake in the world, and merges with the main branch north of Lake Nyasa. Lake Victoria lies in the shallow basin on the plateau between the two rift systems.

CLIMATE AND VEGETATION

Two dominant factors influence the climates of sub-Saharan Africa, and thus also the vegetation. One is the location of so much of the region between the Tropics of Cancer and Capricorn; the other is the large amount of land where elevation modifies both temperatures and precipitation. To most persons from the United States, Canada, and Europe almost the entire region has unfamiliar climates, most of the coastal lowlands being hot and rainy, or hot and semiarid or desert, or hot and seasonally wet and dry. Even in the interior, except in the highest mountains, the coolest months average above freezing, although snow does fall in Cape Province and the Drakensberg Mountains of South Africa, and glaciers have formed within a few degrees of the equator on the summits of Kilimanjaro and Kenya.

Rainfall, both in amount and type, is of greater concern in Africa south of the Sahara than are temperatures. Except for the zone of rainy tropical climate where too much moisture may be a problem, much of the region suffers from low precipitation, either seasonally or in annual total. When it does rain, downpours often lead to rapid runoff with resulting waste of water and erosion. Actual amounts in any given period may vary widely from averages. When the rains fail or when the normal dry season is rainy, crops and grasses suffer.

The climate pattern of Africa is relatively simple. Climatic zones change regularly north and south from the equatorial rainy tropics, except where modified in the east and south by higher plateaus and mountains (Figure 13-7). The change

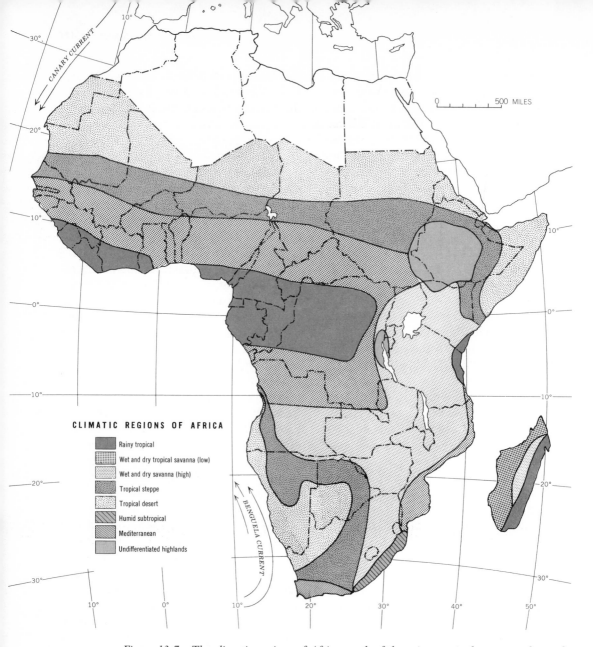

Figure 13-7   The climatic regions of Africa south of the rainy tropical area are almost the same as those north of it. Only in the eastern highlands is there great variation.

from one type to another is a gradual transition, and many exceptions within any given area may occur, by reason of local topographical features. These factors, plus a lack of climatic data, make the drawing of precise boundaries difficult. In some areas climatic boundaries have had to be based on vegetation; but the pattern of related vegetation also needs more study for, like climates, it is often transitional.

RAINY TROPICAL   The largest area of rainy tropical climate is a broad band straddling the equator from the Guinea Coast of Nigeria to the East African highlands. It extends farther north than south of the equator. A smaller area is found in West Africa from Dahomey to Liberia and Sierra Leone. Under the influence of the sun, which is never far from overhead at noon, and of days that are almost even in length throughout the year, a low-pressure zone—the doldrums—is developed. The resultant hot, rainy, and humid climate is typical of lowlands near the equator (Stanleyville). Daytime temperatures are held down by cloudiness and seldom rise above 90°F, but there is little variation month after month, and the diurnal range is too slight to relieve the monotony. With the daily possibility of convectional afternoon rain following midday heat, annual totals generally exceed 60 inches. Douala,

Cameroun, one of the wettest spots in Africa, has an annual average of 156 inches but has recorded over 400 inches in a single year. Also included in this climate type is part of coastal East Africa and the eastern side of Madagascar, where heavy rainfall results from moist southeast trade winds rising over highlands near the Indian Ocean.

The moisture and warmth of the rainy tropics produce a luxuriant rain forest within which a great variety of kinds and species of plants flourish, including tall trees, an understory of smaller trees, and a profusion of vines and parasitic growths. The latter make penetration of the African rain forest difficult, and if the forest is cleared, regrowth occurs rapidly. Here also insect pests, intestinal parasites, and skin infections are constant plagues to

Figure 13-8   *Waterfalls and tropical vegetation on the Lucala River in Angola. (Courtesy of Portuguese Embassy.)*

man. Malarial mangrove swamps flourish along many of the rainy tropical and wet-and-dry savanna coasts of Africa. Rainy tropical is the climate which, with its rain-forest vegetation, is thought by many people to be synonymous with most of Africa south of the Sahara. Climate and vegetation maps show how false this impression actually is.

WET-AND-DRY TROPICAL SAVANNA. This climate prevails over vast regions north,

south, and east of the rainy tropical climate. Low savanna occurs on elevations below 3,000 feet, where the seasonal shift of the high-noon sun north of the equator in the Northern Hemisphere summer, and south of the equator in the Southern Hemisphere summer causes the doldrum belt to shift north and south also. The doldrum effect, however, lags behind the high sun and does not reach the Tropics of Cancer and Capricorn. When the doldrum belt moves southward, dry north-

Figure 13-9   Climate graphs of selected stations.

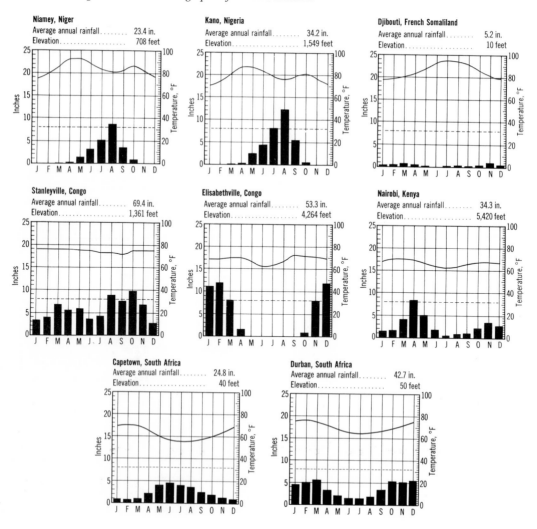

east trade winds off the deserts of North Africa and Arabia take over in the Northern Hemisphere savanna, the rains stop, and the weather becomes dry (Kano). The seasonal reverse is true of the Southern Hemisphere, and although the southeast trade winds blow from the Indian Ocean, they drop their moisture on the eastern escarpment, leaving the interior dry. Thus wet summers and dry winters are associated with the zones bordering the rainy tropics.

The rainy season may average 30 to 60 inches total rainfall, and climatic conditions during this period may closely resemble those of the rainy tropical climate. Actual amounts vary greatly from year to year, and rains may be irregular within any given season. The dry season, whose total rainfall, if any, will often be measured in tenths of an inch, lasts from approximately two months in the transition zone along the rainy tropical climate to as long as seven or eight months on the poleward edges. Bright skies, low relative humidity, and drying winds are characteristic of the dry season. The range in monthly temperature averages is moderate. The coldest months are those near the start or middle of the dry season, but under the influence of clear skies and intense sunshine, average temperatures rise, with the heat maximum coming at the end of the dry season. Daytime temperatures are highest, often above 100°F, just before the rains begin.

High-savanna climate is found in the interior, where elevations are above 3,000 feet and temperatures are lower by 10 to 20°F than those in the lowlands (Elisabethville). The largest concentrations of Europeans live above 4,000 feet in Kenya, the Rhodesias, and the Republic of South Africa, where cooler temperatures and freedom from malaria are combined with zones of fertile land and minerals. In the velds (high savannas) of South Africa frosts are common during the winter months. There is usually less precipitation than in the low savannas or the rainy tropics either because the moisture has been partly lost before the rain-bringing winds reach the interior or because near the equator lower temperatures on the eastern plateaus lessen the effectiveness of convectional forces. The wet-and-dry regime prevails, but near the equator in East Africa it varies by having two rainfall maxima, each following a period of nearly overhead sun (Nairobi). The season of "long rains" is associated with the March equinox and extends from March through May; the "short rains" lag behind the September equinox, with November and December normally being the rainy months.

No one description covers all varieties of tropical savanna vegetation. Most commonly it consists of open woods and tall, coarse grasses. Trees—the dry forests—predominate in the wetter areas, grasses in drier. There are also some areas of bush and scrub vegetation. The trees have various adaptations to the dry season. Most of them lessen transpiration by shedding their leaves and putting down very long roots; many store water in large fleshy trunks. The baobab, which has all these characteristics, is most famous for its enormous trunk, some specimens measuring up to 30 feet in diameter. Where the dry season lengthens and total rainfall decreases, trees become smaller and more widely spaced, and some may be replaced by shrubs. Both trees and bushes may have thorns that enable them to survive elimination by browsing animals —for this is the African big-game country. The savanna is the natural habitat of the herbivorous impala, elephant, giraffe, zebra, and various carnivores, such as the lion, hyena, cheetah, and leopard.

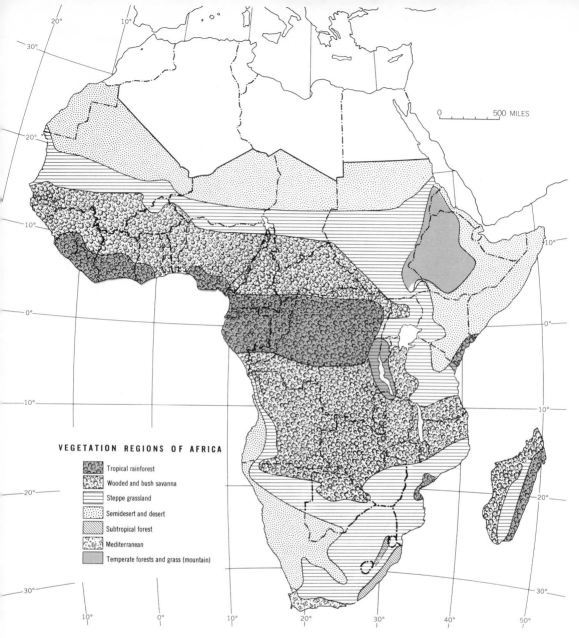

Figure 13-10   The vegetation regions are directly related to the climatic regions. Note the similarity of the two maps.

VEGETATION REGIONS OF AFRICA

- Tropical rainforest
- Wooded and bush savanna
- Steppe grassland
- Semidesert and desert
- Subtropical forest
- Mediterranean
- Temperate forests and grass (mountain)

Except on the drier parts of the high savanna, many mature grasses are taller than a man. The High Veld of South Africa is a zone of 3-foot-high grasses, one of the few African grasslands without trees or other woody growth. Although the grasses of the savanna are lush and green during the wet season, some species are too coarse to be palatable. During the dry season, grasses become so dry and uneatable that even native wild game must depend on grass near water holes. An exception to the unpalatable dry grasses occurs on the drier parts of the veld where, although carrying capacity is low, grazing is good all year.

Figure 13-11   Tropical rain forests are areas of huge trees. Compare the size of the logs with the men, the size of the trees with the trucks. (Courtesy of Uganda Department of Information.)

TROPICAL STEPPE   Tropical steppe climate forms a transition zone between tropical wet-and-dry savanna and tropical desert climates. In comparison with the savanna, the dry season is longer, annual rainfall is less, and rains are more erratic (Naimey). Along with desert, tropical steppe is classified as a dry climate, where potential evaporation exceeds total precipitation. In this semiarid climate there is sufficient moisture for the growth of short grasses (steppe) and in some places for scattered small trees or thorny brush. Annual rainfall may be as little as 16 inches or as much as 30 inches depending on the effectiveness of the rain. The warmer the place, the greater is the evaporation; therefore, less moisture is available for plants. Temperature range increases with distance from the equator, but nowhere is there true winter, although frosts do occur in South Africa. The highest temperatures, well over 100°F during the day, come just before the rainy season as they do in the savanna. There are two zones of tropical steppe climate. The one north of the equator stretches across Africa in a belt 3,000 miles long and averaging about 300 miles in width. The other, south of the equator, is more irregular and to the west has a greater north-south extent because it has formed to the leeward of the eastern plateaus. Since elevation with its cooler temperatures lessens evaporation, it is sometimes difficult in drawing arbitrary boundaries to differentiate between steppe and drier high savanna.

TROPICAL DESERTS   Tropical deserts are among the driest in the world not only because they have very little precipitation, but because high daytime temperatures cause rapid evaporation (Djibouti). The Somali Desert of Somalia and French Somaliland and the Danakil Desert of northern Ethiopia form a crescent around the Horn of Africa. Winds here are either off dry land masses or blow parallel to the Indian Ocean. Rains are heavy in the Ethiopian highlands, but the coasts have low and irregular rainfall with high temperatures. Vegetation is scanty, and the plants must be drought-tolerant.

Southwestern Africa has two tropical deserts, the coastal Namib and the inland

Figure 13-12   Sand dunes in the almost rainless Namib Desert of South-West Africa. (Courtesy of Information Service of South Africa.)

Kalahari. The Namib is about 60 miles wide, extending from northern Cape Province of South Africa, along the coast of South-West Africa, to southern Angola. The Namib is almost rainless. What does come is of the thunderstorm variety, but actual amount and time of fall in any year is most uncertain. Dryness results during part of the year from location in a dry, subtropical high-pressure air mass, and the rest of the year from location on the leeward side of the continent in the belt of southeast trade winds. Offshore the cold Benguela Current causes summer fogs but not rain. The Namib is drier than the larger and higher Kalahari. With short bunch grass and scattered shrubs, Kalahari vegetation indicates more nearly a semidesert, whereas parts of the Namib are completely without vegetation.

MEDITERRANEAN   On the southern coast of Africa in the vicinity of Cape Town, a limited area has Mediterranean climate. Here the 15 to 25 inches of annual rainfall is concentrated in the months of late fall, winter, and early spring when the Roaring Forties shift northward to affect the

Figure 13-13   A flat-topped thorn tree, scattered bushes, and clumps of short grass on stony soil. This is typical of the transitional zone from the tropical steppe to the Kalahari Desert. (Courtesy of Information Service of South Africa.)

southern tip of Africa. Winter temperatures average about 55°F. The coastal region is without severe frost, but the higher and cooler inner edge of the Mediterranean region may not only have frost but also a little snow during some winters. The dry, but not completely rainless, summers average about 70°F. Because of the cold Benguela Current offshore, onshore winds are cooled, and summer temperatures are lower than those in the Mediterranean climate zone of North Africa. Natural vegetation consists of grasses and bushes adapted to dry summer weather. To the east, Mediterranean climate with its winter maximum of rain gradually merges into the humid subtropical with a summer maximum.

HUMID SUBTROPICAL   The humid subtropical climate of southeastern Africa extends only a short distance inland, for the narrow coastal zone is backed by the eastern escarpment, including the Drakensberg Mountains. Rainfall averages vary from about 30 to 45 inches a year (Durban). Although some rain falls each month, heaviest precipitation occurs during the warm season from October or November through March, when the southeast trade winds are blowing onshore. The lesser rains during the winter result from cyclonic storms brought by the northward shift of wind belts. The summer months are hot and humid, averaging as high as 77°F. In Natal the drier winter months average 60°F or above, making this a popular winter resort for South Africa. Vegetation along the coast is dominated by subtropical trees. The higher slopes are covered with a brush and grass vegetation.

UNDIFFERENTIATED HIGHLANDS   In the mountain mass of interior Ethiopia vertical climatic and vegetation changes are

so rapid and pass through such a range of types that they cannot be shown on a large-scale continental map. Therefore the rainy, dissected Ethiopian plateau is designated as a zone of undifferentiated highlands. The vegetation is classified as dominantly temperate forest and mountain grassland although subtropical forests do exist on lower slopes. Similar climatic and vegetation changes occur on the slopes of the East African mountains.

SOILS

Much more study needs to be made of African soils, for they are more complex than originally thought. Unfortunately there has been a tendency on the part of many European settlers to handle soils developed under tropical and subtropical environments as if they were identical with soils of temperate Europe. As a result some agricultural projects have become economic fiascoes. In general, African soils are of poor quality. Because there is no season during which the ground freezes, the weathering process and the decay of organic matter is continuous. Under moist tropical conditions humus rapidly disappears, and soluble minerals are leached by percolating rainwater. Naturally productive soils have developed under specialized conditions and are limited in extent. Among the best are alluvial soils formed on river floodplains and deltas. Fertile soils in East Africa and the Cameroon Highlands are derived from the weathering of igneous rocks. Soils of the tropical steppe and High Veld are rich in humus.

In tropical Africa the most common soils are latosols and other red to redbrown latosolic types. Latosols are a residual soil formed under the forest cover of rainy tropical climate. They may be granular and very porous but easily com-

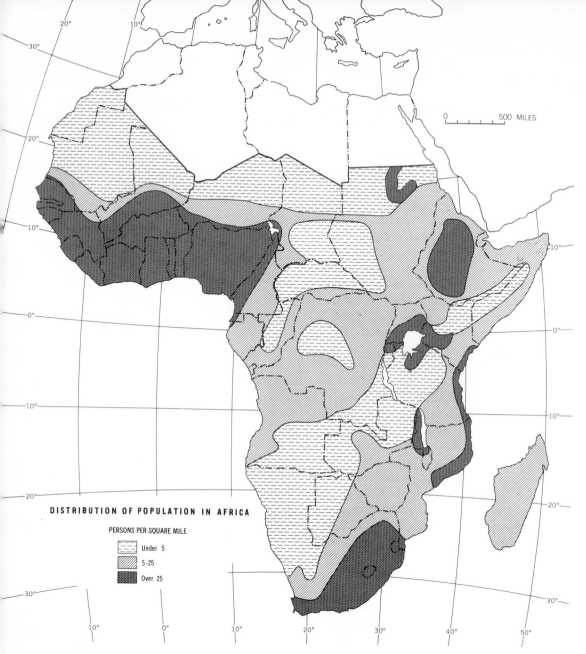

Figure 13-14 Population in Africa south of the Sahara varies greatly according to local conditions. In general, the areas of greatest population are around the large lakes, in the highlands of Ethiopia, and along various coastal areas.

DISTRIBUTION OF POPULATION IN AFRICA

PERSONS PER SQUARE MILE

Under 5

5-25

Over 25

pacted; or they may develop within their profile concentrations of laterite, a red claylike material that, when dry, resembles brick. Latosolic soils develop under ample but somewhat less rainfall than true latosols. Since both have lost most

of their soluble minerals and humus, they are poor to mediocre soils for farming.

The degree of leaching and decay in the wet-and-dry savanna depends on total rainfall, length of the rainy season, and temperatures. Both leaching and decay will be slower with less rain and cooler temperatures. Where associated grasses are tall and humus abundant, soils of the savannas are black and quite fertile. These black soils are among the best in Africa for growing grains and cotton. They somewhat resemble the chernozem or prairie soils of the middle latitudes but must be handled with greater care. On the semiarid tropical steppes where the grass is shorter, there is less humus, and soils are lighter in color. They are fertile but so fine in texture that they require special handling to prevent wind and rain erosion. Desert soils have little humus because of the scant vegetation, but they are unleached and may be quite productive if water is available for irrigation; otherwise they can only support a few animals.

PEOPLE

It is estimated that 190 million people live in Africa south of the Sahara, but this figure may err either way by several millions. For some countries official data are accurate only for the nonindigenous population; other countries, such as Ethiopia, have never held a national census. Regardless of numbers, population distribution is very uneven (Figure 13-14). Concentrations of over 200 per square mile occur in parts of West Africa, in fertile or mineralized zones of highlands, and in the vicinity of the principal ports. Although urban areas are growing, Johannesburg is the only city to exceed 1 million residents. Fourteen other cities south of the Sahara have populations of over 200,000, four being in South Africa. At the other extreme are large areas of tropical rain forest or desert with under five per square mile. Some of the driest parts of the Kalahari and Namib Deserts have no permanent inhabitants.

People of African origin make up about 97 per cent of the population of sub-Saharan Africa, but they are far from being a homogeneous group. Anthropologists do not yet agree on a basic classification, but all recognize certain groupings, some of which are actually determined by language. The problems facing Africa are often closely associated with the varying characteristics of the Africans themselves in regard to native culture, tribal traditions, and degree and type of exposure to European culture.

The relatively primitive Africans include the Pygmies, Bushmen, and Hottentots, all with Negroid characteristics. The Pygmies, usually estimated between 100,000 and 150,000 in number, live in the tropical rain forest of the Congo Basin, where they have survived by hunting wild animals with poisoned arrows and by gathering edible forest products. They are settling down, however, to subsistence agriculture, supplemented by the traditional game and roots, nuts, and

Figure 13-15   Since 1884, when gold was discovered in the Witwatersrand, Johannesburg has grown from a mining camp to the largest city in Africa south of the Sahara. Blocked from view by the tall buildings are the yellow mine dumps. (Courtesy of the South African Information Service.)

fruits of the forest. In more accessible parts of the eastern Congo Basin they serve as a tourist attraction.

The Bushmen, estimated as few as 10,000 or as many as 55,000, are nomadic hunters and gatherers in the Kalahari region of southwestern Africa. They roam the desert and surrounding scrublands seeking water holes, hunting wild animals with clubs or poisoned arrows, and eating any other available food, such as insects, lizards, and roots. Living is a constant and often losing fight for survival.

The Hottentots, as nomadic herders, once ranged over southern Africa with their cattle and sheep, but only about 15,000 pure-blooded Hottentots are left. The Hottentots were pushed into southwestern Africa, north of the Orange River, by the Bantus and the Europeans. They are still herdsmen but now live in

Figure 13-16 Baca women in colorful tribal dress with modern accessories. The Baca separated from the Zulus to form their own tribe. (Courtesy of Elizabeth Eiselen.)

kraals, i.e., semipermanent villages of huts surrounded by a thorn fence that serves as protection for man and animal at night. Pygmies, Bushmen, and Hottentots are declining in numbers and are unimportant in the African economy except as examples of primitive adjustment to three tropical environments: rain forest, desert or scrubland, and wet-and-dry savanna or steppe.

Some 65 million Bantu Negroes inhabit Africa roughly south of 5° north latitude, all speaking variants of Bantu but unable to communicate even among neighboring tribes. To solve the problem Swahili has become the lingua franca in East Africa. The Bantus are split into many groups, some agriculturists, others pastoralists; some warlike, others peaceful. Included are the Baganda of Uganda, the Kikuyu of Kenya, as well as the Bechuana, Basuto, Swazi, and Zulu peoples of southern Africa.

The possibly 55 to 60 million "true" Negroes, also referred to as the Guinea and Sudanese Negroes, rank next to the Bantus in numbers. Separate kingdoms that developed among the Negroes are now represented by a variety of unrelated languages and by strong tribal ties, such as Ashanti, Yoruba, and Hausa. The purest Negro element is found in the forest belt of West Africa, where subsistence agriculture is practiced, supplemented more recently by such cash crops as cacao and palm kernels. Those who live in the wet-and-dry savanna or the tropical steppe to the north of the forests and eastward into the Sudan show Hamitic influence from the Sahara and Ethiopian Highlands. The savanna and steppe dwellers are more dependent on animals than are the forest dwellers. Many have become traders or are skilled in the preparation and working of leather. Much so-called Moroccan leather originates in the savanna of West Africa.

Other anthropological groupings in sub-Saharan Africa are the non-Negroid Semites, or Arabs, and the Hamites. The latter, probably under 35 million in all, are associated with Ethiopia and Somalia, where the wide range of environmental conditions has resulted in the growth of a variety of crops as well as pastoral activities. Mixed Hamite-Negro people of East Africa include the pastoral Masai. The Arabs, possibly 2 million in number, are most numerous in Zanzibar and in some of the larger cities and seaports of East Africa.

An important element in the racial problems of South Africa is the 1.5 million Cape Coloureds. They are the result of racial mixing, since the earliest days of settlement, of Europeans with Hottentots or Bantus or with slaves brought in from West Africa, the East Indies, Malaya, and other areas.

Approximately 4 million Europeans and less than 1 million Asians—mainly Indians and Pakistani—live south of the Sahara. The Asians are concentrated in Natal and former British East Africa. About three-fourths of the Europeans are in the Republic of South Africa, but substantial numbers also live in Zambia, Rhodesia, Kenya, the former Belgian Congo, and Angola. The term White Africa is sometimes used for South Africa and Rhodesia where Europeans are a dominating minority. Many so-called Europeans (in Africa any white person is classified as European) actually were born in Africa. In fact the arrival of the Dutch in South Africa antedated that of the Bantus. In periods of political and racial unrest European emigration exceeds immigration, amounting to a net loss for some countries of several hundred a month when tensions are greatest.

Political divisions ignore ethnic and tribal boundaries. Religious differences also are divisive factors. Out of Africa's approximately 265 million people, not more than 48 million are now professing Christians as compared with 90 million Moslems. Unfortunately, in some countries there are deep cleavages among Christian denominations. Ethiopians are generally thought of as Coptic Christians, but probably more Moslems and animists than Christians can be found in Ethiopia. The majority of Africa's Moslems are in North Africa, but Islam is influential along parts of the east coast and is increasing in much of West Africa, especially along the margins of the Sahara. Except for a growing number of agnostics among the elite, most of the remaining Africans—approximately 127 million—are animists, whose religions are characterized by fears, fetishes, and witch doctors.

The number of educated Africans is small. Illiteracy rates are over 90 per cent in some countries. The universal need for education at all levels and of all types is very evident, although many countries are beginning to introduce some compulsory education for both boys and girls, and some of the new nations have committed as much as 40 per cent of their national revenue to education. That even this may not be enough is evident from data which show gross national product per capita ranging in sub-Saharan Africa from lows of $46 in Ethiopia and $52 in Tanzania to highs of $210 in Ghana and $398 in South Africa. It has been stated that one-third to one-half the Africans are not in the money economy.

THE GEOGRAPHICAL REGIONS

The geographical regions into which sub-Saharan Africa has been divided are Equatorial Africa, Guinea Coast, Sudan Lands, Horn of Africa, East African Plateaus and Zanzibar, South Central Africa,

Figure 13-17 The geographic regions of Africa are based on both physical and cultural factors.

and Southern Africa (Figure 13-17). The basis for these divisions is largely locational and uses political boundaries, but in general, the physical characteristics of each region also help to differentiate it from the others.

EQUATORIAL AFRICA

Equatorial Africa is an area of nearly 1.6 million square miles in which about 27 million people live. It includes the two Congoes, Burundi, Rwanda, and the Central African Republic, which occupy the Congo Basin and adjacent plateaus and mountains. It also includes Gabon, Spanish Guinea, and Cameroun, most of whose rivers drain directly to the Atlantic Ocean. The Congo Basin is broad and flat, with an elevation between 1,000 and 1,500 feet. The land rises to about 6,000 feet in the eastern plateaus and to more than 5,000 feet on the Congo-Zambezi divide. Uplands to the north and west are from 2,000 to 3,000 feet in elevation. Streams descending into the Congo Basin or to the Atlantic tumble over rapids and falls, giving Equatorial Africa great hydroelectric potential. Where rapids and falls do not block transportation, the Congo and its main tributaries are navigable. From Stanley Falls to Stanley Pool above the Congo rapids, a distance of almost 1,000 miles, the river drops less than 6 inches per mile. Many sections of the Congo resemble narrow lakes and are bordered by swamps. The fact that the major tributaries rise both north and south

of the equator helps to even out fluctuations in the flow of the Congo.

Much of Equatorial Africa has rainy tropical climate with tropical rain-forest vegetation and poor soils. Mosquitoes, ticks, flies, and especially the tsetse fly, which transmits sleeping sickness to man and nagana to domestic cattle, are ever-present. To the south, north, and east there is a transition to wet-and-dry savanna climate and vegetation. There are almost no railroads and few all-weather roads, for development of transportation is handicapped by forests, swamps, and dissected uplands. Nevertheless, increasing efforts are being made to improve overland routes, especially those linking navigable sections of main rivers. Air transportation is opening many areas. Leopoldville, Elisabethville, Brazzaville, and Douala have international airports, but more important are the hundreds of small landing fields.

Millions of Africans still live in tribal villages in the sparsely populated interior and have little contact with other people.

Figure 13-18 Many Africans live in tribal villages. Note the structure of the buildings. (Courtesy of Uganda Department of Information.)

They are primarily Bantus but include also primitive Pygmies. Near the villages of thatched huts are small clearings for primitive agriculture. The few towns and cities have developed as river or ocean ports or have grown up where Europeans are developing mineral resources.

Indigenous agriculture in Equatorial Africa is of the subsistence type and contributes little to the economy of the region. The traditional system is that of shifting cultivation, in which a piece of land near the tribal village is cleared, cultivated for two or three years until soil fertility is exhausted, and then abandoned to the encroaching forest until fertility has been regained. The resting period may be as long as fifteen years, but usually is between four and eight years. Methods of work are primitive. The forest is hacked down and burned and the big trees killed by girdling. Plantings are made by crude implements, and yields are low. Cassava, yams, beans, bananas, maize, and millet are staple crops. The fact that all are seriously deficient in protein leads to a problem of malnutrition in addition to insect-borne diseases and debilitating intestinal parasites. When all the suitable land has been used, the village is moved and the process repeated. The settlements are usually near rivers. With the coming of Europeans, palm kernels, palm oil, and wild rubber became products that could be exchanged for hoes, knives, and cloth. Wild rubber is no longer important, but the production of palm products from both planted and wild trees is a leading industry.

Foreign investments and foreign aid are expanding the development of mineral, forest, and agricultural resources. Sawmills are being built along rivers, although the great variety of trees makes the utilization of any one type of wood difficult.

Large reserves of minerals are being located by prospectors. Mining has been important for many years in the Katanga and Kasai provinces of the former Belgian Congo. With the growth of a nonagricultural population, the domestic market for foods has increased beyond the ability of shifting cultivation to supply it, and at the same time the demand for cash crops for export is also increasing. As a result, efforts are being made to introduce modern methods of planting and cultivation as well as new crops, such as the high-protein groundnut (peanut), and to encourage diversified agriculture. Yet millions are still undernourished and chronically ill in a region where doctors and hospitals are too few, and superstition is rampant. Purchasing power is low. Illiteracy rates are high, although school enrollment is increasing. Changes are slow in coming and have frequently been set back by the problems resulting from national independence in a tribal society.

CONGO (capital, LEOPOLDVILLE)   The former Belgian Congo is as large as the United States east of the Mississippi River but has only 14.8 million people. Before independence, the population included about 110,000 Europeans, most of whom lived in the cities, especially in modern Leopoldville and Elisabethville. Since Belgium did not encourage permanent settlement by the Europeans, the majority were there as administrators, technicians, businessmen, and professional persons. With the uprising of Africans following independence, an estimated 35,000 Europeans fled the country, but some have since returned. Although the Belgians emphasized primary education and the training of skilled workers in vocational schools, it is estimated that one-half to two-thirds of the population are engaged

Figure 13-19   Strings of barges are towed on the quiet waters of the Congo River above Stanley Pool. They carry tons of products to Leopoldville for transshipment to the coast.

in shifting cultivation. The Belgians were starting a program of permanent cultivation with emphasis on cash crops.

Tropical rain forest covers the northern half of the country except for a narrow strip of savanna along the northern edge. The rain forest is a sparsely populated region of subsistence agriculture and a few palm oil plantations operated by European companies. Wetter types of savanna climate extend across the southern Congo but become quite dry in the higher east and southeast. In the west on the Congo River is Matadi, the only seaport, and Leopoldville, the capital and chief city. The latter is the downstream terminus for radar-guided cargo and passenger boats. The Inga Hydroelectric Project planned for the lower Congo between Matadi and Leopoldville awaits peace and financing. Kasai province is the world's most important source of industrial diamonds. (In June, 1963, the six provinces of the Congo were divided into twenty-one. Not all boundaries have been settled, so for clarity the names of former provinces, such as Kasai, will be used.) In the higher and more comfortable southeast is Elisabethville and mineral-rich Katanga. In Kivu province of the eastern highlands, cooler temperatures, spectacular scenery, wild game, and colorful Africans were, under the Belgians, the basis for a flourishing resort and tourist industry. Here also were tea and coffee plantations.

Exclusive of minerals, the principal exports of the Congo in preindependence times were palm products from the rainforest region, high-value coffee from the eastern highlands, and cotton from the savanna and drier fringes of the rain forest. Indications are that the output of these crops and of groundnuts, rubber, and wood products has dropped under independence.

Katanga produces 60 per cent of the national income of the Congo, mostly from minerals. Large interlocking corporations control most of the business. The principal corporation, Union Minière du Haut Katanga, has been considered one of the world's most successful mining combines. Katanga annually produces 7 to 8 per cent of the world's copper and about one-half of its cobalt. Shinkolobwe mine was the world's largest uranium producer, but is said to be no longer profitable. Other minerals include beryl, tantalum, and columbium, all heat-resistant and used in missile production. Exports of minerals greatly exceed in value all other products in the Congo. Even when there

Figure 13-20 Tin mines of Manono, Katanga. The open-pit mines of the Katanga region are among the largest in the world and produce some of the highest-grade ore.

is unrest elsewhere in the country, Katanga is able to continue exporting because it has rail connection with Lobito in Angola and Beira in Mozambique.

BURUNDI AND RWANDA   These countries constituted the former Belgian trusteeship of Ruanda-Urundi. Crowded into a mountainous 20,916 square miles are 5 million people, mostly Africans, about 1 million cattle, and 2 million sheep and goats. Native cattle are of poor quality but are treated with veneration. Slaughtering for meat is taboo, and cows give little milk.

Erosion, famine, and poverty are the rule. The Belgians tried with varying success to replace primitive agriculture and grazing with scientific cultivation (for example, terracing and drainage), improved pasture, and better breeds of animals. Small amounts of coffee and cotton are exported. Burundi and Rwanda have tourist attractions similar to those of Kivu province, Congo, and an active tourist industry existed during the period of Belgian trusteeship.

CONGO (capital, BRAZZAVILLE)   Groundnuts, shea nuts, palm products, lumber, and lead are the chief exports, and although the Congo has a highly unfavorable balance of trade, there are a number of possibilities for the future. Iron ore has been discovered. In 1960 production of petroleum began. It is hoped that a dam and power plant on the Kouilou River will lead to aluminum, chemical, and wood-pulp industries. The new manganese mining district of southeastern Gabon is connected by cableway and rail to the railroad which bypasses the Congo rapids, connecting the Atlantic port of Point Noire with the Congo River port of Brazzaville. Brazzaville is smaller and more relaxed in character than Leopoldville across the river. There is free movement across the river between the two cities, especially by members of the Bakongo tribe.

CENTRAL AFRICAN REPUBLIC   The landlocked Central African Republic occupies a rolling low plateau, with tropical rain forest in the south grading north into tall-grass savanna. As elsewhere in Equatorial Africa, subsistence agriculture dominates, but an effort is being made to diversify the economy. Four-fifths of the exports, all small, are cotton, coffee, and diamonds.

Groundnuts and timber are of increasing importance. Most of the external trade moves between Bangui and Brazzaville by way of the Ubangi and Congo Rivers. The country would like to capitalize on its location in the geographical center of the continent by making Bangui an international air center.

GABON   Gabon is hot and humid with tropical rain-forest climate and vegetation. It is well known for the work of Dr. Schweitzer at Lambarene. The country is divided into a somewhat developed coastal lowland and a more backward hinterland of dissected plateaus and some low mountains. Gabon has a very favorable balance of trade. Timber and petroleum are currently the chief sources of wealth, but important discoveries have been made of other minerals, and the hydroelectric potential is good. In the southeast are manganese deposits, including one of the world's largest, which is now being developed by foreign interests. There is some uranium and to the northeast, high-grade iron ore. The oil reserves near Port Gentil, although not large, are among the best south of the Sahara.

SPANISH GUINEA   Rio Muni, the mainland portion of Spanish Guinea, has a growing cacao economy with increasing amounts also of coffee, timber, and bananas entering foreign trade. Mountainous and rainy Fernando Poo, 20 miles offshore, exports coffee, cacao, and forest products.

CAMEROUN   Cameroun, too, depends on the export of coffee, cacao, cotton, and wood but also exports some aluminum, based on the import from Guinea of alumina, which is processed near Douala using hydroelectric power. It is hoped that deposits of bauxite in the northern Ada-mawa area will soon be mined to supply the smelter. The aluminum is shipped to France. Cameroun is hopeful that commercial oil reserves will be found near the coast since it lies between Nigeria and Gabon, sub-Sahara's chief producers.

GUINEA COAST

The Guinea Coast countries of Nigeria, Dahomey, Togo, Ghana, Ivory Coast, Liberia, Sierra Leone, and Guinea include an almost continuous east-west belt of rainy tropical climate changing to tropical wet-and-dry savanna in the interior. Political divisions cut across the east-west physical patterns. Since they also ignore tribal patterns, the tribes ignore political boundaries and move freely across them. Many still consider themselves members of a tribe rather than nationals of a country. The eight countries cover some 799,000 square miles and have a total population of about 57 million persons. In spite of heat, humidity, and considerable tropical rain forest, the Guinea Coast is one of the more populated sections of Africa with rural densities in parts of Nigeria averaging well over 500 persons per square mile. Europeans have tended to shun the Guinea Coast. Since few of those who do live there consider it home, the region lacks race problems, although it does not escape tribal rivalries.

Much of the Guinea Coast zone of rainy tropical climate has one or two dry months when the doldrums have shifted south, but because so much rain falls during the rest of the year, the vegetation is tropical rain forest. Inland, rain forest grades into open woodland, then grassier savannas, and finally in northern Nigeria into thorn scrub. Over large areas, especially in Nigeria, shifting cultivation has ruined the forest and resulted in man-made savannas. During the dry months the dry dusty harmattan of the Sahara may blow over the Guinea Coast, and when it does, the low relative humidity brings a feeling of coolness.

A coastal plain of varying width adjoins the Gulf of Guinea, to which the Niger, Volta, and some shorter rivers are tributary. The Niger delta is a maze of swamps and channels extending inland for about 100 miles. Inland from the coastal plain are rolling low plateaus. Much of the coast is straight and shallow, lacking natural harbors. Mangrove swamps with a network of lagoons and creeks alternate with sandy beaches against which the surf pounds. Small fishing villages and many larger cities are located on the coast. In many places freighters must anchor offshore and lighters shuttle between ships and shore; where there are no piers for the lighters, African stevedores wade back and forth through the surf, often carrying the freight on their heads. A few ports are exceptions: Lagos and Abidjan use deep lagoons protected by sand bars through which channels have been cut; Port Harcourt occupies an estuary. A slowly increasing number of man-made harbors include Tema, which replaces the open roadstead of Accra, and Cotonou. Isolated railroads and roads extend inland from the better ports, and the mileage of all-weather roads is increasing. The airplane is being used more and more. The Guinea Coast has few navigable rivers, with the notable exceptions of the Niger and Benue in Nigeria, but logs are floated to sawmills, and there is some use of rivers for hydroelectric power and, in the interior, for irrigation.

Economic development among the Guinea Coast countries is not uniform, but most of the area is still dominantly agricultural. Migratory subsistence agriculture is practiced along with the production of commercial crops. In the commercial areas yams, cassava, and maize are staple foods. Truck crops are grown for the cities. Export products of the rain forest are primarily "tree crops": cacao, coffee, palm kernels and palm oil, along with some copra and bananas, or, in Liberia especially, rubber. Except for the Firestone rubber plantations, most of the commercial plantings are small and operated by Africans. Hardwoods such as mahogany are cut and exported. In the drier interior, guinea corn (grain sorghum), groundnuts, and millet take over as staple foods, with groundnuts and cotton becoming commercial products. Because of the absence of the tsetse fly in the savanna, goats, cattle, and sheep are raised; hides and skins are export items; and meat—on the hoof or refrigerated—is shipped to the cities of the rain forest.

Where the rural areas are densely populated, an increasing shortage of land for shifting cultivation is creating a problem. The handicaps of the forested Guinea Coast are similar to those of Equatorial Africa: isolation of more remote sections as a result of the difficulties of travel through tropical rain forest; leached and eroding soils; encroaching vegetation; insect-borne and fungus diseases of men, animals, and plants; malnutrition, frequently taking the form of kwashiorkor, a protein-deficiency disease similar to pellagra. Every government of the Guinea Coast is endeavoring to solve these problems.

The interior plateaus are the location of the principal mineral resources of the Guinea Coast, and employment in mining is increasing. Many deposits of iron ore, bauxite, manganese, and other minerals are being discovered and slowly developed. Of considerable importance are the alluvial deposits of tin in Nigeria's Jos Plateau, of gold throughout Ghana, and of diamonds in Ghana and Sierra Leone. Only Nigeria has known commercial reserves of petroleum and coal, but all countries have hydroelectric potential.

One significant change occurring in Guinea Coast countries is an increasing migration of rural peoples to urban areas. They seek jobs in new, small factories, in service industries, or as laborers in the building trades. Some cities are growing so rapidly that not only employment but housing and sanitation lag far behind. Slums are a grim contrast to the modern downtown districts and the better residential areas. Nevertheless, the cosmopolitan nature of the capital cities is reflected in Accra's Ambassador Hotel where a notice reads: "Men must wear long trousers and ties to dinner or African dress as accepted in the best circles."

NIGERIA   Politically Nigeria is a federation of four regions: North, West, East, and, since July, 1963, Mid-West. The latter was formed from the southeastern part of the West. Geographically, much of the North belongs to Africa's Sudan region. Northern Nigeria contains over half of the country and is the center of the nomadic Fulani and Hausa traders and cultivators. The Kano district is the economic heart of the North, which is largely Moslem and has a feudal society. The walled city of Kano, which was a trading center in the days of the caravans across the Sahara, now has a busy international airport and is the site of a missile-tracking station. The West, Mid-West, and East have much of the commercial agriculture, new industries, and trained leadership of the country. Western Nigeria, the center of the Yorubas, is highly urbanized, with Lagos, Ibadan, and several less familiar but large Yoruba cities. Eastern Nigeria is known as Iboland, although like all regions, it contains numerous minority tribes. It includes Port Harcourt and the densely populated Niger floodplain and delta.

Agriculture accounts for some 80 per cent of the exports, supplies almost all the domestic food, and employs possibly four-fifths of the working population. Many of the new factories which are being encouraged by tax concessions process agricultural products. The marketing of export crops is handled by regional produce marketing boards, whose aim is to ensure stable prices, orderly marketing, and improvement in quality. Most of the cash crops are grown by Africans on small farms, but the government is encouraging plantations for efficiency. Exports are well diversified, the leading items being groundnuts from the Kano district, cacao from the West, and palm products from the East. Nigeria ranks among the world's leading exporters of each. Exports also include cotton, Moroccan leather, and kidskin from the North; alluvial tin from the Jos Plateau; and petroleum from the Niger delta, where mangrove swamps create engineering problems. Eastern Nigeria has coal, used mostly by Nigerian and Ghanaian railways and for electricity. The merchantable timber is from the Mid-West, the village of Sapele having one of the world's most up-to-date plywood factories. In recent years Nigeria has acquired a number of industries.

DAHOMEY   Dahomey is one of the smallest but also one of the more densely populated countries. It extends about 430 miles inland from a 70-mile coast. Cotonou's new port should expedite the shipment of Dahomey's chief exports of palm products, coffee, and groundnuts as well as handle increased amounts of foreign trade for Togo, Upper Volta, and Niger.

TOGO   Togo is half the size of Dahomey

and has a low, sandy, harborless coast of only 32 miles. It is another exporter of coffee, cacao, and palm products, along with some cotton and copra. The mining of large phosphate deposits is beginning. Togo has iron ore also.

GHANA   Ghana is well known for cacao, the long-discussed Volta River Project, and Kwame Nkrumah, the first president. The country is primarily agricultural; subsistence crops feed the country, and cacao from small African farms supplies over one-half the exports. Ghana leads the world in cacao production. The Cocoa Marketing Board has managed to keep the industry stable, in spite of plant diseases and fluctuating world prices. The Volta River Project for hydroelectric and aluminum manufacturing plus irrigation finally got under way in 1962 with the start of the first dam. Ghana has sizable deposits of bauxite and manganese, in addition to gold and industrial diamonds. Manufacturing and internal commerce have been growing. Under Nkrumah, millions of dollars have been spent on constructing roads, schools, hospitals, government buildings, and the port of Tema.

IVORY COAST   The Ivory Coast has a thriving economy. It ranks as the world's third largest producer of coffee. Coffee and cacao make up over 65 per cent of its exports, and bananas and timber contribute 25 per cent. Subsistence agriculture has so declined in favor of cash crops that almost one-fifth of the imports are food products from neighboring countries and abroad. Abidjan has many new manufacturing industries, and the port serves Mali and Upper Volta as well as the Ivory Coast.

LIBERIA   For a century after its founding in 1822 Liberia remained one of the most backward and least developed of the African countries. Large sections of the interior are still undeveloped. However, since the Firestone Company established its first plantation in 1926, changes have been taking place. The company's Liberian investment has grown to the point where it employs thousands of Africans. There are no white employees under the top supervisory jobs, and Liberians are being trained to fill these responsible positions. Firestone also has encouraged individual Liberians to grow rubber for purchase by the company. More recently foreign investors plus many Liberians owning a few shares each have begun mining iron ore. Production of 2 million tons of ore a year was reached by the late 1950s, and with the opening of new mines, the export goal is 20 million tons by the late 1960s. In 1961 iron ore moved ahead of rubber in exports. The growing of cacao, coffee, and bananas, the utilization of timber resources, and diamond mining are also encouraged. The government uses its share of the income to build roads, schools, and other much needed requisites for modernizing Liberia.

SIERRA LEONE   Sierra Leone is a small country with a long-standing split between the literate Creoles of the coastal zone, descendants of American slaves, and the largely illiterate tribal peoples of the interior. Diamonds and iron ore make up about four-fifths of the exports. Smuggling has deprived Sierra Leone of some of the diamond income, but the country does produce about one-sixth of the world's gem diamonds in addition to industrial diamonds. The main occupation of the people is still agriculture, but as mining expands the production of subsistence foods, especially rice, declines, and food imports rise. The leading agricultural exports are those of the Guinea Coast: palm products, cacao, and coffee.

GUINEA   The economy of Guinea is largely agricultural of the primitive-subsistence type, but with cash crops of coffee, bananas, and palm kernels for export. Groundnuts are grown on the drier inland savanna. There are undeveloped forest resources and mineral reserves. Diamonds bauxite, alumina, and iron ore are now being exported. The country hopes to expand the mining of bauxite and to construct a dam and power plant on the Konkouré River in order to manufacture aluminum.

THE SUDAN LANDS

Between the Guinea Coast and the Sahara, the steppes and savannas of the Sudan Lands form a strip about 600 miles wide and over 3,500 miles long, extending across the continent from the Atlantic to the Red Sea. The Sudan Lands include the drier parts of the Guinea Coast countries and the northern tier of countries in Equatorial Africa. Facing the Atlantic are Portuguese Guinea, Gambia, Senegal, and Mauritania. Landlocked are Upper Volta, Mali, Niger, and Chad. The country of Sudan, discussed in Chapter 12, fronts on the Red Sea. Mauritania, Mali, Niger, and Chad extend into the Sahara, but their chief centers of population are in the Sudan Lands, and their trade, like their former political allegiance, is to the south and west. Exclusive of the country of Sudan, the region has an area of about 2 million square miles and a population of almost 19 million. The people belong to a mixture of races that includes Hamites, Semites, and Sudanese Negroes. In Senegal alone the tribes are so numerous that about 120 dialects are spoken. The Moslem religion predominates, though there are some animists and a few Coptic Christians. The few Europeans live in the larger cities.

The southern part of the Sudan has wet-and-dry savanna climate with about 45 inches of rain a year, which falls during the five- to six-month rainy season. The effectiveness of this moisture is lessened by high temperatures. Precipitation decreases northward through steppe to almost rainless desert. The Sudan Lands are flat to slightly rolling and somewhat higher to the south and east. In the Sahara portion of Chad is the Tibesti Massif with elevations over 10,000 feet, and in northern Niger is the Aïr Massif with elevations up to 5,900 feet. Western Sudan is drained by the Senegal, Gambia, and Niger Rivers, the eastern portion by the Nile. The Lake Chad basin and a few other broad, shallow depressions have only interior drainage, for the rainfall is inadequate to support rivers tributary to the ocean. Because of uncertain supply, water must be carefully used. Dryness has the advantage of eliminating the tsetse fly.

The economic development of the Sudan is generally primitive. Farming of the migratory subsistence type with some livestock is common in the south. On the most productive land are a few concentrations of population with densities exceeding 50 per square mile. Africans own and cultivate almost all the farmland. Groundnuts and cotton are the principal export crops. In the north pastoral nomads graze cattle, sheep, and goats. On the thorn scrub along the edge of the Sahara thousands of camels are raised. Hides and skins are exported, as is some meat, usually on the hoof. Prospecting is taking place, but isolation of such mineralized areas as the Tibesti and Aïr Massifs will hinder development for years to come. Some mining is under way in more accessible areas.

Lack of transportation, as in so much of Africa, is a handicap. The region has very few railroads, and most of the roads, although being improved, are really trails or tracks and are often impassable after rains. The Senegal, Gambia, Niger, and lower Shari Rivers are navigable, but floods following heavy rains and low water during dry seasons may stop traffic. Domestic and international air transportation is increasing.

PORTUGUESE GUINEA   Although this area has been under the control of Portugal since 1462, it is one of the least-developed parts of West Africa. The coastal lands are a maze of peninsulas and islands, and even in the interior much of the land is low and swampy. Groundnuts account for over half the exports, supplemented by coconuts and some palm oil, but most of the people are subsistence farmers.

GAMBIA   Gambia is an enclave in Senegal. The 5- to 25-mile-wide country stretches 200 miles inland from the Atlantic along both sides of the Gambia River. It has a one-crop economy—groundnuts.

SENEGAL AND MALI   Upon obtaining independence, these two countries tried to form a federation but broke apart in 1960 with such bitterness that the railroad was closed between the excellent seaport of Dakar and the Niger River port of Bamako. As a result, between 1960 and reconciliation in 1963, Dakar lost millions of dollars in trade and services, while Mali had to carry on foreign trade via less convenient Guinea or Upper Volta and the Ivory Coast. The economies of both countries are based on groundnuts. Mali exports, in addition, cotton and cattle and has undeveloped bauxite reserves. Senegal has a new phosphate industry. During World War II Dakar was a strategic naval and air base; it was also the capital of French West Africa. These functions have left their imprint in a very modern city and an airport which is one of the best in Africa. Located in Mali near the great bend of the Niger is legendary Timbuktu, once an Islamic center of culture and education as well as the focus of caravan routes, but now only a small village. Mali hopes to keep up the Office du Niger, which might be called an African TVA—a nonprofit concern started under the French for the construction of drainage, irrigation, and hydroelectric projects in the Niger basin. The land is fertile, and reclamation has increased the output of both food crops and commercial crops such as rice and cotton.

MAURITANIA   The Islamic Republic of Mauritania is one of the poorest and least known of the African countries. Five-sixths of the population live in the southern third of the country. The most productive area is the floodplain of the Senegal River, where Negroes are sedentary farmers. The remaining one-sixth are nomads, mostly descendants of the Moors. They wander, seeking water and feed for the animals and living on millet and dates from scattered oases and on the meat, milk, and blood of their animals. Camels, cattle, sheep, and goats are sold to Mali and Senegal. But the country's economy is changing, for it has large deposits of iron ore and copper, and iron ore at Fort Gouraud is being mined for shipment by a new railroad to enlarged and modernized Port Étienne. Commercial fishing in the cool waters of the Canary Current is expanding. Petroleum exploration is being carried on. The economy of Mauritania is being transformed, but as interest in Mauritania's resources increases, so does Morocco's interest in annexing the country.

UPPER VOLTA   Livestock on the hoof accounts for over one-half of the exports of this landlocked country. Karite seeds (almonds) rank a poor second. Oua-

Figure 13-21 Passengers disembarking from an international jet flight. This is typical of the terminal building at many of Africa's new airports. (Courtesy of Elizabeth Eiselen.)

gadougou is the capital and inland terminus of the railroad from Abidjan, but Bobo-Dioulasso, also on the railroad, is the focus of trade routes and an economic center. Both have international airfields.

NIGER AND CHAD   The cultivation of groundnuts in Niger, of cotton and cottonseed in Chad, and the grazing of livestock in both countries repeat the pattern of the Sudan. They are marginal countries in development because of their isolation and dryness. Only a small percentage of either is under cultivation. Both Niger and Chad, as well as Cameroun, could profit from reclamation around Lake Chad.

HORN OF AFRICA

Ethiopia, Somalia, and French Somaliland, because of their projecting position, form what is known as the Horn of Africa. It covers an area of about 712,000 square miles and has an estimated population of about 23 million people. The dissected plateaus and rocky, desert coastal wastes are a natural defense against invaders, enabling Ethiopia to have an almost continuous record of independence. It is only

since World War II and the coming of the airplane that isolation has begun to break down. The history of modern Ethiopia begins in 1855 with the consolidation of tribal kingdoms, but the royal family claims descent from Menelek I, traditionally the son of Solomon and the Queen of Sheba. Along the Red Sea is Eritrea, federated with Ethiopia from 1952 to 1962, and now a province of that country. There is recurring friction along the boundaries between Somalia and both Ethiopia and Kenya. Much of the grazing land used by Somali nomads lies in Ethiopia, and about one-third of the population of northern Kenya is Somali.

ETHIOPIA   Approximately 90 per cent of the Ethiopians are living off subsistence agriculture. Rough topography limits transportation and isolates small villages. Cattle and sheep, along with millet, wheat, barley, and beans, are the chief foods. Cotton is grown in small patches throughout the country to be woven at home. Since much of the volcanic soil is fertile, agriculture could be greatly expanded if modern methods were used and markets were accessible, for with climates ranging from tropical and subtropical in the valleys to temperate in the highlands, a variety of crops is possible. The livestock industry could be expanded, for the tsetse fly is absent, and vegetation of nearly half the country is classified as permanent pasture and meadow. Hides and skins and coffee are the most important exports. The coffee is gathered from wild trees in the uplands and shipped via the single-track railway which connects Addis Ababa and the free port of Djibouti in French Somaliland.

The United States, the World Bank, and other agencies and countries are helping Ethiopia by furnishing educational and technical specialists as well as financial assistance. Except for native craftsmen, industry has been practically nonexistent, but there are now establishments for tanning hides and processing foods as well as a modern cotton mill. Hundreds of miles of all-weather roads are being constructed. Ethiopian Airlines has regular domestic service to almost forty cities and towns as well as service to neighboring African countries and Europe. Addis Ababa reflects some of the contrasts typical of the country. It still has many unpaved streets, and until recently hyenas served as the city's sanitary force; nevertheless, there are multistory buildings, and groceries sell soup, soap, and other products from the United States. The United Nations Economic Commission for Africa has its headquarters in Addis Ababa; yet Ethiopians still prostrate themselves when His Imperial Majesty Haile Selassie rides by.

FRENCH SOMALILAND   This French overseas territory has a strategic location on the Gulf of Aden and the Strait of Bab-el-Mandeb. Its chief economic significance lies in Djibouti, but Ethiopia's dependence on this port will lessen with the construction of all-weather highways to its own Red Sea ports.

SOMALIA   Somalia is populated largely by nomads. There is some collecting of gums and resins, including frankincense, and hunting of wild animals. Somali leopard skins are considered among the world's best. Agriculture is limited to small areas where irrigation is possible. Bananas for Italy, a little cotton, gums and resins, livestock on the hoof, and hides and skins make up the few exports of this poor desert country.

EAST AFRICAN PLATEAUS AND ZANZIBAR

The independent countries of the East African Plateaus—Kenya, Uganda, and Tanzania—cover an area of about 681,000 square miles and are occupied by some 25 million people. Among these are approximately 100,000 Europeans and 480,000 Arabs and Indians. The regional boundaries extend inland from the Indian Ocean to the line of the westernmost rift valleys. Except for islands, the area is characterized by high plateaus which have broad expanses of level or nearly level surface. They rise from the hot, moist, coastal lowlands of Kenya and Tanzania in great terraces, some over 100 miles in width. The highest elevations parallel Lake Victoria to the east and west and then converge on the Tanzania-Zambia border. Interrupting the plateau surfaces are the rift valleys of East Africa.

Much of East Africa is sparsely populated, but Zanzibar averages 225 persons per square mile, and the fertile, moist lowlands around Lake Victoria have densities up to 400 per square mile. During recent decades the moderate temperatures and healthful conditions of the Kenya plateaus have attracted European settlers, over half of whom have become urban dwellers. Others established stock ranches or plantations, concentrating on the growing

Figure 13-22   The Madhvani Nagar Sugar Works, which have over 15,000 acres under cultivation. (Courtesy of East African Railways.)

of coffee. Uganda's plateaus, lower and sometimes considered less comfortable, and Tanzania's plateaus, lacking fertility and adequate rain, are not so attractive to Europeans. In Kenya some 11,000 square miles of fertile land were reserved for Europeans in the so-called White Highlands. About 3,000 farms were established, the labor on which was done largely by Africans. The Europeans thought they were buying this land from the Kikuyus, but since the idea of private ownership is incomprehensible to them, the Kikuyus came to think that the White Highlands had been stolen from them.

Over 52,000 square miles of territory were reserved for the Africans, including fertile but less accessible land as well as areas suitable only for grazing. But the Africans lacked knowledge of scientific cropping and grazing, and as population pressure increased on their land, loss of fertility and erosion also made their inroads. In the meantime some Africans moved to the cities, especially to Nairobi, where they acquired a desire for a higher standard of living and for greater recognition as Kenyans. Urban and rural frictions developed between Europeans and Africans, who until recently had no real share in the government and who before December, 1960, could not own or lease land in the White Highlands. As a result, the emigration of Europeans and their capital has become pronounced. The large minorities of Arabs and Indians in East Africa live in the cities, on the coastal plain, and on Zanzibar. They operate stores, provide skilled labor, and control much of the commerce.

East Africa has at least 200 distinct indigenous groups, and their close association leads to misunderstanding and friction among the Africans. The majority are Bantus, including the Kikuyus who make up one-fifth of Kenya's population and whose tribal lands have been most affected by European settlement. The progressive Baganda of southern Uganda are Bantus. There are Hamites who moved in from the north and the Hamite-Negroes, among whom are the Masai of Kenya and Tanzania. Some of the Africans are shifting cultivators; others depend almost wholly on low-grade cattle, sheep, and goats. In Uganda the majority practice sedentary farming combined with the grazing of livestock. Although the movement to the cities is increasing throughout East Africa, most of the Africans live poorly on subsistence foods, their wealth being measured in animals.

Many factors handicap economic progress. The uncertainty of rainfall, overgrazing, and erosion make life precarious for whole villages. Insect pests, including the tsetse fly in wet areas, and carnivorous animals, especially lions and leopards, are a constant menace to domestic herds. Grasslands have to be shared with zebras, kudus, and other herbivorous game. Mining has been slow to develop because a deep mantle of weathered rock, and soil hinders prospecting. Where deposits are known, distance to the coast and poor

transportation are problems. High-value, low-bulk diamonds and gold are exceptions. Transportation is inadequate, although railroads have been built from Mombasa into Uganda and from Tanga and Dar es Salaam into Tanzania. The lakes, including Victoria, are used locally. Roads have been improved in the White Highlands and in Uganda, but the majority of East African roads are not all-weather; Tanzania obtained Peace Corps volunteers from the United States to train road builders. The airplane is a valuable addition to transportation; Nairobi and Entebbe are major international air crossways.

Large areas of sparsely populated northern Kenya and Uganda and of interior Tanzania could be used for agriculture if water were available for irrigation. Irrigation would lessen risks from fluctuating rainfall in already developed sections. For years Kenya, Uganda, and Tanzania have wanted irrigation water from Lake Victoria and other lakes and rivers that feed the White Nile, but the 1929 Nile Waters Agreement between Egypt and Great Britain guarantees no upstream construction in any territory under British control except with Egypt's consent. Egypt approved the power dam at Owens Falls on the Nile in Uganda because it does not lessen the flow of the Nile. Permission to divert water is another matter. Now that they are independent, the East African countries consider the treaty obsolete and hope to obtain a share of the water by peaceful negotiation.

For many years tourism has been a major source of income for the region. Tourists have been lured by wild game and the spectacular scenery of the lakes, mountains, and Great Rift Valley, as well as by picturesque Africans and "exotic" Zanzibar. Nairobi has been the

Figure 13-23   A cotton market in Uganda. (Courtesy of East Africa Railways.)

headquarters for outfitting big-game hunters and the departure point for camera safaris.

UGANDA   Uganda is primarily a land of sedentary farmers, although the cities of the south are centers of commerce and small industries. Power from the Owens Falls project supplies Uganda and nearby Kenya. Uganda's cash economy is based on the sale of cotton and coffee by Africans, which makes them the most prosperous of East African farmers. Some of the plots on which cotton, the chief export, is grown are as small as ¼ acre. A few European planters sell coffee, tea, and rubber. Marketing of crops is handled through cooperatives under government auspices. Subsistence foods are bananas, millet, maize, and rice, and some tobacco and sugar cane are grown for domestic use. A little tin and copper are mined in the southwest, and there is an active fishing industry on the lakes. The University College of East Africa at Makerere (Kampala) is instructing representatives of some eighty East African tribes.

KENYA   Kenya is more than twice as large as Uganda, but because of its aridity has only a slightly larger population. It is estimated that only one-third of the country can produce crops. Almost one-half of the exports consists of coffee grown by Europeans on volcanic soils east of the Great Rift, but some African farmers are also producing excellent coffee. By 1964 there were 150,000 registered African coffee growers. From European-owned estates come sisal and tea, the former from drier areas, the latter from wetter lands. The major part of the world's pyrethrum, an insecticide, is grown on the White Highlands. African agriculture includes maize as the principal food crop and livestock. Kenya has over 1 million head of high-grade cattle owned by farmers of all races. A reorganization of scattered small holdings within tribal areas should improve efficiency of farming and encourage cash crops, and there is an active program for resettling Africans on land purchased from Europeans.

TANZANIA Agriculture is the principal economic activity of Tanganyika, although mining developments are outstanding. The most important agricultural enterprise is the production of sisal on European-owned lands near the coast. This commodity accounts for about one-fourth of the country's exports. Kenya and Tanganyika together produce over half of the world's supply. Coffee, 85 per cent of it grown by Africans, and native cotton are important from the more fertile agricultural lands of the northern interior. Cooperative societies handle the produce. Many Africans are cattle raisers, and hides and skins are exported from the drier interior where the tsetse fly is absent. Minerals were unimportant until recent discoveries of gold and diamonds; now the export of minerals is about equal to that of cotton or coffee. Tanganyika has been allocated 10 per cent of the world's diamond sales. Lesser amounts of lead and tin are mined. Coal and other minerals are

known to exist, but are only beginning to be developed.

In April, 1964, Zanzibar joined Tanganyika to form the United Republic. In October the United Republic was renamed Tanzania. Zanzibar included the islands of Zanzibar and Pemba. The population of the islands, dominantly Moslem, is a mixture of Africans, who are subsistence farmers or workers on plantations, Indians, who are the middlemen, and Arabs, a minority who control the economy in general. For centuries Zanzibar was the trading center for East Africa, but since the development of mainland ports, cloves have supported the economy. Since the world demand for cloves is unfortunately dwindling, the government is trying to increase the output of copra and is encouraging the planting of cacao and tea. Cattle are being introduced to improve the local diet.

SOUTH CENTRAL AFRICA

South Central Africa includes independent Malawi and Zambi, the self-governing colony of Rhodesia, and the Portuguese overseas provinces of Angola and Mozambique. South Central Africa covers an area of 1.2 million square miles, with a population of about 21 million. Angola, depopulated by the slave trade, has only about 10 persons per square mile, whereas rugged Malawi averages over 60 persons per square mile. In recent years the population of the entire region has been upset with varying degrees of seriousness by African unrest and European uneasiness.

From both coasts the land rises by terraces to rolling plateaus occupied by the broad basin of the upper Zambezi and its tributaries. The highlands to the east and west of the basin, with elevations of 4,000 feet and above, support the greatest densities of population. Most of South Central

Africa has savanna climate. Specific types of savanna vegetation are related to elevation and latitude, but dry, open woodland predominates. There are large areas where isolation and the problem of year-round water supply still mean a sparse population. The Africans eke out a subsistence living with grazing and shifting cultivation mixed with primitive sedentary agriculture. The Portuguese have established some plantations, and the British carry on general farming of cash crops in the Rhodesian highland.

South Central Africa is a transitional region between Equatorial Africa and the East African Plateaus to the north and Southern Africa to the south. Northwestern Angola has the wet savanna of the lower Congo Basin. Members of the Bakongo tribe move freely across the borders of both Congoes and Angola. Angola administers the tiny enclave of Cabinda north of the mouth of the Congo River. The diamond-bearing rocks of Kasai and the mineralized zone of Katanga extend across the border into South Central Africa. Katanga minerals reach the Atlantic and Indian Oceans by way of railroads through South Central Africa. The Namib Desert of Southern Africa is found in southwestern Angola. The northern part of Bechuanaland is in the drainage basin of the Zambezi River. A railroad links South Africa, Rhodesia, Zambia, and the port of Lourenço Marques serves the South African Transvaal mining districts.

ANGOLA AND MOZAMBIQUE   Angola and Mozambique are considered integral parts of Portugal, and there is a "Welcome to Portugal" sign at the border on the Johannesburg–Lourenço Marques highway. Their combined European population is less than 275,000 out of a total population of over 11 million. Africans, by passing literacy tests, have been able to become "assimilados," that is, *de facto* Europeans with all the rights, privileges, and responsibilities of Portuguese citizens. With a very low standard of living and with illiteracy rates well over 90 per cent in both Angola and Mozambique, few could achieve this status. In 1961 Portugal announced a change in policy. Africans are now citizens, but voting is limited to those who can read and are able to pay what to most Africans is a high tax—$7.00. Angola is more developed than Mozambique, but both suffer from the poverty of Portugal, which limits the money available for schools, roads, and hydroelectric and other modernizing projects. In recent years the migration of selected farmers has been assisted, in order to relieve the population pressure in Portugal.

In Angola the majority of Europeans and Africans are living in the cooler interior. Coffee accounts for one-third of the exports by value, much of it going to the United States for instant coffee; maize is the chief export in tonnage. The more moist plateau inland from Luanda is the center of the coffee industry, whereas most of the maize is grown on the central plateau and is shipped both inland and to the seacoast via the Benguela Railway. Luanda and Lobito are two of the better ports of Africa. Cattle in the drier south, groundnuts, palm products, and cotton also come from the highlands. The drier coastal plain makes its contribution to the economy in sisal plantations and irrigated sugar cane. The cold waters of the Benguela Current provide one of the best fishing grounds off Africa, and with the Portuguese tradition as fishermen, canned fish and fish meal industries have been established. Sun-dried fish are sent inland to African markets to supply needed protein. Industrial and gem diamonds are mined in the northeast. Petroleum production began in 1956 in the Cuanza basin near

Figure 13-24   View of Luanda, chief seaport, largest city, and seat of government in Angola. Note the modern buildings and houses in this city famed for its flowering bougainvillaea vines. (Courtesy of Portuguese Embassy.)

Luanda. Manganese, iron, and copper are now being mined and exported. Portugal has always encouraged the export of raw materials and discouraged manufacturing in its colonies, and this policy continued for Angola and Mozambique even after they became overseas provinces. A recent change in attitude has resulted in several small manufacturing industries to process food, weave cotton textiles, and make cement for the Angolan market. The economic future of Angola will be determined in large part by the outcome of sporadic uprisings of Africans against Europeans, especially in the northwest.

Mozambique occupies the broadest coastal plain in eastern Africa; only in the northwest is there high plateau. Much of the coastal plain has malarial mangrove swamps near the ocean and savanna

Figure 13-25   A broad avenue in Lourenço Marques, the chief seaport of Mozambique. Note the large windows and porches on the buildings planned for tropical living, the many automobiles, and the modern bus. (Courtesy of Portuguese Embassy.)

woodlands inland. Tsetse flies limit cattle. Although the upland is more open and healthier, the economy of Mozambique is tied to the agricultural lands on the coastal plain and to the transit trade of Lourenço Marques and Beira. It is estimated that one-third of the country is suitable for crops, but less than 1 per cent of the arable land is under cultivation. Most of the commercial agriculture of the Europeans is near the ports and on the Zambezi flood-plain and delta. Cotton, cashew nuts, and sugar are the chief exports, along with copra, sisal, and tea. In addition to subsistence agriculture, Africans raise some cash crops to be sold in cities, carry on fishing, and work on European plantations. Over 100,000 Mozambique Africans work in the mines of South Africa. Lourenço Marques is not only the capital of Mozambique and the chief port for the Transvaal, but is also a popular tourist resort for South Africa. The city does not reflect the lack of development or the poverty of so much of Mozambique.

MALAWI, ZAMBIA, AND RHODESIA The rolling uplands, mostly between 3,000 and 5,000 feet above sea level, of Malawi, Zambia, and Rhodesia have varied resources. From a resource standpoint the Federation of the Rhodesias and Nyasaland, which existed from 1954 through 1963, made sense: Northern Rhodesia (Zambia) had mineral wealth; Southern Rhodesia was agricultural and industrial; Nyasaland (Malawi) had a surplus of labor to serve both. Politically the Federation was unable to resolve racial conflicts; throughout the Federation's short life the Africans resented European domination. The ratio of Africans to Europeans was approximately 13 to 1 in Southern Rhodesia, 30 to 1 in Northern Rhodesia, and 300 to 1 in Nyasaland. The majority of Africans still carry on subsistence agriculture or raise low-quality

animals on savanna grasslands. The exceptions are workers in mines or factories or on European farms, as well as those whose cash crops account for over half the exports of Malawi. Europeans have been attracted to the Rhodesian plateau by the minerals and the possibility of commercial agriculture. Malawi has always had less appeal for Europeans. It is more isolated, has fewer minerals, has a high density of population in the highlands, and includes the low, unhealthy Shire River valley.

Almost one-fifth of Africa's mineral output by value is from Zambia and Rhodesia. In Zambia mining, especially of copper, lead, zinc, and cobalt, provides the most important exports. The copper belt in the north is an extension of Katanga's mineralized zone. Zambia is one of the world's leading copper producers and so is one of the richest of Africa's new nations. Southern Rhodesia has a great variety of minerals in geological dikes intruded into the uplands. The Great Dike, more than 350 miles long and 3 to 6 miles wide, cuts across Southern Rhodesia from north to south. It is an important source of asbestos and among other minerals contains the world's largest known source of high-grade chrome ore. Coal production is limited to Southern Rhodesia, especially in the Wankie district from which coal is shipped to Northern Rhodesia and Katanga. Steam power is being supplemented by hydroelectric power. The power plant at the 420-feet-high Kariba Dam on the Zambezi River, about 300 miles downstream from Victoria Falls, began operation in 1960. Electricity is transmitted north to the copper belt and south to Salisbury and Bulawayo. As an added benefit of the project, commercial fishing has started on Lake Kariba on a controlled basis as to size of annual catch.

Figure 13-26   An airview of Kariba Dam on the Zambezi River. Here the river forms the boundary between Northern and Southern Rhodesia, both profiting from this hydroelectric project. (Courtesy of Elizabeth Eiselen.)

African agriculture includes a wide variety of staple crops of which maize is the most important. Tobacco, grown by European farmers in Northern Rhodesia and African farmers in Malawi, is the main export of both countries. In addition to tobacco African cash crops from Malawi include groundnuts, cotton, and tea. The tsetse fly affects much of Zambia, but is less of a problem in drier lands of Rhodesia and the highlands of Malawi. In general the quality of animals, whether European or African, is poor, except on modern farms near the larger cities.

Manufacturing in Zambia and Rhodesia is largely food processing for local use or the smelting of minerals. Much of land-locked Zambia is still wooded and locally sawmilling is important. In both countries conservation of trees and private plantings of eucalyptus, Mexican pine, and wattle are being encouraged, but progress is slow. Fire during the winter dry season is a very serious problem.

Rhodesia has started iron and steel production and before the dissolution of the Federation had hoped to become the industrial heart of Africa, in spite of competition from South Africa. The loss of the potential ties to independent Zambia and Malawi was a damaging blow to such plans. The economy of separate Rhodesia was hurt also when the headquarters of the two largest copper companies were moved from Salisbury to Lusaka, Zambia. The future of the Rhodesias and Nyasaland depends on how successfully they adjust to existence as separate political and economic units.

SOUTHERN AFRICA

Southern Africa includes South Africa, South-West Africa, and the High Commission Territories of Bechuanaland, Basutoland, and Swaziland. The region has an area of 1 million square miles with a population of about 18 million. It consists largely of rolling plateaus with elevations of 4,000 to 6,000 feet except for the Kalahari basin in the center. The latter has elevations under 2,000 feet, creating an area of interior drainage and salt marshes. Along the outer margins the plateaus descend abruptly to narrow coastal plains. Dry steppes and deserts occupy most of the interior and west coast. Rainfall is seasonal and uncertain. When droughts occur, yields of grain are cut drastically, grass for sheep and cattle is scant, springs and water holes go dry, and everyone suffers from the water shortage. Dams for irrigation are being constructed, but more are needed. Erosion is another problem. Much of the rainfall comes in torrential storms, and the formation of gullies on overgrazed grasslands and cultivated fields, especially maize fields, has become serious. The resulting decline in crop production causes men to break up more sod, often on land that is steeper and erodes faster; or the carrying capacity of grasslands declines without reduction in numbers of animals. Thus the problem becomes worse. Control of erosion and an adequate supply of water are dual necessities for the farmer. The arid parts of the interior and west coast hold little promise for economic development except where there are minerals.

Mineral resources—gold, diamonds, and others—as well as agricultural possibilities attracted many Europeans to the country now known as South Africa. Mountainous Basutoland and Swaziland and dry Bechuanaland and South-West Africa held less interest for Europeans. The early pioneers settled first along the coast of southern Africa and then moved into the higher and cooler velds, bringing with them European cattle, sheep, wheat, and maize. Along the southwestern coast they developed Mediterranean agriculture and started irrigation. In the northern parts of the humid subtropical east coast, sugar cane became important. Steep approaches to the interior from all coastal points made railroads and highways difficult and expensive to build and operate. Only the most valuable products from the interior could afford the high cost of transportation.

SOUTH AFRICA   Composed of the provinces of Cape of Good Hope, Orange Free State, Transvaal, and Natal, South Africa is the only European-dominated independent state in Africa and is the continent's most highly developed and industrialized country. Europeans make up about 20 per cent of the population. Of these approximately 58 per cent are of Dutch origin, formerly the Boers but now called Afrikaners. They speak Afrikaans, a dialect derived from the Dutch with modifications from other languages. The Afrikaners con-

trol the government and are primarily ranchers and farmers. Those of British descent make up 42 per cent of the European population, speak English, and are engaged in commercial activities and mining. Bantus number about 68 per cent of the population. Many European South Africans are third-generation in the country and consider themselves to have as much right to the country as the Bantus, who also are migrants into southern Africa. Because of their own long tradition in Africa, the white South Africans do not use the term "African" to designate the black South African, as Europeans do elsewhere on the continent in speaking of the indigenous population. Instead they are all called Bantus. Cape Coloureds account for 9 per cent of the population; Asians, mostly Indians, form 3 per cent. Restrictions based on race are increasing for all non-Europeans. The Coloureds are concentrated largely in western Cape Province. Most of the Indians live in Natal.

Roughly one-third of the Bantus are workers or tenants on European-owned farms, and about one-third are unskilled or semiskilled laborers in mines and factories or are domestic servants. Many Bantus are second- or third-generation, detribalized city dwellers. They have nothing in common with the remaining one-third who still live under tribal organization on Bantu reserves. Most of the men from the latter group spend part of their lives as migratory workers employed by Europeans. Some Bantus are farmers and herders on their own. Bantus own several million each of cattle, sheep, and goats. Only a little over 1 per cent of the Bantus have been able to progress to positions in civil service, medicine, law, or teaching. The generally low social, political, and economic status of the Bantus and Coloureds is cause for much unrest and constitutes one of the country's important problems.

South Africa's physical environment both favors and hinders development. Elevation combined with latitude means cooler and more stimulating climate; but the steep rise of several thousand feet from coastal ports to the interior constitutes a serious problem in the development of adequate and efficient transportation. Nevertheless, road and rail transportation are better developed in South Africa than elsewhere in the continent, and both large cities and small towns are served by South African Airways. Extensive grasslands and the absence of the tsetse fly favor grazing, but other insects, diseases, and uncertain rainfall over wide areas make the industry unprofitable in some years. The sudden and violent nature of much of the rainfall results in rapid runoff, serious soil erosion, formation of deep gullies, and sudden floods on the rivers. Dams are being built to counteract the great annual variation in flow of plateau streams, thus increasing irrigation and hydroelectric potential.

Agriculture is varied. Coastal humid subtropical Natal is especially important in the production of sugar cane. Coastal parts of Cape Province, with Mediterranean climate, are famous for grapes and wine and have winter wheat and livestock. Irrigation in the southern valleys of Cape Province is aiding the production of fruits and vegetables. Agriculture in the dry interior is dominated by sheep and cattle grazing, although projects such as the Vaal-Hartz irrigation scheme north of Kimberley are changing the landscape. With 800 miles of concrete canals the Vaal-Hartz Scheme is one of the biggest conservation projects of its kind in the Southern Hemisphere. Far larger in scope is the Orange River Project, a long-term plan for supplying hydroelectric power and

water for irrigation and industrial expansion to the region extending from Port Elizabeth on the Indian Ocean to Port Nolloth on the Atlantic Ocean. Cattle are seldom surplus, and South Africa usually must import meat. Sheep are especially important in the Karroo, the dry hilly lands between the Kalahari Desert and the croplands of the southeast. Some of the world's finest Merino sheep are bred here. South Africa is second to Australia as a producer of Merino wool, which is South Africa's most valuable farm export. The High Veld on the east side of the plateau has enough moisture for wheat, maize, and sorghum. This is South Africa's "maize triangle." Unfortunately the black soils of the High Veld have lost fertility and are badly eroded; they are less durable under cultivation than the prairie and chernozem soils of the middle latitudes.

For decades the economy of South Africa was dominated by mining, but during World War II manufacturing moved ahead. The four pillars of the mining industry are gold, diamonds, coal, and iron and steel. Gold and diamonds are the chief minerals among the exports, but coal production has now surpassed diamonds in value. Coal is used for domestic power and in the Transvaal's steel mills; some is exported. Durban handled large amounts of bunker coal before ships changed to oil. Since South Africa lacks petroleum, it extracts some oil from coal. Coal seams are widespread, but the southern Transvaal and northwestern Natal lead in production. Iron ore, copper, chrome, manganese, asbestos, and other minerals also are mined, especially in the Transvaal. Uranium is obtained by reworking tailings from the mills after gold has been extracted.

Almost 60 per cent of the world's gold is mined in South Africa. The Witwaters-

Figure 13-27   Sugar cane in Natal. An irrigation canal parallels a narrow-gauge railway line. Irrigation is insurance against the prolonged drought which can affect humid subtropical Natal. (Courtesy of Information Service of South Africa.)

rand—Rand for short—in the Transvaal is the world's greatest gold-mining zone. The principal city of the Rand is Johannesburg, the largest mining center in the world. It resembles a United States city with its tall buildings and dense automobile traffic, but the many yellow hills of mine waste show the source of its wealth. Since 1947 gold has been mined in the Orange Free State. Some geologists believe the richest gold fields in the world lie northwest of Bloemfontein.

Diamonds were first discovered at Kimberley as early as 1866, but the big strike was made in 1871. Although Kimberley Mine—the Big Hole—has been abandoned, diamond mining continues in the Kimberley district. The largest active mine in South Africa at present is the Premier near Pretoria. For years South Africa has ranked third to the former Belgian Congo and Ghana in total production but ahead of both in the more valuable gem diamonds. The latter position is being challenged by South-West Africa.

Manufacturing now contributes the largest share of the national economy. Government capital invested in power development, transportation facilities, and selected industries has been augmented by large investments from the United States and Europe. Expansion has taken place in almost all lines of manufacturing, some of the most noteworthy being in iron and steel production, machinery and electrical equipment, textiles and clothing, chemicals, and building materials. More than half of the raw materials used in manufacturing are produced within the country. Rhodesia is one of the chief markets for manufactured exports. The greatest concentration of manufacturing is around Johannesburg. "Jo'burg" and Pretoria plus the seaports of Cape Town, Port Elizabeth, and Durban account for almost two-thirds of South Africa's industries. Pretoria and Cape Town function also as dual capitals: Pretoria is the administrative center; Cape Town is where Parliament sits. Bloemfontein has the Supreme Court.

Tourism is increasing. Gold and diamond mines can be visited. National parks, of which Kruger National Park is the best known, have been established for the preservation of scenic resources and native wild animals. Resort activities are important along the coasts of Natal and eastern Cape Province.

South Africa faces many problems associated with its physical environment, but the outstanding problem for the country is that of race relations. The government has adopted a policy of *apartheid*, meaning "separate development," which emphasizes racial segregation. Plans have been made for establishing seven "ethnic regions," or Bantu Homelands (popularly Bantustans), in which the separate development of the Bantus would take place. They would be self-governing and develop their own resources. The seven regions cover about 13 per cent of South Africa, located mostly in the hills and mountains of Natal and northern Transvaal, plus Basutoland, Swaziland, and Bechuanaland. The last three regions are essential to the plan, but since the Basutos, Swazis, and Bechuanas are sturdy, independent people, they will undoubtedly continue to resist inclusion in South Africa. Under their present subsistence development, most of the proposed Bantustans are already overpopulated and overstocked, but in terms of industrial potential the Afrikaners con-

Figure 13-28 The pennants name a few of the many tribal groups represented among the contract laborers in Johannesburg's gold mines. Tribal groups, such as these "female impersonators," compete in the Sunday mine dances. (Courtesy of Elizabeth Eiselen.)

sider them underpopulated. They cite, for example, hydroelectric potential on the eastern slopes of the Drakensburg Mountains, and the materials for pulp and paper that could be supplied by forestation. The government plans to provide financial assistance because private white capital and skills are to be barred. European-owned small industries are to be relocated on the border of Bantustans to utilize labor of the Bantus living inside, but ignoring other economic factors. The government is encouraging Bantu education, and the illiteracy rate among the South African Bantus is lower than among the Africans of most sub-Saharan countries. Nevertheless, with numerous restrictions legislated on the Bantus, separate development cannot mean equal development. Broad-minded wisdom is needed to reduce the tensions apartheid has generated. Conflicts must be resolved if South Africa's increasingly complex industrial economy is to continue to expand, for the European's technical knowledge and capital are still needed, as is the Bantu's labor. Peoples everywhere will be watching Transkei, the first tribal state within South Africa to be granted internal self-government.

BASUTOLAND, SWAZILAND, BECHUANALAND These three, under the direct protection of the British government in London, are known as High Commission Territories. South Africa has long sought to absorb them and has close economic ties with each, but all three are seeking complete independence. Basutoland and Swaziland are relatively densely populated, mountainous territories. Basutoland has peaks rising to over 11,000 feet and so-called lowlands between 5,000 and 7,000 feet. Labor for South African mines and the hilly grasslands are virtually the only resources except for undeveloped hy-

droelectricity. Unfortunately overgrazing and erosion have become serious problems, and there is little arable soil. Some wool, mohair, and cattle are exported. Malnutrition is widespread. An average of 43 per cent of the adult male population is working in South Africa at any given time.

Swaziland has a more varied and growing economy, the result of foreign financing of resource development. It has one of the world's largest asbestos mines, and iron is being mined now that rail facilities are available for shipping the ore. Pine trees have been extensively planted on eroded lands and a pulp mill has been erected. Sugar cane and citrus fruit trees have been planted. Cash crops of cotton, tobacco, rice and animal products are encouraged on African farms. Nevertheless, 15 per cent of the Swazi men work on the farms or in the mines of South Africa.

Bechuanaland is sparsely populated and has problems in the Kalahari Desert in the south and the Okavango swamp in the north. The latter has attracted geographers and planners who consider the swamp a potential reclamation area. Cattle raising is the chief occupation; cattle and beef plus a little asbestos and manganese are the only exports. Unfortunately grazing lands are deteriorating here also, and water problems are becoming more acute. About 20 per cent of the male population work in South Africa.

SOUTH-WEST AFRICA   South-West Africa and South Africa are closely tied politically and economically. South Africa administers sparsely populated South-West Africa as a mandate and is responsible for much of the foreign trade. The best port is Walvis Bay, which belongs to Cape Province but is administered by South-West Africa. The region is arid, with the

*Figure 13-29   Clearing the over-
burden to reach diamond-bearing
gravels north of the mouth of the
Orange River. About 98 per cent
will be gem diamonds from this
field. (Courtesy of Information
Service of South Africa.)*

Namib Desert on the west and the Kalahari on the east. In between is a slightly
more moist plateau averaging 3,600 feet
above sea level. The growing of crops is
almost impossible, but sheep, goats, and
some cattle graze on bush and sparse
grasses away from the coast. South-West
Africa is famous for its karakul (Persian
lamb) pelts. Meat is sold to South Africa.
With the fishing grounds of the cold Benguela Current offshore, fish-processing
industries are expanding. Minerals are
the main resources, especially diamonds
from coastal and offshore placer deposits.
Copper, lead, and zinc come from a mine
in the north. The amounts, though small,
are important to a country with so many
environmental handicaps.

AFRICAN ISLANDS

Many small islands, some in groups such
as Cape Verde or the Madeira, others isolated like Ascension and St. Helena, have
significance. The island of greatest area
is Madagascar, which is the fourth largest
island in the world.

MADAGASCAR   The Malagasy Republic occupies the island of Madagascar, 995
miles long and 360 miles wide. Although
only the 250-mile-wide Mozambique
Channel separates it from Africa, the
Malagasy Republic is not an African state.
The indigenous population are Malagasy,
whose ancestors originated in Indonesia
and Malaya rather than in Africa.

Topographically the island is a series of
plateaus and mountains that attain elevations of 2,500 to over 6,000 feet with
mountain peaks up to 9,450 feet. The
steep eastern or windward side of Madagascar has an annual rainfall in excess of
60 inches and in places over 100 inches.
The swift east-flowing streams have
a great hydroelectric potential. The
westward descent is over broad plateaus,
where rainfall is seasonal and varies between 40 and 60 inches. The southwest
lowlands, however, have less than 15
inches of rain and are almost desert.
Temperatures of low elevations are tropical, ranging between 70 and 80°F; the
interior plateaus are 10 to 15° cooler.
Rain forest on the east side and wooded
savanna on the west were the original
vegetation, but migratory agriculture and
burning for pasture have reduced much
of the vegetation to a steppe-savanna

type. Only one-fifth of the island is now classified as forest.

Malagasy depends on agriculture, which suffers from inadequate transportation and the small size of the domestic market. Topography has so limited the construction of roads and railroads that most of the exports come from the coastal regions. Increasing dependence is placed on the airplane; the island has over 100 airfields. Of the eighteen ports used for foreign trade, Tamatave on the east coast is the most important. Coffee, three-quarters of it grown on the eastern coastal plain, accounts for about 30 per cent of the exports. Rice ranks high among the exports and is also the chief item in the native diet, along with cassava, yams, and beans. Other agricultural exports include vanilla, sugar, and tobacco. Cattle raised in the savanna lands are the principal domesticated animals. They can move to the coastal ports on the hoof. Mining is relatively unimportant, although Madagascar is a leading world source of graphite. Some gold and semi-precious stones are exported also.

SMALL ISLANDS   Most of the small islands listed in Table 13-1 are densely populated. Far out in the Indian Ocean are the Mascarene Islands, among which are British Mauritius and French Reunion Island. Both are sugar cane growers. Mauritius is a refueling stop on flights across the Indian Ocean between Africa and Australia. The Seychelles, also British, are a group of 92 small islands north of Madagascar. They export copra, vanilla beans, and cinnamon bark.

In the North Atlantic Ocean are the Portuguese-owned Madeira Islands and the Spanish-owned Canary Islands, both famed for wine. The Canary Islands export quantities of bananas. Farther south are the Portuguese Cape Verde Islands,

which produce excellent coffee. In the South Atlantic are the lonely British Islands of Ascension and St. Helena. Few people now live on either, but in the days of sailing ships they were ports of call to secure fresh water and vegetables. During World War II, Ascension was a base and refueling station for aircraft flying between Natal, Brazil, and Africa. In the Gulf of Guinea, about 125 miles offshore, the Portuguese islands of São Tomé and Principe export cacao, as does Fernando Poo, part of Spanish Guinea. Many of the small islands have the problem of dependence on one crop.

IN PERSPECTIVE

SUB-SAHARAN AFRICA, A DEVELOPING REGION

Since World War II Africa south of the Sahara has been undergoing rapid political, economic, and social changes. During the nineteenth century sub-Saharan Africa passed from rule by native tribal governments to rule by European nations. Now we are seeing a vast and complex transition to independence and government once again by Africans, this time on a national basis. In the words of Nkrumah of Ghana: "We prefer self-government with danger to servitude in tranquility." The people, too, are undergoing change. Millions of Africans are still primitive, uneducated, and superstitious, but millions have abandoned tribal living and now dwell in cities and other communities that offer employment, although most wages for the Africans are very low. A high percentage of Africans are still illiterate, but Albert Luthuli, winner of the 1960 Nobel Peace Prize, is a Zulu. Africa is a continent in which the change from the Stone Age to the electronic age, which took centuries elsewhere, is being accomplished in decades. The major need of Africa is time, but the Africans do not want to wait.

As Europeans moved into the continent, they paid little attention to the claims of the tribes, and seldom made adequate payment for occupied land. Since the Africans were farmers, loss of land was a serious matter. African occupations of subsistence farming and herding were frequently replaced by the development of mines, the exploitation of forest resources, and the starting of plantations. Although sometimes Africans owned and operated farms producing raw materials and foodstuffs for export, generally Europeans managed such operations, paid the Africans low wages, and retained most of the profits. In some colonies such as Nigeria, Uganda, and the Belgian Congo, European settlement and ownership of land was discouraged either by the nature of the environment or by the home government. In other regions, as in Southern Rhodesia and South Africa, a large share of the best land is occupied by Europeans, and rapidly increasing numbers of Africans are unable to secure cropland or grazing land sufficient for their needs. Populations are increasing, in part because Europeans have worked to improve the health, sanitation, and diets of the Africans. Problems of land ownership, racial discrimination, and the usual great disparity between wages paid Africans and Europeans which results in tremendous differences in living standards have made Africans restless and resentful. They are asserting the right to govern themselves and to have a greater share in the development of their own resources.

Few parts of developing Africa are without major environmental handicaps: too much rainfall, too little rainfall, irregular and uncertain rainfall, impenetrable vegetation, no vegetation, grazing lands where grasses are unpalatable in the dry season, infertile soils, badly eroded soils, vast distances, steep escarpments between coast and interior, tsetse fly and locust infestations, malaria-carrying mosquitoes. The list is long. Solutions for many of the problems have not been found as yet by the Europeans, and unfortunately handicaps frequently have been aggravated by European occupation.

Most Africans are poorly nourished. Improvement in food supplies is greatly needed, especially an increase in protein foods. An interesting possibility is the "harvesting" of wild game for meat instead of the raising of cattle and sheep. Comparative scientific experiments seem to be coming out economically in favor of African animals. Many biological and economic problems remain to be solved, but it seems quite certain that the selective harvesting of wild animals would provide meat on marginal land now being used rather unprofitably for cattle. Furthermore, the protein content of the meat of at least one African animal—the hippopotamus—is double that of beef.

As Africans assume responsibility for sub-Saharan Africa, they are going to need assistance, technical as well as financial, but it should be assistance designed specifically for the region concerned. The final report on a 1961 UNESCO conference on Africa states it in this way: "African conditions require technological solutions different from those in the United States, and the store of Western knowledge cannot simply be transferred to Africa. Rather, there is need for radical innovations; in fact, the African situation by its very nature invites invention."

SELECTED REFERENCES

Focus, American Geographical Society, New York. Published monthly except July and August.

Each six-page issue deals with a specific country or region, or with a topic of major interest. Many have been devoted to the developing countries of Africa, including the Congo (Brazzaville), Ethiopia, Gabon, Mauritania, and Somalia. The approach is geographical. Several maps and a brief bibliography are included in each.

Gould, Peter R.: *Africa, Continent of Change,* Wadsworth Publishing Company, Belmont, Calif., 1961.

A collection of selected and edited readings designed to give insight into some of the major political, economic, and social problems of Africa. "Land Consolidation in the Kikuyu Areas of Kenya" is one of the many articles especially pertinent to a geographical study of the continent.

Hance, William A.: *African Economic Development,* Harper & Row, Publishers, Incorporated, New York, 1958.

A series of studies whose common theme is economic development in Africa south of the Sahara. It includes examples in agricultural and industrial development, a discussion of transportation problems, and a consideration of selected African areas.

Hance, William A., *The Geography of Modern Africa,* Columbia University Press, New York, 1964.

An excellent, well-illustrated volume which can serve as both text and reference. The latter use is facilitated by a Subject Index, and an Index on Graphical Names.

Kimble, George H. T.: *Tropical Africa,* vol. I, *Land and Livelihood;* vol. II, *Society and Polity,* The Twentieth Century Fund, New York, 1960. Abridged edition, Anchor Books, Doubleday & Company, Inc., Garden City, N.Y., 1962 (Paperback).

A major study in depth of tropical Africa, i.e., Africa south of the Sahara and north of South Africa, sponsored by the Twentieth Century Fund. It is organized on the basis of subject matter rather than of regions, under the headings of the two volumes.

Stamp, L. Dudley: *Africa: A Study in Tropical Development,* 2d ed., John Wiley & Sons, Inc., New York, 1964.

This revised edition is a good geography of the continent of Africa. A systematic approach to the continent in the opening chapters supplies the background for examination of the countries and regions of Africa, as well as of "African Problems: Past, Present and Future."

chapter 14
CENTRAL EASTERN ASIA

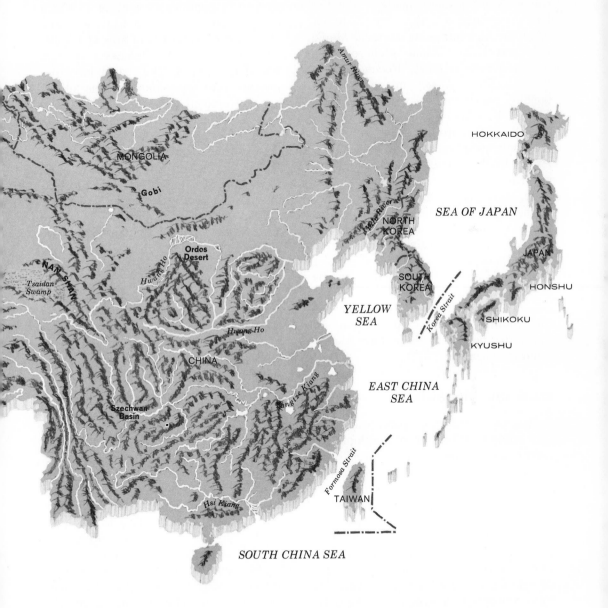

Figure 14-1   Central Eastern Asia has an area of more than 4.6 million square miles. The principal landforms of China are mountains and the high Tibet Plateau. Korea and Japan are also mountainous countries. A large majority of the 860 million persons of the area live either along river valleys, on coastal plains, or on the plains of eastern China.

*A*LMOST ONE-THIRD OF THE WORLD'S population, or nearly 860 million people, inhabit the large part of the East Asiatic countries which tradition has taught us to regard as the mystery lands of the Far East. Associated with these regions in our minds are such intriguing names as Marco Polo and Kublai Khan, such romantic titles as *The Good Earth, Madame Butterfly*, and *The Mikado*, and such world-famous personalities as Generalissimo Chiang Kai-shek, Chairman Mao Tse-tung, Emperor Hirohito, and Chou En-lai. Although these lands are no longer mysterious in the old sense, information for much of the area has again become obscure. How true a picture can we acquire of the lands supporting such masses of humanity? What are the geographical and physical settings against which these Oriental peoples live out the drama of their lives? Can we clear away the cobwebs of mystery and romance and the obstruction of state restrictions, to discern the true culture, livelihood, and activity in which the people of these East Asiatic countries engage?

REGIONAL CHARACTER

Eastern Asia has three parts which, by their cultural and historical development, form natural groupings. These are Northeastern Asia, which is in the Soviet realm; South and Southeastern Asia, which comprises the lands south of eastern China; and Central Eastern Asia, which includes China, Japan, Korea, and Mongolia. The term Far East, traditionally applied to Central Eastern Asia, has been an accepted misnomer for the region. It derives from concepts of geography dating from the time before Magellan proved the earth was round by sailing westward to the Far East. The term no longer makes geographical sense.

SITUATION

The situation in Central Eastern Asia is that of a continental land mass which merges into Central Asia to its west and is fringed by great island arcs of the Pacific to its east. The climates vary from boreal to tropical. The region has commercial, economic, and strategic advantages. Commercially, the eastern parts lie adjacent to one of the major maritime trade routes of the world. Steamers plying between the great Pacific ports of the United States and Southeast Asia often follow a great-circle route that runs past the coast of Japan and China. Korea does not have the same advantage in location, but it does not suffer the landlocked isolation of Mongolia. Strategically, this region is most significant. Its land surface is one-twelfth of that of the entire world, and almost one-third of the world's population is crowded in its more productive lands. On the north and west the region touches the powerful Soviet Union; its eastern island chains and coasts command the west Pacific.

AREA AND GEOGRAPHIC SHAPE

The four countries of this region differ in many respects, including size and shape. The more than 3.5 million square miles of China contrast with the 85,000 square miles of Korea. Japan, with an area of over 147,000 square miles, is less than one-fourth the size of the Mongolian People's Republic, which covers some 606,000 square miles. Area, however, does not necessarily give any idea of capacity for population support. The significance of great area lies in the likelihood of greater mineral wealth and of greater agricultural variety, although it does not guarantee even this possibility. Strategically, China's great area permits the use of space for defense in depth and for a certain amount of mobility in traditional warfare. Its disadvantages lie in the difficulties of communication.

In shape, China and the Mongolian People's Republic are both rather chunky blocks with relatively short boundaries relative to the large area. By contrast, Japan and Korea are elongated countries that lend themselves to segmentation and the outflanking movements of traditional military strategy. They are chiefly maritime in situation, and their coastline boundaries are long in relation to their areas.

CLIMATE

The 35° latitudinal spread of China brings its northernmost limits to the latitude of southern Labrador; its southernmost territory reaches the latitude of Puerto Rico. Although Japan and Korea do not have such an enormous latitudinal stretch, their generally north-south elongations also bring much climatic variety. Yet despite the variety, certain common climatic influences are distinguishable in the region. The huge continental interior of China not only has great continental extremes within itself, but also exerts far-reaching climatic effects upon maritime and peninsular neighbors to the east. In this respect Mongolia shares the position of progenitor with the rest of the Central Asian heartland. It is the existence of this immense land surface, with its great capacities for heat radiation and absorption, that is responsible for the influences creating what is known as the monsoon climate of Eastern Asia. This monsoon differs from the Indian monsoon, however, in having dry, cold winter air masses as the dominant element.

NATURAL RESOURCES

Compared with North America and Northwestern Europe, Central Eastern Asia is faced with a general inadequacy of known resources for large-scale industrial development. There is limited variety in the more important deposits of mineral resources. A few minerals are concentrated overwhelmingly in a few districts within the region; most of this mineral wealth, for example is found in China. Japan has the only large stands of accessible forest resources in the region. China alone has large arable land resources, but because of the large population, that country resembles the others in having only small units of cultivable land per capita. China, Korea, and Japan have certain cultural similarities embodied in the written language, in their backgrounds of Buddhist religion, in Confucian philosophy, and in the careful and intensive methods used for agriculture.

CHINA

China, with an estimated population approaching 800 million, has less acreage of land under cultivation than the United States; yet it supports four times as many people. Both natural and social conditions have helped China to become the most populous country in the world. Favorable natural factors include the large size of the country, the soil, climate, and native plants. There is a large amount of arable land, including fertile alluvial and loessal soils. Much of China has a long growing season and abundant rainfall, with maximum precipitation in the summer when it aids crops the most. More than 9,000 plant species have been described for China, nearly half of which are peculiar to that country, and many of these plants have been domesticated for food production. Social factors include the custom of early marriage and the desire for sons, the use of human labor instead of animal power, and the diet of grain and vegetables rather than of animal products that eliminates the necessity of growing fodder. The animals that supply most of the meat, pigs and poultry, are commonly fed scraps and refuse. On otherwise wasted land, ponds are used to raise bulbs and other water plants, fish, and ducks for food. Chinese are masters of irrigation and of methods of preserving and fertilizing soils to secure maximum yields, even though the pressure of population and lack of public responsibility have resulted in deforestation and erosion. The people are willing to toil long hours to support large families; they remain cheerful and reasonably healthy under crowded and often unsanitary living conditions that would be very depressing to Westerners.

RELIEF FEATURES

RIVERS   China occupies the large eastern segment of the Eurasian land mass and shares in the radial system of river drainages running out from the elevated heart of the continent (Figure 14-1). Flowing northeastward and out of China into the Soviet Union's Pacific maritime province is the great Amur River (Hei-lung Chiang, meaning Black Dragon River). While economically the main stream of the Amur is of greater importance to the Russians than to the Chinese, its tributary, the Sungari (Sung-hua), is the most important river of Manchuria, draining the greater part of the Manchurian Plain. The Russians and Chinese have developed jointly unrealized plans for a vast hydroelectric project on the Amur.

The other large rivers of eastern China run in great bends and loops generally from west to east, emptying into one of the three seas bordering the China coast. The greatest of these rivers is the Yangtze River (Yang-tzu Chiang), over 3,000 miles in length and navigable by steamboats for over half of its course. It empties into the East China Sea near Shanghai. Some of its tributaries are 500 to 900 miles long and also rank as great rivers. Many are navigable by small boats for hundreds of miles.

Draining the southernmost provinces is the West River (Hsi Chiang), forming an important navigation net for the mountainous south where topography is difficult for road construction. The Hsi system brings the trade of the south to the commercial gates of Canton (Kuangchou) and British Hong Kong, although it is importantly supplemented by the southern railroad system.

In North China, the Yellow River (Hwang Ho) long ages ago laid the silt that filled in the great arm of the sea that now is the Yellow Plain. Running out of arid regions and through a dry loessland of fine-particled, easily eroded soils, the Yellow River has created a standing invitation to land-hungry farmers to crowd its plain. At the same time, it has qualified this invitation by the misery it inflicts in frequent, rampaging floods. Although a mighty river, the Yellow River's shifting channels and sand bars restrict its use as a navigable artery. Between the Yangtze and the Yellow Rivers runs the Hwai River (Huai Ho). The Hwai is significant in three important ways. It is a navigable stream now partly controlled by floodgates and dams. It coincides with, and thus marks, the climatic boundary between dry North China and humid South China. The Hwai occupies a low-lying trough in the southern part of the Yellow

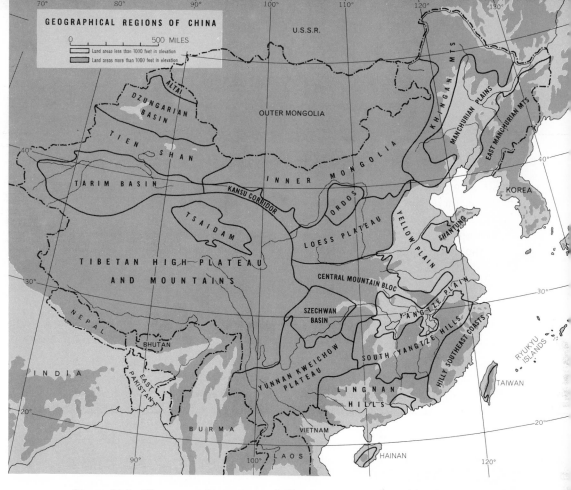

Figure 14-2 The geographic regions of China are numerous and have irregular shapes. The boundaries are largely the result of physical factors.

Plain and often receives Yellow River floodwaters during major breaks in the south-bank dike along Yellow River levees. In spite of strenuous Communist Chinese efforts to control the river, the Hwai plain continues to suffer occasional disastrous floods. Along the mountainous southeastern coast, rivers a few hundred miles long form small delta plains of local significance.

THE GREAT PLAINS   Although rivers form important arteries and bring both blessing and calamity to people in their drainage areas, the valley plains they have carved or deposited are of much greater signifi-

cance for the livelihood of China's large population. The great plains of China are mainly in the north. In northeastern China (Manchuria) the depositional Liao Ho plain of the south joins with the erosional plain of the Sungari (Sung-hua) over a hardly noticeable water divide and forms a continuous surface of some 138,000 square miles. The Liao Ho section is relatively level, the Sungari section, somewhat rolling.

Connected to the Liao Ho plain by a narrow corridor, which is crossed by the Great Wall at the seaport of Shanhaikwan (Shan-hai-kuan), the Yellow Plain runs southward without interruption around the Shantung hill country to merge with the Hwai and lower Yangtze River plains. With the Hwai as a southern boundary, this great plain covers an area of about 125,000 square miles, for the most part level and under 100 feet in elevation.

The Yangtze Plain, although of smaller extent, is more fragmented, more irregular in shape, and extends in a narrow zone much farther inland. Its approximately 75,000 square miles of level surface include the central plains of the Tung Ting (Tung-t'ing) and Poyang (P'o-yang) Lakes as well as the lower Yangtze Plain and the connecting corridors of lowland between them.

MOUNTAINOUS SOUTH   South of the Yangtze the plain extends in narrow slivers up the river valleys to be closed in soon by hills of increasing elevations and ruggedness. Most of South China is in slope land, so that level land for farming is restricted to narrow, scattered valleys and basins whose areas total to a small percentage of the land surface. The largest of these alluvial farmlands occur along the coast.

Separating the Yangtze drainage from that of the Hsi and the small southeast coastal rivers is the great mountain system of the Nan Ling. Running out of northern Yünnan, it reaches eastward as the Tayü Range until about the 116th meridian east, where the mountain system makes a northeastward bend and becomes the Wui Mountains. The general elevations of this Nan Ling system in the eastern sector is from 3,000 to 5,000 feet. From it the land slopes northward to the Yangtze Plain and southward to the Hsi River plain. The latter comprises a network of narrow river floodplains until it fans out into its delta south and east of Canton. Here the so-called Canton Delta spreads over almost 3,000 square miles, the largest and most populous plain south of the Yangtze Plain.

TABLE 14-1   ENGLISH RENDITION OF CHINESE NAMES

Wade-Giles standard	Traditional usage
Ch'ang-sha	Changsha
Ch'in-ling	Tsinling
Ch'ing-tao	Tsingtao
Chou-shan	Chusan
Ch'ung-ch'ing	Chungking
Hang-chou	Hangchow
Hei-lung Chiang	Amur River
Hsi Chiang	Si (West) River
Hsia-men	Amoy
Hsin-chiang	Sinkiang (Chinese Turkestan)
Huang Ho	Yellow River
Kuang-chou	Canton
Kuei-chou	Kweichow
Lu-shun	Port Arthur
Nan-ching	Nanking
Pei-ching	Peking
Shang-hai	Shanghai
Shen-yang	Mukden
Ssu-ch'uan	Szechwan
Sung-hua Chiang	Sungari River
Ta-lien	Dairen
T'ai-wan	Taiwan or Formosa
T'ien-ching	Tientsin
Wu-Han (tri-city)	Hankow, Han-yang, and Wu-ch'ang
Yang-tzu Chiang	Yangtze River

WESTERN PLATEAUS AND BASINS   West of the great plains and the South China hill lands lies the greater part of China's territory. This vast western area generally comprises a number of large plateaus and basin lands of greatly differing characters. Occupying an immense area in the southern part of the far western reaches is one of China's colonial realms, the Tibetan High Plateau, averaging over 12,000 feet in elevation. It is cold, forbidding, and sparsely populated. North of it the land drops into the three great desert basins of Tsaidam, Tarim, and Dzungaria. The first is 9,000 feet high; the latter two are from 1,000 to 4,000 feet above sea level. The Tarim and

Dzungaria are separated by the 18,000 to 20,000-foot-high Tien-Shan Range extending a thousand miles eastward from the Soviet border into China. Still farther eastward from the Tien-Shan stretch the great desert plains of the Mongolian Gobi to the Great Wall of China.

South of the Great Wall, east of the Tibetan High Plateau, and west of the great plains and mountainous south, is an intermediate zone formed by four major topographical units. From north to south, these are the Loess Plateau and valleys, the Central Mountain Block, the Szechwan (Ssu-ch'uan) Basin (also termed the Red Basin), and the Southwest Plateau in Yünnan and Kweichow provinces. Physically speaking, the last one continues into northeastern Burma, where it is called the Shan Plateau, and into northwestern Vietnam and Laos. The Szechwan Basin, supporting over 72 million people, is economically the most important. In its geographical influence upon the climate of the country as a whole, the Central Mountain Block is of the greatest significance.

COASTLINE AND ISLANDS   China's coastline divides roughly into two differing halves. From Shanghai northward most of the coast is flat and low-lying, often suffering inundations during the onshore summer monsoon winds. The only important exceptions are the coast of the hilly Shantung Peninsula and its geologically corresponding Liaotung Peninsula jutting south from Manchuria. Ports on the flat coastlands are few and poor. By contrast, such excellent ports as Tsingtao (Ch'ing-tao) in Shantung and Dairen (Ta-lien) in Liaotung are found along the hilly coasts.

South of Shanghai most of the coast is highly irregular, hilly, and with numerous bays, headlands, and good harbors such as Amoy (Hsia-men) and Hong Kong. Off these hilly coasts also are found most of China's numerous small islands, as well as the two great islands of Taiwan (T'ai-wan) and Hainan. Taiwan is separated by about 170 miles from the mainland and forms part of the western Pacific island arcs. Hainan, on the other hand, is only about 25 miles from the Chiaochou Peninsula and is closely related to the mainland geologically. About 100 miles southeast of Shanghai is the Chusan (Chou-shan) archipelago, noted for its fishing grounds.

CLIMATE AND REGIONAL DIFFERENTIATION

In a general way China may be divided climatically into a higher, dry western half and a lower and more humid eastern half (Figure 14-3). Each half in turn divides generally into two halves north and south with differing climatic characteristics. There are thus four climatic quadrants.

The situation of China is such that most of the moisture obtained by the land is borne in by air masses from the Pacific and, to a lesser extent, from the Indian Ocean. Virtually no moisture is brought in from the Arctic Ocean and only a very small amount comes from the distant Atlantic to water the western frontiers of China. Mongolia, Siberia, and Central Asia build up great pressures of cold air masses because of the high heat radiation during the winters, and the outward movement of these masses brings cold, drying winds to much of China. Winter is not only a season of cold, but also of drought in the north and of greatly decreased rainfall in the south.

During the summer the great heating of the interior of the land mass creates a low atmospheric pressure that draws into the interior warm, humid, maritime and tropical air which furnishes large quantities of rain. Summer in China is the most

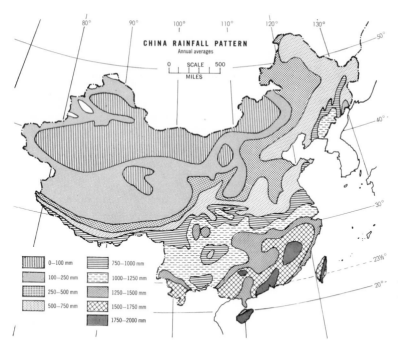

Figure 14-3 The rainfall of China decreases from the coast inland. (One hundred millimeters equals approximately 4 inches.)

important wet season. Several obstacles arise, however, to obstruct the penetration of moist air very far inland. The Himalaya Mountains on the southern rim of the Tibetan High Plateau rob the northward moving air of most of its moisture during the Indian summer monsoon. Although enough moisture blows in along the Brahmaputra Valley into the Ts'ang-pu to give a rainfall that has varied from less than 18 to almost 200 inches per year and has averaged 57.5 inches over a ten-year period, most of Tibet has a low precipitation and is very dry and barren. Evaporation is high because of the large number of clear days and the low humidity. In the western half of Tibet, therefore, streams do not drain out to the sea, but flow into salt lakes.

The high altitude and a southerly location create a climate with great diurnal temperature differences and cold winters. The sunny side and the shady side of a mountain show great temperature differ-

ences. The growing season is limited by the short period between killing frosts.

In the northwestern plains and basins north of the Tibetan High Plateau, precipitation is even more limited and is reduced to 2 to 5 inches annually except on the higher mountain slopes of the Tien-Shan and the Altai, where it may increase to as much as 30 inches. Desert is the characteristic landscape, except in the line of oases that border the Tarim and Dzungarian fringes and in reclaimed portions of the Manass Valley in Dzungaria. Evaporation far exceeds precipitation in most of the area, so that rivers generally become of smaller volume the farther they run, to disappear eventually or flow into shallow salt lakes. Desert gives way to steppe in the moister western part of the Dzungarian Basin and on the northern slopes of the Tien Shan. Even forest growth occurs on slopes from 5,000 to 9,000 feet, above which meadow grasses again furnish feed for grazing livestock.

In the Tarim the climate is more arid, yet warmer because of the protection from northern winds and with a longer growing season. Here, about two-thirds of the population of Chinese Turkestan (Hsin-chiang) make their living in oasis agriculture based upon irrigation.

In the eastern section of the Inner Mongolian region north of the Great Wall, the outer desert of the Gobi gradually changes to steppe as the land comes increasingly within reach of the moist summer monsoon winds from the Pacific. In the vicinity of the Great Wall runs the 14-inch isohyet that moves in wet periods northward into the pastoral nomad land or retreats during dry years to south of the Great Wall. This forms the transition zone between agricultural and pastoral use of the land. Because of exposure to the full force of the Mongolian winter cold waves, extremes of temperatures are great.

In the eastern half of China, moisture decreases generally from the southeast coastal mountain land in a northwesterly direction. It is in this region that the summer monsoon operates most markedly. Its dominance brings about uniformly hot temperatures throughout China in summer. Humidity is much lower in the north, however, and summers are less oppressive.

In eastern China, too, a topographic barrier effects important climatic changes from south to north. Eastward out of the 20,000-foot-high range of the Kunlun (K'un-lun), stretching across the northern Tibetan High Plateau runs the lower but still formidable Tsinling (Ch'in-ling) Range. Forming part of the Central Mountain Block, it first separates the Szechwan Basin from the Loess Plateau with 12,000-foot-high mountains. Then it jogs in a great broken, southeastward arc toward the lower Yangtze at decreasing elevations,

Figure 14-4   Climate graphs of selected stations in China.

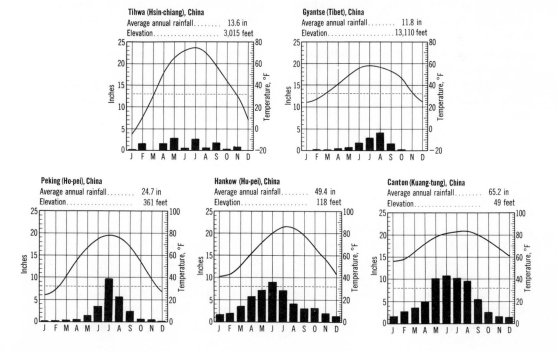

to end in low hills north of the city of Nanking (Nan-ching). The cold, heavy winter air masses of Mongolia cannot surmount the higher portion of this range, so that much of the south is protected during the winter and has mild climates with long growing seasons. This is especially true of the Szechwan Basin, which enjoys an almost year-round growing season. In the lower eastern portions south of the Yellow Plain, cold waves do break through to chill east central and southern China in winter.

In summer, the Tsinling system operates to keep moisture from reaching the north and northwest, so that these areas have a precarious agricultural climate. The cleavage is marked. North of the Tsinling, which continues climatically along the line of the Hwai River, there is a steppe climate of the monsoon type where precipitation ranges from about 30 inches in the south to 14 inches in the vicinity of the Great Wall. Winters are extremely cold, dry, and dusty. Rainfall typically reaches a peak in July, but its occurrence during the growing season is often so irregular that crops may suffer early drought with disastrous results. Violent downpours come upon the easily eroded soils, creating dangerous floods, especially in the lower Yellow Plain north and south of the Shantung hill lands. The growing season varies from 200 to 240 days.

Although northeastern China (Manchuria) does not come under the climatic control of the Tsinling Mountain barrier, its distance from the source of the summer monsoon air masses and the position of the East Manchurian Mountains create a climate similar to that of North China south of the Great Wall, although with lower winter temperatures. Whereas rainfall may be as much as 40 inches on the higher parts of these mountains, on the Manchurian Plain it decreases rapidly from about 30 inches in the lower Liao

Valley to 15 in the northwestern part of the Sungari drainage. The growing season decreases over the same area from about 220 days in the south to about 150 in the northwest.

The more important soils of the north are the calcareous loess of the Loess Plateau, the loess-derived alluvial silts of the Yellow Plain and the valleys of the Loess Plateau region, and the light chestnut and dark prairie earths of Manchuria. To the north of the Tsinling line, steppe and prairie grasses probably form the most widespread original vegetation, although, in the mountains, forests occur.

South of the Tsinling divide, the earth becomes covered with a year-round green vegetation where it is uncultivated. Rainfall in the Yangtze Valley is over 40 inches and increases toward the South China coast to over 60 inches, with much higher amounts in the mountains. Whereas the monsoon brings in most of this moisture, precipitation is caused not only by orography and convection, but also by eastward-moving cyclonic storms. The winter season is mild and also has some precipitation, although it is definitely the driest season. April and May have excessive humidity and are known as the mouldy period, especially all along the Yangtze Valley.

South of the Nan Ling there is no cold weather of a severe type, although temperatures may drop to 40°F at Hong Kong and Canton. Here is a monsoon type of humid subtropical climate, where typical tropical plants may grow. On the 6,000-foot-high Yünnan Plateau to the west and generally in the same latitudes, the climate is one of the most pleasant in China. By contrast, the 2,000-foot-lower Kweichow (Kuei-chou) Plateau is often shrouded in fog, and its valley lands are hot and humid in summer. Off the coast, Hainan Island has a maritime tropical climate, whereas

Taiwan Island to the north has a maritime subtropical regime.

As a whole, the soils south of the Tsinling divide tend to be badly leached. Most of the southern slope lands have sterile red or yellow earths. The alluvial river plains have relatively fertile soils which have been greatly modified through long cultivation, especially in the water-soaked paddy fields. The Szechwan Basin has an exceptional status because its limestone-mixed purplish-red sedimentary earths provide a fertile soil, making possible the most intensive type of slope cultivation. Terracing for paddy rice is highly developed here.

HISTORICAL DEVELOPMENT

China is a land of many cultures and ethnic groups, among which, today, the "orthodox" or Han Chinese form the dominant and most widespread group, comprising over 94 per cent of the population. Some 40 million minority peoples are distributed in the outlying provinces and territories of the south, west, and north. The origin of the Chinese is obscure, but they are believed to have emerged from the northwestern desert oases and to have moved eastward into the region of the lower bend of the Yellow River, where its tributaries, the Wei Ho and Fen Ho, have created alluvial plains north of the Tsinling Range. The earliest reliable Chinese historical records reveal settlement in this plain before 1400 B.C. From here the people expanded eastward into the Yellow Plain and later into the rest of modern China.

Chinese expansion naturally faced the hostility of the different ethnic groups which already occupied the territory that is now China, just as European expansion in the Americas faced the hostility of the American Indians. At the same time, the higher civilization and technology developed by the Chinese attracted the admiration of the tribal peoples. The result was that the large masses of these tribal peoples gradually lost their original cultures and became Chinese. Certain tribes or ruling clans, however, always desired to retain their own cultural dominance. When they found themselves unsuccessful in opposing the Chinese advance, they migrated or fled to mountain fastnesses in areas more distant from Han Chinese power. Thus, we find that in China today, the unassimilated T'ai ethnic groups have made their last stands in the most southwestern and southern frontier regions, while the Miao, Yao, and Yi (Lolo) exist in the higher, less desirable slope lands of the south and southwest.

Historically, in contrast to the steady Chinese population push against the lesser ethnic groups of the south, the Han Chinese have been the object of pressure from the northern and northwestern pastoral peoples. This pressure may be attributable to the difference in security of livelihood between the climatically bountiful south and the precarious steppelands of the north. On many occasions, that insecurity impelled the northern and northwestern nomads to federate themselves and invade the more productive and more densely settled agricultural realm. Thus, during about half of Chinese history, the nomadic or seminomadic peoples became the rulers of much or all of China. Since as a people they were almost literally born to the saddle, mastery of the strategy of mobility may have helped them to achieve success despite great numerical inferiority. Such people were the Mongols and the Manchus. The Manchu conquerors, however, retained empire over the Chinese only at the cost of accepting conquest by Chinese culture.

Tibet, Mongolia, Chinese Turkestan,

and Manchuria were united with China under Manchu rule but were not considered parts of China proper. When the Han Chinese overthrew the Manchu rulers, they also had to take vigorous military steps to keep these colonial regions from breaking away, for in the outer territories, it was only in Manchuria that Chinese formed the majority of the population. The political disintegration of the Manchu empire gave opportunities for foreign imperial interests to intervene both within China proper and in these outlying colonial territories. At the same time, revolutionary ideas from America and Europe were stirring Han Chinese intellectuals into a ferment. Aside from China proper, where most of the powers wished to bring their influence to bear, Russian interests found outlets in all the Chinese colonial realms, since they were along her Siberian and Central Asian frontiers. The British who were in occupation of India intervened in Tibet, and Japan competed with Russia to control the political and economic destiny of Manchuria and, to a lesser extent, Mongolia.

Taiwan has a somewhat special situation owing to its relatively recent occupation by the Han Chinese. The original inhabitants were unorganized primitive tribes of Malaysian people. During the sixteenth century, Japanese pirates had their lairs on the coasts of Taiwan. Portuguese and Dutch explorers made settlements on it, only to be driven out by refugee settlers from China fleeing from Manchu conquest during the middle of the seventeenth century. The Manchus finally extended their sovereignty to Taiwan, but no great development occurred aside from the gradual migration to Taiwan of mainland Chinese farmers, largely from Fukien (Fu-chien) province. More rapid economic development took place after Japan gained control of the island as a prize of

the Sino-Japanese War of 1894–1895. However, the population remained largely Han Chinese. On this basis Taiwan was returned to the existing government of China after World War II.[1]

Among the 40 million minority nationals and colonial peoples of China there are more than 50 officially distinguished ethnic groups with their differing languages. Aside from these, the "orthodox" Han Chinese, though united by a single written language, are divided by seven or eight major spoken languages which are more or less mutually unintelligible to their speakers. Most of these different tongues are in the southeastern coastal hill lands, where isolation has had an important effect upon their development.

POPULATION AND LIVELIHOOD

China has had a large population for 2,000 years; even during the Han Dynasty in the pre-Christian era, official registers claimed a population of 60 million. That the present population is less than thirteen times that of 2,000 years ago indicates the limitations of the existing agricultural technology and the prevalence of Malthusian checks to population growth. Traditional tools and implements present definite limitations to the amount of land a farmer can handle, and this handicap forces him to cultivate only the better soils in order to earn a living. The result has been an excessive concentration of population upon the plains and irrigable valleys and therefore very uneven distribution of people.

Since about 80 per cent of China's population are farm people, the population distribution corresponds closely to the distribution of cultivated land. Some 250 million people are settled on the great

---

[1] Taiwan is now independent of Communist China.

CHINA

Moderately to densely populated agricultural land
(including industrial and urban areas).

INNER MONGOLIAN AUTONOMOUS REGION

SINKIANG

ORDOS

Yellow River

CHINGHAI

Yellow River

TIBET

WEST

Yangtze River

SSUCHUAN

SCALE

0   300

MILES

YÜNNAN

Si River

TAIWAN

HAINAN
ISLAND

*Figure 14-5   The most densely populated rural areas of China are the fertile river valleys
and floodplains.*

Yellow and Yangtze Plains (Figure 14-5). About 50 million are settled on the Manchurian plains. In the Szechwan Basin are another 72 million. Other smaller, heavily populated plains and lowlands include the Wei and Fen plains in the Loess Plateau region, and the various coastal delta plains of southeastern China, especially the Canton Delta.

About 25 per cent of China's population, including some farm people, live in towns and cities, and about 10 per cent

live in large cities. Some of the major metropolitan areas that have developed in China rank with the greatest cities of the world. Fourteen cities had more than 1 million inhabitants each in 1957. Shanghai led with 6.9 million, followed by Peking with over 4 million. The remaining twelve were as follows:

Tientsin (T'ien-ching)	3,220,000
Mukden (Shen-yang)	2,411,000
Wuhan (Hankow, Wu-ch'ang, Han-yang)	2,146,000

Chungking (Ch'ung-ch'ing)	2,121,000
Canton (Kuang-chou)	1,840,000
Harbin	1,552,000
Dairen–Port Arthur (Ta-lien and Lu-shun)	1,508,000
Nanking (Nan-ching)	1,419,000
Sian (Hsi-an or Ch'ang-an)	1,310,000
Tsingtao (Ch'ing-tao)	1,121,000
Ch'engtu	1,107,000
T'aiyüan	1,020,000

(Others nearing 1,000,000 each in 1960 were Fushun and Ch'angch'un in Manchuria.)

Intensive use of hand labor is characteristic of all Chinese farming but is especially true of southern paddy agriculture. A smaller unit of arable land can provide a livelihood for a family in the south because of the ample rainfall and the long growing season which permits double- or triple-cropping during one year on the same piece of land. Thus the greater density of population per unit of arable land in the south does not necessarily indicate greater population pressure there. In the dry and unreliable climate of the north, a lower density per acre may actually coincide with a more marginal standard of living. It may generally be said, however, that the arable land already is supporting the maximum population that can exist on its present productivity with still tolerable standards of living. In the Canton Delta there is less than 0.2 of an acre of cultivated land per person; in the Yangtze Valley required acreage is larger and becomes about 0.4 of an acre; the Yellow Plain has little more per person. In the steppe margins outside the Great Wall, the amount of cultivated land may rise to 1.5 acres per person where agriculture is not mechanized, indicating the greater land area needed for subsistence. Possibly, in Manchuria the density may be lower in relation to the capacity of the land; the mechanization of part of the farming in

state farms here has also decreased average densities.

After millenniums of trial-and-error learning, crops in the various argricultural regions were selected in the pre-Communist era by the farmers to fit the geographical environment of particular localities. Since cultural preference in food has centered upon rice, it has become the dominant crop wherever water availability, soil type, and growing season have combined to permit its cultivation. However, in non-rice lands a variety of crops prevailed because farmers tried to spread their risk. After the Communist regime took over, there was a considerable reduction in the complexity of crop patterns as the Communist agricultural planners tried to rationalize the system to fit planned goals. Efforts were made, with mixed success, to adapt crops to the most suitable soils, and conversely, increased areas under irrigation schemes made it possible to plant rice and other crops more extensively in areas formerly not so used, so that overall crop patterns have been somewhat altered. However, because conditions favorable to rice north of the Tsinling Range are restricted, it is grown chiefly in limited alluvial lands and in oasis areas where ample water is available.

In the north, dry cultivation is the rule, and there is more variety in important crops. The dominant food crops are wheat, millet, kaoliang (grain sorghum), and soybeans. Most of these are grown in the south as well, and crops of barley, maize, sweet potatoes, and many varieties of beans and vegetables are also important.

In much of the Manchurian Plain and the northwest parts of the loess land, low precipitation and cool climate favor the dominance of spring wheat, millet, and kaoliang; soybeans are a prominent export of the Manchurian Plain. South of the Great Wall, winter wheat, kaoliang, and millet are most important. Between the Tsinling Mountain–Hwai River climatic divide and the Yangtze is a transitional zone where winter wheat and summer rice crops are most important. In the rest of South China and the Szechwan Basin, where irrigation water can be led to fields, rice is everywhere the summer crop (Figure 14-6). Rice terraces are common on lower hills, slopes, and mountain ravines. In the winter, wheat, barley, and oilseed plants may be cropped on drained rice fields. South of the Nan Ling, two crops of rice, and sometimes a third, may be grown on a field in one year.

Some regional specialties include the cotton crops in the southeastern part of the Yellow Plain and the northeastern part of the lower Yangtze Plain, the tobacco of Shantung, the sugar cane of Taiwan, Kwangtung, and Szechwan, the tung oil of Szechwan and Hunan, the tea of the southeastern coastal provinces, mulberry (for silkworm feeding) in the lower Yangtze Plain and adjacent hills, and the tropical fruits of the southernmost provinces and of the two main islands. In the northwestern desert oases, almost every annual crop in China is represented, and cotton, grapes, raisins, tree fruits, nuts, and melons are local specialties.

For ages the family has been the cornerstone of Chinese society. Families cared for their unfortunates, and members of a family stood together for mutual benefit. Deference was paid to parents, the educated, and the elderly. On the death of a property owner all the sons shared equally in his land. This custom resulted in minute subdivision of land, a man's holdings often being separated into tiny plots scattered among his neighbors, and it also created land waste and labor inefficiency. Although the Communist collectivized farming has improved these aspects of land ownership, it has also resulted in loss of incentive to production and to land improvement. Millions of disillusioned and discontented farmers have left their dispossessed collective farms and migrated to urban centers to bring rapid rises in city populations. Many of these people were subsequently compelled to return to the farm areas. Most Chinese live in villages, and farmers use much time in going to and from their fields. Hand methods of culture and the use of simple equipment pulled by an ox or water buffalo remain prevalent, since mechanization has made only limited headway. The maximum

Figure 14-6 A field of rice on a Chinese mainland commune, showing close-planting technique. (Courtesy of Hsin-hua News Agency.)

Figure 14-7   A pineapple plantation on newly constructed terraces of leached soil in Kwangtung province of South China. (Courtesy of Hsin-hua News Agency.)

yield from land is sought with disregard for the human labor required. For example, transplanting rice from seedbeds shortens the time the crop occupies a field and permits multiple crops. In South China two crops of rice are grown, and between these, quick-maturing plantings of vegetables are often harvested. In central China two grain crops also are grown, but only one is rice; the other is wheat or another grain. Under the Communists, the typical small farms have been consolidated, and the work on the resulting larger farms is being done by communal groups using improved equipment when available. The mechanization that has been introduced is spotty and limited, being mainly in parts of the great plains of the Yellow River, Inner Mongolia, Sinkiang and Manchuria. Only 5 to 10 per cent of the agricultural land is worked substantially by machines and mechanical equipment.

Living in small farm villages or working for low wages in towns and cities, hundreds of millions of Chinese exist at a bare subsistence level. It is no accident that the common traditional greeting in hungry China has been: "Have you eaten your rice?" rather than "How do you do?"

RESOURCES

The demands of a large population as well as other needs have been responsible for the destruction of most of the forests of China. They have long since disappeared. As a result, in most of the mountain lands no seed-bearing trees remain to reforest the slopes, which are mostly covered with grass, fern, and shrub. Today, important forests are found only in remote parts of the southwestern mountains, in the northern and eastern Manchurian mountain lands, and in mountainous parts of the southeastern coastlands. In South China bamboo is very widespread and is a most important plant for house construction and for a wide variety of other uses.

Fishing is an important occupation along most of the coastal waters and on inland streams and lakes. Because of the limited number of modern fishing vessels, large-scale commerical and deep-sea fishing has had slow development. South of the lower Yangtze, fish-pond culture is a sideline on many collective farms.

On the basis of general geological sur-veys it is believed that China has a moderately good supply of the basic resources needed for modern industrialization. The country has vast quantities of some materials but is deficient in others. Thus China claims second or third rank in the world's coal resources, but her known petroleum fields are inadequate for her needs, though 1964 drilling in Manchuria has added a large supply. Her iron ore reserves in 1962 were claimed to be about 20 billion tons, but many of the deposits are small and of low quality.

The reserves of coal and iron are highly concentrated in single regions. Almost 70 per cent of the coal reserves are in the Loess Plateau provinces on both sides of the Yellow River, where it runs south from its great northern bend. About 50 per cent of presently known iron ore reserves are in southern Manchuria. The Ta-yeh iron mines near Wuhan are reported to be among the world's largest. Most of the exploitation of both coal and iron has been in the area with the best transportation facilities, that is, in south Manchuria, near the sea just north of the Tientsin (T'ien-ching) region, in the Shantung hill

Figure 14-8 Artisans saw and split bamboo for houses and furniture construction in Szechwan province. Bamboo is one of the most versatile and useful plants in Eastern and Southern Asia. (Courtesy of H. J. Wiens.)

land not far from Tsingtao (Ch'ing-tao), and in the Loess Plateau.

Although China needs most of the minerals it produces, the country has a surplus of certain strategic items such as antimony, tungsten, and tin. In the regional distribution of minerals, the north and northeast have most of the coal and iron, the south and southwest the major part of the ferroalloys and nonferrous metals. Abundant ores for the magnesium and aluminum industries are found both in the north and in the south.

Petroleum appears to be found mainly in the northwest desert lands, in Manchuria, and in Szechwan. Oil shale is exploited chiefly in southern Manchuria and at Maoming south of Canton. Together with coal, petroleum and oil shale may form the base for synthetic fuels. Water power potential, in which China claims second world rank, is mainly in the south, but it

Figure 14-9   Construction on a major concrete hydroelectric dam and power plant providing ½ million-kilowatt capacity of power generation on a tributary of the Ch'ien-t'ang River in Chekiang province southwest of Shanghai. (Courtesy of Hsin-hua News Agency.)

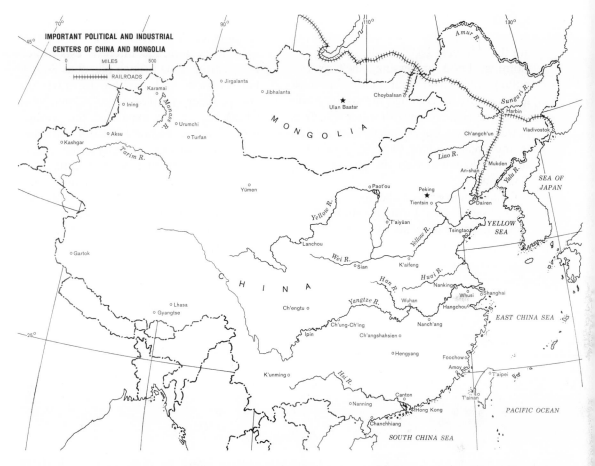

Figure 14-10   The cities and industrial centers are confined largely to China Proper and Manchuria.

is largely undeveloped. Several excellent sites exist for large-scale power development, the most noted being the Yangtze Gorge site, with a reported potential of 13 million kilowatts.

As for minerals, one may say that China has the basis for a considerable degree of industrialization, although per capita mineral wealth is not high. Retarded development may be attributed to past political instability and internal disunity, the lack of large capital accumulations for investments, difficulties in communications, and

social factors inherent in traditional Chinese culture. Rapid mineral exploitation has occurred since 1950.

MANUFACTURING

Although modern industries have made much progress in China, it is safe to assume that about three-fourths of China's domestic needs for manufactured and processed materials are still supplied by traditional handicrafts and home industries, which are now organized as communal or collectivized rather than as private enterprises. The leading industries are those serving basic needs for food and clothing. Food processing, such as rice milling and wheat flour milling, is most important. Rice is milled mostly by traditional methods, often with water wheels as power sources, but wheat flour is ground in the great modern flour mills of cities such as Shanghai, Tientsin, Hankow, and Tsingtao.

China's masses need cheap cotton cloth. Household looms formerly supplied almost the entire demand, but the introduc-tion of modern machinery led to a decay in this branch of home industry. Foreign as well as domestic interests established large cotton mills in such places as Shanghai, Tientsin, and Tsingtao to utilize the cheap labor sources there. Communist China has greatly expanded the production of cotton textiles, which are China's foremost modern industry; the above three cities, together with Peking, Sian, and Urumchi in the north and northwest, are leading textile producers. Silks are especially concentrated in the southern part of the Yangtze delta and at Canton.

Figure 14-11 Blast furnaces of the Pen-chi iron and steel plant in southern Manchuria, where mainland China has her most important heavy-industry concentration. (Courtesy of Hsin-hua News Agency.)

Modern heavy industries such as those connected with chemicals, iron and steel, and machine manufacturing have developed to the greatest extent in southern Manchuria. These industries owe much of their initial growth to the efforts of Japan, which seized the area in 1931 and tried to build up a continental base for political and military expansion in Eastern Asia.

South of the Great Wall, the region from Peking eastward through Tientsin to Shanhaikwan (Shan-hai-kuan), where the Great Wall comes to the sea, is another important area for industries based upon the coal mines located there. Cement, chemicals, glass, and a variety of light industries are found in the larger cities and towns of the area, as well as some iron smelting and steel working. The great labor concentrations in Peking and Tientsin are especially important. Since 1955 the Chinese Communists have built an important iron and steel center at Paotow (Pao-t'ou) outside the Great Wall in Inner Mongolia. A major oil refining and chemical center has also developed at Lanchow (Lan-chou) in Kansu province.

In central China the Hankow (Wu Han) metropolitan area is an important center for iron- and steelmaking, flour milling, dried egg processing, vegetable oil pressing, and textile manufacturing. Farther westward in Szechwan, most of the industrial concentrations are around Chungking (Ch'ung-ch'ing), with a less important region around and south of the provincial capital at Chengtu (Ch'eng-tu). Antimony refining and light industries are found at Changsha (Ch'ang-sha) south of Tung Ting (Tung-t'ing) Lake.

In the triangle formed by Nanking, Shanghai, and Hangchow (Hang-chou) on the lower Yangtze Plain, there is an industrial complex specializing in silk and cotton fabrics; it includes also a great multitude of light industries as well as heavy industry and steelmaking at Shanghai and a major chemicals concentration at Nanking.

In the south, the Canton area and British Hong Kong form the nuclei for a variety of similar light industries, ceramics, shipbuilding, and sugar refining. Sugar refining is even more important on Taiwan. Under Japanese occupation, Taiwan reached a higher stage of industrial development than was attained in the China mainland as a whole. This per capita lead has been maintained since the Nationalist Republic of China established its headquarters on Taiwan. Nevertheless, although only about 50 to 55 per cent of the population on Taiwan are engaged in farming, most Taiwan industries are concerned with food processing. This island is one of the largest world exporters of canned pineapple as well as of sugar. Moderate coal supplies are available, and a large petroleum refining plant utilizes imported crude oil. Hydroelectric power is also important on Taiwan, where a long-established plant manufactures aluminum from imported ore. The manufacture of cotton textiles is one of the leading industries. The one good natural harbor and the port for Taipei (T'ai-pei) is Keelung (Chi-lung), where ships and tankers up to 36,000 tons have been built. Both on the mainland and on Taiwan some automotive manufacturing has been begun.

These examples of modern manufacturing are listed to show that industrialization is making advances in Chinese economic life; but the country has only started on the road to industrialization in the Western sense. In certain key commodities such as cotton textiles, village and home industries have been displaced; in other areas, home industries still play a most important role in filling domestic needs, although on mainland China private organization has been supplanted by collective and state control. The Chinese, by and large, are still mainly farmers.

COMMUNICATIONS AND TRADE

China's communications system has always been inadequate to cope with her geographical immensity and topographic and climatic irregularities. Traditional means of communication are slow and expensive. The value of bulk commodities often could pay for their own transport only for a short distance beyond river or coastal boat transportation. Rutted dirt roads in the north, which become impassable mires in rainy periods, require five times the animal power for pulling carts than would be needed on hard-surfaced roads. In the south, the mountainous character of the land formerly made wheeled vehicles a rarity except in large plains areas. Roads followed the most direct route over mountain ridges and required stone steps. Human carriers and pack animals carried freight and passengers. Fortunately, most of the larger streams of China south of the Tsinling are navigable to flat-bottomed craft over great distances. In the north, winter freezing, low rainfall, high silting, and shifting channels limit the usefulness of rivers. Here wheeled vehicles have been the traditional form of transport.

Railroad construction in China was begun in the late nineteenth century as a result of pressure by Western and Japanese interests wishing to exploit the new materials and markets of China. Because of the strategic and economic importance of Manchuria, historical events have made the railway net here the best in China, and 43 per cent of the 16,650 miles of railroad in 1952 were located in this north-eastern sector of the country. North China had 23 per cent of the mileage, central China 12 per cent, and southeastern mainland China 7 per cent. As a result of Japanese construction, Taiwan then had about 12 per cent of China's railways. Additional construction in the six years following had added 2,732 miles of rail by 1958. Important new construction included the Szechwan railroad from Chungking to Chengtu and extended across the Tsinling to connect with the northwest railroad to Urumchi. A new line also connects the Paotow region with Siberia via the Outer Mongolian capital of Ulan Bator.

Vast areas of China are entirely without railroad facilities. These are mainly in the western half of China, although the southwest and south also are sparsely served. International connections run to North Vietnam, North Korea, Vladivostok on the Soviet Pacific, and Outer Mongolia. China constructs most of her own railway cars as well as some locomotives.

Motor highway construction was launched as a flood-relief project in 1920, but the highway net grew rather slowly because of the high cost of vehicles, gasoline, and oil, most of which had to be imported. However, the Chinese governments have recognized the need for highway development and have added rapidly to the highway net. These include such noteworthy highways as the Burma Road and the Northwest Highway. Highways are generally only dirt-surfaced and often unusable during rainy periods. The highway net has reached about 130,000 miles. A Soviet-constructed motor vehicle factory in southern Manchuria had an annual production reaching 20,000 units in 1959. Most of the vehicles are trucks.

As a result of construction by both Japanese and Chinese military forces during World War II, all major Chinese cities and numerous strategic, though lesser, places have airfields.

China's early trade with the outside world was in high-cost, low-weight, low-bulk commodities such as silk, tea, and opium. Even in the early decades of this century, raw silk was the most consistently important export, with tea ranking next. The rise of cheaper, bulkier raw-material products marked changing export trends in the 1930s. In 1936 silk had dropped by two-thirds because of Japanese competition, and tung oil led all exports, followed by ores and minerals such as tungsten, tin, and antimony. In the 1910 period, cotton goods amounted to nearly one-third of China's imports, but they declined as modern textile manufacturing grew in the large coastal cities. By contrast, such items as metals and machinery, chemicals, kerosene, gasoline, and motor vehicles became increasingly important.

Foreign trade in Communist China is a state monopoly. Postwar imports of the Communist regime have reflected the austerity the Chinese masses have to face to achieve the planned industrial transformation. Large grain and soybean exports up to 3 million tons a year and other agricultural products were sent to the Soviet Union and other Soviet bloc countries in return for complete sets of factory equipment, vehicles, and chemical raw materials. The chief imports from non-Communist countries were rubber, petroleum, fertilizers, and chemicals. After the Korean conflict, the American-initiated embargo restricted Communist imports of strategic materials and equipment from the non-Communist industrial countries.

Up to 1958, from 70 to 80 per cent of Communist trade was with the Soviet bloc countries, and had a value of about $3.5 billion. Subsequent to political conflict with the Soviet Union and because of the drop in agricultural production, total trade declined significantly, and the Soviet portion of the total also declined. China's food needs resulted in major purchases of grain from Canada, Australia, and France. At the same time, China has been striving to increase exports of manufactured goods to the less-developed countries of Asia, Africa, and Latin America.

First among the historically important ports of China is Shanghai, the outlet for the huge Yangtze drainage area; for many years it handled half of the country's trade. Canton has been the major Chinese outlet for South China, although Hong Kong, with greatly superior harbor facilities, has been at once a rival and a transshipment port for Canton. Although Hong Kong no longer occupies the former position of chief supplier for the southeast China ports, its function as a port of entry and distributor for Canton is still significant for Communist China. Tientsin is the most important gateway for the Yellow Plain, although Tsingtao draws off some of this hinterland trade. In southern Manchuria, Dairen (Ta-lien) has been the commercial port of first rank. Dairen, Tsingtao, and Yülin on Hainan Island are important naval and submarine bases.

THE MONGOLIAN PEOPLE'S REPUBLIC

RELIEF FEATURES

The Mongolian People's Republic is the name given by the Communists to the area traditionally called Outer Mongolia. Its separation from Inner Mongolia has no physical basis either in topography or climate and is justified mainly on the rather tenuous grounds of tribal and dialect divisions among the Mongolian peoples concerned (Figure 14-12). In the west, the Altai Mountains constitute a natural boundary separating the Dzungarian Basin and Soviet Kazakhstan from the Kobdo Basin of Outer Mongolia. The country as a whole is part of the great Mongolian Plateau and ranges in altitude from 4,000 to 6,000 feet, although the central Khangai and Tarbagaty Mountains have elevations up to 9,000 feet, and the Altai rise above 10,000. Much of the south and southeast are rather level plains arranged in large shallow basins, or "gobi," often with great patches of barren desert pavement. The western third of Outer Mongolia forms a large basin containing many salt lakes, and the northern frontiers of the country have such mountains as the Sayan, Tanu Ola, and Kentei Ranges.

Since the atmospheric moisture for this area is derived from the distant Atlantic Ocean or from the scanty evaporation from the Arctic, the precipitation decreases the farther south the land extends. Near the northern frontiers, rainfall averages between 10 and 12 inches. At Ulan Bator (Urga), the capital, it has dropped to about 8 inches. The southern half gets less than 5 inches; the southwestern Gobi and the Kobdo Basin receive about 2 to 3 inches or less.

Only the rivers draining from the northern slopes of the Khangai and northern mountains find their way to the sea after running into Siberian lakes and rivers. The vegetation pattern corresponds

Figure 14-12   The Gobi dominates the southern part of Mongolia. Note that rivers and cities are mostly in the northern part of the country.

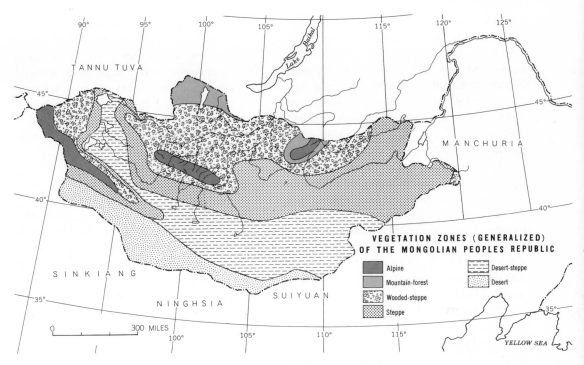

Figure 14-13   The vegetation zones of Mongolia are transition areas between those of the U.S.S.R. and China. Note that in general they extend in an east-west direction.

closely with the rainfall pattern (Figure 14-13). The southwest Gobi region and much of the Kobdo Basin floor have only xerophytic shrubs and grasses. Toward the east of the Gobi, sparse short grass and bunch grass furnish scanty fodder for grazing animals after the early summer rains. Beginning with central Mongolia and proceeding northward, we find that the land gradually provides a more flourishing steppe-grass cover until rather luxuriant grasslands are reached in northern Mongolia. In the higher mountains even forests thrive where they are protected from the ax. With the exception of southwestern Mongolia and drier parts of the Kobdo Basin, Outer Mongolia may be described as one vast range land, much of it eminently suitable for grazing livestock, in what is typically continental steppe climate.

THE PASTORAL ECONOMY

During the first decades of this century, an estimated 13 million domestic animals grazed the Mongolian plains to furnish a livelihood to about 800,000 Mongols. By 1941 the animal numbers had grown to more than 27 million. However, in 1955 the number had dropped to 23 million head. By 1961 the total had been increased by only 2 million. More than two-thirds of the livestock were sheep and goats; sheep in 1955 numbered 13 million. Cattle and horses numbered 1.8 and 2.2 million respectively, and there were about 851,000 camels. The sheep has a significant position. The Mongol drinks its milk, eats its meat and the cheese made from its milk, uses its wool for clothing, felt shoes, and tents, and burns its dung for fuel. Because most of Mongolia is climatically unsuitable for agriculture, the Mongol must adapt himself to the needs of his flocks and seek new pastures as old ones become exhausted. Among the characteristic developments of Mongol nomadism is the yurt, a light and collapsible felt tent that furnishes adequate protection from the fierce winter winds and the −43°F temperatures that may occur.

The Mongol meets many problems in his attempt to make a living. He must adapt himself to great continental extremes of heat and cold. Surface water is scarce and must be supplemented by shallow wells, the water of which often may be brackish. Hard-crusted snow and winter blizzards often bring about heavy losses of livestock through starvation. Natural enemies such as wolves, animal parasites, and diseases may kill off large percentages of the shepherd's flocks and herds. Finally, there is a point of saturation in the capacity of the grasslands to support livestock, so that increased human population must find other means of support or starve. Chinese and Russian efforts to introduce agriculture in the past have met with little success. Today about 1,500,000 acres of land may be in cultivation in the northern humid areas, much of it around Ulan Bator.

Under Soviet influence, continuing attempts are being made to force the nomad to a more sedentary mode of life in which improvements can be carried out more effectively and political control facilitated. Industrial, agricultural, mining, and other technicians from the Soviet Union help direct the present development of the Mongolian People's Republic and the exploitation of Outer Mongolia's resources, although more and more Mongols are becoming trained to carry on such work. Desire for the mineral wealth of the Tannu Tuva sector of Mongolia resulted in its annexation by the Soviet Union in 1946 after more than a decade of Soviet occupation. The other parts of northern Mongolia also have significant mineral wealth, including coal mines presently supplying Ulan Bator's electric power generator and its few manufacturing and processing plants. Coal and oil are also found in the southeastern Gobi.

HISTORICAL DEVELOPMENT

The Mongols became prominent in history at the beginning of the thirteenth century when their famous leader, Genghis Khan, united the divided tribesmen of the steppes through skillful political intrigues and military prowess and launched one of the most amazing empires of all time. This empire proved too large and loosely knit to hold together for long, and Mongol power rapidly declined. In the fourteenth and fifteenth centuries, after the Mongols were driven out of China, the Yellow sect of Lama Buddhism took a firm hold among the Mongols. Church power gained at the expense of the ruling nobles, and the tradition developed that every family should have at least one son in the priesthood. In contrast to the nomadic existence of the Mongols as a whole, the monasteries became the focus of the only large fixed settlements in the country. Some of them had thousands of monks, who were, for the most part, a nonproductive, parasitic element burdening the economy. Today most of the lamaseries have been greatly reduced, and the nobles have been eliminated.

Mongolia became a protectorate of the Manchu rulers in 1691, but when the Chinese revolution of 1911 overthrew the Manchu empire, the Mongol chieftains declared their tie with China dissolved. Although the succeeding Chinese governments refused to recognize this dissolution, Russian and subsequent Soviet intervention, especially since 1931, gradually brought Outer Mongolia into the Soviet orbit during a period of Chinese political and military weakness. Soviet pressure in 1945 forced a reluctant Nationalist Chinese recognition of Outer Mongolian independence from China, but this recognition was repudiated in 1953 by the Nationalists on Taiwan. The Republic of China on Taiwan took the position that Soviet aid to the Chinese Communist rebels in 1947–1949 and Soviet control in Outer Mongolia invalidated the treaty whereby China relinquished sovereignty. Communist China, however, continued to recognize the separation of Outer Mongolia from Chinese sovereignty. Because of the region's historical and political-economic ties to China, rivalry between China and the Soviet Union for influence and dominance in Outer Mongolia may well continue.

Strategically, Outer Mongolia occupies a dominating position in Central Asia. The northern frontiers are only about 100 miles from the vital Trans-Siberian Railway. From southwestern Mongolia, traditionally, it has been easy to cut off access to Sinkiang (Hsinchiang) from China proper via the Kansu (Kan-su) Corridor. In the east, the Great Hsingan Mountains of Manchuria rise little above the plateau edge and have commanding routes into the Manchurian plains. There is no significant topographic obstacle to the advance of mechanized forces from the Mongolian plains southward into China. The levelness of much of the country and the hard pavement of the surfaces in many places permit aircraft landings with minimum or virtually no preparation. It is small wonder that Soviet Russia has been and is eager to maintain its dominance over this strategic country.

THE REPUBLIC OF KOREA

RELIEF FEATURES

Topographically, Korea is an elongated block tilted from northeast to southwest, with an area of 85,286 square miles. Its greatest length is about 450 miles and its width from 100 to 150 miles. North of the 40th parallel, most of it is a deeply incised plateau and mountain land forming part of the East Manchurian Mountains. In the central part of this north section lies the Kaima Plateau at an elevation of some 5,000 to 6,000 feet. A mountain backbone not exceeding this height, known as the Taebaek (Tae-baek) Range, follows the east coast the length of the peninsula. The highest elevation is about 9,000 feet on the dead volcanic peak of Baek-tu San, which lies on the Manchurian frontier between the sources of the Yalu (Ya-lu) and Tumen Rivers. Cutting across the peninsula from Seoul northward to the east coast port of Wōnsan (Won-san) (Figure 14-14) is a lowland corridor or depressed valley that forms a strategic communications route.

The westward dip and the situation of the high-water divide less than 30 miles from the east coast bring short, steep drops to the streams flowing into the deep Japan Sea, with small alluvial plains near their mouths. Most of the drainage flows westward, except in the southern part and where the river valleys trend southward. The slope of the land is more gradual, and the alluvial plains widen where the rivers deposit their silt-laden waters into the shallow Yellow Sea. The agricultural development, therefore, has largely been in the western and southern parts of the country. Here level land is more abundant.

Because of the land connection of northern Korea along a broad front, the

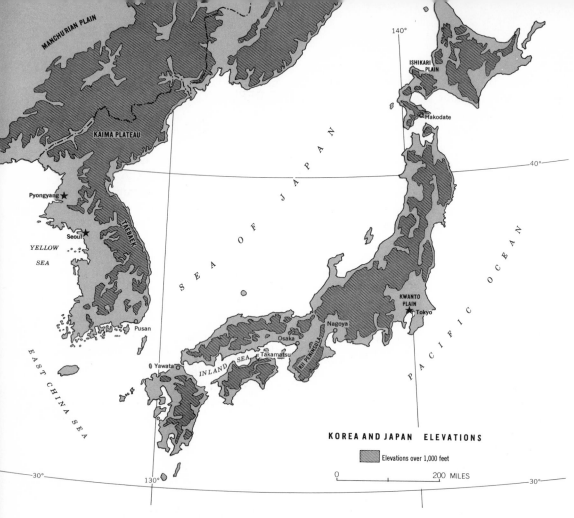

Figure 14-14 The interior of each of the principal islands of Japan has elevations greater than 1,000 feet. In Korea the highest land is in the north and along the east side of the peninsula. In both countries the highlands cause transportation problems.

continental climatic influence is strongly felt, and the higher elevation of the north also increases the severity of winter extremes. By contrast, the southern maritime parts of Korea have a mild marine climate, owing to the effect of the warm Japan Current bathing its shores. Although southern Korea is almost 300 miles north of Shanghai, its mild climate resembles that of the lower Yangtze Plain. Climatic contrasts between north and south are analogous to those between North China and the Yangtze Plain. Along

the northeastern coastlands, the cold currents moving southwestward from the Tatar Strait chill the atmosphere and produce damp, gloomy, and often foggy weather that restricts some forms of agriculture. There also is a striking contrast between the tidal rise of 2 or 3 feet along the eastern coast and the differences of over 20 feet between low and high tide along the western coast where the inrolling tide piles up the water in the shallow Yellow Sea. The tide creates difficulties for shipping in the western ports.

AGRICULTURE

Since in Korea, as in China and Japan, rice is the cultural preference in the staple diet, it is raised wherever possible. The rainfall ranges from less than 20 inches in the northeast coastal region to over 60 on the southern mountain slopes. Paddy rice, therefore, is chiefly a southern crop, although it is found in low-lying alluvial land in the north, including the Yalu Valley (Figure 14-15). Millet and winter wheat are most important in northern Korea; soybeans are grown everywhere. Barley, which takes up about three-fifths as much land as paddy rice, is the second most important crop, and its cultivation, too, is largely concentrated in the southwest part of the peninsula. The sweet

Figure 14-15   Plowing with yellow oxen in harvested wet-rice fields in Korea. The seeding season begins about the middle of April and ends in early May. (Courtesy of Korean Research and Information Office.)

potato is also an important crop in the south. Wheat is most important in the great peninsula jutting westward between the North Korea city of Pyŏngyang and the capital at Seoul. From Seoul southward, cotton and tobacco become increasingly significant industrial crops, although both are grown to a certain extent in North Korea. Mulberry and silkworm cultivation is prevalent in the southwest and south central provinces of the country. The north, with its short growing season, has only one crop per year of field grains, whereas the south grows two on the same land.

Although intensive hand tillage is carried on here as in China and Japan, there are differences in agricultural practices. The use of night soil as fertilizer is less important in Korea, especially in the

Figure 14-16   A small village among agricultural fields in Korea. Houses of the farmers have thatched roofs. (Courtesy of Korean Research and Information Office.)

north, although its use has probably increased under Communist Chinese influence in the north. Green (vegetable matter) fertilizers are widely used, and have caused the denudation of much mountain vegetation, the destruction of which has been hastened by needs for fuel and by the 250,000 farm households mostly located in North Korea that are engaged in shifting slope cultivation.

Under Japanese occupation, Korea was an important rice exporter to Japan. This export meant that Koreans had to be content with less desirable foods, and large quantities of millet and kaoliang were imported from Manchuria to fill the deficit left by the rice export. Although Korean population density per square mile of cultivated land was less than half of that of Japan, agricultural yields per unit of land also were only about half of Japan's yields. Moreover, farm income of Koreans under Japanese occupation before 1945 was only about one-third of that of Japanese farmers. These figures indicate only one aspect of the impoverishment of Korea under Japanese exploitation. Until United Nations forces drove out the Japanese in World War II, one-third of all cultivated land in Korea was held by absentee Japanese landlords, often by corporations.

Postwar development in politically divided Korea followed different lines in north and south. North Korea has followed the collectivized system of Communist China, and individual ownership has been abolished. In South Korea, land reform has brought land ownership to the majority of the farmers (Figure 14-16). Although moderate progress has been made in agricultural technology, for example, in the use of improved seed and plant selection, pest and disease control, and chemical fertilization, food production has not met domestic demands.

South Korea's 70 per cent of the total Korean population in 1959 required a 25 per cent production increase to satisfy their needs. Per capita arable land was then only 0.8 of an acre, and farm size averaged less than 2 acres. The flight of North Korean refugees to the south reduced the population pressure on North Korean land, but both areas continue to suffer from extremely low living standards.

FISHERIES

Off the Korean coasts are important fishing waters, which were largely exploited for Japanese benefit before World War II. The mixing of cold and warm ocean currents in the Sea of Japan has led to exceptionally productive fisheries. Korea, however, had no registered shipping while it was part of the Japanese empire, since all ships were of Japanese registry. Most of the motorized ships were sunk during World War II or withdrawn to Japan, and the development of Korean fishing has had to start with serious disadvantages. Moreover, fishing rivalries among Japan, the Soviet Union, and Korea make for added conflicts in the Sea of Japan. Korean marine food production has not reached pre-World War II levels under Japanese control. Total Korean production in 1960 reportedly reached about 1 million metric tons, of which about two-thirds were claimed by North Korea, whose waters are more productive.

HISTORICAL DEVELOPMENT

Korea has served as a cultural link between China and Japan for over 1,500 years. For about 1,000 years of the region's history, much of Korea formed part of the Chinese empire. During many years it was divided into several kingdoms. Unification of the country under a separate rule occurred during the tenth century, but like other countries peripheral to China, Korea sent periodic tribute to the Chinese emperor until the nineteenth century. Korean history records many attempts by its neighbors to dominate its affairs, including several invasions by Japanese armies. Before the nineteenth century these incursions had aroused in the Korean people a tendency toward extreme isolationism and seclusion, fortified by savage resentment of even accidental intrusions by early trading ships.

The struggle between China and Japan for domination of Korea became acute after Japan emerged from its own period of isolation in 1852 and began to emulate its Occidental teachers in the art of empire building. The defeat of China in the Sino-Japanese War of 1894–1895 eliminated China's influence in Korea for fifty-five years. The struggle shifted to a competition between Japan and Russia. As a relative newcomer on the scene, Russia brought her East Asian frontiers southward to North Korea in 1858 after acquiring a slice of Chinese-claimed territory on the Pacific. Japan's victory in the Russo-Japanese War of 1904–1905 gave her a free hand over a Korea ruled by a corrupt, inept, and backward court. Japan annexed Korea in 1910 and for the next thirty-five years tried, by police-state methods, to stamp out Korean culture and national consciousness. She succeeded only in instilling the deep-seated resentment that resulted in the ousting of the Japanese after Japan's defeat in 1945.

The Yalta agreement, bringing the Soviet Union into the war against Japan two weeks before the latter collapsed from the American and Allied attack, permitted Soviet forces to occupy North Korea and led to the splitting of the country in 1948 into two contending halves. This was demarcated by a boundary, the 38th parallel, meant only for temporary expediency. The determination of the United Nations to form a united independent Korea met with the equally determined Soviet ambition to control the entire country. In the clash that came in 1950, the failure of the Soviet Union's indoctrinated North Korean armies caused strategical difficulties for the Soviet Union which could be solved only by bringing in the forces of its much more powerful satellite, Communist China. Thus China, newly oriented to an alien ideology, was restored to its historical position in the struggle for control over northern Korea. From 1953 onward North Korean development followed the direction of Chinese Communist leadership. In this division, South Korea was left with the smaller half of the land surface (38,031 square miles), but with more arable land.

RESOURCES AND INDUSTRY

Korean resources are so modest that there is little hope for a high degree of industrialization in any near future. Coal reserves of usable quality have been estimated at only 34 tons per capita, about one-seventh of Japan's reserves and a small fraction of China's. Because of low quality, much of the coal must be mixed with imported coal to be satisfactory for industry. North Korea, however, is fortunately located to import good coal from Manchuria. In iron ore Korea is better situated. Other important minerals include gold, tungsten, and graphite. The country has significant water power potential.

In regional distribution of resources there is great disparity between north and south. Korea north of the 38th parallel has 70 per cent of the existing forests, 67 per cent of the coal reserves, 80 per cent of the iron ore, 63 per cent of the gold, and most of the hydroelectric power as well

Figure 14-17   Korean women grind flour with this primitive animal-powered stone mill in front of their mud-walled, straw-roofed house. (Courtesy of United States Army.)

as the better fishing waters. It is not surprising, therefore, to find that the south, with 70 per cent of the 36 million population in 1960, is mainly agricultural, whereas the north, with the bulk of the industrial potential, has the greater industrial development.

During the first two decades of Japanese occupation, Japan's chief interest was in extracting food and raw materials from Korea, and she made little attempt to develop industry there. After 1935 a change in policy toward industrialization resulted from Japan's strategic plans. Nevertheless, in 1938 Korean industry employed only about 200,000 Koreans (including miners but excluding traditional handicraft workers) or about 3.8 per cent of the gainfully employed population. The Korean conflict resulted in such heavy destruction in both north and south that mining and manufacturing were almost brought to a halt. South Korea's coal production of 5.4 million tons in 1960 was just about one-half of that claimed for North Korea. The latter's claimed production of 841,000 tons of steel in 1960 contrasted with the few tens of thousands of tons in the south. But the combined iron ore production of the two parts of Korea in this same year was still far below Korea's 3-million-ton production under the Japanese in 1944. South Korea's cement production in 1960 was less than one-fifth of that claimed for North Korea, and the South Korean chemical fertilizer production, vital for agriculture, was even smaller by comparison.

This unfavorable contrast for South Korea is the result not only of the preponderant concentration of minerals, except for tungsten, in North Korea, but also of the location of most of the water power potential and the best hydroelectric sites in the higher, rougher topography of North Korea. In contrast to North Korea's 9,139 million kilowatt hours of electric power in 1960, mostly derived from water power, South Korea produced only 1,697 million kilowatt hours, or about one-fifth, largely from her coal-burning thermal plants. However, although North Korea outshines the south in heavy industry and power, the south has a superior position in light industries, especially in textiles. The warmer, moister climate favors cotton growing and silk-

Figure 14-18 *A modern chemical fertilizer plant in Chung-ju, Korea. Korea's leached soils require heavy fertilization for adequate production of crops. (Courtesy of Korean Research and Information Office.)*

worm breeding in the south, and a much larger volume as well as greater variety of textile fabrics are manufactured, including rayon and nylon.

North Korean industry is especially concentrated in and about its chief city and capital Pyōngyang, at the port of Chinnampo to the southwest, and at Sinūiju near the Yalu River mouth. Hamhung and Wōnsan on the east coast of North Korea are industrial centers supplied with power from hydroelectric dams and plants in the Kaima Plateau gorge lands to their northwest.

South Korea's most important and most varied industrial complex lies at the capital at Seoul and between that city and its seaport of Inchon. Other important industrial centers are the large (million-class) southern port city of Pusan and the medium-class cities such as Taegu farther north, Kunsan and Mokpo on the southwest coast, and Samchok on the east coast. The latter has the largest single coal mine in Korea and emphasizes chemical industries.

In South Korea, food and beverage manufacture constitute approximately one-third of all industry by value added. Textiles add another 17 to 20 per cent,

Figure 14-19 *Textiles are the chief product of Korea's relatively underdeveloped modern industries. This interior view of a factory in Pusan is duplicated in Seoul, Pyongyang, and Kunsan, which are textile centers that use domestic cotton. (Courtesy of United States Army.)*

with metal manufacturing comprising only about 12 per cent. Chemicals, rubber, and paper products constitute other major categories. The smallness of modern industry is revealed by the mere 242,000 people in such employment in South Korea in 1957, out of a population of over 22 million, a little over 1 per cent of the population.

The paradoxical situation and the grave

economic problems of Korea are revealed by the fact that, in spite of the low position of industrial development in South Korea, farm population was estimated at only 63.7 per cent in 1957 and 58.2 per cent in 1960. The large surplus urban population and associated unemployment derive chiefly from the refugee flight from North Korea as well as from the saturation in farm and rural employment.

Korea's 3,250 miles of railroad before World War II provided a fairly adequate network for the economic needs of the country. A 600-mile double-track line ran the length of the country from the southern port of Pusan to the Yalu railroad bridge into China at Sinŭiju. The most strategic and only transpeninsular line then followed the Seoul-to-Wŏnsan corridor. The division of the country has cut both lines near the 38th parallel. Destruction during the Korean conflict and ob-

Figure 14-20   A view of the harbor and port of Pusan in southernmost Korea. This important commercial center and the terminus of the railroad from Seoul now has over 1 million inhabitants. (Courtesy of Korean Research and Information Office.)

solescence by 1958 had reduced the total rail net of Korea to about 2,500 miles. The South Korean government in 1960 completed a 21-mile extension across Korea's mountain backbone to permit rail passage in ten hours from Inchon on the west coast to Samchok on the east coast.

Korea's highway net, by contrast with her rail net, has been considerably strengthened. Compared with the 14,000 miles of dirt highways for all of Korea in 1937, construction by 1960 had brought South Korea's highways alone to almost 17,000 miles. Possibly nearly an equal mileage existed in the northern half of the country.

Rail and road connections with China provide through routes of trade and transportation. During Japanese occupation, Pusan was an export port for transit freight from Manchuria, and it still is the leading port, whereas Najin (Na-jin) and Chongjin (Chong-jin) near the Soviet frontier served as outlets for northern Manchuria. The better natural ports are on the east coast, such as the important port of Wōnsan, although the western and southern ports have the more significant economic hinterlands. Chinnampo (Chin-nam-po) is the port for the North Korean capital of Pyōngyang (Pyongyang). Inchon (In-chon) is the port for Seoul, and Kunsan (Kun-san) and Mokpo (Mok-po) form industrial centers and ports for the southwest. Division into North and South Korea hurts seriously industrial development and both inter-regional and Korean foreign trade.

JAPAN

RELIEF FEATURES

Japan differs from the other countries of Central Eastern Asia in being entirely insular; it is one of the volcanic island chains that form scalloped arcs off the mainland of Eastern Asia. Though hundreds of islands are included in Japan, all except four are of very small size. Among the four, Honshu with 88,031 square miles is by far the greatest and is known as the "mainland" of Japan. Hokkaido, somewhat detached and northernmost, is second in size, 30,077 square miles in area, or slightly smaller than Maine in the United States. The two southern, smaller islands, Kyushu and Shikoku, together with the southwestern arm of Honshu, form the bounds of Japan's Inland Sea. Kyushu, the southernmost, has an area of 13,768 square miles and is about the size of Massachusetts and Connecticut combined. Shikoku, with 6,857 square miles, is larger than Connecticut, but smaller than Massachusetts.

Their recent geologic origin has had marked effects on the Japanese islands. They are composed mainly of high and rugged mountains, parts of a gigantic and partly submerged range rising from the seabed. From the elevated parts of the range forming Japan extend several island arcs, revealing the existence of further submarine ranges. From northeastern Hokkaido, the Kurile (Chishima) Chain stretches toward the Kamchatka Peninsula. Southward from Tokyo Bay runs the Bonin Chain. Southwestward from Kyushu, the Ryukyu (Liu-ch'iu) Chain reaches Taiwan. Okinawa, an important island in the middle part of the Ryukyu Chain, has been developed as an American military air base since World War II. The Korean mountains extend in a submerged arc toward southwestern Honshu, while the Sakhalin mountains dip under Soya Strait to emerge again in Hokkaido.

Where these mountain chains meet in Hokkaido, in central Honshu west of Tokyo, and in Kyushu, high, complex mountain knots, with clusters of volcanoes, occur. The highest mountains are found in central Honshu, with Mt. Fuji (Fuji-yama) rising over 12,000 feet. In submarine topography, the 30,000-foot depth of the Tuscarora Deep southeast of Japan contrasts with the shallow Yellow Sea or even the 12,000-foot-deep basin of the Sea of Japan. Japan's coasts are bordered by many promontories and indentations that give the country a coastline of 16,000 miles, or four times that of the much larger country of China.

Characteristically, Japan's topography comprises a mountainous center enclosing small interior basins and narrow valleys, surrounded by coastal alluvial plains. These plains are surmounted near the mountains by former lowland plains which have been raised by earth movements to make high, level, but river-cut terraces. Rivers are short, with steep profiles that make most of them unnavigable, except for short delta stretches. They have limited backup reservoir capacities. The plains and terraces on which the majority of the population live bring the people into close contact with the sea. These lowlands are generally small and scattered; the Kwanto Plain, some 5,000 square miles, dominated by Tokyo, is by far the largest. Following this in size are the plains of Hokkaido, the most important, the west-central Ishikari Plain covering only 800 square miles. Much of the plains are agriculturally cultivated, but farmland has been increasingly encroached upon for urban and industrial use. The coastal plains are most often bordered near the sea by dune ridges, which create drainage difficulties but which also serve as settlement sites. Favorable factors affecting occupancy of the coastal lowlands include a long growing season, abundant rainfall, and opportunities for fishing.

CLIMATE

Adjacency to the east coast of the Asiatic land mass brings Japan into the monsoon climatic regime, but it is a regime greatly modified by maritime influences. The northward-moving warm Japan Current divides around Kyushu, flows poleward along the northwest coasts of Japan to Hokkaido, and washes the southeast coast as far as Tokyo Bay. To the north of this latitude and around Hokkaido, southward-moving cold currents chill the northern coasts.

The southeastern half of Japan has the familiar midsummer monsoon rainfall peak, with an added peak during the typhoon period in late summer and early fall. Cyclonic storms moving northwestward from the Yangtze Valley also produce the moldy period of the "plum rains" (maiyu), characterized by oppressive heat and humidity. Winter continental winds bring cool, drier weather to the southeast but heavy precipitation to northwest coastal mountain regions. Much of that precipitation is in the form of deep snow, which thaws rapidly in spring and causes serious floods. Although no part of Japan suffers drought as it is understood on the continent, northern Hokkaido and the Inland Sea in the south have only about 40 inches of precipitation in contrast to 57 inches at Tokyo and 84 inches at Kagoshima in southern Kyushu. Moreover, the mountain-ringed Inland Sea region has mild, pleasant winters. Summers in the southern half of Japan are hot and oppressive. In northern Honshu and Hokkaido summer fogs are frequent.

The long latitudinal stretch of over 1,000 miles between northern Hokkaido and southern Kyushu leads to considerable climatic differences. Hokkaido has

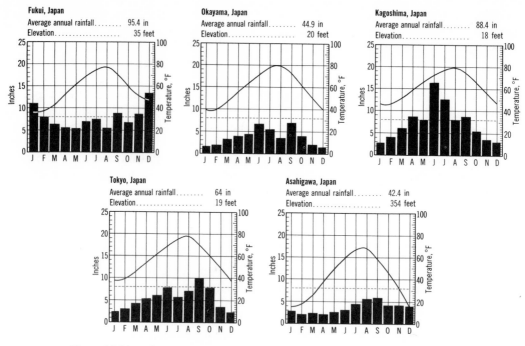

Figure 14-21   Climate graphs of selected cities in Japan.

climatic similarities to Maine; Kyushu resembles Florida. In the south especially, altitudinal zonation brings a range of vegetation that equals that produced by many of the latitudinal changes at low altitudes. Vegetation varies from subtropical forests in southern Kyushu, southern Shikoku, and the Kii peninsula of southeastern Honshu to subboreal coniferous forests in the heart of Hokkaido.

HISTORICAL DEVELOPMENT

The earliest known inhabitants of Japan were the Caucasoid Ainu, a short, stockily built race with the hairiness characteristic of Europeans. The Mongoloid Yamato race entered Japan via the southern island of Kyushu. Gradually, with the aid of improved weapons and armor, they drove back the fiercely resisting Ainu and pushed them far into northern Honshu and Hok-

kaido. Today only a few thousand pure-blooded Ainu are found on Hokkaido and on Sakhalin Island.

Archaeological finds that include Chinese bronze artifacts dating back to about the beginning of the Christian era indicate some Japanese cultural contacts with the mainland as early as that period. Most of the advances of early Japanese civilization, however, were based upon cultural importations from China subsequent to the Christian era. Korea formed the bridge over which they flowed. Conflicts with the continental areas came through Japanese raiding expeditions against parts of southern Korea, through Japanese pirate raids along the China coast, and through two unsuccessful attempts by Kublai Khan to invade Japan with huge naval fleets. Contact with the West began with the arrival of Portuguese Jesuits in the middle of the sixteenth century. Their numerous converts became embroiled as a group in the political rivalries of the time. Fear of foreign aid to enemies of the reigning Shogun (military dictator) caused the latter to banish the missionaries and suppress Christianity. For two centuries Japan withdrew into cultural and commercial seclusion. Serious internal economic, social, and political unrest developed in Japan in the early nineteenth century, coming to a head at a time when China's weakness before the aggression of well-organized European naval powers was becoming apparent. Fear of falling into the same situation decided Japan to come out of seclusion in 1853 when Commodore Perry of the United States made a show of arms in Tokyo Bay in a move to open the country to foreign trade and intercourse.

Japan now exerted itself to develop those aspects of technology that appeared to have made the Western powers strong. Foreign experts were invited to help in guiding the development of a modern army and navy, of education, science and industry, and agriculture. Trade restrictions and the need for dependable markets and sources of raw materials eventually provoked the Japanese to seek them by force of arms. Through skillful political maneuvering and military pressure timed to exploit the struggle for power among the Western nations, Japan by 1937 had built up an empire of great magnitude. Between 1876 and 1879, Japan occupied the Ryukyu Islands, vaguely claimed by China. Taiwan was acquired by the Japanese victors in the Sino-Japanese War of 1894–1895. Korea was annexed in 1910 after a military intervention and threatened war with China. Russia ceded the Kuril Islands in 1875 in exchange for the southern half of Sakhalin Island. When Japan defeated Russia in the war of 1904–1905, she took back southern Sakhalin, which she called Karafuto. In return for

entry into World War I on the Allied side, Japan was permitted to oust the Germans from their Pacific Islands in 1916 and to occupy what became the mandated Pacific Islands under the League of Nations (the present United States Trust Territory of the Marshall, Caroline, and Mariana Islands). She was already entertaining ambitious dreams of a continental empire, which began to take form with the occupation of Manchuria in 1931 when China was too disorganized and weak to resist effectively. These and subsequent moves in China and Indochina threatened the power balance in the Pacific and the interests of the United States and its allies. Because the United States finally took resolute measures to oppose these advances, Japan made the attack on Pearl Harbor that led to open warfare in the Pacific. Insatiably ambitious, Japanese militarists had overestimated the geographical foundations of their power. At the end of World War II, Japan was stripped of her empire; it was finally reduced to the home islands.

POPULATION AND LIVELIHOOD

Part of the urge for expansion resulted from the rapid population increase that began after 1850. Economic poverty, disease, and practices associated with the feudal system had kept Japan's population fluctuating around 30 million for two centuries. By 1941, the population level was 2½ times as high. In 1960, Japan had more than 93 million people, but the increase rate had been drastically reduced to less than 1 per cent per annum. In the century from 1860 to 1960, Japan's population had tripled, whereas land under cultivation had increased by only one-third. Japan in 1960 had only 15.8 million acres of cultivated land, compared with 313 million acres of harvested land in the United

States, or a ratio of 1 to 20. Japan's 93 million people compared with the 180 million for the United States during the same year—a ratio of about 1 to 2. Japanese land resources were equal to only one-tenth of the cultivated land resources per capita of the United States; and Japan did not have the pastoral and mineral resources also available to the United States. The potentially unused arable land of Japan, moreover, is negligible. In 1960, required food imports amounted to about 6 million tons, although there were also exports of processed foods, mostly of marine origin. Intensive land use and intense exploitation of fisheries, therefore, have been necessary to cope with the food needs (Figure 14-22). Moreover, like the

farm households with 37.8 million people. In the same year the United States, with a much greater population, had only 23 million people on farms. Agriculture still is the leading occupation of the Japanese, and its relative decline has been due in large part to the fact that virtually no good agricultural land remains to be utilized.

Even more than in China and Korea, rice is the cultural preference of the people, so that even in such subboreal climates as those of Hokkaido, rice growing is pushed wherever water, soils, and growing season permit. More than 55 per cent of the cultivated land is in rice crops. Nevertheless, the area of cultivated land in dry crops far exceeds that used for paddy. This seeming paradox is explained by the fact that

Figure 14-22   Edible seaweed gathered from the shallow beach flats at the head of Tokyo Bay is sun-dried in square patches preparatory to packing and selling. (Courtesy of H. J. Wiens.)

British, the Japanese also must manufacture and export to live.

AGRICULTURE

Though the percentage of Japanese population employed in agriculture has dropped from 80 to 40 per cent during the past century, the total number has increased somewhat; in 1950, there were 6,176,422

winter dry crops are grown on the paddy fields, whereas rice cannot be grown on most of the land permanently used for dry crops. The long growing season from the Kwanto Plain southward permits such double cropping, so that the equivalent of 4.48 million acres of crop area is added to the actual cultivated land surface. Technical improvements and widespread mechanization have brought about a rev-

Figure 14-23   A rice-harvest scene in the Kwanto Plain of Honshu, Japan. The cut bunches of rice are hung on racks made of bamboo poles to dry before threshing. (Courtesy of H. J. Wiens.)

Figure 14-24   Lake Toya on Hokkaido Island. (Courtesy of Japan Travel Information Office.)

olution in Japanese farming, and bumper crops have become standard.

Climate is one of the less significant factors limiting agricultural production, although it becomes important in northern Honshu and Hokkaido. Sixty-five per cent of the land is over 15 degrees in slope, and poor drainage and other factors further reduce the land fit for use. With soils generally well leached, because of the high rainfall, production depends heavily on fertilization. Though maximum use is made of organic fertilizers such as night soil and farm manures, there is increasingly heavy dependence upon chemical fertilizers, most of which are manufactured in Japan, although some are imported.

Pressure of population upon the land is shown by the small amount of land in industrial crops, by the high yields that indicate the most intensive cultivation, and by the high percentage in cereal and starchy tubers which yield the most calories per unit of land. Before World War II, 81 per cent of the calories consumed were from grains, 95 per cent from grains and tubers, and 68 per cent from rice alone. Postwar dietary changes have led to increased use of wheat products and other improvements in the diet, including interest in dairy products.

In the south, fall-sown wheat and winter barley are associated with summer rice together with soybeans on field borders and dikes. A great variety of crop associations occur on the dry fields. Oats are important only in Hokkaido, and barley, naked barley, wheat, millet, and buckwheat are widely grown. Sweet potatoes are conspicuous in the southern parts of Japan and white potatoes on Hokkaido. Large quantities of vegetables are grown on the diluvial, upland dry fields.

Some regional specialties include tobacco and hemp on the northern part of the Kwanto Plain, tatami reeds for mats in the Okayama and Hiroshima coastal plains, green tea and tangerines in the Shizuoka vicinity, flax, pyrethrum, peppermint, and sugar beets in Hokkaido, rapeseed and sesame seed in Kyushu and between Lake Biwa and Ise Bay, and mulberry, especially in the west Kwanto upland plain and central Honshu mountain basins. Dairying is important in Hokkaido, in central Honshu, and in the hill lands surrounding the Osaka-Kyoto region.

FISHERIES

For about the last fifty years Japan has been the foremost fishing nation of the world, an aspect of livelihood partly attributable to its insular advantages, partly to population pressure upon limited farmland, and in great measure to the natural productiveness of the seas around Japan. In 1940, one-fourth of the world's fish catch was made by Japan. Fish and other marine products follow rice in importance in the diet of the average Japanese. Because most of the farming areas are on the coastal plains, many thousands of farmers are part-time fishermen. In 1959, there were in addition some 628,000 regularly employed fishermen. The recent trend has been toward the increased development in large-scale, deep-sea operations and the general break up of the small-scale fishing enterprises.

Prior to World War II, up to half of the catch were herring and sardines, which now constitute only about 10 per cent of the total haul. The catch of mackerel-type fish and of squid has greatly increased. Coastal and offshore waters of the home islands account for about 80 per cent of the catch. The loss of prewar-empire areas dealt Japan a severe economic blow, and extensive claims to offshore waters by

Korea, Communist China, and the Soviet Union have further restricted her fishing grounds. Nevertheless, by 1960 Japanese fishing fleets had surpassed the prewar 4-million-ton annual catch by 2 million tons. Japan thus equaled or surpassed Communist China's annual production and made approximately double the catch of each of the next ranking nations, the United States and the Soviet Union.

INDUSTRY

Japan cannot live without importing about 6 million tons of its food needs, and it can pay for this food only through exports. With limited amounts of raw materials for export, Japan must export labor in the form of manufactures and processed goods. Furthermore, the country is poor in the minerals required for modern industry and must import both fuel and raw materials to supplement meager home supplies. Strategically, therefore, Japan is very vulnerable. Virtually all its raw cotton, wool, phosphate rock, crude rubber, nickel, bauxite, magnesite, and tin must be imported. The import requirement for iron ore is about 82 per cent, for heavy coking coal, 70 per cent, for crude oil, 88 per cent, and for salt, 80 per cent.

Of the important metals, only zinc is adequate. Except for moderate supplies of chromite, ferroalloys essential for high-grade steels are seriously deficient. Fortunately, sulfuric acid, one of the most important of the heavy chemicals, can be adequately supplied from pyrite and is a by-product in the smelting of copper, zinc, and lead. Much of Japan's needs in copper can be met from domestic mines.

Of coal, the production of which exceeds in value that of all other minerals combined, Japan has an adequate supply. At the annual rate of mining of about 50 million tons, there is sufficient coal to last two hundred years, but industry needs to import much coking coal. Although Japan has much smaller reserves than China, until 1954 it had been the largest producer in Asia. (Communist China now far surpasses Japan in coal output.) Nearly half of the coal reserves are in Kyushu. About 40 per cent are found in the northern island of Hokkaido; the remainder is scattered throughout Honshu. Fifty-five per cent of all coal mined comes from Kyushu, mostly from the Chikuho field in the north; about 25 per cent comes from Hokkaido, mostly from the Ishikari field. Supplies for the Tokyo industrial area come from the Joban field just north of the Kwanto Plain.

A combination of unfavorable factors in recent years has seriously depressed the Japanese coal industry. Conversion to oil in many plants has led to the closing of many mines. More important, getting coal out of the thin, broken seams characteristic of many Japanese deposits involves crushing expense. Japanese coal is high in waste content when compared with American coals. These and other factors made coal imported from as far as the United States $5 per ton cheaper in Japan than domestic coal. That the Japanese mines have continued large-scale production is in part due to the greatly increased efficiency of production, which rose from 5.5 tons per man monthly in 1946 to 20 tons in 1960.

Petroleum reserves are meager. They supply only 10 to 12 per cent of the needs, and Japan produces annually less than the United States does per day. However, Japanese refining capacity based on imported crude oil is large. Most of the domestic reserves are found near the northwest coast of Honshu and in the Ishikari region of Hokkaido.

Japan's hydroelectric power potential is about equal to that of Italy and is one-

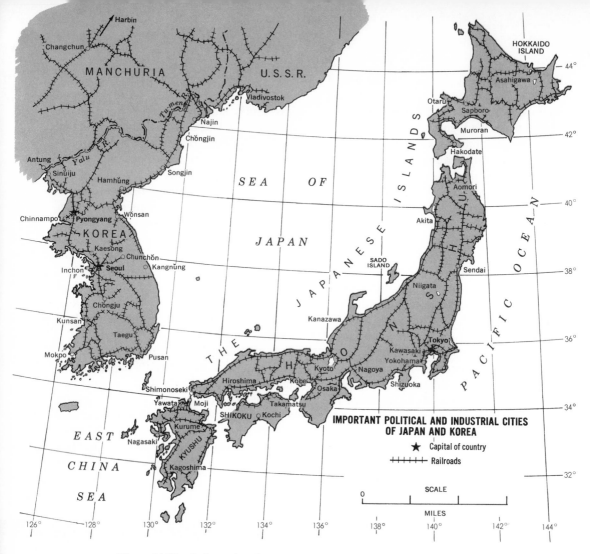

Figure 14-25   Industrial and commercial centers of Japan and Korea.

fourth that of China. Before World War II, however, Japan held third rank in the world in developed hydroelectric power. Only about 60 per cent of the potential is now being utilized. The development of hydroelectric power suffers the seasonal limitation of the monsoon system and is based on a stream flow of an average of about six months per year. Ninety-two per cent of the hydroelectric facilities are run-of-the-river type, which produces erratic quantities of electricity and hence requires standby steam plants. Unfortunately, the damming of the few large reservoir sites

available requires submersion of needed agricultural land. Postwar power demand increased so enormously as to make obsolete the earlier hydropower generation. Large thermal plants now are the major source of supply, with plants of a reservoir type serving as supplementary sources; most of the present development is along the rivers in the central mountain knot of Honshu. In general, high-cost coal, petroleum, and hydroelectric power constitute difficult problems in Japanese industrial development. Great interest has been focused upon power generation by nuclear plants, prototypes of which were under construction in 1964.

Iron ore is largely imported from such suppliers as Malaysia, the Philippines, India, and, before 1945, China and Korea. Ninety per cent of the small home production comes from two districts: 60 per cent from the Kamaishii and Senin mines in northeastern Honshu north of Sendai, and 30 per cent from the Kuchan mines in southern Hokkaido. Since the ore goes to the coal regions for smelting, about 70 per cent of the pig iron is produced in northern Kyushu, the center for heavy industry, where about one-half of the country's steel is produced.

Manufacturing in Japan is concentrated in the belt running along the southern side of Honshu and along both shores of the Inland Sea, from the Kwanto Plain to and including northern Kyushu, in which 75 to 80 per cent of the industrial activity is located. Nearly 85 per cent of the value of industrial goods comes from this area. The reasons for such a concentration are to be found in the abundant labor, excel-

lent water and land communications, fine harbors, adjacent agricultural and mineral resources, and the historical focus of the region as the heart of the country. Sixty per cent of the industrial activity is divided about equally betweent the Osaka region and the Tokyo region; 10 per cent is found in north Kyushu and 10 per cent around Nagoya. Although heavy industry is the principal activity in northern Kyushu, the other areas are noted for their great variety of industries. Nagoya specializes mainly in light industries, but also manufactures motorcars and aircraft. Metalworking, the making of machinery, motors, chemicals, textiles, and food processing are of major importance in the three eastern centers. A limited amount of heavy industry occurs in southern Hokkaido. Earlier industrial development was centered mainly on cotton and silk textiles, but the war buildup of the late 1930s brought increasing attention to heavy industry and machine making. The relative position of heavy and light industries by 1957 had become the reverse of that in 1935, with heavy in-

Figure 14-26   Pottery being dried in the sun before firing in kilns. Japan is noted for numerous small pottery and chinaware enterprises. (Courtesy of H. J. Wiens.)

Figure 14-27   Tokyo, the capital of Japan, is one of the largest cities in the world. This view of the principal business district shows large, modern office buildings as well as several means of communication. (Courtesy of Japan Travel Information Office.)

Figure 14-28   Although Japan is one of the major textile manufacturers of the world, much of the processing is done by home industry or by other small producers. This photo illustrates the process of drying silk cloth after it has been dyed. (Courtesy of H. J. Wiens.)

dustries leading by about 10 per cent in value. Textiles, which in 1935 constituted 32 per cent of the value of manufactures, in 1957 reached only 15 per cent. Chemicals accounted for 15 per cent of the value of manufactures in 1935 but only 9.5 per cent in 1957.

Japan's industrial output has been growing faster than that of any other country in the world and has made remarkable progress. In production of steel ingots, Japan in 1960 ranked fifth among the nations, after the United States, the Soviet Union, the United Kingdom, and West Germany. It became the world's largest shipbuilder in 1956 and in the following year built 29 per cent of the world total. Japan's cement production in 1960 reached 22.5 million tons to place her fourth in world rank. She also became the world's largest producer of rayon staple, cameras, sewing machines, and transistor radios, and reached second rank after the United States in the manufacture of synthetic fibers and television sets. An amazingly rapid increase took place in the production of automotive vehicles. From a postwar beginning of about 15,000 units in 1946, production jumped to over 111,000 in 1957; and high rates of growth of about 36 per cent and 58 per cent in 1959 and 1960 brought production in the latter year to over 400,000 units, with almost as large an output of passenger cars as the Soviet Union and approximately twenty times the automotive production of Communist China.

Over 6 million workers labored in factories with four or more workers. Although Japan at the beginning of 1958 had 477 large plants (15 per cent of the total) each with over 1,000 employees, 78 per cent of Japanese factories employed less than 500 people each. Yet in the overall industrial picture, in spite of her rank

among the world's industrial powers, Japan is still overwhelmingly dominated by small and medium-size enterprises.

COMMUNICATIONS AND COMMERCE

As a rugged mountain land with most of its productive areas fringing the sea and with good harbors in abundance, it is natural that Japan should be a seafaring nation. Dependence upon commerce for a livelihood spurred the creation of a large merchant marine, and Japan's strategic ambitions led her to build up one of the most powerful naval fleets in the world. The merchant fleet reached a prewar peak of 6 million gross tons in 1941, but was reduced to 1.34 million tons in World War II. The war also resulted in the sinking of virtually the entire navy. By 1961, however, Japan had rebuilt her merchant marine to about 6.7 million tons and is continuing to increase this shipbuilding rapidly.

Coastal trade between the home islands and ports has required 1 to 2 million tons of shipping, for land communications are difficult and costly because of the rugged terrain. Nevertheless, even before World War II, 15,000 miles of well-equipped railroads served the different islands. Railroads are more important for passenger than for freight hauls, however, and passenger transport brings greater gross receipts—a very unusual situation in railroading. The most important line is the Tokaido, which follows an ancient and famous highway route connecting Tokyo with Kyoto and Osaka. In 1962 the Japanese government decided to construct a new high-speed railroad, completed in 1964, paralleling the existing line to enable trains to travel at speeds of over 100 miles per hour between Tokyo and Osaka. Motor-car travel and truck transport are

Figure 14-29   Zamami Shima is one of the islands of the Okinawa Gunto. Like most of the islands, the topography is very rough and rugged. All land that can be cultivated is in production. There are many small but good harbors.

increasingly common in Japan; in 1961 over 3.35 million motor vehicles were registered. Trucks and motorcycles in about equal proportion accounted for 2.8 million units. Most country roads are narrow and poor. Military considerations led to the construction of the undersea railway tunnel connecting Honshu and Kyushu between Shimonoseki and Moji; it was completed in 1944. A parallel undersea highway tunnel, the second longest in the world, was completed in 1958. Proposals have been considered for an undersea tunnel connecting Honshu with Hokkaido for railroad use. Bridge or undersea-tunnel

connections are also contemplated for Honshu and Shikoku in the future.

The chief ports for foreign trade are Yokohama-Tokyo, with a combined population of some 10.3 million in 1960, Osaka-Kobe, nearly 4.1 million, Nagoya in Ise Bay, over 1.5 million, and Moji at the Shimonoseki Straits. Japan's foreign trade in 1960 was over four times its annual value in 1934–1936. There has been extensive reorientation both in trading partners and in the importance of import and export categories. During the prewar period, the major countries trading with Japan, in order of their importance to

Japan, were China, the United States, Germany, and Great Britain. In the postwar era, China has occupied a relatively unimportant position, but Southeastern and Southern Asia have taken one-half of Japan's exports and provided about one-third of her imports. The United States is Japan's best customer. She sold Japan about one-third of that nation's imports, valued at $1.5 billion in 1960, and bought a little less than one-third of Japan's exports, valued at $1 billion in 1960. Following the United States, Hong Kong, the Philippines, and Australia, in that order of importance, were the most important export markets for Japan. Australia, Malaya and Singapore, and Kuwait were the main sources of Japan's imports. The leading exports in order of rank in 1960 were iron and steel products, cotton fabrics, ships, chemicals and drugs, clothing, fish products, and spun-rayon fabrics. The chief imports were petroleum, raw cotton, machinery, wool, chemicals and drugs, iron and steel scrap, and iron ore. Japan must import food and raw materials. To buy these, she must obviously export her labor power in the form of manufactures.

IN PERSPECTIVE

CENTRAL EASTERN ASIA, PROBLEMS OF POPULATION AND RESOURCES

Central Eastern Asia's problems are numerous and differ according to the geographical environment and technological development. Generalizations often require exceptions, but we may probably say of this region that population increases faster than food production, and that there is therefore a general nutritional deficiency for the majority of the people. Of the four nations considered in this section, mainland China appears to be suffering the greatest difficulty in providing adequate food and nutrition to its population. In spite of an initially rapid increase in the first decade of Communist rule, agricultural production, beginning in 1958 (the so-called year of the "great leap forward"), suffered a series of disastrous setbacks resulting from a combination of climatic calamities and Communist mismanagement. Whereas in Taiwan, Japan, and Korea, agricultural production rose by 3 per cent in 1960–1961, according to a United Nations survey, mainland China suffered a decline. Mainland China's population continued to increase by over 16 million per year. By contrast with China's over 2 per cent rate of population increase, Japan has reduced her rate of increase to only about 1 per cent. This still means that about 1 million more people are born every year. Japanese agriculture, however, has made significant production advances, and because of industrial gains, Japan has the highest standard of living in East Asia. Taiwan has managed to achieve near self-sufficiency in food production amid an expanding industrial complex; but the population growth rate of 3.6 per cent per annum arouses concern about food deficiencies in a near future.

South Korea's economy has been kept from collapse in the postwar era only through American aid. Her imports in 1960 amounted to ten times the value of her exports, and more than two-thirds of her imports were financed by foreign aid. No reliable information is available on the state of the North Korean economy. It can probably be fairly said, however, that the maintenance of a viable Korean economy without a disastrous drop in the already low living standards cannot be expected without continued foreign aid.

Hong Kong has experienced a decade of prosperity in spite of the problems of the refugee influx from mainland China.

Industry has overtaken the former primacy of commerce at Hong Kong, although the latter continues its vital role.

In the Mongolian People's Republic the winds of change have also blown some degree of industrialization into the three or four cities of this remote land, though reports to the outside world give insufficient basis for economic diagnosis. Pastoral dominance continues for the 937,000 inhabitants estimated for this land in 1960.

In general, in Central Eastern Asia poverty and low purchasing power are associated with small savings and lack of surplus for capital accumulation. Except in Japan, where literacy is high, poverty is also associated with low literacy rates. Children must start earning part of their living at an early age, bringing their cheaper, less efficient labor into competition with that of adult workers. In general, skilled labor is lacking in most of the area except Japan, but the number of trained workers is gradually developing in the other areas, especially at Hong Kong and in Taiwan. Agriculturally, the region still overemphasizes individual crops such as rice and suffers from a relatively low state of development in pastoral industries except in Mongolia and in the west and northwest periphery of China. The backwardness of dairying is partly attributable to earlier cultural distaste for dairy products. Meat-producing animals are raised in great aggregate numbers but are few per capita. Raising animals for food is mainly concentrated on the scavenger type, such as hogs and fowls, which compete little with man for the food-growing land. In Japan and Mongolia, however, the pig is less important.

Although progress is being made in industrialization and technical modernization, many aspects of society still follow old traditions. Where the forms of tradition have been overthrown, as in Communist China, the earlier pattern of autocracy and rule-from-the-top persists as strongly as ever. This may well lead to rapid technological progress in some spheres under the ruthless drive of Communist dictatorship, but such a process also involves a sacrifice of the finer values of civilization. In technology and economic advancement, Communism in mainland China has not demonstrated its superiority over modified free-enterprise systems operating, for instance, in Japan or Taiwan, where human welfare has taken precedence over worship of an ideological system.

SELECTED REFERENCES

Cheng, Chu-yuan: *Communist China's Economy, 1949–1962: Structural Changes and Crisis,* Seton Hall University Press, 1963.

The 193 pages of text and appendixes provide an objective evaluation of the Communist transformation of China's agriculture, industry, and social economy. Although written from the viewpoint of an economist, the study is valuable in interpreting China's economic geography in 1963.

Cressey, George B.: *Land of the 500 Million,* McGraw-Hill Book Company, Inc., New York, 1955.

The author presents a 356-page discussion of China from two points of view. In the first seven chapters he describes the country as a whole: its peoples, cultures, landforms, climates, agriculture and attendant problems, natural resources and their utilization. In the second half of the book he describes China by six major regions, each with five to six subdivisions. A final chapter assesses China's prospects as of 1955.

Friters, Gerard M.: *Outer Mongolia,* The Johns Hopkins Press, Baltimore, 1949, chap. 1, pp. 1–43.

Chapter 1 contains most of the discussion of interest to the economic geographer. The rest of the 358-page book discusses Outer Mongolia's international relations.

Ginsburg, Norton, and others: *Pattern of Asia,* Prentice-Hall, Inc., Englewood Cliffs, N.J., 1958, chaps. 3–14, pp. 46–289.

The first four chapters on Japan are by Norton Ginsburg; Chapter 6 on Korea is by Shannon McCune; and Chapters 8–14 on China and the Mongolian Peoples Republic are by Herold J. Wiens. This discussion provides a detailed topical description of Central Eastern Asia. Maps included show the railroad net, cities categorized by size or importance, climatic charts for six localities, major land uses, and vegetation.

Japanese Ministry of Foreign Affairs, Public Information and Cultural Affairs Bureau: *The Japan of Today,* 1962.

A convenient summary of developments in Japan as of 1962, beautifully illustrated. Pages 5–20 and 37–74 are especially relevant to students of geography.

McCune, Shannon: *Korea's Heritage,* Tuttle Company, Rutland, Vt., 1956.

The first six chapters of this social and regional geography of Korea are devoted to the political history, social character, and demography of the country. Then follows an analysis of the "basic," or primary, economy of Korea and of its "modern industrial" economy. The latter half of the text discusses regional Korean geography. The appendixes on minerals and industrial distributions supply prewar data.

Trewartha, Glenn: *Japan, a Physical, Cultural and Regional Geography,* The University of Wisconsin Press, Madison, Wis., 1945.

Although much out of date for economic and cultural aspects, it is still the classic and only detailed discussion of Japan's physical, climatic, and regional geography in English, and the discussion still is valid for most of these aspects and for the agricultural geography, with minor exceptions.

chapter 15

SOUTH ASIA

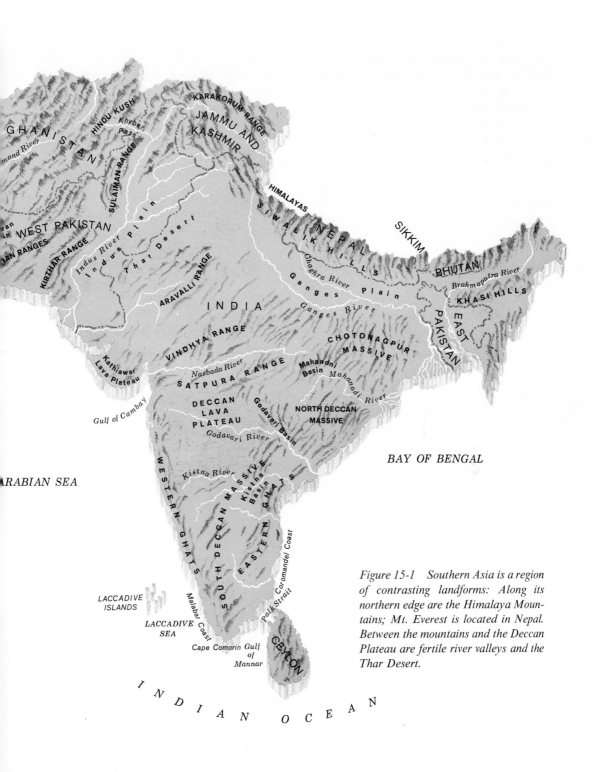

Figure 15-1 Southern Asia is a region of contrasting landforms: Along its northern edge are the Himalaya Mountains; Mt. Everest is located in Nepal. Between the mountains and the Deccan Plateau are fertile river valleys and the Thar Desert.

*I*NCLUDED IN SOUTH ASIA IS THE VAST subcontinent of India, with the countries of India and Pakistan, and the formidable Himalaya Mountains, in which Nepal, Sikkim, and Bhutan are located. Landlocked Afghanistan is to the west and the island of Ceylon to the southeast.

The lands of South Asia exhibit most of the extremes associated with the continent: maximum range in elevation from Mt. Everest to areas below sea level, temperature range from the perpetually snow-covered mountains of the north to the steaming tropics, and maximum world rainfall, dropping to the extreme aridity of the Thar Desert. Villages untouched by modern influences are in close proximity to Westernized industrial cities, and the more primitive tribal groups contrast sharply with cultured and sophisticated urbanites. Within this complex there is great diversity in race, language, and religion, but for several millenniums the dominant human activity has been subsistence agriculture supplemented by part-time home industries or handicrafts.

Dispensing Western ideas along with material goods, the European colonial system reached its zenith in the nineteenth century but rapidly disintegrated after World War II. Under the impact of Western material culture ancient customs and practices are changing. Both the old and the new countries of South Asia are employing Western science and technology to increase their productive capacity in order to provide a better living for their 560 million people. South Asia has some of the oldest independent nations in the world—Afghanistan, Nepal, and Bhutan—and some of the newest—India, Pakistan, and Ceylon, formed in 1947.

Jammu and Kashmir are claimed by both India and Pakistan. These are now considered Trust Territories of the United Nations, but a plebiscite is to be held.

THE SUBCONTINENT OF INDIA

PHYSICAL SETTING

Physically isolated from the great land mass of Asia by mountain barriers, the subcontinent of India may be divided into three major natural regions: the mountain wall separating it from the Asian land mass; the contiguous plains of the Indus, Ganges, and Brahmaputra Rivers; and the compact triangular peninsula thrust into the Indian Ocean (Figure 15-1).

RELIEF FEATURES The mountain wall to the north is symmetrically arranged with the massive Himalayas in the center and the Baluchistan and Burmese Ranges on the west and east. From the gorge of the Indus to the gorge of the Brahmaputra, the Himalaya Mountains extend eastward in an arc for about 1,500 miles. With an average crest line of 20,000 feet, several of the world's highest peaks are found here; Nanga Parbat in Kashmir, Mt. Everest in Nepal, and Mt. Kinchinjunga farther east rise to almost 30,000 feet. For more than 1,000 miles there are only two commonly used routes through this lofty barrier. The western follows the Jhelum River to the Vale of Kashmir, thence via the upper Indus Valley; the eastern route is via Darjeeling and Sikkim, thence through the Chumbi Valley to Tibet.

On the west the less formidable Sulaiman and Kirthar Ranges extend southward to the delta of the Indus. There are two major passes in this mountain wall, the most famous being the strategically important Khyber Pass, which for centuries provided major access to the plains of northern India. Farther south, where these ranges converge, is the Bolan Gate, the best natural route from Southwestern Asia.

To the east the gorge of the Brahma-

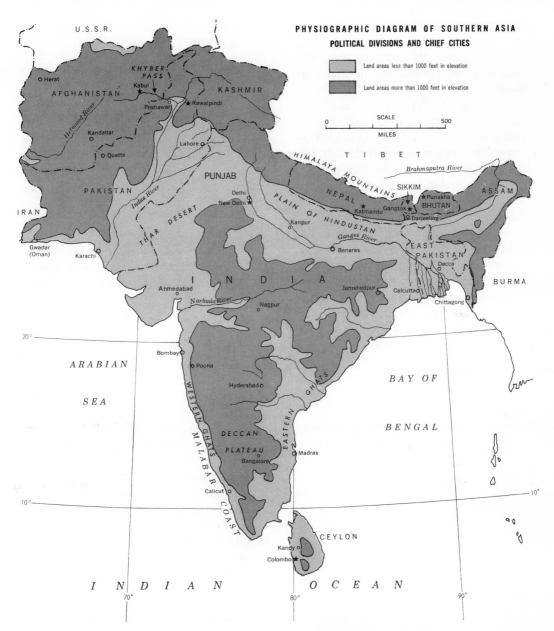

PHYSIOGRAPHIC DIAGRAM OF SOUTHERN ASIA
POLITICAL DIVISIONS AND CHIEF CITIES

Land areas less than 1000 feet in elevation

Land areas more than 1000 feet in elevation

SCALE

0   500

MILES

Figure 15-2   Countries and principal cities of South Asia.

putra is difficult, and the Burmese Ranges are a practical barrier. Passes are high in these folded mountains, and they have been little used. During World War II a military highway, the Ledo Road, was constructed to the railhead in Burma. It was officially abandoned in 1945.

The Plain of Hindustan is one of the largest and most important in the world; historically and culturally it is the heart of India. More than 2,000 miles long and from 150 to 200 miles wide, the plain is remarkably level throughout, the slope gentle, and the alluvium fine in texture. It is drained by three major rivers, the Indus, Ganges, and Brahmaputra, and their tributaries. All three rivers are fed by melting snows of the Himalayas and by summer monsoon rains, and though volume varies with the seasons, they provide considerable water to irrigate the intensively cultivated and densely populated plain.

Peninsular India, lying south of the Hindustan Plain, is a dissected plateau with great physiographic diversity. The western escarpment, known as the Western Ghats Mountains, rises to elevations of 3,000 to 5,000 feet; the eastern escarpment is a discontinuous chain of lower hills called the Eastern Ghats. The western coastal plain is narrow, gradually widening toward the south into the fertile Mala-

Figure 15-3   Kashmir, the land between China and Afghanistan, has been a subject of dispute between India and Pakistan since the formation of the two nations. The village at the foot of the mountains is Gulmarg. (Courtesy of Consulate General of India.)

bar Coast. On the east the Coromandel Coast, with alternating plains and deltas interrupted by many small hills, extends more than 1,000 miles.

Major rivers of the plateau rise on the slopes of the Western Ghats and flow eastward to the Bay of Bengal. Fed by the monsoon rains, these rivers vary greatly in volume and in the dry season are of scant value for either navigation or irrigation.

CLIMATE   Except for climatic extremes associated with mountain barriers, the tropical monsoon is dominant throughout the habitable portions of the subcontinent (Figure 15-4). Annual range in temperature is often 20 to 40 degrees, but seasonal rhythm in rainfall is more significant. The year is sharply divided into wet and dry seasons, the area receiving 75 to 97 per cent of the annual rainfall during the summer (Table 15-1).

Rainfall variability, increasing from east to west, is a serious problem. For example, a station with a 6-inch average has recorded 20 inches of rain in 24 hours; heavy downpours of this type cause flooding and erosion. Sometimes the rains are late, the season short, and total precipitation less than normal. Population pressure is so great that one or two seasons of rainfall shortage or maldistribution may cause crop shortages and famine.

The success of agriculture is, therefore, largely dependent upon the summer monsoon. President Sam Higginbottom, of Allahabad Christian College, said of northern India:

If the rains fail, there is no work for the farmer or for the very large number of casual landless laborers. Without the rain the fodder crops cannot be grown, neither can the fields be prepared for the grain crops which are grown in the cold season. There the failure of the rains means the absence of work for twelve months or until the

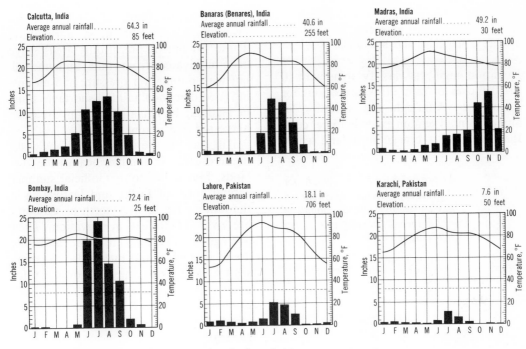

Figure 15-4   *Climate graphs of selected cities.*

TABLE 15-1   WET AND DRY SEASONS

Station	Altitude, ft.	Annual precipitation, in.	Rainy season, June–Oct.	Dry season, Nov.–May	Months with less than 1 in.
Peninsula:					
Bombay	37	74.0	72.8	1.2	7
Calicut	27	116.2	97.3	18.9	3
Bangalore	3,021	36.8	27.0	9.8	4
Madras	22	48.9	39.0*	9.9†	4
Ganges Valley:					
Calcutta	21	60.8	50.3	10.5	3
Patna	183	44.5	40.6	3.9	6
Benares	267	40.6	37.9	2.7	7
Delhi	718	27.7	23.8	3.9	7
Hill stations:					
Darjeeling	7,376	121.8	105.5	16.3	3
Simla	7,232	68.0	51.5	16.5	1
Indus Valley:					
Multan	420	7.1	5.0	2.1	10
Jacobabad	186	4.1	2.7	1.4	10
Karachi	13	7.7	6.1	1.6	10

* August to December.
† January to July.

next rains, and the absence of work means absence of wages and the absence of wages means absence of food, therefore starvation.

Irrigation engineers classify areas with 10 to 50 inches of rainfall as precarious for agriculture. Although the variation in annual rainfall seldom exceeds 15 per cent, that variation is crucial in a land where more than two-thirds of the people are primarily dependent upon agriculture. These so-called precarious areas have been cultivated from time immemorial, but with population pressure and mounting food demands, rainfall shortages must be made up by irrigation if crops are to be harvested and famine averted.

Hill stations are used by persons wishing to escape the summer heat of the lowlands. Simla, the former official summer capital north of Delhi, and Darjeeling in the famous tea district north of Calcutta are over 7,000 feet in elevation. Their average temperatures in June and July are 66 and 61°F, but this is also the rainy season, and skies may be overcast for many consecutive days. Octacamund, luxurious resort in the Nilgiri Hills southwest of Madras, is noted for its scenery and gardens.

CULTURAL FACTORS

POPULATION   Predominantly rural, population is widely dispersed in thousands of villages averaging about one hundred houses. The dot map of population distribution (Figure 15-6) shows a marked concentration in the well-watered and intensively cultivated Ganges Valley and Delta where certain districts have 800 persons per square mile. A second area of concentration is in the southern tip of the peninsula, especially along the Malabar Coast, where coconuts and two crops of rice a year are the main support of more than 1,400 people to the square mile in Cochin. Inland, population is clustered around the Kolar goldfields of Mysore. Settlement in the Indus Valley has grown with the development of its water resources, and the present population pattern correlates closely with irrigated lands. Another lesser grouping is in the northern Deccan, noted for its cotton. In marked

Figure 15-5   Climate graph for Cherrapunji, India. This station has an average annual rainfall of 427.8 inches; almost 100 inches falls during July.

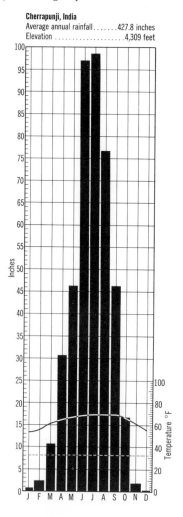

Cherrapunji, India
Average annual rainfall.......427.8 inches
Elevation ....4,309 feet

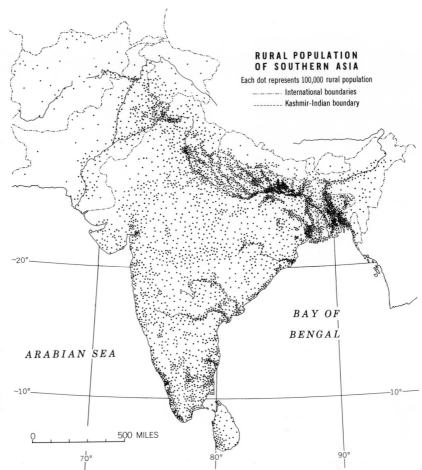

**RURAL POPULATION
OF SOUTHERN ASIA**

Each dot represents 100,000 rural population

‑‑‑‑‑‑‑‑ International boundaries

‑‑‑‑‑‑‑‑ Kashmir‑Indian boundary

−20°

*BAY OF
BENGAL*

Figure 15-6 Note that rural population is concentrated largely in river valleys and along the coast. Contrast the density of population in East Pakistan with that in West Pakistan.

ARABIAN SEA

−10°

10°

0 _____ 500 MILES

70°

80°

90°

contrast are the sparsely populated mountains and the arid lands of Baluchistan and Rajputana.

Since the first census of India in 1872, the growth curve has been consistently upward. Since 1900 the population has increased from 283 to 441 million, and in the decade 1951–1961 the net increase was 49.9 million or about 5 million a year.

While the population has always been predominantly rural, a trend toward urbanization is apparent. The most striking feature is the increase in the larger cities; six cities now have a population of more than 1 million each, and a number

have over ½ million. This urban growth may be attributed to war stimulus, resettlement of peoples following Partition (as the separation of India and Pakistan is called), and increasing industrialization.

LANGUAGES   Successive invasions and conquests of past centuries have left their imprint and, in its complicated ethnic history, the subcontinent has received both cultural and material gifts from each of the invaders. Linguistically this area is highly complex; four main stocks are broken down into 179 languages and several hundred additional dialects. Except

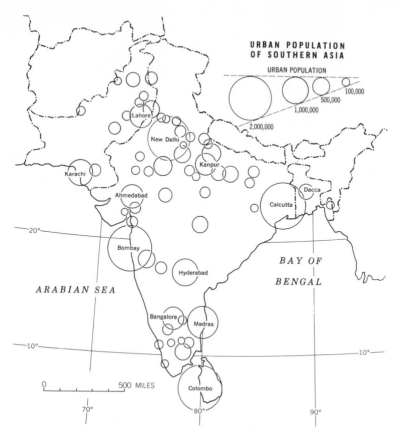

Figure 15-7 India is a country of town, village, and city dwellers. Note the large number of cities in India as compared with their scarcity in Pakistan and Afghanistan.

in isolated districts, most people are bilingual or even multilingual. Multiplicity of languages reduces intellectual contacts and creates educational problems; in Madras, for example, instruction is given in four indigenous languages. While under British control, elementary instruction was commonly in the vernacular, with English taught in the high schools. Most university instruction was in English; already the language of government and business, it also became the language of the intelligentsia.

Although it recognizes fourteen languages and has officially adopted Hindi, the Republic of India will continue to use English until 1972. Pakistan has officially adopted Urdu and Bengali but in practice continues to use English.

RELIGION   Religion plays a dominant role since it often regulates customs, diet, occupations, and other aspects of life. Hindus accounted for 251 million or 66 per cent of the total population in 1941; second was the large Moslem minority, with 92 million or about 24 per cent.

Six other religious groups were represented in the remaining 10 per cent—Buddhists, Sikhs, Jains, Parsees, Jews, and Christians. Several of these minor religions have millions of adherents; for example, over 6 million Sikhs are concentrated in the Punjab and more than 6 million Christians in the southern part of the peninsula. The small community of Parsees, mainly in the Bombay area, is highly influential in economic and political affairs.

Hindus recognize four main castes, and there are some 3,000 subcastes. Traditionally a person born into a particular caste engages in the occupation and observes the social and religious customs of his particular stratum. The system carries stratification to an extreme degree by enforcing rigid marriage rules, regulating contacts between different castes, and making occupations hereditary. While it has provided an element of stability, the rigidity of the caste system has undoubtedly contributed to widespread poverty.

SEPARATISM AND PARTITION   As an outgrowth of racial, religious, and linguistic complexity, separatist movements developed. In the early 1930s the name "Pakistan" identified the movement for a separate Moslem state. Indian nationalist sentiment also grew steadily, and in the long struggle for freedom the various groups worked together. When the British withdrew, however, internal differences and antagonisms came to the surface. After a year of bitter fighting the country was partitioned along religious lines, both India and Pakistan becoming dominions within the British Commonwealth (1947). In 1950 India became a republic, and in 1956 Pakistan became the Islamic Republic of Pakistan. Both countries voluntarily retained their association with the British Commonwealth.

Partition left the problem of minorities unsolved. India still has a minority of 35 to 40 million Moslems, and Hindus account for about 13 per cent of Pakistan's population.

One-third of India was formerly made up of Native States under their own hereditary rulers, the largest and most important being Hyderabad. With independence and the establishment of national governments, the Native States have acceded to either India or Pakistan; the status of Kashmir is still unsettled.

TRANSPORTATION   Historically, the great centers of Indian civilization were in river valleys; streams served as major arteries of transportation, and overland movement was made largely by bullock cart or pack animals. The railway era began in 1853, and by 1900 the main pattern was almost complete. Originally designed for political and economic control, railroads not only contributed to the growth of Indian trade and industry but also to the rapid movement of food in time of famine.

The railway pattern indicates European interest in commerce; most lines focus on the major ports of Karachi, Bombay, Madras, and Calcutta. The densely populated plain, extending from the Punjab to the Ganges Delta, is served by the most extensive rail net in Asia.

Under Partition, transportation facilities that had been developed to serve a single country were divided into three parts. India received 34,000 route miles of railways, and Pakistan 7,000 route miles, about three-fourths of which are in West Pakistan, and one-fourth in East Pakistan. The three major ports of Calcutta, Bombay, and Madras are in India; Karachi and Chittagong serve Pakistan.

In contrast to railroad construction, highway building has lagged. There are only 90,000 miles of all-weather roads in the entire subcontinent and at least twenty times as many bullock carts as motor vehicles. Waterways are of great significance in Bengal, where a network of canals and channels provides access to many areas not served by land transport. In East Pakistan a large portion of the jute, tea, and paddy crops are moved via waterways which ramify over most of the Delta.

THE REPUBLIC OF INDIA

The Republic of India supports a human population of 445 million and an animal population of 300 million. Predominantly rural, 86 per cent of the people in 1960 gained their livelihood from agriculture. In few countries is the pressure upon the land so great. As population increased through the centuries of India's history, farms decreased in size, the per capita land resource gradually declining to less than 1 acre. Under Hindu and Moslem inheritance laws, a small farm may be divided into several smaller parcels to assure all heirs a fair share in each type of land, such as wasteland, upland, or floodplain. Repetition of these divisions generation after generation has resulted in excessive fragmentation; thus agriculture is often inefficient and uneconomic.

The first concern of farmers is to satisfy their daily food requirements. Major edible crops fall into three groups, cereals, pulses, and oilseeds. About 75 per cent of the cultivated area is devoted to grains, including rice, wheat, sorghums, millet, maize, and barley; rice alone occupies one-third of all the cultivated land. Pulses, an important source of protein, rank second in acreage, followed by the oilseeds: peanuts, rape and mustard, linseed, and sesame. Of the fifteen crops occupying more than 1 million acres each, all are edible except cotton and jute.

In addition to being one of the most populous countries, India ranks first in the number of cattle—approximately 160 million. Oxen are used for working the fields as well as for transport. The sacred cows are not worked, but their milk is a valuable addition to the diet. The 40 million water buffaloes are valued as work animals; their milk is larger in quantity and higher in butterfat content than that of Indian cows.

Crop yields per acre are lower than in many other Asian countries. Contributory causes include unreliable precipitation, erosion, soil depletion, and poor seed, as well as inadequate fertilizer. Since dung is in great demand for fuel, probably less than half of the animal manures are applied to the fields, and India makes no systematic use of night soil, a common practice in both Japan and China. Land is too scarce to be planted to soil-building cover crops, and chemical fertilizers are too expensive.

The drier lands carry some 60 million sheep and goats and ½ million camels. Horses, ponies, and donkeys are used mainly for transportation in towns and cities. Animal husbandry has received scant attention, but India collects and exports annually some 65 million dollars' worth of wool, hides and skins, bristles, and bones.

Considerable intensive gardening is carried on in areas accessible to urban markets as well as on estates for the large-scale cultivation of export commodities such as tea and coffee. Although estates employ large numbers of laborers and provide valuable exports, peasant agriculture, with its great emphasis upon food, is infinitely more significant.

AGRICULTURE

FOOD CROPS   One of the world's major cereals, rice, is preferred by the half of the human race living in Southern and Eastern Asia. Rice is accorded highest prestige value and dominates the local economy to such an extent that social customs and religious celebrations are in many areas closely related to its growth cycle.

With approximately one-third of the world's rice acreage, India ranks first in land planted but second to China in total harvest. Paddy (rough rice) is a summer crop of the wet lowlands, thriving under temperatures of 75°F and 50 to 80 inches of precipitation. With less than 40 inches, however, irrigation is necessary. Produc-

Figure 15-8   A farm family at work in a paddy field. Note the absence of machinery. (Courtesy of Consulate General of India.)

tion is heaviest in the well-watered coastal plains and windward slopes of the Western Ghats. One crop a year is usual, but a few well-watered areas are double-cropped. In villages, husking and polishing are done by hand, but in the larger centers, milling is mechanized. Paddy is generally consumed in the locality where grown, but any small surplus is moved to nearby markets by bullock carts or small boats.

Wheat, the most important commercial grain, is grown principally as a winter crop on the alluviums of the Ganges Valley west of Benares, and on deep, black soils of the peninsula which retain sufficient moisture to carry it to maturity. Yields vary considerably, the national average being 12 bushels per acre. With 24 million acres in wheat, India ranks third in the world. The entire crop is consumed locally, and additional wheat and flour are imported. Rice and wheat are expensive cereals eaten by the upper-income groups, whereas the cheaper but highly nutritious millets constitute the major food supply of middle- and lower-income groups.

Many varieties of millet are grown throughout India, but production is most heavily concentrated in the peninsula. It is generally a winter or dry-season crop grown in rotation with cotton, although in a few places it is planted at the beginning of the rainy season. Millets occupy 67 million acres, ranking after rice (80 million) but ahead of wheat (30 million). Millet will produce 500 to 1,000 pounds of grain per acre, and it is customary to interplant pulses. Millet is primarily for

Figure 15-9   Husking rice by driving animals over it to knock the grains from the husk. (Courtesy of Consulate General of India.)

human consumption, but the poorer grain and the stalks are used for animal feed.

Corn and barley are grown extensively in the Ganges Valley and in Kashmir, mainly for human consumption. More than 7 million acres are planted to each. Corn, the chief food grain among certain hill tribes, gives way to barley at higher elevations.

Pulses include a variety of peas and beans, an indispensable source of protein in the predominantly vegetable diet. Most important of the pulses is gram, or chickpea, which is scattered throughout India—20 million acres—but with a major concentration in Uttar Pradesh. Barley and gram are cheap, staple foods in north India.

Although sugar cane is widely grown, it is concentrated on the Gangetic alluviums. Because it competes with food grains for land, it tends to be a minor crop—4 million acres. Two-thirds of the cane is crushed in small local mills worked by animal power and the juice boiled down to make gur (unrefined sugar); one-third of the cane goes to mills using the centrifugal process. The entire output is absorbed by the domestic market and supplemented by imports. Sugar is also obtained from several varieties of palms.

India leads the world in the production of peanuts, the major areas being Bombay, Madras, and Hyderabad. Domestic markets absorb the larger share of the crop. High in fat and protein content, peanuts are crushed in local power mills and the oil made into ghee. Other edible oilseeds are cotton, sesame, rape, and mustard. Nonedible linseed and castor oil are used in industry.

Although commercial production is limited, fruits are grown in thousands of individual gardens. Bananas and papayas are basic foodstuffs, but the mango, mangosteen, and durian are more highly esteemed. Oranges are widely distributed, and apples, pears, and grapes are grown in the cooler areas. The coconut has a multiplicity of uses, yielding edible oil and many by-products.

Spices, which attracted early traders, are still grown along the Malabar Coast, especially nutmeg, cloves, and pepper. Chili, ginger, and mustard come from other areas. Indian curry powder is compounded of many pungent spices.

NONEDIBLE CROPS   The tobacco crop of 570 million pounds annually is second in

Figure 15-10   The village cultivators bring their cotton to market, and the dealers pack it first into 100-pound bags. These bags are then sewed into 300-pound bundles and loaded on oxcarts for transportation to mills or railheads. (Courtesy of Government of India.)

size only to that of the United States, the Indian leaf coming from the fields and garden patches of small farmers. Coir, made from the fibrous husk of the coconut, is the basis of a profitable cottage industry in south India. Coir yarn as well as mats and matting are exported. Dozens of other crops are locally significant and are traded in the village market.

Most of the Indian cotton, which is high in quantity but low in quality, is grown under the natural rainfall of the summer monsoon rather than by irrigation. It is cultivated in the middle Ganges and in the peninsula, but the leading region is the Deccan Plateau inland from Bombay. Here the fertile black soils have been formed by the weathering of old lavas, and although the rainfall is 20 to 35 inches, the soil is sufficiently tenacious to retain moisture until the crop matures. In a region where rainfall is precarious, the Deccan cotton crop fluctuates from year to year, and the average yield is low, about 100 pounds per acre.

Until the end of the eighteenth century India was one of Great Britain's major sources of raw cotton, but as advances in the textile industry called for a longer staple and finer fibers for higher-quality cloth, India lost most of the Lancashire market. Large quantities of short-staple cotton are sold to Japan and other industrial countries which manufacture cotton textiles for markets with low purchasing power. Part of the 3.5-million-bale crop is used locally by the handloom industry as well as by many large mechanized mills.

India was exporting cloth handwoven from jute in the eighteenth century, but large-scale use of the fiber did not begin until about 1840. New machinery and methods pioneered by Scottish weavers in Dundee opened wider markets for this cheap but strong fiber, and India secured a virtual world monopoly in raw jute.

Optimum growing conditions are found in the lower Ganges-Brahmaputra basin, where favorable climate and alluvial soil, enriched by annual inundation, ensure high yields.

Before 1950 all jute mills were in or near Calcutta, although more than two-thirds of the fiber was grown in Pakistan. To supply its mills on the Hooghly, India has recently doubled jute acreage.

ESTATE AGRICULTURE   In the Indian economy, estate agriculture is completely overshadowed by small-scale cultivation. The total acreage in tea, coffee, rubber, and cinchona is minimal compared with that of the major food crops. The million wage laborers on plantations are insignificant in comparison with 240 million peasant farmers and their families.

Tea is India's leading plantation crop. The type grown is of indigenous origin and differs in quality from that domesticated elsewhere in Asia. Large-scale planting began in the late nineteenth century. Tea can be grown in the lowlands, but it thrives best on well-drained slopes between 1,000 and 4,000 feet in elevation. About one-half of the total acreage is now in Assam, with a smaller region in the vicinity of Darjeeling; 60 per cent of the Indian tea industry is owned by long-established British firms that employ many Nepalese laborers.

In the Madras and Travancore highlands, the gardens are about 4,000 feet in elevation. Labor is recruited from the more densely settled parts of India. Distinctive quality and flavor are associated with different districts, Darjeeling tea having a preferential rating in the United States. In addition to the large home market, India exports 445 million pounds of tea, or about one-half of the total entering world trade.

Slope land with good drainage, temperatures averaging 80°F, and afternoon rains provide a suitable habitat for rubber. British estates are localized along the Malabar Coast, but most Indian-owned estates have been established at higher elevations of 1,000 to 2,000 feet. About 100,000 acres of trees are being tapped; the annual harvest is processed mainly by Indian mills.

COTTAGE INDUSTRIES

For centuries small-scale and cottage industries were an integral part of the self-sufficient village economy of India. Utilitarian articles were produced everywhere; in certain areas specialized skills were highly developed, and artistic products were frequently carried long distances by sailing ship or caravan. India claims to have been the original home of cotton weaving and for several thousand years exported fine cloth.

From the sixteenth into the nineteenth century varied textiles including muslins, chintzes, and calicoes were exported, as were embroidered shawls, silks, and carpets. Apprentices under master craftsmen attained skill in metalwork, brass, copper, bronze, and silver; most of these artisans worked at home with simple tools. Integrated into the local economy, such handicrafts enabled India to sell competitively both at home and abroad.

The industrial revolution, with its outpouring of machine-made goods, had the effect of depressing craft manufacture in India, and many small industries gradually disappeared. After a long period of stagnation in cottage industries, the national government is officially encouraging their revival as a means of reducing unemployment as well as of increasing production for both local and foreign markets. The handloom industry now produces about 20 per cent of the nation's cloth and employs 14 million workers, five times as many as all factories combined. Weaving silk, wool, and rugs by hand supports additional tens of thousands. Inlaid metals, filigree, lacquer and horn articles, brassware, and ivory are made for world markets.

Figure 15-11 Carpet weaving in an Amritsar factory. The two strips of paper on the loom contain design and color instructions for the weaver. (Courtesy of Government of India.)

LARGE-SCALE INDUSTRY

India possesses most of the requisites for modern large-scale industry. Coal reserves are large, India ranking seventh in world production; 90 per cent of the present output comes from the Damodar Valley. Railroads consume about one-third of the coal, and lesser amounts are used by the steel and textile industries, for thermal electricity, and for export.

The most highly mineralized area extends from the coalfields of the Damodar Valley to the goldfields of Mysore. Actively worked minerals include high-grade iron ore, the ferroalloys—manganese and chromite—bauxite, and mica. Agricultural materials most available to industry include cotton, jute, wool, oilseeds, hides, and skins. Although half of the developed hydroelectric power is in the vicinity of Bombay, the greatest potential is along the Himalayas, in the Western Ghats, and in the southern hills.

TEXTILE INDUSTRIES It was not until 1856 that the first cotton mill began operation in Bombay, where there were many natural advantages; three years later a second was established at Ahmedabad. Coincident with railway building, the industry spread inland to Nagpur, thence southward through the cotton-growing districts of the peninsula. In the Ganges Valley the first mills were in Cawnpore and Delhi, later in Bengal.

The cotton textile industry, employing some 600,000 persons, is widely dispersed, but over one-half of all the mills are concentrated in Bombay and the Ahmedabad district. For many years India exported raw fiber and imported machine-made cloth, but with the development of the domestic industry that situation has been reversed. India still exports short-staple fiber but imports the long-staple cotton required for higher-grade textiles. The country has become the world's leading exporter of cotton cloth.

Jute manufacturing, concentrated along the Hooghly River, developed after the Bengal coalfields were opened in connection with railway construction. Bengal jute and available coal for power provided the impetus for large-scale mechanization. Jute manufactures fall into the four main classes of gunny bags for rice and wheat, burlap for baling cotton or wool, coarse rugs and carpets, cordage and yarn. Jute manufactures add 240 million dollars annually to Indian exports.

Indian silks have long been famous for their fine color and distinctive patterns, but when local sericulture declined, India became an importer of silk yarn to supply both the cottage industries and the mills. Certain kinds of high-quality handwoven materials are in demand at home and abroad, Benares being noted for its silks interspersed with metallic threads. Machine manufacture has developed slowly, the mills being concentrated in the Ganges Valley.

Wool is the smallest of the mechanized textile industries. Because of the warm weather over much of India, there is little need for woolen clothing, but in the north there is some demand for handmade cloth and blankets. Punjab mills manufacture short-fiber local wool into blankets, carpets, and felts. The better-quality woolens and worsteds are made of long-fiber wool imported from Afghanistan, Iran, and Australia. In several localities carpets and rugs are woven for Western markets.

IRON AND STEEL The area southwest of Calcutta has varied resources for heavy

Figure 15-12   Blast furnaces of the Bhilai Steel Plant, Bhilai. (Courtesy of Consulate General of India.)

industry, all conveniently grouped within a relatively small radius. Coking coal from the Damodar Valley, high-grade iron ore from Orissa, and a range of ferroalloys, including manganese and chrome, can be brought together at moderate transport cost.

The Jamshedpur mill, 150 miles west of Calcutta, began pouring iron in 1911 and has expanded into the largest steelmaker in India. An exporter of both pig iron and steel, Jamshedpur is also a fabricator, making tin plate, wire and nails, plates, and structural steel. Jamshedpur has become a little Pittsburgh, attracting numerous subsidiary industries.

Large reserves of bauxite are available in the same general area, and aluminum fabrication has been added to the Indian economy.

CITIES

Delhi is situated near the low divide between the Indus and Ganges Valleys, with the ruins of many previous capitals nearby. Made prosperous by trade, old Delhi expanded under the impetus of irrigation agriculture. When caravan routes in the area were succeeded by railroads, the city became the hub of the Indian rail net and increased in popula-

tion to over 900,000. A walled city with mosques, palaces, and narrow congested streets, Delhi is famous for its beautiful handicrafts. Local cotton is spun and woven in large mills, and there is considerable handloom weaving and other cottage industries; the finer manufactures include jewelry, carved ivory, and embroidery in gold or silver thread.

Five miles south, a new capital was dedicated in 1931, its broad boulevards flanked by government buildings, fine residences, and foreign embassies. The hotels, apartment houses, and colonnaded luxury shops along Kingsway in New Delhi cater to officialdom and the well-to-do. The two Delhis with a combined population of 2.3 million are complementary in function.

Calcutta, established in 1690 as a fort and factory of the East India Company, is well located on the Hooghly River. Westernmost of the Ganges Delta channels, the Hooghly is navigable far inland. Calcutta soon became the commercial entrepôt for all of eastern India. One-quarter of the country's factory production is now on Hooghly-side, where a 60-mile stretch of river has become a great industrial conurbation with Calcutta as its node. Factories line both banks, the heavier industries directly at waterfront, where handling costs for raw materials are minimal. This is the world center for jute spinning. Consumer goods manufactured include soap, tobacco, paper, and cotton textiles, and also wares made of iron, brass, and copper. Calcutta has a population of 3 million, with another million in the metropolitan area.

Bombay, whose population is 4 million, is situated on an island off the west coast of India; it resembles Calcutta in commerce but is less diversified in industry. Based on raw material from the Deccan, cotton spinning is the leading industry. Bombay has one-quarter of all Indian cotton mills as well as other manufacturing, including rubber, chemicals, machin-

ery, and automobile assembly. The Cotton Depot has warehousing for 1 million bales, and the Grain Depot provides ample storage for wheat and oilseeds.

Madras, the third largest city, is the major industrial and commercial center of south India. Early English enterprisers who traded in handwoven cloth and cotton textiles are still dominant. The big mills do more spinning than weaving, the thread being purchased by local handloom operators. Leather is tanned in many large and small factories. Located on a broad coastal plain, Madras is less congested than most Indian cities.

Hyderabad, not to be confused with

Figure 15-13   Bombay is the largest city in western India. It is as modern as any American or European city. (Courtesy of Government of India.)

Hyderabad, Pakistan, is a city of 1.3 million and the long-time capital of the feudal state of the same name. Its princely Moslem rulers drew part of their wealth from diamond mines, one of which produced the famous Koh-i-Noor; but cotton, cattle, and food crops raised by tank irrigation are the main sources of income. Modern industry includes locomotive and railway car building, but skilled Oriental crafts are the predominant occupation in old Hyderabad, which is less Westernized than the other large Indian cities. Ahmedabad, located in the cotton-producing area of Gujarat, is also a leader in textile manufacturing.

THE ISLAMIC REPUBLIC OF PAKISTAN

The Islamic Republic of Pakistan is divided into two parts separated by 1,000 air miles, about 1,200 surface transport miles, and more than 3,000 miles by sea. Both the land and the population are unequally divided. West Pakistan, with 311,406 square miles of area, has 41 million inhabitants, or 131 per square mile; East Pakistan supports 53 million people on 54,501 square miles, or 969 per square mile. West Pakistan is hot, arid, and barren, the struggle for water transcending

Figure 15-14 Customers looking over the wares of one of the sidewalk merchants. Such scenes are common in the cities of India. (Courtesy of United Nations.)

Figure 15-15 The Badshahi Mosque, Lahore, Pakistan, as seen from the southeast, showing the façade of Prayer Hall. (Courtesy of Embassy of Pakistan.)

all else; East Pakistan, hot and humid but well watered by the summer monsoon, is green with luxuriant vegetative cover, a land where floods and drainage pose serious problems. The Republic as a whole is predominantly rural, but in West Pakistan settlements are clustered along rivers and canals, whereas in East Pakistan they are dispersed. Mainly agricultural, West Pakistan produces wheat, cotton, millet, hides and skins; East Pakistan is noted for its rice, jute, and tea. Moslems account for 86 per cent of the 94 million people, the Hindu minority, 13 per cent.

WEST PAKISTAN

West Pakistan is a rectilinear area extending from the Himalayas some 800 miles to the Arabian Sea, and from Afghanistan-Iran on the west to the Thar Desert on the east, with the valleys of the Indus and its affluents as the productive heart of the area.

PHYSICAL SETTING

INDUS SYSTEM   Rising in Tibet, the Indus cuts through the Himalayas and then flows the full length of West Pakistan to the Arabian Sea. On the west it is joined by the Kabul River from the highlands of Afghanistan, but the more significant tributaries are to the east: the Jhelum, Chenab, Ravi, Beas, and Sutlej. All have their headwaters in India. The largest and best-developed part of the Punjab consists of the combined valleys of these eastern affluents which rise in the Himalayas and, fed by melting snows and monsoon rain, become rushing torrents laden with debris and silt. The fan-shaped plain of the Five Rivers is floored with alluviums of great depth. Extending for several hundred miles along the mountain front, the plain in the south is pinched to a narrow gap between the Sulaiman Mountains and the Thar Desert. The Five Rivers, merging into a single stream, enter the Indus halfway to the Arabian Sea.

CLIMATE   Climatically, both the Punjab and the Sind (lower Indus Valley) are deserts. Punjab summers are hot, averaging 90 to 95°F although daily maxima may reach 110 to 120°F; winters are cool, 50 to 55°F. Rainfall is scant in total amount, ranging from 7 to 20 inches with marked concentration in July and August (Table

15-1). Light winter rains are invaluable. Except for the northern foothills, the area is too dry for agriculture, and nearly all crops must be irrigated.

The Sind is a true desert with high average temperatures (Jacobabad: June, 97°F, January, 57°F), clear skies, and low relative humidity except along the coast. Precipitation is both scant and erratic. Hyderabad, which averages 8 inches annually, has recorded a 10-inch downpour in one day.

WATER   Crossed by successive waves of conquerors, ancient Pakistan was a transit land with occasional settlements along the rivers or close to the northern mountains. More than two thousand years ago lands in the Indus Valley were being irrigated. The lowlands could be inundated by simple stream diversion, but to raise water to higher levels various devices were used, including the scoop, shadoof, and Persian water wheel. Underground sources were tapped by wells, and the water was lifted by animals or manpower.

In 1849, soon after the province was annexed, the British began rehabilitating old canals that had fallen into disuse. Many of these were on the lower Indus, Jhelum, and Sutlej Rivers. It was the lower Chenab Canal, however, which first called attention to the high productivity of the soil when irrigated, and to the effectiveness of canal colonies in the settlement of arid but fertile lands. By 1920 the irrigated area had increased to 1.5 million acres, and thousands of miles of canals and distributaries carried the waters of the Five Rivers to the undulating plains of the eastern Punjab, whose deep alluviums now support over 90 per cent of its people. Since the water of the Five Rivers flows through India, where it is diminished by irrigation removals be-

fore entering Pakistan, control of the sources of these rivers might constitute a threat to the agriculture of the Indus Valley. Completion of projects on the Indus and reclamation of land in the western Punjab will lessen the risk. The great Sukkur Barrage, in northern Sind, was built across the Indus in 1932. Nearly a mile long, it supplies one of the world's largest irrigation districts, covering about 5 million acres. The Kotri Barrage on the lower Indus near Hyderabad, begun in 1950, now provides an assured water supply for an additional 3 million acres.

Major irrigation systems have thus far been confined to the lands lying east of the Jhelum, but the new multipurpose Thal Project, with its Jinnah Barrage now under construction on the Indus, will add two hydroelectric plants and 1.5 million crop acres to the Western Punjab. The Warsak Project on the Kabul River near Peshawar will also irrigate 100,000 acres, but its main purpose is to supply power for industries in the local area and to the Punjab power grid.

Throughout West Pakistan irrigation projects have given greater stability to agriculture and a better living to smallholders. The main problem is alkalinity as an aftermath of irrigation.

AGRICULTURE

CROPS   In West Pakistan food crops occupy three-quarters of the cultivated area, with wheat in first position—12 million acres. It is sown as a winter crop in the Sind and the Punjab, the latter being the major wheat-growing province. The Sind plants nearly as much rice as wheat, and part of the surplus goes to more densely populated East Pakistan. Corn is grown in various districts. The millets, low water users, are especially suitable for many acres and supply an inexpensive bread-stuff at all seasons. Oilseeds—linseed, sesame, and rape—occupy a much smaller acreage than grains but are expanding, and sugar cane is cultivated in many irrigated areas.

In contrast to India, where the Deccan cotton crop is dependent on natural rainfall, in Pakistan cotton is entirely under irrigation. The fiber is indigenous to the Indus Valley, but higher-yielding American upland varieties have been introduced and constitute 90 per cent of the Pakistan crop. The staple now ginned is nearly 1 inch in length, grading higher than most Indian fiber; some long-staple Egyptian cotton is also grown.

With new irrigation projects, the area in cotton has expanded. Led by the production in the Punjab and Sind, the total crop is 1.3 million bales per year, of which about 400,000 are exported.

DOMESTICATED ANIMALS   In the Punjab plains bullocks and buffaloes are used for plowing the fields, cow buffaloes for milk, and camels for riding and plowing. In the Sind cattle are raised in irrigated areas. Beasts of burden include horses, donkeys, and camels; the last are the most valuable for transport, and there is an extensive network of camel paths in the Sind Desert. In the mountainous frontier provinces and in Baluchistan to the west, the people are pastoral nomads, keeping sheep, goats, donkeys, and camels and migrating seasonally from lower to higher elevations.

The wool, hides, and skins from millions of animals provide the basis for many home industries, such as weaving, leather-working, and shoemaking. Local tanning and wool weaving are increasing, but Pakistan annually exports some $35 million worth of hides and wool.

INDUSTRY AND CITIES

Before Partition, West Pakistan produced one-third of the Indian cotton crop but had few mills; it provided most of the skins, hides, and wool processed in India. Cottage industries included the making of lacquer, pottery, embroidery, and carpets and the spinning and handloom weaving of local cotton and wool. Large-scale industries were limited to several cement and flour mills and two petroleum refineries. The government has inaugurated a program of economic development, giving priority to irrigation, electrification, and manufacturing. Power fuels are in short supply; developed water power is inadequate and must be supplemented from India over the Punjab grid. But an extensive natural gas field near the Indus, connected by pipeline to Karachi, has added to the industrial potential. Mineral resources include petroleum and coal in commercial amounts.

Factories using power-driven machinery are now manufacturing cotton yarn and cloth, cement, steel ingots, rubber tires, sugar, and vegetable oils. Industries tend to be concentrated in the northern Punjab between Peshawar and Lahore, but lower Sind has cotton ginning, tanneries, salt, and cement.

Both the agricultural and the industrial future of West Pakistan depend upon the development and wise use of water resources for irrigation and for power.

A small fishing village when acquired by the British in 1843, Karachi had a deep natural harbor but a desert hinterland of scant value. A railway up the Indus Valley made it the recognized outlet for the wheat and cotton lands of the Punjab. With the opening of the Suez Canal, Karachi became a major stop on the trading route from Europe to all Asiatic and Australian ports. It serves as outport for the Afghan trade and is the beneficiary of all irrigation expansion in the Punjab and Sind. Its world significance is enhanced by its strategic location on international air routes. From 1947 to 1959 Karachi was the capital of Pakistan, and its area enlarged from 30 to 566 square miles. The population has increased to 1,400,000 since Partition.

Lahore, second city of Pakistan and capital of Punjab province, developed at a crossing of routes between the Ganges and Indus Valleys and the mountain passes to the northwest. Long established as a Moslem culture center, Lahore has expanded as a result of irrigation developments. Produce marketing, flour, cotton, and woolen mills, and modern railway car shops help to support a population of about 1 million.

Hyderabad, a railway junction and market center, is the capital of Sind province. Through the ancient caravan station of Peshawar, near the northwest frontier, passes much of the Afghan trade with India and Pakistan. Sialkot and Rawalpindi serve as market centers for mountain-flank regions, the latter receiving goods from Kashmir. In 1959 the capital was shifted from Karachi to a site, to be called Islamabad, near Rawalpindi, in which the government maintains its offices.

EAST PAKISTAN

East Pakistan consists of the eastern three-fourths of former Indian Bengal, which was divided to make two new provinces; West Bengal remained with India, and East Bengal formed the larger part of East Pakistan. A portion of the highland of Assam was also transferred to the new eastern province.

BENGAL FLOOD PLAIN

East Bengal occupies the larger portion of the great plain formed by the joint floodwaters of the Ganges, the Bramaputra, and numerous lesser rivers from the peripheral hills and mountains. In their lower reaches the two larger streams are joined by the shorter Surma-Meghna system, which rises in the Assam Hills. Fed by monsoon rains, these streams annually inundate a great part of the lowlands, their waters reaching the Bay of Bengal by a series of interlaced and constantly shifting delta mouths.

The multiple deltas are active areas of land building, as loads of stream-borne silt extend the coastline seaward. The newer delta lands are not immediately available for agriculture. An immense area along the south coast is occupied by the Sunderbans, a wilderness of mangrove swamp and forested jungle cut by numerous creeks and tidal channels. The more active mouths of the larger distributaries are in East Bengal, sometimes called the new delta. In contrast to West Bengal, where old channels are silting and only the Hooghly carries much water, East Bengal has 2,600 miles of navigable waterways.

LAND USE

With its high temperatures and 60 to 80 inches of annual precipitation, East Pakistan is a green land where vegetation is luxuriant and most wet crops flourish. Great expanses of flooded paddy and jute fields are interspersed with smaller patches of sugar cane, oilseeds, peas, and beans, coconuts in the south, and tea in the eastern hills—all indicative of an abundant tropical rainfall. Eighty per cent of the total area is under cultivation, mainly by small farmers owning a few acres, or by tenants of the large landowners.

There are few cities and not many large market towns, for East Bengal is predominantly rural. Dispersed habitation is more common than settlement in villages. Individual farmsteads, thickly scattered across the low plains, are placed on artificial mounds of earth which serve as safety islands during the flood season. Even these raised bits of land are not idle; patches of tobacco, vegetable gardens, various tree fruits, and coconuts or bamboo surround the thatched houses. Population density in East Pakistan is over 770 persons per square mile.

AGRICULTURE

JUTE   The broad flood plains of Bengal have long been the center for the cultivation of jute, one of the world's cheapest but most valuable fibers. Known as early as 800 B.C., the plant leaves were used for food, the fibers extracted and twisted into cordage or woven into coarse cloth. In 1750, sackcloth made on handlooms was a common item of Bengal commerce; the East India Company traded in gunny bags and shipped raw jute to England for the manufacture of rope and twine.

In 1822, a consignment of jute reached Dundee, Scotland, a famous flax-weaving center. In addition to practicing better methods for spinning and weaving jute, these mills developed hessian cloth, a tightly woven and durable fabric suitable for grain sacks. They bleached the fiber, made waterproof canvas and tarpaulins, and mixed jute with cotton and wool to make carpets, curtains, and upholstery fabrics. Modern jute milling spread from Dundee to the Hooghly district of India, and the rising world demand for cheap textiles created a ready market for the fiber.

Figure 15-16 After being retted and washed, Bengal jute is hung on bamboo racks to dry in the sun. (Courtesy of Government of Pakistan.)

Optimum conditions for jute cultivation in the Ganges-Brahmaputra lowlands include the 60- to 80-inch rainfall, high humidity during the growing season, a well-saturated soil, and ample water for retting. Flooded fields, with fresh alluvium being added annually, can be cropped year after year for high yields, but lands above flood level need fertilizers or crop rotation.

Sown in a well-prepared seedbed, then weeded and gradually thinned, Bengal jute develops a canelike stalk that reaches a height of 8 to 10 feet in a 5-month growing season. The stalks are cut by hand with a sickle, tied in bundles, and soaked in streams or ponds for ten to twenty days. During this process, known as retting, the pith ferments and disintegrates, so that the fibers can be stripped loose.

After it has been washed and dried, the soft yellowish fiber is ready for market. Few major crops require more man-hours of tedious labor.

Middlemen travel through the Bengal countryside buying dry jute, which is transported to collecting centers by bullock cart or by cargo boats and small steamers on the Delta channels. At the warehouse the loose bundles of fiber are sorted and graded, then compressed into standard 400-pound bales for export.

The great Bengal plain produces 98 per cent of the world's jute, two-thirds of it in East Pakistan, where it is the most valuable cash and export crop, exceeding $140 million per year. Before Partition all the jute mills were in West Bengal along the Hooghly, and most of the crop was shipped westward via the long Calcutta and Eastern Canal which bisects the Delta. Smaller exports were made through Chittagong.

The newly created East Pakistan of 1947 had few baling stations or warehouses and no jute mills. India is now planting more jute in West Bengal, and East Pakistan is building mills. Large mills near Dacca, at Khulna, and at Chittagong, are weaving burlap for the foreign market, several more are under construction, and Pakistan hopes to export less raw fiber and more manufactured jute. Part of the crop is still exported in bond through Calcutta, and Hooghly mills buy East Bengal jute for processing, the United Kingdom being the next best customer.

TEA   The eastern borderlands of Bengal extend into the Assam Plateau. On these hill slopes, particularly in the upper Surma Valley tributary to Sylhet, there are 82,000 acres of tea plantations. Sylhet has a rainfall of more than 150 inches annually, the other natural conditions being similar to the larger Assam tea region across the Indian border. Some 10 to 12 pickings are made annually; the East Pakistan tea crop averages 50 million pounds. Tea chests move by rail to dockside at Chittagong and are shipped to the domestic market in West Pakistan or overseas to the London tea auctions. In the export trade of East Pakistan, tea is second only to jute.

RICE   Although jute is the great cash and export crop, the East Bengal farmer depends on rice; in contrast to 8 to 10 per cent in jute, paddy is grown on three-quarters of the cultivated land. Rainfall is ample, two-thirds of the 60 or more inches coming during the four hottest summer months; the annual inundation enriches many soils with new alluvium, although excessive flooding is often a serious problem. Where moisture is sufficient, a second crop of rice is planted in the same year. Many different varieties are grown; floating rice, whose stalk lengthens as waters rise, is a specialty in East Bengal floodlands.

Although the Pakistan paddy crop averages 27 billion pounds annually, one-third that of India, East Bengal is a deficit area, obtaining additional rice or substitutes from West Pakistan. Land under paddy has been increasing at the rate of 150,000 acres yearly, mainly at the expense of jute. More acreage might be added by the drainage and reclamation of the Sunderbans, the unused jungle of the lower deltas.

CITIES

Dacca, the new capital of East Pakistan, was the capital of Bengal three centuries ago. In the days of cottage industry exports, the city was a famous center for fine muslins. Surrounded by the richest rice and jute lands in Bengal, Dacca has

Figure 15-17   Threshing paddy by hand in East Pakistan. (Courtesy of Government of Pakistan.)

Figure 15-18   A street scene in Dacca, East Pakistan. Note the variations in styles of clothing and transportation. (Courtesy of Embassy of Pakistan.)

grown rapidly since its recent selection as capital of East Pakistan, and the population, including its port, Narayanganj, now exceeds 600,000. New industries include cotton and jute weaving.

East of the Ganges-Bramaputra Delta, the small coastal city of Chittagong has become the major port of East Pakistan. Situated some 10 miles upriver from the Bay of Bengal, it was used as a trading post by the Portuguese in the sixteenth century, but was not so well located for Bengal commerce as Calcutta on the Hooghly. Considerable jute moved across Chittagong wharves, and the Assam-Bengal Railway made the city a shipping and supply port for the upcountry tea planters of the Assam Plateau.

After 1947 jute shipments expanded rapidly, cargo through Chittagong rising from 4 to 16 million tons in the five years after Partition. New facilities included jute mills, harbor expansions, and a water power installation in the Chittagong hills;

a new paper factory uses quick-growing bamboo, produced locally but formerly shipped to Calcutta paper mills. Many Pakistan imports and exports are now channeled through the expanded port rather than via Calcutta, and there is regular passenger-freighter service to Karachi.

INDIAN BORDERLANDS

On India's northern border in the central and eastern Himalayas are the landlocked independent kingdom of Nepal and the Indian protectorates of Sikkim and Bhutan.

NEPAL

Nepal, comparable in size to Wisconsin, supports some 8 million people mainly by agriculture and cottage industries; but population pressure upon the limited arable land causes steady emigration, especially to Sikkim and Darjeeling. Because of rugged topography, transportation is heavily dependent upon porters. The capital city of Katamandu, which dominates the largest valley, is extremely isolated by land but easily accessible by air.

Figure 15-19 Gateway into the Hanuman Dhoka Square in Katmandu. Notice the tile buildings, the systems of transportation, and the dress of the people. (Courtesy of United Nations.)

SIKKIM

Sikkim, tiny enclave between Nepal and Bhutan, commands the main trade route between India and Tibet via the famed Chumbi Valley. Cultivation and dispersed settlements are usually above 3,000 feet, and there is a well-developed system of transhumance. Except for Gangtok, capital and chief market place, villages tended to develop around monasteries or to serve as staging points on the Tibetan trade route. Pack animals crossed the 12,000-foot pass bringing Tibetan wool to India in exchange for cottons, silks, and other manufactures.

BHUTAN

Bhutan, like Sikkim, is a Buddhist country with many monasteries. Located in the eastern Himalayas, it is cut by high ridges and deep valleys. Many of its settlements are concentrated along the track connecting with the Chumbi Valley route. Subtropical crops are grown in the southern lowlands, but upland cultivation, largely of maize and millet, is of the shifting type. Bhutanese are skilled in working wood and are also noted for their metalware and handicrafts.

Oriented toward the south, Nepal's contacts are mainly with India; Bhutan is physically and culturally oriented toward Tibet, now under Chinese control. The 70-mile Sikkim corridor normally functions as a strategic route between the Indian lowlands and the vast Tibetan plateau.

KINGDOM OF AFGHANISTAN

A diverse and massive highland covers three-fourths of Afghanistan. Extending westward from the central mountain core of Asia, the Hindu Kush varies in height from 15,000 to 20,000 feet; including the lower ranges attached to it on the west and south, this mountain complex is continuous for 600 miles. The broad valley basin surrounding the capital, Kabul, has an elevation of 6,000 feet. On the north the Hindu Kush slopes gradually to a 2,000-foot plain, where the Amu Dar'ya marks the Soviet border. On the south a flatter tableland of 2,500 to 3,000 feet is rimmed by the border mountains of Pakistan.

Much of Afghanistan's 250,000 square miles is semiarid, precipitation varying from 11 to 15 inches, but vast areas are drier, the Seistan Desert receiving only 2 to 3 inches annually. Although rainfall is both low and irregular, snowfall in the higher mountains is usually dependable. Highland temperatures drop below zero in winter, and there is also below-freezing weather in the southern deserts. Summer heat is everywhere extreme, with high temperatures, strong winds, and blinding dust storms.

Most of the rivers drain to the landlocked Aral Sea or evaporate in various deserts. The waters of the Kabul River, however, reach the ocean by way of the Indus.

LAND UTILIZATION

GRAZING   In areas of scant rainfall and extensive mountain slopes, grass is the most valuable resource; an estimated 2 million of the 14 million inhabitants are pastoral nomads. Grazing is widespread, and transhumance is common; the herdsman with his camels and black tents drives his animals to the mountains in spring, then returns to lower pastures in autumn. Cattle, camels, and goats are grazed, but sheep, a source of milk, meat, wool, and skins, are most numerous. Wool is exported or made into rugs, blankets, and coarse cloth. The north flank of the

Hindu Kush sloping to the rich grasslands of the Oxus plain is the recognized center for the 4 million black sheep whose lambs provide the curly karakul (Persian lamb) sold in world fur markets.

AGRICULTURE   Agriculture is dependent on mountain snows that feed the many streams. Meltwater in spring swells the Amu Dar'ya, the Kabul, and the extensive Argandab-Helmand system of the south. Where fertile soil can be reached by small diversion canals, ribbons of cultivation follow the rivers and spread out into the plains. Thousands of tiny streams become miniature oases, where husbandmen build their mud huts and till subsistence plots of wheat or barley, rice, vegetables, and fruits. Corn, millet, and alfalfa are grown for feed. Intensive patch farming is practiced in remote mountain valleys, often at high altitudes and by means of terraces.

The hot summer sun speeds the ripening of fruits, and markets in season are piled high with grapes, apples, figs, apricots, peaches, and many varieties of melons. Fruits are preserved or sun-dried for winter use, and raisins, dried apricots, and figs reach the export market in quantity. Certain valleys are famous for their almonds, walnuts, and pistachios.

PROBLEMS OF MODERNIZATION

Afghanistan's independence was achieved after a long history of invasion, conquest, and pressure politics; during the past century, it has been a buffer nation between an expanding Russia on the north and the British in India. Though railways reach the borders in several places, Afghanistan has not embarked upon railway building. The ancient caravan routes have become the present-day road pattern, including a line of highways connecting Kabul with the various provincial capitals.

Mineral surveys have been made, the larger cities electrified, and a few government factories established to supplement local cottage industry.

The greatest potential resource in Afghanistan is the mountain meltwater that floods the rivers in early spring and summer, much of which goes to waste in the great deserts. Several new reclamation projects are now under construction, including two large dams above Kandahar, which will store sufficient water to irrigate ½ million acres of arable land. In addition to subsistence crops, commercial agriculture, including long-staple cotton, sugar beets, and tobacco, will be expanded and electricity provided for local industry.

Technical assistance from outside countries is being employed, but the government is reluctant to grant concessions to foreigners. The age-old problem of Afghanistan has been how to develop the country and expand the economy without losing its cherished independence.

THE DOMINION OF CEYLON

Situated near the south tip of India, Ceylon is connected to the mainland by a 22-mile ferry across Palk Strait. Sixty per cent of its area, the northeast, is a flat, dry plain, but southwest Ceylon is dominated by a mountain mass some 50 miles in diameter, with upland plateaus and valleys between high ranges. In contrast to the plain, this southwestern highland is verdant throughout the year; numerous small rivers radiate from it. Many shallow salt-water lagoons fringe the island coasts.

THE TWO-SEASON MONSOON

Ceylon has two well-defined rainy seasons, May to August and November to January. The summer monsoon strikes the southwest coast and the central mountains with full force, whereas the lowlands of eastern and northern Ceylon are left almost rainless. The northeast monsoon gives the plains an average precipitation of 40 to 60 inches and provides additional rainfall in the mountains. The southwestern third of Ceylon, with a well-distributed rainfall of 70 to 150 inches (Colombo, 90 inches), is known as the wet zone, the extensive northern and eastern plains, the dry zone. Both the agricultural economy and the population pattern are closely related to these regions of adequate and inadequate precipitation.

Population is concentrated in the wet zone; the fertile coastal area and the intensively tilled upland valleys have a population density of 500 to 1,000 per square mile. Here the Sinhalese comprise two-thirds of Ceylon's 10.6 million inhabitants. One and a half million Tamils, recent Hindu migrants from India, predominate in the dry zone, which averages less than 100 per square mile. Wide expanses of scrubland and jungle are almost uninhabited.

PEOPLE OF CEYLON

Migrating from the Ganges Valley some twenty-four centuries ago, the early Sinhalese first settled in the dry north where dense forests were lacking; they used the intermittent rivers to develop a civilization based on water storage and irrigation. The ancient Sinhalese kings built great tanks, or reservoirs, 10, 20, or 30 miles in circumference, and developed irrigation agriculture. With the decline of their civilization, partly as a result of wars, the tanks and irrigation canals reverted to scrub and jungle. Most of the people moved to the better-watered southwest, where the difficulty of clearing the rain forests had repelled the first settlers.

Early Arab navigators skirting the south Asia coast made Ceylon a base for spice and silk operations. The Portuguese settled at Colombo in 1505, the Dutch on the east coast in 1640; both developed shore stations to exploit the wild cinnamon. Arriving at Trincomalee in 1782, the English soon expelled the Dutch, conquered the kingdom of Kandy, and made the island a British colony. In 1948, it became a self-governing member of the Commonwealth.

Ever since the days of the early spice traders and sea rovers, Ceylon's location near the tip of India has made it a natural port of call. Modern steamship lines converge at Colombo to the virtual exclusion of the smaller ports. Colombo had no natural harbor, but several breakwaters provide ample anchorage. The immediate hinterland includes the densely populated southwest plain and the prosperous up-country estates with their tea and rubber. Kandy, a former capital and famed for its Buddhist temple, is located in the mountainous interior.

AGRICULTURE

Early experimental planting included sugar, coconuts, and indigo, but coffee soon became the standard crop on hundreds of British estates around Kandy. When a leaf blight swept the coffee lands in the 1880s most planters turned to tea.

Ascending from sea level to 1,600 feet, the railway from Colombo to the Kandy Plateau traverses one of the best-cultivated sections of the wet zone. Here three export crops meet, although each has a well-defined region of concentration: coconuts on the coastal plain within a 60-mile radius of Colombo, rubber at higher elevations, and tea in the mountains.

Most of the large tea estates are at altitudes of 2,000 to 6,000 feet where there is an annual rainfall of 80 to 200 inches. Tamils from south India clear the land, then plant, mulch, and prune the trees. The estates, which average about 300 acres, were mainly British, but Sinhalese planters are increasing in number. The tea leaves are hand-plucked, wilted, fermented, rolled, fired, sifted, and packed. Sold at the weekly auctions in Colombo, tea makes up one-half of the export trade, Ceylon ranking second only to India.

Rubber is well suited to the almost continuous rainfall of the double monsoon. Some rubber is tapped by small cultivators, but most of it comes from large estates owned by British or Sinhalese, employing many workers and processing the latex mechanically. Among Ceylon's exports, raw rubber is second only to tea.

Coconuts, third largest export, are mainly tributary to the port of Colombo. As the special prerogative of the small Sinhalese grower, coconuts are part of a diversified system that includes rice, fruits, and vegetables. Home-dried copra is a ready source of cash, and the wood husks and fiber have innumerable household uses. Most copra is processed in Ceylon, but coconut oil and desiccated coconut now outrank copra and coir products in the export trade.

Cacao in Ceylon thrives in hot and humid uplands with rainfall of 60 to 80 inches; the leading centers are at 500 to 2,000 feet in valleys well sheltered from winds. Many estates interplant cacao between rubber trees, and it is found at considerable altitudes in the tea region. Numerous shut-in valleys in the Kandy district market cacao of high quality. Cinnamon, first exploited as a wild tree native to the wet lowlands, is now cultivated in gardens. The bark is peeled, fermented, dried, and made into quills, chips, or cinnamon oil for export.

Rice is the main foodstuff and has the widest distribution of any crop. Two-thirds of the paddies are in the wet zone, interspersed with coconut and rubber holdings, and extending into the tea-growing region, where terraces line many mountainsides. Paddies fringe the lagoons in the semiempty dry zone of the northern plain. The 900,000 acres of paddy are insufficient for home needs; Ceylon imports 1 billion pounds of rice annually. In an attempt to remedy this deficiency, many of the ancient tanks are being rehabilitated, and new storage projects such as the Gal Oya irrigation dam are opening up paddy lands in the dry zone.

IN PERSPECTIVE

SOUTH ASIA, LANDS OF RELIGIOUS, POLITICAL, AND ECONOMIC CONFLICT

Extending from the snow-covered Himalayas to the Indian Ocean and from Iran to Burma, South Asia is dominated both economically and politically by the large and populous Republic of India. Neighboring countries are Pakistan with its arid West and humid East, the tropical island of Ceylon, the small mountain states of Nepal, Sikkim, and Bhutan, and landlocked Afghanistan to the northwest.

Throughout South Asia, the economy is predominantly agricultural and dependent upon the monsoon rainfall. Where double cropping is practiced, irrigation is generally necessary. Agricultural expansion in arid West Pakistan and Afghanistan awaits large-scale reclamation and irrigation. The population of South Asia, well over 500 million, is heavily concentrated in the fertile floodplains and deltas as well as in certain favorable coastal areas. Population pressure is great, but there is scant hope of relief until agricultural practices are improved and water resources more efficiently utilized.

Except in Ceylon, with its heavy emphasis on export crops such as tea, rubber, and coconut products, small-scale subsistence agriculture is widespread; it is supplemented by handicrafts or cottage industries which provide part- or full-time work for millions. The competition of foreign machine-made goods and the growth of large Indian mills formerly caused a general decline in cottage industries; now, however, governments are encouraging their expansion for increased employment as well as goods for export.

Large-scale manufacturing is best developed in India, especially cotton, silk and wool textiles, iron, steel, and its subsidiary industries. Most of South Asia has foreign technological assistance in agriculture, mining, and hydroelectric development. Despite the attention focused upon multiple-purpose projects and expanded mechanization, greater production of foods and handicrafts is basic everywhere. Population increase is rapid and continuous. Improvements in nutrition, health, and living standards are contingent upon a comparable increase in production.

SELECTED REFERENCES

Aubert de la Rue, Edgar, François Bourliere, and Jean-Paul Harroy: *The Tropics,* Alfred A. Knopf, Inc., New York, 1957.

An ecological study of tropical lands between the Tropics of Cancer and Capricorn, with special emphasis on South and Southeast Asia. Highly valuable for its text and many illustrations, including more than 100 in color. A sensitive discussion of landscape, life, and migration in the tropics; it includes peoples, animals, and crops.

Davis, Kingsley: *The Population of India and Pakistan,* Princeton University Press, Princeton, N.J., 1951.

The author looks "at the region against the background of population developments and economic conditions elsewhere." Includes the overall picture: natural increase—past and future; migration—its direction and extent; social structure and change, including urbanization, education, caste, religion, Partition, as well as economic achievement and population policy. It contains many maps and graphs and a selected bibliography.

Kuhn, Delia, and Ferdinand Kuhn: *Borderlands,* Alfred A. Knopf, Inc., New York, 1962.

Includes four borderlands in South and Southeast Asia—areas "close to someone else's political and cultural boundary." Included are the Islands of the Sulu Sea (between the Philippines and North Borneo), Burma's borderland with China, Sikkim —the edge of Tibet—and landlocked Afghanistan. The authors recognize the British pioneer role in these comparatively empty borderlands.

Spate, O. H. K.: *India and Pakistan,* with a chapter on "Ceylon" by B. H. Farmer, E. P. Dutton & Co., Inc., New York, 1954.

This book is a standard source of permanent value containing a wealth of varied information on the Indian subcontinent. Shows internal diversities of regions, societies, and economies, stressing the enduring rural basis. Valuable for economic and bibliographic data, and its frequent use of simplified maps.

Vakil, C. N.: *Economic Consequences of Divided India,* Vora & Co., Ltd., Bombay, 1950.

Sums up the fundamental interdependence of the subcontinent at the time of Partition. Emphasizes the economic and social problems created when dry, scantily peopled West Pakistan and humid, densely peopled East Pakistan were separated from larger, more populous, and better-developed India. Valuable source for facts and figures.

chapter 16
SOUTHEAST ASIA

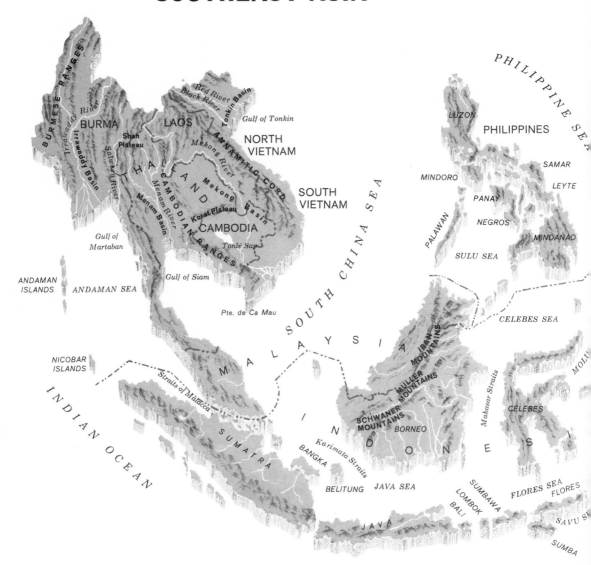

SERAM

URU

NDA SEA

NEW GUINEA

MOR

ARAFURA SEA

TIMOR SEA

Figure 16-1   Southeast Asia is an area of mountainous peninsulas and islands.

*T*HE PENINSULAR AND INSULAR LANDS east of India and south of China are often grouped together as Southeast Asia. They include Burma, Thailand, and the Indochina Peninsula states of Cambodia, Laos, and the two Vietnams, North and South. Extending southward from the mainland, the Kra Peninsula and Malaya form a land bridge to the two great archipelagoes of Indonesia and the Philippines. Culturally, many of these lands are age-old; politically, most of them are new and inexperienced; only Thailand has never been a colony. Newest of the nascent states—if it is a state—is the Federation of Malaysia created in 1963 by the Union of Malaya, Singapore, and British Borneo.

Of recent occurrence, the countries of Southeast Asia have had an experience in common—four years of war and occupation while the wheels of production turned slowly and sometimes stopped. In mines, factories, and oil fields much valuable equipment was destroyed. Estate agriculture was badly disrupted, buildings burned, labor forces dispersed, and management expelled. Even the economy of the small farms was seriously disturbed. Returning colonial governments were met with demands for immediate independence, and in the following decade most former colonies attained varying degrees of sovereignty. In addition to suffering from administrative inexperience, the new countries are faced with shortages of matériel and personnel. Preindustrial, impoverished, and illiterate peoples have been finding the problems of independence as dismaying as those of colonialism.

PHYSICAL SETTING

Rugged physical features with deep valleys and high peaks are characteristic of Southeast Asia. The mountainous peninsula extends from eastern Tibet southward into the tropics until it terminates in the long, narrow Malay Peninsula. Approximately three-fourths of it is above 3,000 feet in elevation, and in the north, mountain ranges rise to 19,000 feet (Figure 16-1). The lofty northern border is characterized by many sharp ridges and deep gorges which spread out fanwise toward the south. Several ranges extend through Burma to the Bay of Bengal; another range forms the backbone of the Malay Peninsula. The broader Annam Mountains lie near and follow the coast of Vietnam. Much of this mountainous interior is inaccessible, almost uninhabited, and of little economic significance.

The great Salween and Mekong Rivers, rising in eastern Tibet, together with the shorter Irrawaddy, Menam Chao Phraya, and Red River (Song Hoi), dominate the economic life of Southeast Asia. Rivers serve as natural arteries of transportation; small craft are aided upstream by the onshore monsoon winds and downstream by the river current. In their upper reaches all the rivers have cut deep gorges with steep, precipitous banks, but as they approach the coast they become sluggish, broaden, and build floodplains and deltas. Most extensive in the valleys of the Irrawaddy, Menam Chao Phraya, and Mekong, these alluvial lands provide the only sizable areas of good soil; hence each of the three river basins has become the site of a culture and a political unit.

Most of Southeast Asia experiences hot, humid summers and mild winter climates (Figure 16-2). Over the region as a whole, annual temperatures average 75 to 80°F. Singapore has a mean annual temperature of 81°F, with less than 5° contrast between the warmest and coolest months. The annual precipitation of 95 inches at Singapore varies from 4 to 16 inches per month, the only seasonal contrast being from rainy to less rainy.

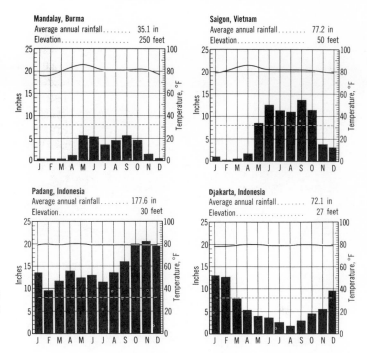

Figure 16-2 Climate graphs of selected cities in Southeast Asia.

Farther north, average temperatures become lower, and seasonal contrast is greater. Burma, Thailand, and the Indochina Peninsula lie in the path of both summer and winter monsoons. The Annamitic Cordillera separates the lands to the west, with their summer rainfall, from the Annam coast to the east, which is watered by the winter monsoon. Rangoon, with an annual rainfall of 99 inches, receives 94 inches during the wet season from May to October and only 5 inches during the dry season. Northward along the Burma coast, the yearly rainfall is 203 inches at Akyab but only 35 inches at Mandalay in the mountain trough. Maximum summer precipitation often causes serious floods in the lowlands. Burma, Thailand, and most of Indochina are in the rain shadow during the winter months, while the Vietnam coast is in the direct path of the northeast monsoon. Hué gets two-thirds of its 102 inches of rain from September to December.

The tropical monsoon dominates the climate of the East Indies and the Philippines, which receive precipitation from both the summer and winter monsoons, areal distribution being influenced by the trend and height of the mountains. However, the northwestern coast of Luzon, the southern half of Celebes, the eastern one-fourth of Java, and several smaller islands in the vicinity of Java and Celebes may experience long and severe droughts. Temperatures in the mountains are uniformly high, with little seasonal contrast except where modified by high elevations, which may give so-called temperate-zone conditions in the tropical highlands.

High elevation and rugged topography predominate, with a maximum of land area in mountains and plateaus and a minimum in lowlands. Except for a few isolated areas, the lowlands are intensively cultivated and densely populated. A large percentage of the 220 million Southeast Asians are concentrated in these lowlands,

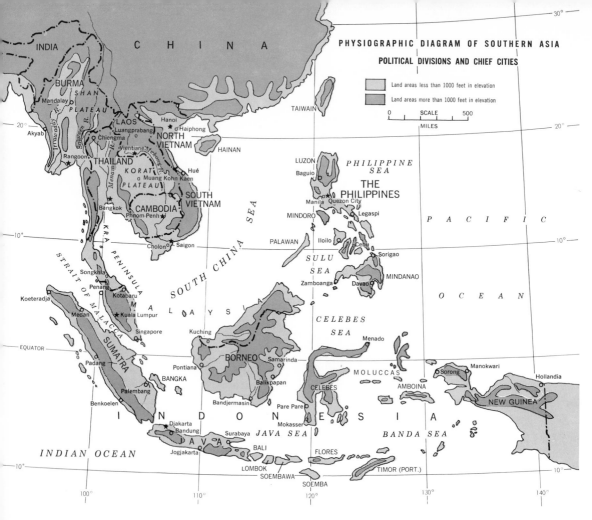

Figure 16-3   Countries and principal cities of Southeast Asia.

chiefly on floodplains and deltas, where agriculture is most rewarding. The majority of the people depend upon small-scale subsistence farming. The rice economy is dominant.

IMPACT OF EUROPEAN TRADE

An advance guard of Western enterprisers reached Southeast Asia about 1600, inaugurating a new commercial era. Europeans constituted only a fraction of the total population but possessed superior commercial training, industrial tech-

niques, and organizing ability. They gradually established the colonial mercantile system. Cultivation, organized along plantation lines, emphasized crops with the highest export value. The new estates were widely distributed but were most numerous in the East Indies and Malaya, largely because of favorable soil and climate, abundant labor, and European control. Since climate varies with elevation, altitudinal zonation of crops is common both on the mainland and in the islands. Coconuts and sugar cane are usually found in lowlands, rubber at moderate elevations or in rolling hill country, coffee and tea on hillsides and mountains up to 5,000 feet, cinchona at still higher altitudes.

At its best, the plantation system stimulated agricultural production, developed latent natural resources, and improved communications. It provided new sources of employment for native peoples, improved their living conditions, and brought them a certain amount of Western-style prosperity. At its worst, it paved the way for economic or even personal vassalage. It inevitably entailed foreign political dominance and a persistent denial of local self-determination.

The normal emphasis in Southeast Asia is upon food crops with a complementary development of home industries. Throughout the centuries highly skilled arts and crafts had tended to develop, certain cities and regions becoming famous for their designs and fine workmanship in metal, lacquer, woods, and textiles. When superimposed upon this foodstuff and handicraft economy, European commercialization disrupted the old social and economic organization and frequently destroyed even the skilled handicrafts. Emphasis on tropical raw materials for world markets exposed these preindustrial peoples to external economic forces over which they had no control. With the old balance upset, employment has been irregular over much of Southeast Asia, with frequent loss of wage income; a fluctuating food supply has not always kept pace with the rapidly increasing population.

BURMA

After unification under the powerful Mongols and various invasions by border rulers, Burma was annexed piecemeal by the British, beginning in 1826. Long a province of India, it was occupied by the Japanese in 1942 and attained its independence in 1948.

Figure 16-4   In Southeast Asia handicrafts are of greater significance than power manufacturing. Javanese silversmith (left) making a repoussé bowl by hand. Silver work of many types is crafted in various countries including Thailand, Burma, and Cambodia. Batik making (right) is a highly skilled craft in Java. Workers in Jogjakarta apply melted wax to percale before dipping it in selected colors to form the design.

PHYSICAL SETTING

RELIEF FEATURES   A high mountain rim surrounds Burma on three sides, walling it off from its neighbors. On the east this rim becomes a broad plateau, the Shan Plateau, from which a longer mountain range extends southward to form the Malay Peninsula. Within the U-shaped enclosure, the Salween River flows southward from Tibet through the Shan Plateau, cutting a deep and narrow trench. In contrast, the Irrawaddy and its major affluent, the Chindwin, rise on the Chinese-Tibetan border and transverse two

Figure 16-5   Many parts of Southeast Asia are densely populated. Java is said to be the most densely populated island in the world. Note the size of the capital of each country in relation to other cities within the country.

broad valleys separated by a narrow mountain range. The Irrawaddy and other rivers end in deltas on the south coast, combining to form broad coastal lowlands interlaced by many channeled waterways.

For its basic economy Burma is dependent on the Irrawaddy River system; its fertile valleys and deltas contain most of the arable land and support the larger part of the 23 million inhabitants. Forest and mineral wealth is tributary to the river; cities and commerce rely upon it. The Irrawaddy has long been the transport lifeline of the country. Craft of all types—rice boats, sampans, timber rafts, petroleum barges—ply the river, and government-owned steamers ascend to Bhamo, 872 miles from Rangoon. Within the delta alone are over 2,000 miles of navigable waterways.

CLIMATE   All of coastal Burma, high or low, is well watered. The high mountain ranges of Lower Burma, in the direct path of the southwest monsoon, are drenched by a rainfall of 150 to 170 inches annually; the exposed coastal lowlands have over 100 inches. Rainfall diminishes inland; halfway to Mandalay it drops to 40 to 50 inches, this section of Upper Burma being known as the dry zone. The Shan Plateau to the east receives 60 to 80 inches, and the high mountains of the northern border 120 inches or more. During the rainy season, Burmese rivers rise to flood proportions, spreading sheets of muddy water over the lower valleys. Great loads of alluvium are deposited in the deltas, which are still extending seaward.

LAND UTILIZATION

With its heavy rainfall from May to September, Lower Burma is the region of maximum rice cultivation. The narrow coastal plain of the Arakan and Tenas-serim Mountains have a similar agriculture on a small scale. Upper Burma, with its broad interior valleys centered around Mandalay, its lower rainfall, and higher summer temperatures, is better suited to mixed farming.

The surrounding mountains and plateaus are largely forested or grass-covered. Small mountain valleys are often intensively tilled and even terraced. With limited areas of good soil, patch agriculture of a subsistence type is common among hill tribes, such as the Shans, Kachins, and Karens.

FORESTS   The nonagricultural lands include thousands of square miles of forests, some worthless, others suitable for exploitation. The most valuable wood is teak, in which Burma has long held first rank. The most extensive teak forests are tributary to the upper reaches of the Irrawaddy. Trees are killed by girdling and allowed to stand for two or three years, then cut, dragged to watercourses, and floated to receiving stations on the larger rivers. Here they are made into rafts for the long trip down the Irrawaddy to mills on the Rangoon waterfront. Five to ten years may elapse between the girdling of

Figure 16-6   Teak logs in the north Burma highlands are worked by elephants.

a tree on the upper Chindwin and the arrival of the log at the mill. Ironwood and other less valuable species now exceed teak in annual cut, but the latter is still the export leader.

MINERALS   Several oil fields on the Irrawaddy and lower Chindwin Rivers have made Burma a long-time petroleum producer. Oil reaches the refineries near Rangoon by river barge or by a 320-mile pipeline. Lead-zinc-silver ores are mined in the Shan Plateau as well as in the Tenasserim area of the Malay Peninsula; the latter is also noted for its tin and tungsten. Gold, rubies, and jade are also produced.

AGRICULTURE   Two-thirds of the cultivated area in Burma is in paddies, in the adjoining deltas of the Irrawaddy and the Sittang. The apex of these great alluvial lowlands is 180 miles inland; their base stretches for 150 miles along the coast. The 100-inch rainfall is sufficient to mature a crop without additional irrigation. With the opening of new markets abroad in the 1870s, upland farmers from the dry zone migrated to the delta to clear, dike, and drain the swampy jungle, the movement reaching its height between 1880 and 1910. Ten million acres in Lower Burma were reclaimed.

Rice seedlings are transplanted during the warm rains of midsummer, and harvest begins in November, with hand cutting, drying, threshing, and sacking. Seasonal laborers from India seek harvest employment in Burma. Intersecting the delta in all directions, tidal creeks provide ready access by boat. Some 600 rice mills throughout Lower Burma receive the rough paddy by water, then husk and prepare it for overseas shipment. Rangoon is the recognized marketing and shipping center for the overseas rice trade, the country's most profitable business.

Upper Burma, the extensive central basin around Mandalay, is the second most productive region. Here many valleys converge, and at this focus of routes Mandalay has long been the historic regional capital.

Although called the dry zone, this district of lower rainfall and higher summer temperatures is highly suitable for multicropping; here is self-sufficiency in rice but little for export. Because of its low water requirement and drought tolerance, millet is a favorite grain; peas and beans are cultivated for protein, sesame and peanuts for cooking oils. In the area south of Mandalay, cotton provides a ready cash crop. Work bullocks and water buffaloes are raised for sale to the great commercial paddy lands of Lower Burma. Unlike the paddy workers of the delta, the small farmers of Upper Burma are largely independent and own their own land, on which they practice diversification and crop rotation.

INDUSTRIES AND CITIES

Rangoon, situated on a deep channel of the delta 21 miles from the Indian Ocean, is the capital, the metropolis, and the dominant port. Canals connecting with the Irrawaddy and Sittang Rivers make the city the focus of the interior river trade as well as of the delta traffic. It is the assembly point for rice, upriver teak, and petroleum; its major industries are the milling and refining of such export commodities. More than 80 per cent of Burma's foreign trade passes through Rangoon.

Mandalay, the principal city of Upper Burma, has both rail and water connections with Rangoon. The traditional industries include jade cutting and silk weaving, and the city is noted for its numerous temples and monasteries.

THAILAND

Originally migrants from southwest China, the Thai have had a long record of successful resistance to encroachment, first by powerful rulers in Burma and Cambodia, later by the rival colonial empires of France and Great Britain. Sovereignty was preserved during a period when independence was rare in South Asia. Long known as Siam, the name was changed in 1939 to Thailand—"Land of the Free."

Thailanders in general are water-conditioned, with the population concentrated mainly on the central floodlands and the long, wet coastlands; the inhabitants are habituated to salt- or fresh-water living. Throughout the central plains, rivers and connecting canals are navigable even in the dry season. They serve as main highways and are thronged with rice boats, passenger launches, floating bazaars, and sampans for transport or habitation (Figure 16-7).

Bangkok, capital of the kingdom since 1782, is the hub of rail and water transport and handles 85 per cent of the country's foreign trade. Below the city on the 15-mile channel of the lower Menam Chao Phraya are situated the rice and teak mills as well as most of the port facilities. Chinese merchants and entrepreneurs buy rice, deal in teak, build boats, monopolize moneylending and banking, and control 80 per cent of the trade.

Thailand's topography—a rim of varied highlands surrounding central lowlands—is similar to that of Burma. The Menam Chao Phraya and numerous smaller rivers rise on the borders, their silt-laden waters flowing into a broad interior plain, thence south to the Gulf of Siam. Lower central Thailand, some 60 miles wide, is a maze of interlaced channels built up by

Figure 16-7 *The floating market in Bangkok is an assembly and shopping center for all types of goods and produce. (Courtesy of Government of Thailand.)*

continuous sedimentation; the coast is still extending southward.

Although much shorter than the rivers of Burma, the streams are sluggish and subject to annual floods. During the monsoon rains, the Menam and its affluents regularly inundate some 5,000 square miles of central plain. During this hot, wet season the paddy farmer of lower Thailand has ample need for his house on stilts and his sampan. The Salween on the west and the Mekong on the east are border streams of minor significance to the Thai economy.

Shared with Burma as a common boundary, the high range on the west is continuous for 1,000 miles. The Kra Peninsula, longer than all the rest of the country, is locally called Siamese Malaya. On the east, the broad Korat Plateau, 1,500 feet high on its western edge, slopes toward the Laos border.

From May through October the summer monsoon operates with full force. The higher mountain ranges and the Kra Peninsula receive 100 to 125 inches of rain annually, but the central plain and the Korat Plateau, partly in the rain shadow, get a maximum of 60, decreasing to 35 inches.

NATURAL RESOURCES

North Thailand is similar to the mountainous Shan Plateau on its western border. Here forest lands are the chief resource and teak the most valuable tree. State forests cover 41,000 square miles, with 10,000 in teak, a much smaller area than it occupies in Burma. Chiangmai, the northern railhead, is a primary assembly station, but logs from many tributaries are rafted down the Menam Chao Phraya to the Bangkok mills. Some logs are taken out by way of the border rivers, the Salween and the Mekong. Formerly exploited at the rate of 1 million logs annually, production has declined, but teak is still regarded as a substantial national resource.

The commercial minerals are tin and a much smaller output of tungsten, both from the Kra Peninsula. The mines are foreign-owned and worked by Chinese labor. Tin ores, third largest Thai export, are shipped to Malaya for smelting.

THE RICE BASIN

The economic life of Thailand is most closely interwoven with rice, which is grown on 95 per cent of the cultivated area, most of it in the flat central plain. A large part of these great lowlands has a rainfall of only 40 to 50 inches yearly but receives a copious water supply from the Menam. This complex river system is fed by many affluents from the circle of northern highlands. When its major channel is bank-full, it disgorges a mass of surplus water into various effluents—distributaries which branch off from the lower Menam Chao Phraya, sometimes rejoining it downstream. Smaller parallel rivers contribute their volume of water, and during the monsoon season much of the plain becomes a vast shallow lake.

Flood time is rice-planting time for the small cultivator. The heavy and impervious soils of the central plain are highly productive. Since single-cropping is usual, however, the average yield of 30 bushels per acre is low in comparison with that of countries growing two crops annually. One-quarter of the paddy area is in floating, or deepwater, rice, which grows in 6 to 7 feet of water. For the past half-century, paddy acreage has been expanding at the rate of 40,000 acres per year. New reclamation projects will provide additional irrigation, better flood control, and greater rice production.

The yearly rice consumption in Thailand, 450 pounds per person, leaves a large surplus for sale. Assembled at Bangkok, it is milled and shipped to deficit countries, among which, high on the list

Figure 16-8   Rural house of bamboo and thatch near Ayuthia is raised on stilts above the flood level. Note water storage jar at left corner of the house. (Courtesy of Government of Thailand.)

of buyers, are Hong Kong and Singapore, the latter serving as middleman for Malaya. Rice accounts for one-half of Thailand's export trade.

UPLAND FARMING

Above the flooded rice lands are scattered zones of upland diversified farming where soybeans, corn, sorghum, sesame, peanuts, tobacco, and cotton are cultivated. These crops are sometimes intertilled between rows of rice, maturing after the latter has been cut. The largest mixed-farming area is in the upper Menam Chao Phraya Basin, extending to Chiangmai. The small upland cultivator relies heavily on vegetables for the family support, grows bananas, mangos, papayas, and

keeps pigs, goats, and poultry, especially ducks.

In comparison with wet paddy on the lower floodplain, the drier mixed farming of Thailand is small. Some of the new irrigation projects serve the higher benchlands, providing water for upland crops such as cotton, tobacco, sesame, and peanuts. The Korat Plateau, in area nearly one-third of the kingdom, includes a broad plain a few hundred feet in elevation, where considerable rice is grown during the flood season along rivers tributary to the Mekong. Except for these valley paddies, farming throughout the plateau consists of mixed dry-land crops. Cheap upland pasturage favors livestock raising, the Korat region producing half of the work bullocks and buffaloes used by

Thai farmers. These animals are frequently sold to other Southeast Asia countries.

RUBBER IN THE PENINSULA

Rubber from Thailand ranks third in the world, after that produced in Malaya and Indonesia. It is grown far south in the peninsula, where convection showers bring 75 to 100 inches of well-distributed rainfall. There are few large estates, but many Chinese have small holdings of 2,000 to 3,000 trees; rubber is the second most valuable Thai export, accounting for 20 per cent of the total.

The coconut palm is at home everywhere in coastal Thailand, but the largest acreage is in the Kra Peninsula.

THE INDOCHINA PENINSULA

East of Thailand, the Indochina Peninsula includes two great river basins, the Red River (Song Hoi) in the north and the Mekong in the south, connected by the long, narrow coastal plain of Annam. Behind this plain, the Annamitic Cordillera forms a continuous mountain range of 5,000 to 8,000 feet in elevation, declining on the south and west to a series of plateaus which drain westward to the Mekong.

The Cordillera serves as a climatic divide; its western slopes and the Mekong Basin receive peak rainfall during the southwest monsoon; the eastern slopes get the rains of the northeast monsoon. Over most of the area summer is rainy, followed (except in the northeast) by a dry season from December through March. Annual rainfall in Saigon is 80 inches, in Hanoi 72, but some of the higher mountains have over 200 inches.

Within this area, the Tonkinese, Annamese, and Cochinese are of Mongol origin, but the Cambodians are descendants of the ancient Khmers. After a thousand years of independence—with indirect control from China—colonialism began in 1863, when Cambodia ceded Cochin China to France. Later, French protectorates were established over Cambodia, Annam, and Tonkin, consolidated in 1887 as the Union of Indochina, with Laos added in 1893.

Following the Japanese occupation, 1941 to 1945, a republic was proclaimed in the north by Tonkinese opposed to the return of French rule. An eight-year struggle ended in 1954 with French withdrawal, Indochina becoming four independent countries—Cambodia, Laos, North Vietnam, and South Vietnam; a line near the 17th parallel divided Annam between the two latter countries. Each of the new states is trying to organize and perfect its own separate economy.

SOUTH VIETNAM

In South Vietnam, both Cochinese and Annamese occupy the extensive floodplains of the lower Mekong or cluster thickly along the coastal plain between the Cordillera and the South China Sea. With the exception of the Saigon-Cholon area, the population of the republic is predominantly rural and village-dwelling; it includes small paddy farmers and former farm laborers on the large estates. Many hill peoples are scattered thinly throughout the forested plateaus and on mountain slopes.

Like the Irrawaddy and the Menam Chao Phraya, the Mekong River has built up one of the great floodplains of Southeast Asia. The apex of this delta is in lower Cambodia, but three-fourths of it is in old Cochin China (now Vietnam), where rice paddies are the basis of the national economy. Most of the occupants are small farmers, but in certain areas sharecroppers cultivate rice estates that were drained and reclaimed by earlier French enterprisers. Since the ratio of paddy to population was large, old Cochin China was a reliable rice exporter, much of the surplus going to overcrowded Tonkin in the north. The rice trade was and still is handled by Chinese middlemen; fleets of junks on the delta waterways move the unhusked paddy to the Saigon-Cholon conurbation for milling and shipping.

Introduced in 1897, *Hevea* rubber was planted on a large scale, some holdings reaching 100,000 acres. Most of the plantations are on the red-earth uplands between the Mekong and the Cordillera. Young rubber trees are intertilled with tea, coffee, or sugar cane. The estates, most of them within a short radius of Saigon, produce latex of high quality. Unlike Malaya, Vietnam has few small growers. Rubber leads all exports.

Far less productive than rice, corn is cultivated in paddies as a second crop, but more often in uplands unsuited to rice. The many river banks bordering the watercourses are thickly planted to such nonirrigated crops as tobacco, beans, sugar cane, and cotton, which mature during the dry and sunny November-to-

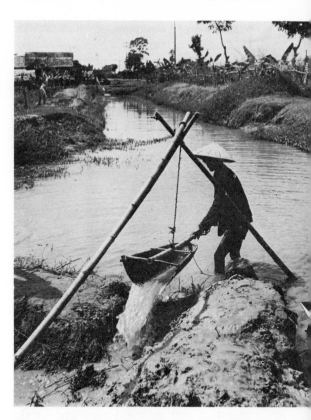

Figure 16-9 To help settle over ½ million refugees, South Vietnam is expanding its arable paddy acreage. Irrigation by hand scoop is often necessary.

TABLE 16-1 THE NEW STATES OF INDOCHINA (Estimates)

Country	Area, sq. mi.	Population
Republic of South Vietnam	65,709	13,800,000
Communist North Vietnam	61,516	16,000,000
Kingdom of Cambodia	53,650	5,000,000
Kingdom of Laos	91,482	2,200,000

Sources: for area, *Rand McNally World Atlas,* Rand McNally & Company, Chicago, 1960; for population, the *Statesman's Year Book, 1962–1963,* St Martin's Press, New York, 1963.

April season. Yams are a food staple everywhere.

In addition to the large rubber holdings under French management in the red-earth uplands, tobacco, tea, and coffee estates extend into the cooler Moi Plateau at the south end of the cordillera. Here small farmers also grow tobacco and tea as cash crops.

Saigon, 50 miles up the Saigon River, is the metropolis, capital, and trade center of South Vietnam. Besides local rice and rubber, most of the Cambodian and Laotian trade passes through it. Including its nearby rice-milling suburb, Cholon or "Great Market," this conurbation has a population of 1.6 million, of which 600,000 are Chinese.

Since the partition of 1954, some 800,000 refugees from Tonkin and northern Annam have fled to the south; many are still living in temporary camps and villages in the vicinity of Saigon. One of the most pressing problems of the new regime is refugee resettlement on upland farms or on newly reclaimed paddy lands in the delta.

KINGDOM OF CAMBODIA

The kingdom of Cambodia, almost encircled by Thailand on the northwest and Vietnam on the southeast, is a basin-like lowland drained by the Mekong River system. With its various tributaries and delta channels, the Mekong dominates the life of Cambodia. The best agricultural land has been built up by silt-laden rivers that enrich the fields annually. The floods provide ample water for paddy irrigation and sufficient moisture for the broad natural levees where most nonirrigated crops are grown. The watercourses determine the agricultural pattern, set the village-habitation pattern, and serve as the oldest and best transportation arteries.

The most productive section is southeast Cambodia, which includes the upper quarter of the Mekong delta lands with their flooded paddies and extensive areas of river-bank cultivation. Two other agricultural regions extend upcountry from the apex of the delta. The first follows the Mekong two-thirds of the way to the Laos border; it includes the red-soil uplands with their French-owned rubber estates. The second extends northwest from the river, two belts of paddy land forming a broad ellipse around Tonle Sap Lake and almost reaching the Thailand border. Methods of rice-paddy and river-bank

farming are similar to those in Vietnam, but there is little double-cropping in Cambodia. Despite its 5 million people, the kingdom is not overcrowded. Although the yield per acre is low, large amounts of paddy are grown, one-quarter of it surplus for export. The river-bank farmers plant nonirrigated food crops such as corn, beans, and peanuts; cotton and tobacco are processed locally. Less than 15 per cent of the country is under systematic cultivation, and much of it is in forest and almost uninhabited.

Most farmers in Cambodia are part-time fishermen, gaining a portion of the family livelihood from nearby river or lake. Tonle Sap, in the central plain, is a great shallow lake connected with the Mekong by a 75-mile channel. At low water the lake covers some 1,000 square miles, but when the Mekong is in flood after the monsoon rains, surplus water pushes up the channel into Tonle Sap Lake, which expands and inundates an area of 3,500 square miles. During the following dry season the surplus water is slowly disgorged back into the Mekong. This unique lake supports a rich and varied fishing industry; the marketing of fish—fresh, dried, or salted—reaches millions of dollars annually.

Phnom Penh, with ½ million inhabitants, capital and only large city, is situated at the juncture of three waterways, the Mekong, the Bassac (a major delta channel), and Tonle Sap River. A single line of railway connects the capital with the Thai rail system, but Cambodia's foreign trade is handled mainly by river to Saigon. Vessels of 16-foot draft, including junks and river steamers, ascend to Phnom Penh to lift rice, rubber, corn, and other cargoes. A new ocean port at Sihanoukville on the Gulf of Siam has been linked to Phnom Penh by motor highway.

KINGDOM OF LAOS

The mountain kingdom of Laos, in the isolated and heavily forested drainage basin of the upper Mekong, is 650 miles long from Yünnan to the Cambodian border and has some 2 million thinly scattered inhabitants. Its mountain valleys and dry dissected plateaus support a limited rice-corn-tobacco-cotton economy. Resources for sale are meager, but pigs, cattle, hides, and coffee from its southern plateau, teak, stick lac, and other forest products reach market via the Mekong River to Saigon. Because of its long frontier with North Vietnam, Laos is vulnerable to infiltration from its Communist neighbor and has become one of the political trouble spots of Southeast Asia.

NORTH VIETNAM

Tonkin, in the drainage basin of the Red River (Song Hoi), was the northernmost of the states that constituted former French Indochina. Together with the northern half of Annam, it is now North Vietnam and is closely allied with Communist China.

Rice occupies three-fourths of the cultivated land in the Red River delta and Annam coastal plain, the secondary crops including corn and sugar cane. When floods rise, a network of dikes and canals diverts water from the river to the paddies, which are small, averaging 3 acres to a household. More than one-half of the paddy land grows two crops annually, but flood damage is sometimes extensive. Unlike Cambodia or South Vietnam, North Vietnam seldom has rice for export and must frequently make up shortages by importing from the less densely populated Mekong delta. Considerable upland rice, corn, and other food crops are grown in the plateaus and in the mountain valleys that stretch to the borders of China.

Most of the active mining is north of the Red River and near the border of China. The best coal measures in Southeast Asia are tributary to Haiphong, a 100-mile field containing rich seams of anthracite and high-grade bituminous coal, easily worked and near the coast. Lode ores of tin-tungsten are an extension of the Yünnan tin field of China.

Hanoi, a coastal port in ancient times, has been left some 55 miles inland by the seaward extension of the delta by river silting. Developed by the French as the administrative center for all Indochina, Hanoi has cotton-textile factories and serves as marketing center for the Red River basin. Haiphong has good port facilities for rice trading, coal shipping, and general cargo handling. Like agriculture, most industry and commerce is state-controlled, and trade is largely with China.

THE PHILIPPINES

Soon after their discovery by Magellan in 1541, the Philippines became a commercial outpost of Spain and were ruled by the Spanish for three centuries. This long period of occupation left its cultural imprint upon the religion, language, and customs of the archipelago. A half-century of American control after 1898 also made its contribution to educational, economic, and political development. Self-rule, which began with Commonwealth status in 1935, was interrupted by the Japanese occupation, then followed by full independence, with the establishment of the Republic of the Philippines in 1946.

The archipelago consists of some 7,000

islands with an area of 115,000 square miles. Numerous folded ranges, some reaching elevations of 10,000 feet, extend in a north-south direction. There are many volcanic peaks, both inactive and active, some of which have erupted in recent times. Broad interior plains between ranges on the larger islands and narrow coastal plains on the smaller islands contain the best agricultural lands and support the larger part of the 30 million people. Almost one-half of the population live on Luzon.

The larger islands include Luzon on the north, with many peninsulas and embayments, rugged Mindanao on the south, and undeveloped Palawan on the west. Between them are six smaller islands known as the Visayan group: Samar and Leyte on the east, Panay, Negros, Cebu, and Bohol on the west. Despite certain similarities throughout the archipelago, various areas have recognized specialties. The broad Cagayan Valley of northern Luzon is mainly devoted to corn and tobacco. Extending from Manila Bay to the Lingayen Gulf, the rich central plain of Luzon grows rice, sugar cane, and coconuts and is the economic heart of the Philippines. The limited but highly productive coastal plains of Mindanao grow abacá, rubber, and coconuts. With few exceptions, all the better valleys and coasts throughout the islands are carefully tilled and densely populated.

With high temperatures and high relative humidity, the climate of the lowlands is oppressive most of the year. The highlands are pleasant; Baguio at 4,756 feet averages 15° cooler than Manila. The summer monsoon brings heavy rain to the western regions, the annual amount varying from 50 to 180 inches. Manila receives more than one-half of its 80 inches during the three midsummer months. Eastern sides of the islands receive their maximum rainfall in winter and have no pronounced dry season. Baguio gets 250 inches a year, most of it during the summer monsoon. North of Mindanao, typhoons frequently destroy crops and damage property.

NATURAL RESOURCES

Over one-half of the area of the islands is covered with timber, including some 80 species of commercial value. Except for large stands of pine in the mountains of Luzon, these forests are mainly broadleaf hardwoods; 1 billion board feet are cut and sold annually. Much of the wood is used locally, but the finer hardwoods such as narra (Philippine mahogany) are suitable for interior finishing, furniture, and cabinet work, and enter the export trade. Minor forest products include rattans, bamboo, resins, and tanning materials.

Minerals are widely distributed, with gold from the rich mining district near Baguio ranking first, closely followed by copper. Large reserves of iron ore in northern Mindanao and of chromite in both Mindanao and Luzon lie near the surface and can be worked by open-pit methods. There are also scattered manganese and silver deposits.

AGRICULTURE

Agriculture is predominant; much of the land is carefully tilled, and double-cropping is general. The food favorite, rice, is most heavily grown in central Luzon and on Panay, but even in the mountains, steep slopes are terraced for paddy. Farms average less than 5 acres, and the entire family helps to transfer the young plants from seedbed to field and to harvest the grain.

Since Spanish times the Philippines have been a rice-deficit area, importing from the surplus countries of Southeast

Figure 16-10   The water buffalo is the common work animal of Southeast Asia. These are preparing a field for planting. (Courtesy of the Philippine Embassy.)

Asia. Under both Spanish and American administration, new lands were cleared for export crops such as abacá, coconuts, sugar, tobacco, and rubber, but little attempt was made to increase the paddy area.

Corn, commonly cultivated on land unsuited to rice, is the second breadstuff of the Philippines. Acreage is largest in the Cagayan Valley, where it is frequently a succession crop after tobacco. Cebu and Negros depend heavily on corn, and it is a food staple in most upland areas. Camotes (sweet potatoes), manioc or cassava, taro, peanuts, and bananas supplement rice and corn in the diet. Shifting cultivation is widely practiced in upland areas.

Sugar cane is the major field crop, accounting for one-quarter of the total exports. The central plain of Luzon, together with Negros and Cebu, ships 1 million tons of sugar annually. Despite the long trans-Pacific voyage, preferential entry for Philippine sugar makes the United States the most favored market.

South of Manila, coconuts fringe nearly every coast, with high concentrations in certain volcanic areas that have favorable slope and drainage. This highly productive tree occupies one-quarter of the cultivated area and is second only to rice in the local economy. The individual grower sun-dries the meat, but on large plantations mechanical dryers prepare copra of higher quality. Small trading vessels circulate through the archipelago buying sacks of copra, which they sell to the oil mills. Coconuts are exported in the form of copra, oil, meal, or desiccated coconut, the Philippines supplying one-third of the total entering world trade.

The Philippines long had a virtual monopoly in the production of abacá, a fiber valued for its strength and resiliency. Under the trade name "Manila hemp," it is used chiefly for rope. The tall banana-like plant is cultivated in the Legaspi Peninsula of Luzon, and around the Gulf of Davao in Mindanao. In Luzon, abacá is grown by small farmers or tenants and stripped by hand, but in the newer lands of Davao, where the plantation system has been introduced, the large-scale stripping of fiber is mechanized. Abacá and the cordage made from it in Manila are among the leading Philippine exports.

CITIES

Founded in 1571, Manila has been the capital and chief port of the Philippines since early Spanish times. The bay provides commodious anchorage for ocean shipping and the many interisland steamers. The city is more commercial than industrial, since manufacture is mainly processing, coconut oil pressing, sugar refining, rope making, and the preparation of tobacco. Including its suburban periphery and nearby Quezon City, the new political capital, Manila has 2.3 million inhabitants. Iloilo on Panay, Cebu City on Cebu, Bacolod on Negros, and Zamboanga and Davao on Mindanao serve as regional centers for the provinces.

INDONESIA

The Indonesian archipelago[1] is the largest in the world, extending some 3,000 miles along the equator and 1,500 miles north-south. Included are large islands with small populations like Borneo and small islands like Java and Bali that have large populations. Sparsely peopled Borneo (Kalimantan), Celebes (Sulawesi), and New Guinea (Irian) have interiors so mountainous, rugged, and jungle-filled that they have never been completely explored or mapped.

[1] Most of the archipelago is controlled by the Republic of Indonesia, but the eastern half of the island of Timor is held by Portugal and Papua (eastern New Guinea) was mandated to Australia after World War II.

Physically, Indonesia is a continuation of a southward-trending arm of the Himalayas. The folded and volcanic Sunda arc includes Sumatra, Java, the lesser Sundas, and Celebes-Halmahera. The mountain backbone of both Sumatra and Java is mainly volcanic, with 100 or more peaks, 20 of them from 8,000 to 10,000 feet. Both Java and Sumatra have many active volcanoes and frequent earthquakes.

Generally tropical in location, Indonesia has considerable climatic variation because of altitude. Lowland temperatures average 75 to 80°F, with less than 5° annual range. At higher elevations, the lower temperatures permit altitudinal zonation in agriculture. Many lowland cities have nearby hill stations for recreation and for health. Djakarta (Batavia), with an average annual temperature of 79°F, is in contrast to Bandung at 2,500 feet with an average temperature of 72°. Cooler nights in the uplands are an attractive feature.

Over much of the archipelago, variations in temperature are less significant than variations in rainfall. Situated between the land masses of Southeast Asia and Australia, western Indonesia is in the direct path of the summer and winter monsoons, Djakarta receiving 75 inches; Medan, 80; Pontianak, 130; Macassar, 115 inches; and stations at higher elevations even more. Relative humidity is generally high.

PEOPLE AND POLITICS

The ancient Indian kingdom in Java included both Buddhists and Hindus. Borobudur in central Java, built in the eighth or ninth century, is the most famous of the Buddhist monuments. The Islamic infiltration began in the thirteenth century with the arrival of Arab traders; by 1600 Islam had superseded both Hinduism and Buddhism. Later Portuguese, Dutch, and

English companies became active competitors for the trade of the Indies, the Dutch emerging as the victors. Their posts and plantations spread throughout the islands, and by 1900 the Netherlands East Indies had become the world's largest colony specializing in tropical foodstuffs and raw materials.

Dutch rule in the Indies ended during World War II; with the surrender of Japanese occupation forces, Indonesians at once declared their independence. Dutch attempts to reimpose colonialism failed, and the Republic of Indonesia was established.

Through the centuries, migrations from Asia and the Pacific have created a complex social structure. The majority of the people are Moslems, with relatively small groups of animists, Hindus, and Christians. Among the nonindigenous peoples, Chinese are most numerous and control much of the small business and trade. Although many different languages and dialects are in use, a variant of Malay is the official Indonesian language. In addition to racial, linguistic, and religious diversity, there is great contrast between the cultured Javanese and Balinese, and the migratory food-gathering peoples of Borneo and western New Guinea.

AGRICULTURE

Like their Arab and Portuguese predecessors, the Dutch in the Indies came in search of spices—cloves, pepper, cinnamon, nutmegs—and then cultivated other tropical crops. Coffee was introduced into Java about 1700; the Dutch East India Company made the first large shipment to Amsterdam in 1712.

Under the culture system practiced from 1830 to 1870, which included compulsory planting, forced native labor, and collection at fixed prices, the coffee gardens expanded into the highlands above Djakarta, and the East Indies became the world leader in coffee. Overproduction and price declines broke the market; other crops were substituted, and the culture system gave way to long-term plantation leases.

The upland of Java between Buitenzorg, 800 feet, and Bandung, 2,500 feet, was the first area of large estates. Here

TABLE 16-2   INDONESIA

	Area, sq. mi.	Population census, 1930	Population estimate, 1955*	Population census, 1962, millions
Java and Madura	51,032	41,718,364	51,637,572	63.0
Sumatra	182,859	8,254,843	11,371,233	15.2
Borneo (Kalimantan)	208,285	2,138,691	3,092,206	4.1
Celebes (Sulawesi)	72,986	4,231,906	6,065,145	7.0
Moluccas (Maluku)	191,681	893,400†	685,704‡	—
Timor Archipelago	24,449	1,657,376	2,183,545	—
Bali and Lombok	3,973	1,802,683	2,579,187	—
				97,085,348

* Estimate by Election Committee for Parliamentary Election, Government of Indonesia, September, 1955.
† Including Irian (western New Guinea).
‡ Excluding Irian.

coffee was superseded by tea and rubber. Most plantations are in the highlands, the main exceptions being those devoted to sugar cane, tobacco, and sisal. Tea, rubber, and cinchona predominate in west Java; east Java grows rubber, tea, and coffee; central Java is the major sugar cane region. The island has been a great garden

Figure 16-11   Beginning work at daybreak, the rubber gatherer makes his rounds on an estate in Sumatra. Cutting a thin shaving of bark permits the sap, or latex, to drip slowly into the cup.

Figure 16-12   The latex is trucked to the estate factory and poured into shallow trays to coagulate. The highest-quality rubber comes from the estates rather than from smallholders.

for plant introduction, where hundreds of promising crops have been tested.

The estate system reached Sumatra about 1865 when large-scale jungle clearing and tobacco planting began near Medan. Tea, abacá, the oil palm, and rubber were gradually added.

The optimum elevation for rubber is about 1,000 feet. *Hevea* saplings, started in nursery beds, are set out in rows, usually with catch crops such as corn, beans, or sweet potatoes, planted during the years before tapping begins. Most estates are mechanized, some of the largest being on the east coast of Sumatra, now the recognized center of foreign rubber concessions. Considerable liquid latex is exported in tankers.

Small growers everywhere have increased their holdings, the farmer and his family in Java, Sumatra, or Borneo tapping his trees, coagulating the latex, and processing the sheets of crepe by hand. Since they grow various food crops for home use, smallholders are not greatly affected by fluctuating world prices. Small-scale rubber planters now account for 75 per cent of the total output. South Sumatra rubber is marketed through Palembang. Growers in southeast Borneo ship downriver to Bandjermasin. Ranking second only to Malaya, Indonesia produces over one-third of the world's natural rubber.

Throughout much of Indonesia, groves of coconuts surround the native villages or kampongs. Together with bananas, papayas, and mangos, coconuts help to augment the food supply and are a ready source of cash income. Drying and collecting copra is a year-round business, and some 5,000 native vessels (prahaus) cruise the islands as copra traders. Many types of coconut products are significant.

Tobacco is still a favorite estate crop in Java, although little patches on small farms now contribute the larger share of locally used leaf. Door-to-door buyers collect the crop and sell it to the cigarette factories. In Sumatra high-quality tobacco for cigars is grown along the Deli River in the Medan district, where pioneer Dutch enterprisers secured concessions. Since tobacco can be grown on a field only once in eight or ten years, large acreages are imperative. The famous Deli leaf brings high prices from cigar makers.

Coffea robusta, a hardy variety introduced from Africa, is cultivated on terraced slopes in east Java, the optimum elevation being 1,500 to 2,000 feet. Estate production has declined, but small cultivators have increased the number of their trees to supply the home demand; Indonesia consumes far more coffee than tea.

Tea from Assam was introduced into the highlands of west Java, where volcanic soils and well-distributed rainfall of 100 to 200 inches provide suitable natural conditions. The carefully managed Java estates are between 1,500 and 4,000 feet in elevation. In Sumatra production is localized in the hills east of Lake Toba.

Picking is continuous. The leaves are factory-processed and packed on the estates, and small growers sell their green leaves to the nearest factory. With a tea export of 75 to 80 million pounds annually, Indonesia ranks third in the world, exceeded only by India and Ceylon.

The oil palm, a wild forest tree from equatorial Africa, was introduced into Sumatra in 1911. Oil palms in the Medan area are grown on highly mechanized estates of 3,000 to 20,000 acres, employing Javanese or Chinese laborers. Careful selection of trees has increased the oil yield per acre from 500 to approximately 2,000 pounds. After being cooked and pressed, most of the oil is shipped in tankers to Europe or the United States. One-third of the world's palm oil comes from Sumatra. In Indonesia it is used in the manufacture of soaps and edible fats.

Sugar cane is one of the oldest estate crops. Large and small growers as well as the sugar factories are concentrated in the lowlands of central and east Java. Stimulated by high world prices, sugar output rose to a peak of 3 million tons, 10 per

Figure 16-13   Clusters of palm fruit are cut by hand and hauled by tractor to the factory, where oil pressing is fully mechanized.

cent of the world crop, in the early 1920s, only to suffer later from overproduction and low prices. Since most Java cane is grown on paddy land in rotation with rice, the output was readily reduced by substituting essential food crops.

Spices, which supplied the original motivation for the East Indies trade, are still cultivated for local use and for export. The Moluccas specialize in nutmegs, cloves, and cardamon. White and black pepper and cinnamon come chiefly from Sumatra and Borneo.

The cinchona tree, successfully transplanted from highland Peru, thrives at altitudes of from 4,000 to 6,000 feet. Over 90 per cent of the world's supply of cin-

chona bark, from which quinine is extracted, was formerly produced in Java, where it is also manufactured. Synthetic quinine, developed in 1945, broke this Dutch monopoly based on Javanese cinchona.

Indonesia has the largest rice production per acre of any Southeast Asian country. The area in paddies, called sawahs, almost equals that of all other crops combined, two-thirds of it being in densely populated Java. Water is obtained from simple stream diversion or reclamation projects built by the government. In Bali and Lombok, as well as in Java, many steep slopes have been terraced for sawahs. The growing season is continuous,

Figure 16-14   Terraces in southern Bali are flooded for wet rice. In the dry season these sawahs will be planted to nonirrigated crops such as sweet potatoes, maize, or beans. (Courtesy of Government of Indonesia.)

Figure 16-15   Rice harvest landscape in south Bali. Cut by hand with a small knife, the rice stalks are tied in bundles and stacked by the roadside. Workers then carry the bundles on their heads to the home village. Note the coconut palms fringing the coast. (Courtesy of Frances M. Earle.)

with planting, cultivation, and harvest going on simultaneously. Seedlings are transplanted to the prepared fields, and after harvest a second crop is planted. If sufficient water is available, additional rice is preferred; otherwise, the farmer plants a dry crop such as corn, cassava, sweet potatoes, or soybeans. Rice now exceeds prewar production, although Indonesia has not yet achieved self-sufficiency.

Corn (maize) is grown almost everywhere from sea level to 7,000 feet. Cultivated in the sawahs as a succession crop after paddy, it is also a favorite in the uplands, where it is rotated with hill rice. Sweet potatoes, cassava, and bananas grow in almost every garden but lack the prestige of rice. Villages are surrounded and houses shaded by trees bearing papayas, tamarinds, coconuts, bananas, and mangos.

Smallholders often cultivate cash crops such as tea or cotton. Both peanuts and cassava exceed local demand, the latter being marketed as cassava flour or tapioca. Valuable fibers include sisal, abacá, kapok, and coir.

MINERALS

The petroleum fields are widely dispersed, extending from northern Sumatra to western New Guinea (Irian). The Sumatran fields are inland from Palembang on the mountain flanks and run along the north coast. Oil is produced near Surabaya and Rembang in east Java, in the Balikpapan and Tarakan fields of east Borneo (Kalimantan), and in the Vogelkop of western New Guinea. Output dropped to zero during World War II, but is again approaching normal. Petroleum is processed in local refineries; gasoline, lubricating oil, and kerosene account for one-fifth of Indonesia's exports.

The tin deposits of Bangka, Belitong, and Singkep, islands in the Java Sea, are a continuation of the tin belt of Malaya and were exploited by Chinese in the early 1700s. On Bangka, the mines are a government monopoly and are worked largely by Chinese labor. Tin ore in placer deposits is worked either by hydraulic pumps or by dredges. Indonesia produces one-half as much tin as Malaya, ranking second in the world. Most of the ore is smelted in Singapore.

Good steam coal is mined in southern Sumatra, and other islands have workable deposits of bauxite and nickel. Pearls and shell come from eastern Indonesia.

INDUSTRY AND CITIES

With the exception of cotton textiles and consumer goods such as oleomargarine and soap, most industry has been based on estate crops. Sugar and rubber mills, coconut oil plants, cigar and cigarette factories, and petroleum refineries process local materials. Throughout Indonesia, handicrafts are generally more significant than mechanized industry.

Old Djakarta, at the mouth of the Chilliwong River, was burned by the Dutch in 1620, then rebuilt and named Batavia. Centrally located for the commerce of the Indies, it became a great trading and shipping port. When river silting made the old harbor too shallow, a new deepwater port was developed at nearby Tandjung Priok. With Indonesian independence the name Djakarta was restored, and as capital of the republic, the city now has an estimated population of 3 million.

Surabaya has a well-protected harbor and is the trade center for east Java; Semarang serves a similar purpose for the rich estate lands of mid-Java.

In Sumatra, the upriver port of Palembang handles rubber and other tropical exports as well as petroleum products from the local refineries. Developed by the rubber and tobacco corporations, Medan is a planter capital rather than an Indonesian city; it has a nearby hill station on a 4,500-foot plateau. Bandjermasin is the outlet and trade center for southeast Borneo. Many other regional and insular centers are merely agglomerations of kampongs or native villages.

Because of its close proximity and crossroads position, Singapore is a natural clearinghouse for a large volume of Indonesian trade.

MALAYSIA

The original federated Malaya, organized as a member of the British Commonwealth in 1957, has become the basis for a much larger Federation of Malaysia approved in 1962. The new country includes the independent state of Singapore as well as North Borneo and Sarawak, both on the island of Borneo. The central government and parliament of the new nation is now located at Kuala Lumpur in the Malay Peninsula. Predominantly Malayan and Chinese, the Federation will include many other races of Southeast Asia.

MALAYA

Modern Malaya dates back to the trading activities of the British East India Company, which occupied Penang in 1786 and Malacca in 1824. From these two Straits Settlements, Great Britain extended a protectorate over nine Malay states. In 1948, the Federation of Malaya was formed, and with Kuala Lumpur as capital, it attained full independence within the British Commonwealth in 1957. The Federation's 7 million population includes 3.5 million Malaysians, 2.5 million Chinese, and about 1 million other Asiatics, predominantly Indian and Pakistani.

The central core of Malaya is a highland 3,000 to 7,000 feet in elevation, which slopes abruptly to a coastal plain, narrow on the east coast, broader on the west along the Strait of Malacca. The short rivers are sluggish in their lower courses, and the coast is fringed by freshwater

TABLE 16-3 MALAYASIA

	Area, sq. mi.	Population, 1963 (est.)
Malaya	50,647	7,220,000
Singapore	289	1,775,000
North Borneo	76,455	2,255,000
	127,391	11,250,000

marshes and mangrove swamps. Situated well within the equatorial belt, Malaya has a precipitation averaging from 75 to 125 inches annually but reaching 175 inches in the central mountains. As elsewhere in the rainy tropics, the afternoon shower prevails, and heat and humidity are high.

The west-coast plain from Singapore to the border of Thailand is the most productive part of Malaya. Varying in width from 15 to 50 miles, this 400-mile-long belt encompasses most of the improved land, the main subsistence and export crops, the largest population, and the main cities.

AGRICULTURE Two-thirds of all cultivated acreage in Malaya is occupied by rubber, an industry that employs some 500,000 workers and is the largest single source of income. Soon after its success in Ceylon, *Hevea brasiliensis* was introduced into the older coastal settlements of Malaya. Following the completion of a railway up the peninsula from Singapore to Penang, numerous inland estates were cleared during the rubber boom of 1909 to 1919.

The British-owned estates, with thousands of acres in trees, are managed like factories, using work crews of Malays, Chinese, or Tamils. Estates produce one-half of the Federation's export rubber; the other half comes from Malay or Chinese smallholders with less than 100 acres each. The 345 acres under *Hevea* trees in 1897 have increased to 3.5 million acres, and

Malaya has become the leader in world rubber production, with an annual export of 700,000 tons.

Other cash crops include the coconut, oil palm, and pineapple. An almost unbroken belt of coconut groves, ½ million acres, fringes the west coast and extends up many river valleys. Kiln-dried for market, copra is shipped coastwise to Singapore or Penang, where the oil is extracted. The oil palm, which was introduced from Africa, is best suited to large-scale operation. British-owned estates employing Indian labor do their own pressing, and the oil is marketed through Singapore. Pineapple canning in south Malaya is largely controlled by the Chinese.

Many small farmers cultivate paddies in the lower floodreaches of the rivers. In contrast to Burma and Thailand, with their heavy rice exports, Malaya grows less than one-third of its requirements.

TIN MINING The great placer tin belt of Asia extends from Yünnan through the Malay Peninsula to Indonesia, its most extensive deposits occurring in Malaya.

Figure 16-16 A floating tin dredge near Kuala Lumpur. These giant machines eat their way slowly across the countryside, mining the tin-bearing gravels of Malaya. (Courtesy of Straits Times, *Singapore.)*

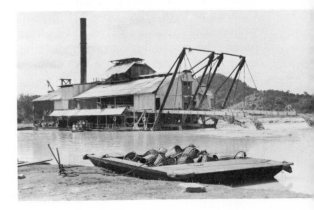

The richest alluvials are in the valley bottoms and foothills around Kuala Lumpur and in districts farther north. Tin-bearing gravels are worked by two methods, a simple washery operation using a gravel pump and the more costly but efficient floating dredges. Both pumping and dredging are on the increase, but lode mining in the mountains is still limited. With its rich surface ores and low-cost mining, Malaya has long supplied over one-third of the world's tin. The concentrates are consigned to the great smelters in Penang and Singapore.

SINGAPORE

Because of its crossroads location, Singapore has become one of the great world seaports. Ocean shipping between Europe and the Far East passes through the Strait of Malacca, a narrow sea lane between Sumatra and Malaya, with the island of Singapore at its southern end. It was purchased from one of the Malay sultans in 1819, became a highly profitable trading station for the East India Company, and later was an outport for the rich tin and rubber trade of Malaya.

Serving some 4,500 ships annually, Singapore has many miles of wharves and docks; over them passes a stream of imports and exports, raw, semifinished, or ready for consumption. Much cargo is transshipped in the open roadstead. Commercial activities have two broad bases. The city serves as metropolis and major port for the Federation, through which move rubber, tin concentrates, copra, palm oil, and canned pineapple. Rice, textiles, and consumer goods needed by upcountry planters are procured through Singapore, which handles nearly 90 per cent of all Malayan foreign trade.

Its second function is that of general entrepôt for the wares of South Asia and the East Indies, Singapore serving as a transit port for Indonesia, Burma, and Thailand. Tin concentrates from Bangka Island, rubber from Sumatra and Borneo, and copra from the South Seas are assembled here. The city deals in pepper, cloves, nutmegs, and curry materials from all over Southeast Asia. Bulk shipments to Singapore are redistributed throughout Australasia.

Industries are mainly restricted to the preparation of raw materials in transit. Tin ores and concentrates are shipped to Singapore for smelting, and the bars and ingots are sold to refineries in the United Kingdom and the United States. Copra, rubber, woods, and other tropical materials are also prepared for market.

Singapore's transshipment function includes banking, shipping, and commodity brokerage. As the trade and transfer emporium for much of South Asia, it has attracted a diverse population. Chinese of Malayan nationality have increased to 1,200,000; the Malays and other Asians are in the minority in this city of 1,775,000.

BORNEO (Malaysia)

The Chinese, Indians, and Arabs were early Asiatic traders along the coasts of Borneo and were followed by European rivals, the Dutch, Portuguese, and English. In 1821 Sarawak on the northwest coast was ceded by a Malay sultan to James Brooke, the so-called White Rajah of a domain extending 450 miles along the South China Sea and 100 miles inland to the crests of the central mountain complex. Brooke and his descendants ran Sarawak both as a trading post and as a limited plantation operation.

Through a treaty with the Sultan of Sulu, triangle-shaped North Borneo was acquired in 1878 and its development begun in 1881 by the British North Borneo

Figure 16-17   Two common activities of Southeast Asia: (left) *mining tin-bearing gravels by dragline;* (right) *drilling oil wells in a tropical area where bananas are growing.*

Chartered Company. In addition to trading, newly cleared plantations produced the standard tropical crops of the Indies: coconuts, tobacco, pepper, and the sago palm. With the rubber boom of World War I, extensive plantings of *Hevea* trees were made. Rubber became the leading crop, grown on estates and by 100-acre smallholders. A Bornean saying is, "Rubber sustains the state." The coastal trade in copra is also flourishing, and the leading towns have been known as planter's settlements.

The upcountry interior, mountainous and heavily forested, is the home of various indigenous groups, such as the Dusuns, Muruts, and Kelabits. These people

are largely self-sufficient and have little contact with the coast settlements. The more primitive tribes are still in the hunting and gathering stage of culture; others practice shifting cultivation of the firefield type. More advanced groups farm upland valleys or plateaus, growing either paddy or hill rice, corn, beans, yams, and bananas, in addition to breeding cattle.

Trade between the highlands and the coast is based on hardwood timber, rattan canes, gums, gutta percha, and other forest products, which are boated on the long rivers that reach the sea through thousands of miles of jungle. The widely spaced coastal villages, basically Malay with their houses on piles, are engaged in fishing and patch agriculture, including sago growing and sometimes paddies. Native villages also fringe the rivers at wide intervals. Partly as a result of the immigration of Chinese and other Asians, population is increasing in the Europeanized towns.

As in Dutch Borneo, the swampy and mangrove-fringed coasts were explored for oil; rich strikes in Sarawak date back to 1909. In Brunei, not yet a part of Malaysia, the highly productive Seria oil field of 1929 continues to provide most of the employment and pay all the expenses of the sultanate, a British protectorate. Petroleum and its products rank first in Brunei and Sarawak exports.

IN PERSPECTIVE

SOUTHEAST ASIA, PROBLEMS OF EMERGING NATIONS

Extending southward from the borders of India and China, Southeast Asia includes several peninsular countries such as Burma, Thailand, Cambodia, South Vietnam, and Malaya, as well as the archipelagos of Indonesia and the Philippines. Well watered by the tropical monsoon, the great river valleys with their deltas, as well as the richer coastal plains, are devoted in the main to a system of agriculture in which rice is dominant.

Ancient kingdoms with high cultural attainments flourished at various periods, but most of them had declined in power and significance before the advent of Europeans. With the exception of Thailand, all Southeast Asia came under colonial rule. Following the development of large estates, tropical products such as tea, coffee, cacao, coconut oil, palm oil, fibers, drugs, and spices have been exported in a steady flow. Since environmental conditions are especially suitable for the rubber

tree, Indonesia and Malaya have become the two greatest world sources of natural rubber. The three great river basins in Burma, Thailand, and Cambodia and South Vietnam produce a surplus of rice, in the export of which the region leads the world.

Under colonialism, mineral resources were developed, transportation improved, and commerce expanded. Cities like Singapore, Djakarta, and Manila, with strategic locations on trade routes, have become world entrepôts. Upriver delta cities such as Rangoon, Bangkok, and Saigon are more local in function.

The new countries are faced with problems of land ownership, population redistribution, and resource development. They wish to retain the material benefits achieved under colonialism; but except for the Philippines, they lack administrative personnel with experience in government, and they have few skilled technicians. To complicate the problem further, some 12 million Southeast Asians are Chinese. Able and industrious, they have long been the merchants, middlemen, and moneylenders, and with the withdrawal of Europeans they are becoming small capitalists. Although long resident in countries such as Malaya, Thailand, and Indonesia, the millions of Chinese, many of whom claim dual nationality, add an element of political uncertainty.

SELECTED REFERENCES

Hall, D. G. E.: *A History of South-East Asia,* St Martin's Press, Inc., New York, 1955.
A cultural history of one of the world's great crossroads. With his long and varied experience in this region, the author discusses authoritatively both the indigenous cultures which developed along individualistic lines and also the successive pene-

trations and pressures of outsiders—the results of Asiatic as well as of the more familiar European territorial expansion—ending with the fall of colonialism. A standard one-volume reference on Southeast Asia.

Landon, Kenneth P.: *Southeast Asia, Crossroads of Religions*, The University of Chicago Press, Chicago, 1949.

A brief introduction to the widespread influence of nonindigenous religions. These lectures center upon Sinicized Annam, Hinduized Siam, and Islamized Indonesia; the author recognizes that peoples have also been influenced by other Oriental religions. One Western religion, Roman Catholicism, is dominant in the Philippines.

Spencer, Joseph E.: *Asia East by South*, John Wiley & Sons, Inc., New York, 1954.

A geography of the Indian subcontinent, Indonesia, the Philippines, Japan, and neighboring lands. A detailed treatment of topics and countries, with emphasis on habitat, society, and economy. Extensive maps and good bibliography.

Spencer, Joseph E.: *Land and People in the Philippines*, University of California Press, Berkeley, Calif., 1952.

A source study emphasizing man-land ratio in food production under different systems, as affected by a steadily increasing and urbanized population. A good type study for Southeast Asia under two colonial regimes as well as under Philippine independence. Excellent rural study with author's own photographs; many tables; notes and bibliography.

Thompson, Warren S.: *Population and Progress in the Far East*, The University of Chicago Press, Chicago, 1959.

Discusses changes in, and development of, population in South and Southeast Asia. Analyzes agricultural and industrial bases of population growth and the effect of illiteracy on social and economic progress. Extensive bibliography.

chapter 17

AUSTRALIA, OCEANIA, AND ANTARCTICA

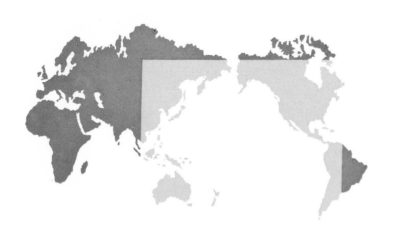

Figure 17-1   The southwestern part of the Pacific Ocean has more islands than any other equal area. The islands vary in size from New Guinea to mere dots of land. Australia, the smallest of the continents, is also in this area. Note the absence of islands in much of the northeastern Pacific.

*T*HE PACIFIC OCEAN IS THE LARGEST single earth feature, covering two-fifths of the surface of the globe, an area larger than all the land masses combined. It lies between the Old World continents to the west and the Americas to the east. Although so large, the Pacific was long unknown to Europeans and was among the last parts of the world they explored. Moreover, they were not enlightened by stories told by voyagers, which often gave erroneous impressions concerning the natives and their customs. Most Americans had small interest in the Pacific until World War II, when the names of obscure islands were headlined in the newspapers.

The regional unity of the Pacific is its vast extend of water. The land areas are very small in comparison; even Australia is smaller in area than the United States. Stretching southeast from Asia is a series of mountain folds, the tops of which form the elongated islands of Indonesia, New Guinea, the Bismarck Archipelago, and the Solomon group. The folding continues through New Caledonia, the New Hebrides, and other islands to New Zealand. The Australian continent lies to the south and west of these mountainous islands. Further seaward, east and north, are other folds mostly underneath the waters of the Pacific, though a few peaks, often of volcanic origin, rise above the open ocean to form small, widely scattered islands. The most remote islands are of either volcanic or coralline origin. The volcanoes generally form high islands; those of coral are low, and except for a limited number of raised coral islands, have a height of only a few feet above sea level. Characteristically, the oceanic islands on a map appear arranged in arclike festoons because they rise, sometimes from great depths, above curving lines of weakness in the earth's crust.

Compared with the eastern Pacific in which islands are rare, the western Pacific has numerous islands. The north Pacific between the Aleutian chain and the tropics has practically no islands except near the continents. In the vast southern ocean between New Zealand and Antarctica, only a few isolated volcanoes rise above the apparently boundless sea.

AUSTRALIA

Australia may well be called the island continent because of its isolation from the great land masses and because it is the smallest of the populated continents, having an area of about 3 million square miles. Down-under Australia and Antarctica are the only continents wholly south of the equator. The similarity of conditions and problems in some parts of Australia to those of the United States and the British ancestry of most of the people make Americans at home with the Australian people.

The Commonwealth of Australia was established in 1901 by the union of six British colonies. The former colonies, now called states, are New South Wales, Victoria, Queensland, South Australia, Western Australia, and Tasmania. In addition there is a Northern Territory. The capital of the Commonwealth is Canberra. The country is a self-governing member of the British Commonwealth. Australia also governs the eastern half of New Guinea and several smaller islands.

Australia's natural characteristics have important human relationships. Much of the continent is very ancient, with old crystalline rocks predominating, and it has the lowest average elevation, hardly 1,000 feet, of any continent. Only 6 per cent of the country has an altitude of over 2,000 feet. Low elevation, combined with its location in the trade winds and under

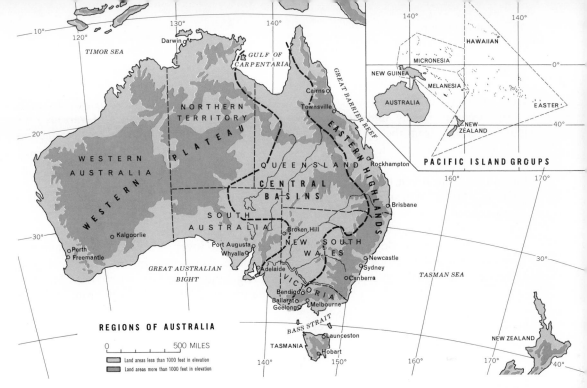

Figure 17-2   Australia is divided into three large regions. Each could be subdivided into many smaller ones. Most of the population of the nation live in the eastern and southern part of the mountain area. Western Australia is largely a desert area.

areas of high atmospheric pressure, precludes much rainfall; hence one-half of the continent is arid and one-fourth semiarid. No drainage reaches the ocean from this dry interior, and temporary streams and lake basins contain water only after occasional rainstorms. Hardly one-fourth of Australia is blessed with a humid or subhumid climate. Most of the streams in the humid regions are short, but some have been developed for power; in the southeast interior, the Murray-Darling-Murrumbidgee drainage area supplies much water for irrigation. In northern Australia, the rivers vary in volume from flood stages during the summer rainy season to intermittent during the dry winter. Australia extends almost 2,600 miles from east to west and 2,000 miles from north to south. It is compact, and the infrequency of indentations makes Australia's coastline the shortest, compared with the

land area, of any of the continents. There are few good harbors, no active volcanoes, and the highest peak, Mt. Kosciusko, is only 7,328 feet above the sea.

PHYSICAL SETTING

REGIONS   Australia is divided into three major regions: the Western Plateau, the Central Basins, and the Eastern Highlands (Figure 17-2).

The Western Plateau occupies three-fifths of the continent. Most of it consists of very old rocks that have been worn down by erosion to a peneplain. Only low knobs and a few ranges rise above the monotonous surface, most of which has an elevation of about 1,200 feet. Around Spencer Gulf, in South Australia, earth movements have resulted in elongated ridges and depressed blocks called rift valleys. Only in the north and southwest is the rainfall adequate for trees and good pasture for livestock. Wheat and other crops are raised in the southwest.

The Central Basins include the lowlands extending from the Gulf of Carpentaria on the north to the Murray River basin and the Great Australian Bight on the south. From north to south, the Carpentaria, Great Artesian, and Murray Basins together include 800,000 square miles, or over one-fourth of the country's area. The basins are underlain by dipping layers of sedimentary rocks, chiefly clay and sandstone. The Carpentaria Basin has generally poor soils and is covered with scrub trees and tall grass. Some cattle are kept by the few settlers living in the region.

In the Great Artesian Basin, water enters the sandstones in high ground along the eastern rim and is held in the pervious beds by impervious clay above and below. The water is under pressure and when reached by bores (drilled wells) flows out on the surface. Although most of the water is too salty to be used for irrigation, it is usable for watering livestock and makes possible a cattle industry in grassy areas devoid of surface water. The lower part of the basin is desert, and Lake Eyre, whose elevation is 39 feet below sea level, contains water only after heavy rains. The best grazing coincides with the area of greater rainfall in the eastern part, especially in the Darling Downs of southern Queensland that are drained by the Darling River, a tributary of the Murray.

The Murray Basin has fertile soils and is important for wheat, cattle, and sheep production. It is well watered toward the eastern and southern rims, but the climate becomes drier along the lower course of the river. Here irrigation projects, using the waters of the Murray and Murrumbidgee Rivers, make possible the raising of citrus fruits, grapes, alfalfa, and other crops.

The Eastern Highlands cover about one-sixth of the continent. The region consists of uplifted plateaus, tilted crustal blocks, and folded zones of various rock types, along with small disconnected areas of lowland and coastal plain. Although parts of the Highlands are thinly populated, the region contains two-thirds of Australia's inhabitants, in part because it is the best-watered in the continent. Elevations are moderate and vary from under 1,000 to over 3,000 feet, with summits above 7,000 feet in the southeast. The Highlands continue across Bass Strait to Tasmania, which is a very rugged island composed of two uplands separated by north-south extending lowlands. In southern Victoria fertile lowlands (Gippsland), trending east-west, lie between the Highlands and lower coastal hills. Here the large majority of the state's population live. A remarkable feature off the Queensland coast is the Great Barrier Reef that parallels the mainland for over 1,000 miles.

The Highlands have a rainy climate throughout their length. The temperature changes, however, becoming warmer from south to north. Forests cover most of the region, but there are also well-watered grasslands for grazing. Dairying and livestock industries are important and some specialty crops are grown, such as sugar cane, bananas, and pineapples in Queensland. The drier inner slopes of the southeast are devoted to wheat and animal industries. The Gippsland area, near Melbourne, and the central lowlands of Tasmania support dairying, diversified farming, and apples and other fruits of mid-latitude climates.

CLIMATE   The climate of Australia is affected by its location between 10° and 40° south latitude, the general low elevation of the land, and the position of the Eastern

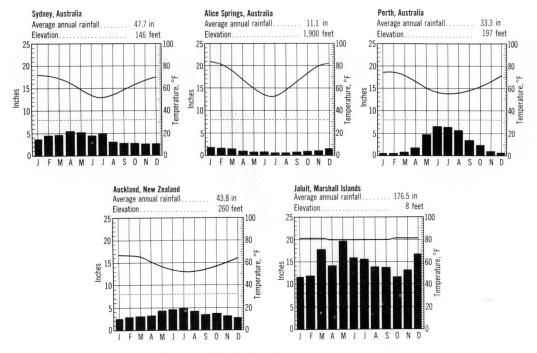

Figure 17-3   Climate graphs of selected cities.

Highlands (Figure 17-3). The location south of the equator causes the seasons to be reversed from those in the Northern Hemisphere—summer coming from December to February and winter from June to August. The shifting of the wind belts with the seasons determines the time and location of the rains.

In summer heavy rains drench northern Australia, which is then in the tropical calms. Winter is the dry season, when the tropical rainy belt shifts equatorward. Throughout the year the temperatures remain generally high. Northern Australia, then, has a wet-and-dry tropical or savanna climate, except for Cape York in the northeast, where rain falls throughout the year and the climate becomes rainy tropical.

Rainfall diminishes toward the interior. From central Australia to the west coast is a hot trade-wind desert, dry at all sea-

sons. Not only is the rainfall scant but it is extremely unreliable. The desert touches the south coast at the Nullarbor (treeless) Plains. Between the desert and the savanna and east-coast regions is the tropical steppe, with rainfall enough for grass and bushes but not for trees.

Southwestern Australia, the coast of South Australia, and the area near the mouth of the Murray River have a Mediterranean type of climate with mild rainy winters and hot, dry summers. In winter the prevailing westerly winds shift north, and the accompanying cyclonic storms furnish the rains. Cyclones down under whirl opposite to those in the Northern Hemisphere, the winds rotating clockwise instead of counterclockwise. Inland, the steppe climate begins at about the 10-inch annual rainfall line—a contrast to northern Australia, where the savanna is replaced by steppe at about the 20-inch rainfall line. The difference is accounted for by the higher rate of evaporation toward the equator.

Southeast Australia has a humid subtropical climate with rainfall throughout the year, mild winters, and warm summers. The winter rains are cyclonic; the summer rains are associated with easterly winds from the Pacific.

Tasmania and southern Victoria lie in the westerly winds and have a marine west-coast climate resembling that of western Oregon. Winters are cool and wet. Summers are mild and somewhat less humid. Snow may occur in the highlands in the winter months.

Figure 17-4 Kangaroos are abundant throughout Australia and Tasmania. These marsupials graze on hills and plains, hopping on their long legs. The young are only about 1 inch long when born and are suckled in a large pouch in the mother's body. (Courtesy of Australian News and Information Bureau.)

NATURAL VEGETATION   Because of Australia's long isolation from other continents, most of the trees are peculiar to the continent and consist dominantly of two types —acacias and eucalypts. There are hundreds of species of each, which have adapted themselves to the various climates, as have the many unique flowering plants and other vegetation. Patches of rain forest occur in the wet tropical zone; in the savanna regions are tall grasses and stunted woodland. The steppes have grass, usually in clumps, small acacia brush (mulga), and saltbush. The rainier parts in the Mediterranean climate possess excellent commercial forests of eucalypts. With less rainfall, the forests are replaced by shrubs called mallee. In the Eastern Highlands and the southeast and southwest corners of Australia are forests of eucalypts interspersed with grass and open woods. Forests originally covered most of Tasmania, but the continent itself is not rich in timber; commercially valuable forest trees cover less than 2 per cent of the area. Vegetation in the desert consists of scattered spinifix (a grass), saltbush, and a few stunted mulga bushes. Native trees are hardwoods, except for some misnamed "pines" in Tasmania and the Eastern Highlands.

ANIMAL LIFE   The native animals of Australia are mostly unique in that they lack close relatives in other continents. This condition results from the long separation of Australia from other lands; the higher animals never reached the island country. Two-thirds of the species in Australia are marsupials, primitive creatures whose young are carried in an external pouch. Examples include many species of kangaroo, the opossum, koala (tree bear), and wombat. Tasmania had two carnivorous marsupials, the Tasmanian wolf and the Tasmanian devil. Australia has the only

AUSTRALIA, OCEANIA, AND ANTARCTICA *665*

egg-laying mammals in the world, including the platypus, which has the bill of a duck, the tail of a beaver, webbed feet, is covered with fur, lays eggs, and nurses its young. The only higher mammal is a wild dog, the dingo, brought into the country by the early aborigines. Snakes, lizards, and crocodiles are numerous. In coastal waters of the tropics are found big sea turtles and the dugong or manatee. Birds include the emu, which resembles the ostrich, a black swan, the lyre bird, many cockatoos, and the kookaburra, a kind of kingfisher with a cry so strange that it is called the laughing jackass.

Besides bringing in the domestic animals, the British introduced rabbits, which throve and multiplied to hundreds of millions, eating grass needed by sheep and cattle. Rabbits are slaughtered in great numbers in an effort to reduce the pest, and their pelts are exported by the tens of millions to be used for cheap furs. Some are eaten, but most of the carcasses are unused. After rabbit-proof fences proved only partially successful, in the 1950s "myxomatosis," a contagious disease of rabbits, was introduced and has greatly reduced their numbers with resulting benefit to the grazing for livestock.

ECONOMIC DEVELOPMENT

The Commonwealth is in an early stage of economic development. It primarily produces and exports foodstuffs and raw materials, and imports many of its needs for manufactured goods, although industrial output has greatly increased since World War II. A hindrance to manufacturing expansion and diversification, however, is the fact that the rather small population does not provide a sufficiently great market for mass production of comprehensively varied goods. Important exports include wool, wheat, hides and skins, beef

and mutton, lead, zinc, and other metals. Imports include needed manufactures, lumber, and petroleum products.

PASTORAL INDUSTRIES Australia is world-famous for sheep and important for cattle. Livestock are favored by extensive natural pastures, mild winters that obviate the necessity for supplementary feeding except during occasional droughts, and the absence of natural enemies except a few wild dogs. Since wool, meat, and hides are in demand, ships come from all parts of the world to secure them.

Australia leads all other countries in the production and export of wool. Sheep number about 152 million, a ratio of a dozen sheep to each person in the country, but the number of sheep may vary by millions, depending on whether a year has drought or adequate rainfall. The large majority of sheep are found in semiarid climates from southern Queensland across interior New South Wales to Victoria and South Australia. Formerly they were handled on huge stations (ranches) leased from the government; now sheep runs have been reduced in size, and flocks usually consist of about 1,000 animals, mostly merinos and mixed breeds. Shearing is done by machines. The wool is delivered to storage warehouses in centers like Sydney and Melbourne. There some wool is scoured, graded, and baled, but a large proportion is sold in a greasy condition. Australia's wool is of premium quality and totals about 1.4 billion pounds annually, one-fourth of the world's clip. Wool is the leading export of Australia, accounting for about one-eighth of the total domestic income and sometimes for over one-third of the country's income from exports. Sales of lambs and mutton are often greater than those of any other country, although in some years New Zealand ranks first. Annual production of

Figure 17-5 A mob (flock) of sheep at a station (ranch) in New South Wales. (Courtesy of Australian News and Information Bureau.)

mutton, beef, and pork is about 1½ million tons.

Beef cattle rank next to sheep in number and value of products. About 11 million beef cattle and 5 million dairy cows are kept in Australia. Queensland leads in cattle, with over 6 million head. Beef cattle are favored over sheep in the tropical savannas and near deserts, but in the cooler areas they generally cannot compete with the more profitable sheep. Packing plants are located in centers convenient to supply, for example, in Brisbane. About one-fourth of the beef slaughtered is exported, primarily to England, the

business being favored by a reciprocal trade agreement.

Dairying is carried on chiefly in the moist coastal lowlands and lower Eastern Highlands in New South Wales, Victoria, southeast Queensland, and Tasmania. The industry is favored by mild weather and good grazing. Over 190,000 tons of butter and 42,000 tons of cheese are produced annually.

AGRICULTURE   Wheat is the most important crop in Australia and occupies well over one-half of the 25 million acres tilled. Production of wheat varies from 50 million to more than 200 million bushels annually; the great differences depend on weather conditions and world prices. In most years nearly 100 million bushels of wheat are shipped. The United Kingdom is the best customer. Wheat farming is highly mechanized. The wheat belt has a crescent shape and is situated where the annual rainfall is 12 to 25 inches, on the inward slopes of the Eastern Highlands in New South Wales and Victoria. South Australia and southwest Western Australia also grow wheat. Adelaide and Port Lincoln in South Australia are among the wheat-exporting ports.

Sugar is raised, but because of the labor situation, costs are high compared with those of most foreign producers; hence the industry is protected by a high tariff. The cane is grown by the plantation method in some places along the coast of Queensland where fertile soils are available.

Fruits that need a tropical climate, such as bananas, pineapples, and papayas, are grown in coastal Queensland and northeast New South Wales for sale in Sydney and other cities. The chief citrus region is along the lower Murray River in South Australia, New South Wales, and northern Victoria, including sections of the Murrumbidgee Valley. Fruit is raised by irrigation in all these inland locations. Mildura is a chief center for citrus fruits, grapes, currants, and raisins. Wine is made near the vineyards, especially in South Australia.

Apples, pears, cherries, and berries are grown in Tasmania, the cool southern lands of Victoria, Western Australia, and the uplands in New South Wales. Apples are exported to Europe. Fruits are often canned; they are also made into preserves and marmalade.

WATER RESOURCES   Water is stored and used extensively for irrigation in the Murray River basin where the Hume dam, which also generates hydroelectricity, is noteworthy. Another dam is the Burrinjack, which stores water for the irrigation of the Murrumbidgee Valley. Compared with that of other continents, Australia's potential water power is small because of the lack of large, swift rivers. A few hydroelectric plants are located in southeastern Australia and Tasmania, but big coal-fired plants, like Yallourn, Victoria, supply 90 per cent of the total electrical power. The Snowy Mountains development is a multiple-purpose dam for irrigation and power, which will eventually provide 3 million

Figure 17-6 The 16-mile bore, near Alice Springs, is the last watering point for drovers traveling their cattle down the north-south stock route to the railhead for shipment to Adelaide. (Courtesy of Australian News and Information Bureau.)

kilowatts of power and 1.8 million acre-feet of water for irrigation in the Murrumbidgee and Murray Basins.

MINERALS   Australia is quite well supplied with mineral wealth. For example, some gold is mined in every state and territory, the annual output being valued at about 38 million dollars. The ancient rocks in Western Australia have many gold deposits, the mines at Kalgoorlie being especially productive. During the 1850s gold was discovered in New South Wales and Victoria, and soon the Bendigo and Ballarat mines in Victoria became great producers. Victoria has mined gold worth over 1½ billion dollars, but during late years the output has been small. The Commonwealth is also important for its production of lead, zinc, and silver, the combined value of which is approximately 75 million dollars annually. The greatest center for these metals is Broken Hill, a city of 30,000 in the desert of western New South Wales. Copper and tin are mined in sufficient quantity to supply domestic demands. The country supplies most of its needs for iron and steel. Annual production is about 2 million tons. Iron ore is mined in South Australia and Western Australia; most of it is then taken by boat to Newcastle and Port Kembla, where coking coal is available for smelting. A steel mill is also located at Whyalla in South Australia. Bauxite occurs on Cape York Peninsula and will be shipped for reduction to aluminum to New Zealand, where hydroelectric power is available. Very beautiful opals and sapphires come from Australia. Uranium is mined at Rum Jungle, 60 miles south of Darwin, Northern Territory.

Australia has the largest known coal reserves in the Southern Hemisphere. The annual production is approximately 21 million tons, of which one-third is lignite. The best coal underlies the coastal area north and south of Sydney. Coal is also mined from several deposits in Queensland. Victoria has extensive beds of lignite; the bed at Yallourn, east of Melbourne, is nearly 200 feet thick. This deposit, mined by the open-pit method, is used by steam plants to generate electricity for use in Melbourne and other cities. Some shows of petroleum have been discovered, but production is insignificant.

MANUFACTURING   Since 1915 manufacturing has greatly expanded, in part because during both world wars it was difficult to import finished goods. Heavy manufactures of iron and steel have made notable advances. Lead smelters operate at Port Perie, South Australia, and near Newcastle. Automotive vehicles are built in Adelaide and railroad equipment in terminals like Melbourne and Port Augusta; shipbuilding and ship repair is carried on at the major ports. Light manufacture of textiles, especially woolens and other consumer goods like household articles and electrical supplies, now supply much of the domestic market. The processing of raw materials, sugar, metallic ores, oil shale, and wool is characteristic. Oil refineries at Melbourne, Sydney, and Fremantle operate on imported crude petroleum. Meat slaughtering, meat packing, and flour milling are carried on for both local sale and export. A tariff protects many recently developed industries. The higher cost to consumers is compensated for by increased employment; about one-third of the over 3.7 million workers in the Commonwealth are employed by manufacturing industries, mostly concentrated in the southeast.

TRANSPORTATION   The concentration of population and industries in southeast and southwest Australia and the great expanse of unpeopled desert markedly affect the location and construction of railroads and highways. Furthermore, until 1900 each state developed its transportation routes independently, focusing on the capitals, which were also the chief seaports. This individuality is shown by the use of three railroad gauges—broad, standard, and narrow—though some are being converted to similar gauge. Only one railroad built well to the south for strategic reasons crosses the continent from east to west. A narrow-gauge railroad to Alice Springs, in central Australia, and a highway from there to Darwin in Northern Territory is the only well-traveled route across the "Never-Never Land" of the interior from south to north. The government owns and operates about 90 per cent of the 28,000 miles of railroads.

Many of the highways in Australia are unimproved, but 20,000 miles are called improved, and long stretches are paved. The best roads connect the major cities. Over 1 million motor vehicles are licensed, and the Commonwealth ranks high among the countries of the world in per capita ownership of motor vehicles. Most of the principal cities are on the coast, and exchange of freight among them is largely carried by ships rather than by rail or trucks. Sydney, Melbourne, Adelaide, Brisbane, Fremantle (the port of Perth), and Hobart have freight and passenger service by sea to Europe, Asia, the Americas, and other places.

Airlines connect the principal cities, and air travel in this thinly populated country of large size is of great importance. Overseas airlines connect Australia with many countries of Europe, Asia, Africa, and the Americas, as well as with New Zealand and numerous Pacific islands. Doctors and nurses fly to remote ranches when emergencies arise.

POPULATION

Of about 10.9 million people, more than 80 per cent are native-born, and the large majority are of British ancestry. Since World War II over a million immigrants have moved to Australia; about one-half of them have been British, but there were also many Dutch and Italian people. A scant 75,000 aborigines and half-breeds still survive, living mostly in the interior dry lands and northern sections.

For a country only partially developed, Australia has a surprisingly large urban population. The six state capitals—Adelaide, Brisbane, Hobart, Melbourne, Perth, and Sydney—contain one-half of the population in the Commonwealth; Sydney and Melbourne together have one-third of the people. Except for Port Adelaide, outside the city limits of Adelaide, and Fremantle, a few miles from Perth, the capitals are the chief ports, handle most of the exports and imports of their respective states, are the principal railroad centers, lead in the manufacture and distribution of goods, and are paramount in business management, government, education, and cultural life. Important for governmental activities is Canberra, the capital of the Commonwealth. In addition to the six state capitals, there are about 140 smaller cities. Less than 3 million people, hardly 30 per cent of the population, are classified as rural, and some of them live in villages rather than on farms.

Sydney and Melbourne rank fourth and fifth in population among the world cities in the Southern Hemisphere. Each is a

Figure 17-7   An aerial view of Sydney looking southwest across the harbor bridge and ship-ping wharves. Sydney, the capital of New South Wales, is the largest city in Australia and has a population of over 2 million. (Courtesy of Australian News and Information Bureau.)

modern, well-built metropolis with sub-stantial public buildings, office and busi-ness structures, big warehouses on the waterfront, factories, fine residences, thea-ters, and parks. The other state capitals also present an attractive appearance. Sydney ranks with San Francisco in its landlocked harbor, which, like its Ameri-can counterpart, is crossed by a huge bridge at the narrows.

Although widespread aridity reduces its capacity to support great numbers of people, Australia has room for more than double the present population. To be sure, the Eastern Highlands reduce the useful-ness to agriculture of the well-watered southeast, and poor soils and tropical cli-mate in northern Australia make that region unattractive to white settlers, who are the only ones acceptable; colored peo-ple are excluded. Large areas of good grazing, generally fertile soils in consider-able parts of southeast and southwest Australia, important deposits of metals and coal, a healthy and invigorating cli-mate over the southern half of the conti-nent, and a citizenship of a high order are favorable factors for the development of the Commonwealth.

The country is very advanced in social legislation and direct government. The secret ballot, old-age pensions, arbitration of strikes, government loans for housing, social security, the recall of public officials, government ownership of railroads, the initiative, referendum, and other measures were adopted in Australia before they were accepted in the United States. Education has received universal support, and the percentage of illiteracy is very low. Universities are located in each of the state capitals.

OCEANIA

The term Oceania may be taken to include New Guinea and other mid-Pacific islands north and east from Australia, south to New Zealand, and north to Hawaii, the only insular state of the United States. The islands of the Republic of Indonesia, the Philippine Republic, and Taiwan are discussed in connection with Asiatic areas. It is customary to divide the islands of Oceania into three areas: Melanesia, Micronesia, and Polynesia (Figure 17-2). The Bismarck Archipelago, the Solomon, New Hebrides, and Fiji groups, New Caledonia, and associated smaller islands are called Melanesia (black-inhabited islands) from the complexion of the natives. Micronesia (small islands) includes the numerous but usually small islets of the Caroline, Mariana, and Marshall groups east of the Philippines and generally north of New Guinea and Melanesia. Polynesia (many islands) covers a huge triangular area on both sides of the equator in the middle Pacific from Hawaii on the north to New Zealand on the south and Easter Island on the east.

The native inhabitants are as varied as the islands. Negroid peoples of various types live in New Guinea and Melanesia. Micronesians resemble Malays; they are of medium size and have brown skins. Polynesians have a mixed ancestry and are generally a tall, good-looking race of light brown color.

Native people migrated to the Melanesian and Micronesian islands thousands of years ago, and the Polynesians have lived on their islands for a dozen centuries or more. Europeans, however, have known about these island areas for only a few centuries. During the two and a half centuries following the crossing of the Pacific by Magellan in 1521, Dutch, English, Spanish, and French navigators made voyages of discovery. The most renowned explorer of all was Captain James Cook, an Englishman, who made three voyages between 1768 and 1780; his maps of the Pacific showed well all essential features of that ocean and its islands.

Europeans of various sorts and occupations followed the explorers. The impact of whalers, traders, missionaries, merchants, and other settlers was often disastrous to the natives. For example, in less than two centuries the number of Polynesians is believed to have been cut by three-fourths, and Micronesians and Melanesians have suffered in a similar way.

Control over the Pacific Ocean lands is divided among several powers. Politically, New Zealand is a self-governing member of the British Commonwealth of Nations. The United Kingdom, France, and the United States are now the principal island-governing powers. During the years between the two World Wars, Japan controlled the Marianas (except Guam), the Carolines, and the Marshall Islands. Since World War II, however, the United States has governed these islands as a United Nations Trust Territory. Of the smaller powers, Chile owns isolated little Easter Island in Polynesia; and the eastern part of Timor belongs to Portugal. Australia governs the eastern half of New Guinea, and along with New Zealand rules several Pacific islands under trust agreements. Western Samoa became an independent republic in 1962, and Tonga is an independent kingdom under the protection of the United Kingdom.

POLYNESIA

Of the native peoples in Oceania, the Polynesians were most admired by the European navigators. They were a large, fine-looking race of mixed ancestry and high intelligence, although culturally they were still in the Stone Age. Scientists believe that the Polynesians were derived from the intermarriage of many peoples, including those of Asiatic, Melanesian, and Caucasian origin. Although they declined in numbers after the arrival of Europeans in islands like Hawaii and New Zealand, the Polynesians have freely married with the English, American, and other nationalities, and these new mixtures now constitute an important element in the population.

In most of Polynesia the scenery is exceedingly attractive to tourists and other visitors, for it is often spectacular, with startlingly steep cliffs covered with tropical verdure, clean beaches shaded by waving palm trees, active volcanoes, and in New Zealand, snowcapped peaks and glaciers. Paintings, photographs, moving pictures, plays, books, and stories about Polynesia, although popularizing the islands, have sometimes resulted in odd and exaggerated notions about the ease and pleasures of tropical living and the relationships to be expected from the natives.

Except for New Zealand, Polynesia lies in the tropics on both sides of the equator. It is broadest from Samoa and Tonga on the west to lonely Easter Island on the east. Of the dozens of groups and hundreds of islands scattered around this part of the Pacific, some are quite large and populous, but the greater number are small, and many are uninhabited. Always the extent of ocean vastly exceeds the area of land.

NEW ZEALAND   By far the largest land area in Polynesia is New Zealand. Americans feel at home here, for the people are mostly of British ancestry, and both the climate and landscape resemble parts of Europe and the United States. The industries of the country are familiar, and many of its economic problems are similar to those in certain parts of the United States.

New Zealand is situated about 1,200 miles southeast of Australia and consists of two large islands and several smaller ones, having an area of about 104,000 square miles and a population of nearly 2½ million. In contrast to Australia, New Zealand is mountainous and has a generally rainy climate. It possesses many fine harbors and has active volcanoes, numerous geysers, and many glaciers.

The natural environment of the islands varies greatly. With a latitudinal extent approaching 1,000 miles, the country has a generally humid west-coast climate, with temperatures modified by the surrounding ocean but getting progressively colder toward the south. North of Auckland snow is unknown, and the climate is subtropical. Snow and frost are rare on the lowlands of all of North Island. The southern end of South Island has cold winters. Its west coast is very cloudy with heavy precipitation, and snow piles up in the high mountains to feed numerous glaciers. The eastern side of South Island, leeward of the high mountains, has less rainfall, and most of it has a subhumid climate with a fairly large range of temperatures. New Zealand lies in the belt of prevailing westerlies, and for this reason cyclones provide much of the rainfall. Mountains cause large local differences in rainfall and temperature.

The backbone of South Island is a high and rugged mountain chain, culminating

Figure 17-8   The Southern Alps on South Island of New Zealand are noted for their tourist resorts. Behind the hotel is Mt. Sefton, 10,345 feet, and on the right is Mt. Cook, New Zealand's highest peak, 12,349 feet. (Courtesy of Matson Lines.)

in Mt. Cook or Aorangi (cloud piercer) 12,349 feet above sea level. Some seventeen peaks reach elevations of 10,000 feet or more. The southwest coast, called Fiordland, is indented by a score of fiords that were scoured out by prehistoric glaciers. Beautiful lakes, snow fields for skiing, glaciers, serrated peaks, and the fiords are tourist attractions in South Island. Both islands offer the tourist excellent fishing, sandy beaches, and protected harbors. North Island mountains are not so high as those in South Island, but central North Island has active volcanoes and also many hot springs and geysers, those of Rotorua being world-famous.

Like Australia, New Zealand was long isolated from other land masses, and this isolation greatly affected the native flora and fauna. Many plants are peculiar to the islands. Southern pines and beeches, tree ferns, ferns, and laurels are charac-

teristic. Tussock and other grasses supply excellent grazing on the semiarid slopes and plains. Notable is the Canterbury Plain, famous for sheep and wheat, on the east of South Island. In both North and South Islands, much of the original "bush" has been cleared and planted to grasses on which the dairy industry is based.

Except for marine animals and the bat, native mammals are lacking. Flightless birds, many now extinct, were once common; one of these, a moa, stood 12 feet tall. The nearly wingless kiwi and the kea, a type of parrot, are unique. The tuatara, one of the lizards, has a rudimentary third eye. Some introduced animals, like rabbits and deer, have become pests.

The economic resources of the country are varied. Among the minerals, coal easily leads in value although proved resources total under 1 billion tons, of which only one-third is bituminous. It is mined in several localities, but the chief production and best coal comes from the west coast of South Island near Greymouth and Westport. Although the coal output is 2.5 million tons annually, small amounts are imported, chiefly from Australia. Clay products, cement, and lime are manufactured for local consumption, and a little natural gas has been discovered. Gold is the principal metal, but the once large production is now small.

Although most rivers in New Zealand are short, many are swift and have enough volume to form considerable potential water power, and much is being developed. Natural underground steam is used for industrial power in the hot volcanic region of North Island.

The forests that originally covered much of the country have been damaged by careless grazing, logging, and fire, and only about 17 million acres of forest remain. The annual cut of lumber exceeds 500 million board feet. Although the cut of rimu (red pine) is the largest, other softwoods and beech are important sources of lumber for construction and furniture. Kauri, one of the tallest trees in the world, is a superior timber, but most of the stands of this fine tree have been logged. Kauri gum is valuable for varnish manufacture. Much fossil gum is dug from marshes in which it has been preserved.

Animal industries form the chief economic base. The generally mild, rainy climate favors both native grasses and the introduced species that give the grasslands a high carrying capacity. Farmland is mostly devoted to grazing. Even most crops are feed for livestock; of 20 million acres of improved land, only 1.5 million acres are in field crops. Animal products such as wool, meat, hides, and dairy products constitute over 90 per cent of the exports from New Zealand.

The dairy industry is the leading source of income for a majority of the farmers of

Figure 17-9   The Canterbury Plains are one of the chief agricultural areas of New Zealand. The town is Amberley. (Courtesy of Matson Lines.)

North Island, although many also raise sheep, beef, and pigs. Since neither dairy cows nor sheep require shelter, but little supplemental feeding is needed. Purebred animals predominate among the nearly 2 million dairy cows. Methods are sanitary and efficient, and New Zealand dairy products have a good reputation. Cheese, butter, and dried and canned milk are exported, in particular to the United Kingdom.

Sheep are raised extensively on both islands, North Island having 55 per cent and South Island 45 per cent of the country's 42 million sheep; the number exceeds the human population in the ratio of 20 to 1. New Zealand follows Australia in exports of wool, but leads all countries in exports of mutton.

Most of the wheat is raised on the Canterbury Plain, which has a subhumid climate. Production is adequate to supply local demands. Oats, potatoes, and apples are among the other crops grown.

Aside from the processing of dairy products and meat slaughtering, New Zealand is unimportant in manufactures for export. Clothing, flour, woolens, lumber, and other products are manufactured for the domestic market.

New Zealand has a population of upwards of 2½ million including the Maoris. These natives originally lived in villages, cultivated the sweet potato and some other crops, built canoes, caught fish, and wove cloth from the fiber in the long leaves of New Zealand flax. They were a tall, kindly, fine-looking, and intelligent people, culturally far in advance of Australia's aborigines. Clever carvers of wood, the Maoris had no knowledge of metals or of pottery. Although reduced in numbers, about 158,000 still survive, including part-breeds from mixtures with Europeans, and they form a self-respecting integral part of the country's population.

The great majority of the settlers of New Zealand came from the British Isles. They introduced new plants and animals and thereby changed the entire economy of the country. Social changes were equally important. Education is universal; universities are located in the chief cities. Social legislation is advanced, and the people pride themselves on the absence of poverty and the fact that equal opportunities are open to all. Life in New Zealand resembles life in rural regions of the United States. Farmers have trucks, automobiles, milking machines, tractors, and a variety of other equipment, along with telephones and mail delivery. Many farms are electrified. Principal highways are graded and paved. Railroad passenger and freight service is good; the lines are operated by the government.

Auckland is the largest city and also ranks first among the seaports. Wellington is the capital and the second port; it is located on a good harbor on Cook Strait. On South Island, Christchurch and Dunedin are the largest cities.

New Zealand governs the Cook Islands, Niue, and the Tokelau group. It also exercises control over nearly unpopulated islands in the far south Pacific.

SMALLER ISLANDS OF POLYNESIA   Except for New Zealand, most of the islands of Polynesia are divisible into two types—high volcanic islands and low islands built of coral. A few of the coral islands have been elevated; some others are made of a combination of volcanic and coralline material; and there are examples of volcanoes surrounded by coral reefs and islets.

The high islands generally are larger and have more rainfall, better soil, and a greater variety of vegetation than the low islands. Having more resources, the volcanic islands can support more people and provide a greater variety of goods than

Figure 17-10   Auckland is the largest city in New Zealand. Queen Street, shown here, extends from the business center to the wharves. (Courtesy of New Zealand Embassy.)

the flat strips of coral thinly covered by sand and only a few feet above sea level. Examples of the high islands are the Hawaiian, Samoan, Society (Tahiti), and Marquesas groups. In contrast, the Tuamotu Archipelago, Ellice, Phoenix, Tokelau, Line, and most of the Tonga (Friendly) Islands, except for a few active volcanoes, consist of numerous coral islets. The Cook Islands include some that are of elevated coral, as is also Nauru, famous for its phosphate rock. The Tubuai (Austral) Islands are of both volcanic and coral origin. Remote Pitcairn and Easter Islands are volcanic.

Hundreds of the coral islands in the tropical Pacific are atolls—low, narrow strips of coral, usually of an approximately oval shape, surrounding a lagoon. The coral ring may be continuous, but more often it is broken into motus (parts). Sometimes an atoll has a score or more of these islets. Atolls vary in size from lagoons with a diameter of a few miles to some of 100 miles or more. They are often built on platforms that rise from great ocean depths. Many geologists believe atolls were once fringing reefs around volcanoes that have disappeared, leaving only the coral strands.

Sea birds that resort to some of the low islands for nesting are everywhere. With the exception of bats, land mammals are lacking, except for those introduced by man. The people have a saying that the sea is the poor man's garden. They catch fish and turtles, gather shellfish and certain seaweeds, and sometimes obtain porpoises or other sea mammals for food.

Coconut palms, pandanus, and a variety of bushes constitute the principal native plants on the coral islands. The coconut supplies a great variety of products. The meat is eaten fresh; the milk of immature nuts is a refreshing drink; a fermented drink is made from the sap; the living crown makes a delicious salad; and from the dried meat, called copra, is pressed oil for cooking, skin lotion, and other purposes. The trunk serves as posts for huts; the leaves are used for roofing material and fuel, the fiber, for ropes, fish nets, mats, and sails, the shells for dishes. In fact, every part of the coconut palm is put to some use. Pandanus leaves are also woven into mats and clothing, and the fruit, resembling a pineapple in looks but not in flavor, is edible.

Coral sand is poor soil; hence if the people want gardens, they dig pits in which various wastes are allowed to rot. They then can raise vegetables and fruits on these places, which, although small in size, supply the chief food crops like taro. Coral atolls support limited numbers of people, ranging from several hundred down to a few families. The natives live in villages. They build excellent sailing canoes, often equipped with outriggers for stability, and in the old days, they lived without using money and with little trade. A limiting factor of life on some low islands was the small supply, or even absence, of drinking water.

Before the arrival of Europeans, the natives on the high islands raised taro, a starchy root planted in an artifical swamp, arrowroot, sweet potatoes, breadfruit, and several other crops. They kept a few pigs and chickens, gathered sea food and the eggs of sea birds and turtles, caught fish, and sometimes raised mullet in fishponds.

Cooking bananas grew in the mountains; oily nuts were used for seasoning along with sea salt. The natives carved hardwood into many useful articles and used birds' feathers for decorative costumes. They built villages usually near the sea, and they made long voyages in sturdy outrigger canoes.

Today, after contact with Europeans, the number of natives in Polynesia has declined greatly. Tuberculosis and other diseases, wars, and the destruction of the old ways of life wrought havoc with the Polynesians. Only in a few places, for example the Tonga Islands, are the natives as numerous as in the past.

The United States owns several isolated little islands, south and west of Hawaii. These include Wake, Johnston, Baker, Howland, Palmyra, Kingman Reef, and Jarvis. Most of these islands are used for air bases. By mutual agreement, the United States and the United Kingdom maintain a joint administration and use of most of the Line Islands and the Phoenix Islands that are south of the equator. These tiny low atolls also have strategic value as air bases. Canton Island has been developed as a major fueling stop on flights between Hawaii and Australia or New Zealand.

The Samoan Islands are high, and the rocks are mainly volcanic. Savaii and Upolu are the principal islands of Western Samoa, which became an independent republic in 1962. It has an area of 1,120 square miles, and a population of about 104,000. Tutuila and a few small islands in eastern Samoa belong to the United States. The landlocked harbor of Pago Pago on Tutuila is a superior strategic base for ships and aircraft. The village of Apia, on Upolu, is the chief trade center for Western Samoa.

French Polynesia includes the Society Islands, largest of which is Tahiti, the

Figure 17-11 Siva-Siva is the native dance of Sanwa. The dance tells a story in motion. The dancer takes the lead while those seated chant and keep tune. (Courtesy of Matson Lines.)

Tuamotu Archipelago, the Marquesas Islands, and the Tubuai Islands. Tahiti grows vanilla for export in addition to copra, which is produced on most of the islands. Pearls are secured by divers in the lagoons of the Tuamotus. Pearl shell, tortoise shell, and dried trepang or *bêche-de-mer,* a sort of sea slug, are other exports. The little city of Papeete on Tahiti is the chief center for trade in eastern Polynesia. Artists and writers have given the world an enticing view of the attractive people, the lush tropical vegetation, and the steep-walled mountains of Tahiti.

MELANESIA

The land area included in Melanesia is large, but except for Fiji, the islands are little developed economically, and most of the natives have a primitive culture. The white population is small.

NEW GUINEA   The second largest island in the world is New Guinea. It has an area of 312,000 square miles and is nearly 1,500 miles long by 500 miles at its greatest width. The western half is controlled by Indonesia; the eastern half is governed by Australia. The northeastern quarter, together with the Bismarck Archipelago and Bougainville Island of the Solomon group, is part of an Australian United Nations Trust Territory: the southeastern section, called Papua, is directly administered by the Commonwealth.

Very high ranges, over 12,000 feet in elevation, extend the length of New Guinea. Peaks reach 15,000 to 16,500 feet, high enough to be snowcapped all or part of the year. The mountains are a great barrier to ground travel, but do provide man with cooler sites for villages. From the mountains descend large rivers that could be used to generate millions of horsepower in hydroelectric energy if and when developed.

New Guinea has a rainy tropical climate, and most of the island is covered with jungle growth or a dense rain forest. The coastal areas and river floodplains are largely mangrove swamp, very difficult to traverse. Groves of sago palm that flourish in the swamps are a source of starchy food for the natives. Important deposits of gold have been found on the island, and the placers yield about 10 million dollars per year.

Both the flora and fauna are mixtures of Asiatic and Australian types. Among the animals is a species of kangaroo. Birds are in great abundance and singular variety, including the bird of paradise, the cockatoo, and the flightless cassowary.

Among the natives are pygmies, living in remote mountain areas, Papuans, who are tall Negroes with woolly hair, and Melanesians, who have dark skins, frizzly hair, and a somewhat higher culture than the Papuans. Natives live in villages, plant gardens, process sago palms for food, raise pigs, and make a variety of stone implements and other articles. They build large houses without nails. The dwellers by the sea construct big sea-going canoes. In the swamps the houses are built on piles. New Guinea is little developed, and most of the natives continue to live in a self-sufficient way as they have done for centuries.

The few whites who have settled on the big island engage in trading, gold mining, and managing coconut plantations.

BISMARCK ARCHIPELAGO New Britain, New Ireland, and many smaller islands form the Bismarck Archipelago. The two principal islands are narrow and mountainous. Active volcanoes are located around the fine harbor of Rabaul, the chief trading center. Lowlands are small but contain most of the scattered native villages. Copra is the leading export.

EASTERN MELANESIA Fiji, Santa Cruz, and the Solomons, except for Bougainville Island, are governed by the United Kingdom. New Caledonia is French, and the New Hebrides are under a condominium (joint government) by France and England. There are many coral reefs and coral islets. Generally the large islands are very mountainous, and several contain active volcanoes. Volcanic rocks predominate, but older rocks also occur, especially in New Caledonia and Fiji, where they are associated with deposits of metals. These include nickel, chrome, cobalt, and iron in New Caledonia, and gold in Fiji. The Melanesian islands all have a rainy tropical climate, and except for grasslands in part of New Caledonia, dense rain forests prevail. The Solomons are little developed except for copra plantations.

Fiji has an area of 7,036 square miles

Figure 17-12   Suva, capital of the Fiji Islands, is located along a good harbor at the foot of low, rolling hills. (Courtesy of Matson Line.)

and a population of nearly 400,000. It consists of two large islands, Viti Levu and Vanua Levu, and over 250 small ones. Although some gold, manganese, hardwood timber, and kauri pine are exported, the chief products are agricultural. Sugar plantations export about 200,000 tons annually. Bananas, rice, cacao, and copra are among other products of the land. Indians, mainly Hindus, were brought in as plantation workers and now equal the native Fijians in number. Many Indians run small businesses or operate little farms. The chief port and capital is Suva, an important communications center by sea and air.

New Caledonia is 250 miles long by about 30 miles wide and is the largest French territory in the Pacific, with an area of 8,548 square miles. Offshore are barrier reefs and coral islets. Besides nickel and chrome, the island exports copra, coffee, and beef cattle. The population of about 70,000 includes some 28,000 natives, nearly 20,000 French, and many Asiatics. Noumea, the capital and chief seaport, is an important supply, trade, and communications center by both sea and air. Its industries include a nickel smelter.

MICRONESIA

Most of Micronesia is now controlled by the United States. Spain established ownership over the islands in the sixteenth century and continued as governing power until the Spanish-American War. In 1898 Spain ceded Guam to the United States and sold the rest of the islands to Germany. During World War I the islands were taken by Japan. In World War II they were captured by the United States, which now governs them, excluding Guam, as the Pacific Trust Territory, under trusteeship from the United Nations. Included

are the Mariana (Ladrone) Islands, except Guam, the Caroline Islands, and the Marshall Islands. The Gilbert Islands and Ocean Island are controlled by the United Kingdom, and Nauru is a trust territory of Australia.

MARIANAS   The largest island of the Marianas, Guam, is an important United States naval and air base. On the west coast is Apra Harbor, with Agaña, the capital, a few miles away. Many of the native Guamanians (Chamorros) work for the government or are supported indirectly by government funds. Most families have a plot of ground on which corn, vegetables, and fruit are raised. Cattle are kept both for draft purposes and food, and a little fishing is done. Copra is exported.

Saipan, Tinian, and Rota were commercially developed by the Japanese, who planted sugar cane, manioc (tapioca), vegetables, coffee, bananas, and other fruits. A sugar mill on Saipan was destroyed during World War II, and the Japanese were removed from the islands after the war. No sugar is now produced, and farming has declined, only subsistence crops being raised.

CAROLINES   The Caroline Islands, situated just north of the equator, are scattered over an ocean area one-half the size of the United States. The Carolines include more than 900 atolls and several volcanic islands, but their land area totals only 461 square miles. The population is about 52,000, most of whom are Micronesians. The principal volcanic islands are the Palau and Yap groups toward the west, the Truk Islands near the center, and the islands of Ponape and Kusaie at the eastern side. These five islands or groups account for about 430 square miles of the Carolines and have 70 per cent of the inhabitants. The volcanic soil is fertile, and the variety of resources is greater than on the atolls. Hundreds of the atolls are unpopulated, and those that are inhabited support populations ranging from a few families to a few hundred persons. People make their living by subsistence agriculture and fishing. They live in villages in huts built of native materials. Life is slow, but the natives are happy and satisfied with simple things. Some copra is exported, and handicrafts are made for sale in America.

Palau consists of eight islands and scores of islets, together with a large lagoon surrounded by coral reefs. Phosphate rock is exported for fertilizer, especially from Angaur, an island at the south of the group.

Yap, composed of several closely adjacent islands, is used as a cable base. The Yapese have retained traditional customs and have rejected Western dress, which they consider too warm. They continue to value their unique stone money; some specimens have the size and shape of millstones.

Truk is a group of half-submerged hills that are the eroded remnants of a large volcanic dome rising from a submarine platform. There are six sizable islands and many small ones, in the midst of a lagoon about 25 miles across. The lagoon is surrounded by an irregular coral reef. Ponape and Kusaie are high, compact islands with a tropical climate and forest-covered mountains. In both islands are sites of ruins of ancient walls and stone structures built by man.

EASTERN MICRONESIA The Marshall and Gilbert groups and Nauru and Ocean Islands are the chief land areas of eastern Micronesia. The atolls that form the Marshalls are in two chains, an eastern and a western. Their land area is only 70 square miles compared with 4,500 square miles for the enclosed lagoons. The population is about 15,000. A few of the islands are large enough for good air bases. Some of these islands, like Bikini, have been the sites of atomic bomb experiments.

British islands include the Gilberts, low islands located on both sides of the equator, and Nauru and Ocean Island just south of the line. Tarawa is the capital and chief port of the Gilberts. Nauru is a trust territory of Australia. Ocean Island is governed by the British. Both these islands export phosphate rock obtained from large and valuable deposits.

ANTARCTICA

Surrounding the South Pole is Antarctica, an unpeopled continent almost completely covered with mile-thick ice. The land mass has an estimated area of 5 million square miles, covered by four-fifths of the world's ice. It is the coldest of all continents, temperatures seldom rising above freezing. Antarctica is essentially without life, save for the penguins that live on the shore ice. The Weddell seal is abundant but rarely hunted. Whales are taken in the adjacent seas during the summer, and sea mammals resort to the shores of storm-swept South Orkney, South Georgia, and other islands, where man may slaughter them for their fat. From Antarctica great icebergs break off and float away to melt in the ocean. The interior is a white, monotonous plateau surface, whose elevation at the South Pole is nearly 10,000 feet. Through the snow and ice mountain ridges sometimes emerge, especially near the ocean margin. Coal has been reported, and other minerals may exist beneath the ice. There is an active volcano, Mt. Erebus. Shelf ice is lodged on the continental shallows.

IN PERSPECTIVE

THE PACIFIC AREA, DISTANCE AND LOW POPULATION DENSITY

Throughout the Pacific's vast extent, its islands, both large and small, and its peoples of varied ancestry, are of increasing importance in their world setting as they emerge from obscurity to play a part in global strategy. Islands so insignificant or remote that formerly months or even years elapsed between visits by outsiders, have become landing fields and fueling stations on air lanes between North America, Asia, and Australia. Some islands are the sites of great supply depots and strong defense bases for naval, army, and air forces. The beauty and unique life on South Sea islands attract increasing numbers of pleasure seekers. To care for this expanding tourist industry, many new hotels and other facilities have been constructed, and additional plane and ship transportation has been provided. Many inhabited islands of the Pacific now have radio communication and keep in daily contact with the world news.

In Australia, New Guinea, and other places that contain old crystalline rocks, new occurrences of metals are being found. From the sedimentary rocks petroleum is produced in New Guinea and coal in Australia and New Zealand. Deposits of phosphates have been developed on several islands that are built of coral limestone. Such discoveries are bound to increase in number and variety with more thorough geological exploration, and large expansion in the exploitation of the mineral industry seems a certainty for the future.

Fish resources are inadequately developed. The use of radar and sonic devices to detect swarms of fish in the ocean depths, and of helicopters to locate schools near the surface and areas of floating plankton on which fish feed, are applications of science that are assisting the growth of the fishing industry. Quick-freezing and packaging of the catch along with the operation of floating canneries and other modern practices will aid in marketing fish caught in waters remote from world markets.

Science applied to agriculture will increase production of food crops and export staples, especially in the undeveloped regions of Australia, New Guinea, and other oceanic islands. Medical science has helped to improve the health of native peoples, although much remains to be done in instituting health measures. With increased education and knowledge about the world, improvements in culture, health, and self-government will be made among many native groups that now live in a primitive manner. The advance made in a century by the Maoris of New Zealand, and the Fijian and Tongan people provide examples of what can be expected to happen even more rapidly in coming years. With improvements in knowledge, the lands and waters of the Pacific will become increasingly useful to the nations and peoples of the world. Even parts of icebound Antarctica are claimed by several nations, and that continent may become a source of coal and other minerals as well as of the whales now taken near its coasts. Scientific studies in Antarctica, such as those begun during the Geophysical Year of 1957–1958, may improve our knowledge of atmospheric circulation, the origin of cyclonic storms, and the causes of weather.

SELECTED REFERENCES

Coulter, John Wesley: *The Pacific Dependencies of the United States,* The Macmillan Company, New York, 1957.

This valuable book extensively describes in Part 1 the territories of the United States: Hawaii (now a state), Samoa, and Guam. Part 2 includes the Trust Territory of the Pacific Islands: the Marianas, Palua, Yap, Truk and Ponape, the Marshall Islands, Pingelap, and Mokil. The text covers the relief features, climate, products, and people of the various islands.

Cumberland, Kenneth B.: *Southwest Pacific,* McGraw-Hill Book Company, Inc., New York, 1956.

The book well describes Australia and its neighboring islands, including the New Hebrides, the Solomon Islands, New Guinea, New Caledonia and Norfolk, New Zealand, and its neighboring islands, including outlying ones like the Cook Islands, Niue, Tonga, Western and American Samoa, Tokelau Islands, Wallis and Futuna, and Fiji.

De Laubenfels, David J.: "New Zealand," *Focus,* New York, September, 1960.

A concise description, with five maps, of the landforms, land use, regions, rainfall, and features of the country.

Freeman, Otis W.: *Geography of the Pacific,* John Wiley & Sons, Inc., New York, 1959.

Covers the setting, peoples, exploration and settlement, trade, and political geography of Australia, Melanesia, Micronesia, Polynesia, and Indonesia.

Scofield, John: "Australian New Guinea," *National Geographic Magazine,* vol. 121, no. 5, pp. 483–637, May, 1962.

A popular article, beautifully illustrated with colored plates and maps, descriptive of both Netherlands and Australian New Guinea.

Wiens, Harold J.: *Pacific Island Bastions of the United States,* D. Van Nostrand Company, Inc., Princeton, N.J., 1962.

This is a popularly written book on the physical features and the human and political geography of the Pacific islands, dedicated to those who are "seriously" minded.

Wiens, Harold J.: *Atoll Environment and Ecology,* Yale University Press, New Haven, Conn., 1962.

A detailed study of a specialized type of island widespread in the tropical Pacific.

CONCLUSION: PEOPLE IN THE CHANGING WORLD

IN THE PRECEDING CHAPTERS THE AUTHORS have sketched the geographical environment of the various regions of the world and pointed out the principal geographic relationships within and among them. Thus this study may be considered a background against which to view current happenings and possible future developments.

In many ways the modern world is dynamic, a place of rapid change; yet in other ways changes are so slow that conditions seem almost static. Since 1910, two major world wars, as well as several minor engagements, have affected every country to such an extent that it can now be said that no nation is so independent as to be unaffected by events outside. Within the present century wars have raged and brought numerous political changes. Old empires—Serbia, Austria-Hungary, Russia, Germany—have disappeared. Several old nations which had been absorbed—Latvia, Lithuania, Ukraine, Hejaz—were revived, existed for a brief period, and were then again absorbed by a neighboring larger or stronger power. Several countries—Poland, Finland, Czechoslovakia, Hungary, South Korea, Burma, and others—regained their independence and survive as independent or semi-independent nations, although they have had to

make numerous boundary adjustments. Still others—Saudi Arabia, the Soviet Union, the Philippines, Yugoslavia, the Republic of Indonesia, Israel, Mali, Somali—have come into existence as new nations, each exerting influence, if not on a worldwide basis at least regionally. War and the consequences of economic change have forced many nations, long thought of as world leaders—the United Kingdom, France, Germany, Italy, Japan—to shrink their national boundaries and yield all or parts of their former colonial empires. The latest surge of nationalism which has created, or re-created, such countries as Libya, the Sudan, Gabon, Malagasy, Congo, Jamaica, Trinidad, Laos, and numerous others is but a continuation of the search for political freedom. Every nation, even the United States because of its additional world responsibilities, has been affected by the continually changing political geography of the world.

Despite the changes in the political boundaries of nations, large or small, much of the geography of the world remains the same. Whoever controls them, the mountains still have their heights and barrier effects; the major rivers and streams continue to flow in the same directions; the winds continue to move in the same general pattern and bring their life-sustaining rains; and the soils of the plains remain the principal producers of food. The earth continues to revolve and rotate so that man may depend on a succession of seasons and know that day will follow night. However, man has modified his environment in many ways. Some of these effects, such as the reclamation of land, the harnessing of water power, and the extraction of metals from ores, are beneficial. Other effects are harmful as can be seen, for example, when man's activities cause soil erosion, forest fires, and the spread of pests and diseases. Natural changes are usually very slow, but those resulting from human activity may be quite rapid. Man, more than nature, is the real variable in the geography of the world.

PROBLEMS OF DISTRIBUTION

The uneven distribution of minerals, fertile soils, and life-giving water produces an equally uneven distribution of population and resource utilization. Man can utilize these resources to better his standard of living through work, peace, and prosperity, or eventually to destroy himself completely by war and famine. In the previous chapters, "have" and "have not" regions have been discussed. What, then, is the world point of view?

POPULATION

The total area of the earth is 197 million square miles. Of this area, 140 million square miles are covered by oceans, seas, and lakes; another 10 million square miles are either too cold, too dry, or too rough for permanent settlement by large numbers of people. This leaves an area of 45 million square miles in which man does live; but of this, approximately one-half

is subhumid or semiarid. More than 3 billion persons are thus confined largely to 23 million square miles of the earth's surface.

Not only is the world's total population increasing more rapidly than ever before, but the normal span of life is also longer. Between 1900 and 1960, the increase in world population was over 1 billion persons, or an average of more than 48,000 per day. Since 1960, the average daily increase has approximated 67,000. The population of India alone is now being increased by about 17,000 living births per day, that of the United States by over 6,000. Because of lower infant mortality, increasing medical knowledge, and a somewhat better distribution of food, the expected life span in the United States has increased by more than 22 years since 1900. In 1960, there were 16,658,000 persons in the United States sixty-five years of age and over. By 1970, it is estimated that there will be 20,035,000 in this age group, and by 1980, it will number over 25,000,000. Life expectancy, although increasing in other countries, has not risen as much in most places as in the United States.

The countries with the largest total populations are China and India; but people are not evenly distributed throughout their areas. Because of various physical factors, the people of China are concentrated on the narrow southeastern coastal plains, along the valleys of such rivers as the Hsi, Yangtze, and Yellow, in the many smaller stream valleys, and in some instances on the sides of terraced highlands. Large parts of the interior are too dry and far too elevated to support many people. In India the situation is similar; the Ganges Valley and the narrow coastal plains are densely populated, but the rougher parts of the Deccan Plateau and drier interior areas are less densely settled. When applied to the country as a whole, population density means little; when considered for the areas of arable land, it is significant. For example, the density for China is 190 persons per square mile. Since the different parts of the country vary greatly in their ability to produce, the density ranges from zero in the deserts to more than 2,500 per square mile in the arable areas. This is a density of three persons per acre—probably twice the number who could be fed by agriculture alone. In the United States at least 2.3 acres of arable land per person are needed to maintain the present standard of living. In many ways India and China are typical since they emphasize the problem of too many people for too small an amount of arable land.

Part of the Northeastern United States, much of West Central Europe, and sections of South Asia, Southeastern Asia, and Central Eastern Asia have large areas in which the density of population exceeds 250 persons per square mile. Each of these areas contains not only a considerable amount of productive land but other favorable features, such as minerals, suitable climates for particular crops, and sufficient water supply. People in some areas do not take as much advantage of these factors as they might; nevertheless, the potentiality for development is theirs.

Advancing scientific knowledge will, perhaps at a date not too far in the future, enable man to use large areas of land not now in production. If, by using atomic power, it becomes feasible to process sea water and pipe it to desert areas, vast amounts of now unproductive land could be put to work. New methods of cultivation, new and improved plants, better methods of processing and preserving—all will aid, to a certain point, in caring for the increasing world population. Popula-

tion pressure upon the land is, then, world problem number one.

NATURAL RESOURCES

MINERALS Minerals are one of the principal bases of modern civilization, or of the modern standard of living. Iron, copper, uranium, coal, and petroleum are the most important of the major mineral resources. Many of the minor minerals—minor only in the sense that they are not produced in such large quantites—help to make the basic minerals far more usable than they would be otherwise. Thus vanadium, limestone, and other minerals are as essential to producing certain kinds of steel as are iron ore and coke.

Some nations because of their large areas—the Soviet Union, the United States, Canada—have a variety of minerals; others because of smallness and location—Italy, Liberia, Bulgaria, Thailand—have only a few, if any, minerals in significant amounts. Several nations produce one or two minerals—Malaya, tin; Sweden, iron ore; South Africa, gold and diamonds; Saudi Arabia, petroleum—but, because they lack other substances necessary for their processing, they export vast quantities as raw material.

Minerals are of little if any value, until put to work. Since much of the modern standard of living is based on minerals, nations have often attempted to gain control of the properties of their neighbors. Obviously, the unequal geographic distribution of minerals is a problem to be solved if the world is to remain at peace.

WATER Most essential of all the natural resources is water. Without water, plants cannot grow even in fertile soil; unless he has water to drink, man dies in a few days. Yet overabundance can be just as disastrous to an area as a scarcity of water; the Amazon Valley is no more densely populated than large areas of the Sahara. Not all plants need the same amount of water to thrive. Some, such as the great forests of the selvas, need at least 70 to 80 inches of rainfall fairly evenly distributed throughout the year; others, like numerous desert plants, can thrive on 5 inches or less of moisture per year. Corn does best in a region that has long, warm summer days wherein the moisture is supplied by afternoon thundershowers. Wheat produces well if it has about 20 inches of rainfall, provided that it occurs at the right time. Other plants also have their peculiar water needs, which in many respects are the result of adjustment to their environment. Where a surplus of fresh water is available and irrigation can be practiced, numerous crops can be produced, and the problem of food production can be partly settled.

Water is as essential in the life of cities as it is in rural areas. In the United States, where urban population is rapidly increasing, the limitations of the function of several major cities are determined by the amount of water available. Cities throughout the world attempt to solve their water problems in diverse ways. Gibraltar has cemented sides of the Rock, to create catchment basins; Los Angeles pipes water completely across southern California; and Athens rations its supply. New York is constantly searching for new places to build dams and thus ensure a permanent supply of water. Until the water problem is solved, approximately 9 million square miles of the earth's surface will be of little value to mankind.

SOILS The soils capable of producing the most abundant crops are, like minerals and water, also unevenly distributed. Poor management and constant utilization have put hundreds of thousands of acres out of production, some permanently. Large areas in northern China, parts of North Africa, especially near Carthage, and sections of Italy were in ages past good producers of food. Many farms in the southern part of the United States are so badly gullied that the land is no longer usable. Dust storms in the subhumid parts of the Soviet Union, China, and the United States are but warning signals that grasslands are being put to improper use.

Man has gone far in solving some of his current soil problems. Rotation of crops, contour plowing, strip-cropping, gully control, and fertilization are but a few of the conservation measures that have been developed. To carry out such programs is costly, in most instances requiring government aid in addition to what the owner contributes. Frequently, land must be taken out of production for a short period of time, and in areas where food production is at a subsistence level, the diminished crops might mean starvation. To help solve its soils problem, the world needs a better distribution of foods and a closer unity among nations.

FOOD PRODUCTION

Each part of the world specializes in some crop or crops. The principal agricultural products of an area are usually those that do best in that particular environment. Farming in most parts of the world is thus an adjustment to the natural environment of soil, water, and climate. Irrigation and other specialized types of agriculture are, of course, exceptions.

The two great food crops of the world, wheat and rice, are basic foods for more than 90 per cent of the world's people. Rice is intensively cultivated in the monsoon lands of Asia, most of which are densely populated. Wheat is an extensively cultivated plant of the semiarid and subhumid lands of Central Eurasia, central North America, southeastern South America, northern China, and southwestern Australia. Most of the rice produces four or five times as many bushels of grain per acre as wheat. The per capita consumption of wheat for the world as a whole is 180 pounds, for rice, 150 pounds In general, the standard of living in wheat-producing and wheat-consuming lands is considerably higher than it is in the rice areas. The areas producing rice depend much more upon the current crop than do the wheat-producing areas. In some parts of the United States and Canada, beef has replaced wheat as the chief staple food. If the rice crop in an area fails, famine and starvation are common since there is no surplus from previous years and no money to buy the surplus from other regions. Most wheat areas have a surplus from previous years or have some means of securing grain from another region.

Rye, corn, barley, and oats are also important grain food corps. Potatoes form the principal part of the diet in certain sections of Europe and the Americas. Supplementary foods, such as vegetables and fruits, vary with the locality.

Animals suitable for meat live in most parts of the world. In areas having the highest standard of living in the Western world, beef, mutton, pork, and poultry are essential items of diet. The consumption of meat products varies greatly from region to region, depending upon the amount of land available for pasture, the religion of the people, and the general prosperity of the area. The average annual consumption of meat per capita for the world is 50 pounds, ranging from 20 pounds per person in Asia to 220 pounds in Australia and New Zealand. The per capita consumption in Anglo-America is about 160 pounds.

Usually enough food is produced each year to feed the people of the world if it were evenly distributed. Should production be low in some area there is generally enough surplus in another to make up the deficiency. But wars and lack of transportation or money to buy food may prevent needed shipments. Food production in every part of the world can be increased by more efficient land utilization, improved methods of harvesting, and plant betterment, but improvement in transportation and in the economy of poverty-stricken peoples is also needed.

MANUFACTURING

The processing of goods, in some form or other, is carried on in every part of the world. Complex manufacturing, however, is confined primarily to the Northeastern United States and the most densely populated section of Western and Central Europe. Most areas within these two regions have, or did have at one time, large quantities of coal and iron ore, water power, access to rivers, lakes, or oceans for cheap water transportation, fairly level topography or gaps through inland barriers so that land transportation was not handicapped, access to sufficient quantities of food and necessary raw materials, and a reputation for skilled workmanship. Outside these two principal regions there are numerous smaller developments, such as the Texas Gulf coast and the Los Angeles areas of the United States, the Donets and Ural areas of the Soviet Union, the Jamshedpur and Calcutta areas of India, and the Sydney area of Australia. Many of the smaller centers are areas of specialization.

In most instances, the nations with the

highest standard of living are those that have the easiest access to manufactured goods. Machines used in producing a specific item decrease the amount of labor required for making that item. Ultimately, however, mechanization creates more new jobs. The worker has more time for educational and recreational activities. Each nation attempts to increase its output of manufactured goods for sale in foreign countries, since the sale of these goods adds purchasing power; yet simultaneously, each nation develops protective tariffs to encourage its own industries and to discourage the sale of foreign goods within its own boundaries. Many nations could use their resources to better advantage by developing agriculture, mining, or other activities than by trying to compete in the market for manufactured goods. By such reasonable adjustments, manufactured goods could flow more freely to the areas where they are needed and thus aid both producer and consumer.

WORLD LEADERS

The two most important and influential nations today are the United States and the Soviet Union. Each is a giant in area; the Soviet Union, with 8.6 million square miles, ranks first in size, the United States, with 3.6 million, ranks fourth. Each has a large population—the Soviet Union with 220 million persons ranking third, the United States with 190 million ranking fourth. Neither country is densely populated. Both have large areas for agricultural production, and both have great mineral wealth and vast industrial activities. Each is the leader in its sphere of influence. There, however, most of the likenesses end, for in political activity and political thought the two nations are diametrically opposed.

The Soviet Union, in building its sphere of influence, has brought many of the nations that border it partly or completely into the Communist bloc. China, which is one of the most important additions, has more than three times the population of the U.S.S.R. and is larger than the United States in area. Beyond the adjacent areas, the Communist doctrine has been successfully spread in parts of Africa, Asia, North America, and South America. This particular bloc of nations actually controls more land area and a larger population than any other group.

The United States has attempted to build its sphere of influence by working with other nations through mutual-aid programs. The United Kingdom, France, Greece, Vietnam, Thailand, and other countries have worked with the United States in the development of these programs. In addition to building a joint armed force, economic aid has been given where needed in an attempt to better agricultural and industrial development. The Peace Corps is now assisting in many African and South American nations. The United States has borne most of the cost; most of the immediate benefits have gone to the countries assisted in an effort to improve the standard of living and increase the educational opportunities.

The third bloc of nations of special importance, although minor when compared with the two previously named groups, is known as the Islamic world. With the exception of the Republic of Indonesia, Malaysia, and Eastern Pakistan, these nations form a compact group in North Africa and the Near East. The population of over 300 million is held together largely by common religious belief, since more than 90 per cent of the people are Moslems. Approximately two-thirds of the inhabitants live in Turkey, Pakistan, and Indonesia. In these three countries there is a variety of agricultural activities as well as some complex industrial development. In the remaining countries the standard of living is low; most of the people eke out a living by farming near an oasis or in an area where irrigation is possible. In some countries many lead a nomadic life by following their flocks. The Near East area is the location of large oil developments and reserves. The Islamic world is not aligned with either the Communist world or the Free World. Turkey is a member of the North Atlantic Treaty Organization, and Pakistan belongs to the Southeast Asia Treaty Organization, both of which groups are anti-Communist.

A fourth large bloc of nations is joined together in the Organization of American States. This group is made up of the Latin-American Republics and the United States. Its primary purpose is to encourage peaceful development of the area through the betterment of economic conditions. At a 1964 meeting, most O.A.S. countries voted to censor the activities of Cuba and to apply economic and political sanctions, thus indicating their intent to remain politically free.

PLACE OF GEOGRAPHY

What, then, is the place of geography in this world of unequally distributed natural resources and unsettled peoples? Study of the many facets of human activity must not be regarded as a study of uncorrelated facts. To understand the activities of mankind, one must have knowledge of the various factors, physical and cultural, that make up man's environment. These factors may or may not determine what man will do in or about a specific area. They will of necessity, however, influence both his thinking and his actions about the problems that face him.

The study of geography will help individuals in our region of the world to understand better the people and problems of other regions. Only through sincere and sympathetic mutual understanding of one another can the people of the world hope for lasting peace. An understanding of geography will definitely contribute toward this goal of good international relationships throughout the world.

GLOSSARY

Alluvium Material deposited by running water, such as a floodplain or a delta.

Anticline An upfold in the earth's crust.

Arable Suitable for cultivation by plowing or tillage.

Archipelago A group of islands, or an area of ocean or sea interspersed with islands.

Arroyo A stream-cut valley in dry lands. Usually it will have water in it only during and immediately after rains.

Artesian Referring to an underground water supply, usually under enough pressure to cause the water to rise to the surface in a well.

Barrens Areas of poor soil that are covered by scant or scrubby vegetation.

Basalt A dark-colored and heavy rock of volcanic origin.

Benches Elevated areas of flat land, a topographic terrace or shelf.

Bora A violent, cold, northerly wind of the Alps and Adriatic area.

Braided stream A stream or river in which there are many joining and rejoining channels of water and in which sediments are usually being deposited.

Browse Low tree growth or bushy growth eaten by animals.

Campos A wet-and-dry tropical region in central Brazil covered with scrub and grass vegetation.

Chernozem A class of soils found along the dry margins of black prairie lands, originally covered with a thick mat of grass roots at the surface; rich soils.

Chinook A warm, dry wind that moves with high speed down the leeward side of mountains, especially the east slope of the Rocky and Cascade Mountains.

Cirque An amphitheater-shaped, steep-walled head of a glaciated valley in mountains.

Combine A machine which harvests, threshes, and cleans grain while moving over the field.

Condominium A country or region governed by two or more powers; joint dominion or sovereignty.

Coniferous Cone-bearing, like the pine tree.

Conurbation Cities and towns so near together that they form a large and almost continuous urban area.

Convection A process of heating the atmosphere; rapid uplift of masses of moist air in a vertical or nearly vertical stream, which may result in convectional heating and thunderstorms.

Cordillera A combination of mountain ranges or a system that forms a large unit such as the Andes or Himalayas.

Currents, ocean Movement in a definite path of large quantities of ocean water such as the Gulf Stream or the Japanese Current.

Cyclone A region of low atmospheric pressure, about which the winds blow counterclockwise in the Northern Hemisphere or clockwise in the Southern.

Deciduous Shedding leaves during the winter or dry season, as the oak or hickory does.

Delta The deposit of sediment at the mouth of a river caused by decreasing velocity of the stream.

Diurnal Daily, recurring every day.

Diversified farming Farming in which two or more crops are produced each year; a combination of stock and crop farming.

Doldrums A transition zone between the trade-wind belts, characterized by calms and weak winds.

Drift, ocean A movement of oceanic circulation slower than a current, such as the North Atlantic Drift.

Elevation Height above the level of the sea.

Escarpment A long, high, steep face of rock; steep cliffs such as the "Break of the Plains."

Estancia A large stock ranch in Latin America.

Estuary The drowned mouth of a river; a river mouth where the tide meets the river current.

Extensive agriculture Use of land with a minimum of labor and outlay, such as wheat farming on the Great Plains.

Fallow Land tilled but not planted for a season or two. Weeds and insects are destroyed and water is conserved so that one crop may be produced every two or three years.

Fathom A depth measurement of water; one fathom equals 6 feet.

Faulting Slipping or breaking of rock structure under pressure. Many faults form scarps or steep cliffs.

Fazenda A plantation in Brazil, for example, a coffee fazenda.

Finca A farm in Latin America, for example, a coffee farm in Colombia.

Fiord A narrow inlet of the sea between high banks or mountains, which has been gouged out by glaciers as along the coast of Norway or southern Alaska.

Floodplain An area along the sides of a river where the river overflows and deposits its sediments.

Foehn wind A relatively warm, dry wind which descends a mountain front when a cyclonic storm causes air to cross the range from the opposite side of the divide.

Gallery forest A forest along the banks of rivers that flow through grasslands. Tree crowns meeting over the stream give the impression of going through a green tunnel.

Ghee A semifluid type of butter used in India.

Growing season The period of plant growth between the last killing frost in spring and the first killing frost in fall.

Hogan An earth-covered lodge of the Navaho Indians.

Humus Partly decayed plant and animal matter in the soil; the organic portion of the soil.

Hurricane A tropical cyclone.

Hydrophyte A plant that grows in wet situations.

Hydrosphere The liquid sphere of the earth, chiefly water, such as the oceans, seas, bays, and lakes.

Igneous Formed by solidifications of molten material into rocks, such as granite and lava.

Intensive agriculture The use of the land to produce as much as possible in a given area and period of time by the expenditure of much labor and capital upon it.

Isobar A line on a map connecting places of equal atmospheric pressure.

Isohyet A line on a map connecting places of equal amounts of rainfall.

Isotherm A line on a map connecting places of equal temperature.

Jungle Dense undergrowth or second growth in the rainy tropical forests.

Kampongs Native villages of Indonesia.

Karroo A dry tableland of South Africa.

Karst A land surface formed by the solution or underground erosion of limestone rocks, as in the Highland Rim or the Karst area of Yugoslavia.

Lacustrine Formed by or in a lake; is applied to a plain formed by deposition in an old lake bed.

Laterite soil Reddish clay soil of the subtropics and tropics where the process of laterization is dominant.

Leaching The removal of calcium and other elements from the soil by water seeping through it.

Lithosphere The solid part of the earth.

Llanos Tropical plains covered with tall grass, located in the interior Orinoco Basin of Colombia and Venezuela.

Loess Deposits of windblown soils, usually found in the zone between dry and humid areas or in front of the former limits of glaciation.

Meltwater Water from the great ice-age glaciers.

Metamorphic rocks Rocks changed and formed by heat and pressure.

Metropolitan area The densely populated area around a large city such as the Greater New York or greater London areas.

Migratory agriculture Primitive agriculture, usually in the tropics, where the larger trees are killed and the brush burned, with only a few crops grown on one field before the field is abandoned.

Milpa A term applied to plot under migratory agriculture especially in Africa and the Americas.

Monsoons Seasonal winds that reverse their direction. For example, the summer monsoon blows toward Asia, but the winter monsoon blows away from Asia.

Moraine An accumulation of unassorted clay, earth, stones, and other materials deposited by a glacier.

Muskeg A swampy area in the subarctic or Arctic regions; usually has spruce and sphagnum moss.

Nagana The African name for trypanosomiasis, a cattle disease transmitted by the tsetse fly.

Naval stores Pitch, tar, and turpentine which are extracted from the pine forests of the middle latitudes.

Oblast A province within one of the states of the Soviet Union.

Okrug A district or circuit within a state of the Soviet Union.

Orographic Referring to precipitation caused when moist air is forced to move over mountains.

Outcrop A series of rocks exposed at the surface of the earth.

Outwash Material carried from a glacier by meltwater. Laid down in stratified deposits.

Paddy A field in which flooded rice is grown; unmilled or rough rice, whether growing or cut.

Pampa Grassland of South America especially in Argentina.

Paramo A cold, treeless zone above the tree line in the highlands of the tropical Americas.

Paramos High, bleak plateaus or similar areas in mountains.

Pedalfer A class of leached soils in which many chemical elements except aluminum and iron have been removed.

Pedocal Soils of dry areas in which little leaching has taken place; much calcium still present in a zone of accumulation in the subsoil.

Peneplain An old land surface worn down by erosion to almost a plain.

Permafrost The permanently frozen layer of the earth beneath the surface as in the polar or subpolar regions.

Placer mining The removal of minerals from an alluvial, wind, or glacier deposit by the use of water.

Podsol Leached soils developed in humid and usually cool regions, especially under cover of conifers.

Polder A tract of lowlands reclaimed from the sea by dikes and dams, as in the Netherlands.

Polyes Basin meadows or large sinkholes.

Pulses The edible seeds of legumes, usually beans and peas.

Raion An area or division of an oblast.

Residual soil Soil that is covering the bedrock from which it was formed.

Retting The process of soaking or exposing to moisture of certain fibers such as flax or jute.

Rift valley A valley formed by faulting in contrast to one formed by erosion.

Sawah A term used in place of paddy in Indonesia.

Scablands An extremely desolate region north of the Palouse country in the state of Washington, which is made up of wide, steep-sided, interlacing, dry channels.

Scarp A steep slope caused by faulting or erosion.

Scrub Vegetation chiefly of dwarf or stunted trees and shrubs, as in the "bush" area of Australia.

Sedimentary Formed from the accumulation of sediments deposited in water; a class of rock.

Selva A rain forest in Brazil.

Sensible temperature The combination of temperature and humidity as it feels to the body.

Sericulture The production of raw silk by the raising of silkworms.

Sirocco A hot, dry wind blowing from the Sahara.

Skerry A rocky isle, a reef.

Steppe Usually a plains area in a semiarid or subhumid region that is covered with short grass.

Subsistence agriculture Cultivation of the soil for the immediate needs of the family; very little, if anything, to sell.

Syncline A downfold in the earth's crust.

Synclinorium Folds of strata dipping toward a common line; a series of folds that create a trough.

Taiga Extensive northern forests, predominantly of conifers, in North America, Europe, and Asia.

Tierra caliente Hot lands in tropical highlands of the Americas, up to elevations of 2,500 feet.

Tierra fría Cool lands in tropical highlands of the Americas, with an elevation of about 6,500 to 12,000 feet.

Tierra templada Temperate lands in tropical highlands of the Americas, with an elevation of approximately 2,500 to 6,500 feet.

Till Unsorted and unstratified glacial drift deposited directly by the melting of ice, with sand, gravel, clay, and boulders mixed.

Timber line The elevation on a mountain above which trees do not grow; it varies with latitude and exposure. A lower tree line may result from deficiency in rainfall.

Trade winds Winds blowing toward the equatorial area from the subtropical high-pressure belts.

Transhumance The movement of herds between upland and lowland pastures with the seasons.

Troposphere The layer of the atmosphere next to the earth.

Tundra An area poleward of the taiga, whose vegetation is composed of lichens, mosses, and low bushes.

Typhoon A hurricane near Asia.

Velds Semiarid grasslands in which there may be scattered trees, as in South Africa.

Wadi A channel or bed of a watercourse which is dry except during or immediately after a rain, as in desert or semidesert areas.

Xerophytes Plants that are adapted to growth in areas of drought.

Index